Recovering the Lost World

A Saturnian Cosmology

Volume 2

Recovering the Lost World

A Saturnian Cosmology

Volume 2

(Toronto Edition)

Jno Cook

Saturnian Press

This book is generated from the website saturniancosmology.org. The website
includes search and locate utilities, access to 3000 related files, and active
links elsewhere. If you need these sources, please visit. If you have comments
or questions, feel free to contact the author at jno@saturniancosmology.org.

ISBN 978-0-9972379-2-4 (paperback)

Front cover: Saint Jerome in His Study, Albrecht Dürer, AD 1514
Fonts: Liberation Serif, Liberation Mono
Conversion: Calibre 2.41.0, custom Python scripts

Saturnian Press, LLC
4207 SE Woodstock Blvd #420
Portland, Oregon 97206
saturnianpress.com

Printed in the United States of America

Recovering the Lost World, Volume 1

1: Introduction and Background

Preface (index.php, 12K)
> Contents: The starting premise of this text; who I am, why I wrote this text; accolades; file hits.

Chapter 1: Introduction. (lost.php, 57K)
> Contents: What this site is about; the sledgehammer of ignorance; the history of objections; collation and synthesis.

Chapter 2: A Synopsis. (syn.php, 62K)
> Contents: A synopsis of the website; verification of notions by others; items completely missed by other researchers.

Chapter 3: The Osiris Mystery. (intro.php, 71K)
> Contents: The Osiris mystery; David Talbott's "Saturn Theory"; Wal Thornhill's plasma connection; the combined model and objections.

Chapter 4: The Nevada Conference. (nevada.php, 49K)
> Contents: The Nevada Conference; a comet's path; ice cover; seasonal plants; periodic extinctions; a new set of postulates.

Chapter 5: The Absu and Speculation. (cos.php, 67K)
> Contents: The equatorial rings detailed; methods of forming postulates; accusations of speculation; Peratt's wrench in the works.

Chapter 6: Alternate Cosmology. (planets.php, 61K)
> Contents: The standard and some alternative cosmologies; Saturn as a misfit in the Solar System; life on Earth.

2: Established Archaeology

Chapter 7: Ice Ages and Humans. (ice.php, 70K)

Contents: Recent glaciations; Homo erectus; the Acheulean Handaxe; Homo sapiens.

Chapter 8: Tunguska and Chicxulub. (tung.php, 128K)
Contents: preliminary planet interactions; stratospheric dust; Tunguska; Chicxulub; Grand Canyon; a Great Lakes atomic detonation.

Chapter 9: Event of the Younger Dryas. (dryas.php, 130K)
Contents: Firestone's paper of 2007; the Laurentide Ice Sheet; a likely sequence of events; the Great Lakes; the Carolina Bays.

Chapter 10: The Peratt Column. (peratt.php, 105K)
Contents: The Peratt Column; the Opossum; Nazca lines; Ley lines; Job; Carnac; Manu; Lepenski Vir; Sheela Na Gigs; Mari; Neith; Oannes; Kojiki; Cerberus.

Chapter 11: A Timeline and Gimbutas. (gim.php, 84K)
Contents: Earth placed below Saturn; the Hypsithermal; the Saturnian planet stack, a time line, Marija Gimbutas and Neolithic figurines.

Chapter 12: Saturn and Archaeology. (arch.php, 91K)
Contents: Revisiting the Acheulean Hand Axe; the caves of Lascaux and others; Catal Huyuk transitional period.

3: Mythology and Remote Antiquity

Chapter 13: The Creation. (polar.php, 99K)
Contents: Starting from Chaos; an unexpected flood; the egg; creation; the eye of Ra; petroglyphs; the city on the horizon.

Chapter 14: The Start of Time. (time.php, 62K)
Contents: The God visits Earth; the start of time; the first land; Horus the Hawk; gifts of the Gods; living in paradise.

Chapter 15: The Era of the Gods. (gil.php, 107K)
Contents: The King list; dating the Age of the Gods; barrows, henges, temple platforms.

Chapter 16: The World Flood. (flood.php, 84K)
Contents: The worldwide flood of 3147 BC; the battle of the Gods; the Absu.

Chapter 17: The Gods Leave. (leave.php, 62K)

Contents: The Gods leave; return of the Axis Mundi; a new era.

Chapter 18: Pyramids and Henges. (oldk.php, 122K)
Contents: Horus on his mountain; the Palermo Stone; the pyramids; barrows after 3100 BC, henges after 3100 BC.

Recovering the Lost World, Volume 2

4: Narratives of Ancient History

Chapter 19: The Midnight Sun. (sun.php, 104K)
Contents: The Midnight Sun; histories; something is missing; developing consciousness; the flood of Noah.

Chapter 20: The Flood of Noah. (noah.php, 123K)
Contents: The flood of Noah reconsidered; the fall of the Absu; a flood from the Sky; the Moon on fire; the extinction of Jupiter.

Chapter 21: Day of the Dead. (jup.php, 162K)
Contents: Blood and alcohol; the ten suns; Day of the Dead; Tower of Babel; Return of Mars; Sodom and Gomorrah.

Chapter 22: The Exodus of Moses. (moses.php, 145K)
Contents: The terror of Venus; Moses and Yahweh; the Ark; the psychosis of Moses; Joshua.

5: The Start of Modern History

Chapter 23: Destructions by Mars. (quet.php, 138K)
Contents: Destructions by Mars; calendar reforms; a blast from heaven.

Chapter 24: The Tablets of Ammizaduga. (bolt.php, 107K)
Contents: The Tablets of Ammizaduga; the bolt from Jupiter; the fall of Phaethon; the twins.

Chapter 25: The Hour of Phaethon. (hist.php 110K)
Contents: Dating the thunderbolt of Phaethon; the start of history; the sky in disarray; change in the equinox.

Chapter 26: Hezekiah and Babylon. (star.php, 133K)
     Contents: The star in the crescent; Hezekiah, Babylon; philosophy, religion, science; the presence of God.

Chapter 27: The Sibylline Star Wars. (sib.php, 76K)
     Contents: The Great Year, new locations of the stars; Nonnos; two meteors; Denderah.

6: The Parallel Mesoamerican Record

Chapter 28: Language and Causality. (lang.php, 137K)
     Contents: Consciousness; languages; becoming human; boat people; children.

Chapter 29: The Maya Calendar. (maya.php, 76K)
     Contents: The beginning of time; the first calendar; Tzolkin; Haab; Long Count; Katun Cycle, four ages.

Chapter 30: The Chilam Balam Books. (chil.php, 230K)
     Contents: The Katun cycle, the Thirteen, the Nine; Nine Lives; 2349 BC; the burning tower; 8th century; Katun 3-Ahau; Nine Fragrances.

Recovering the Lost World, Volume 3

7: Long Range Mesoamerican Astronomy

Chapter 31: The Olmec Record of the Past. (rec.php, 144K)
     Contents: A 40,000 year record; the three-cornered stone; the endless nights; God wakes up; survey of the world; the Third Creation.

Chapter 32: Olmec Site Alignments. (olmec.php, 160K)
     Contents: A crisis with the Sun; Izapa; Edzna; San Lorenzo; La Venta; Teotihuacan; Monte Alban; Pleiades.

Chapter 33: The Day of Kan. (kan.php, 106K)
     Contents: The Day of Kan; the course of the "may"; the third conquest; summary.

Chapter 34: The Popol Vuh. (popol.php, 152K)
Contents: Northern Gods, southern Gods; Seven Macaw; Zipacna and Earthquake; Hunahpu and Xbalanque; the ballgame in Xibalba; Tulan.

Appendixes

Appendix A: Notes on Chronology. (chron.php, 173K)
Contents: Sources for dates of the King lists; parallel chronologies; calendars; Carbon-14 dating; Precambrian.

Appendix B: The Celestial Mechanics. (mech.php, 190K)
Contents: Asteroid belt; outer orbits, inner orbits; plasma interactions; 52-year cycle of Venus; close encounters of Mars.

Appendix C: Mesoamerican Site Alignments. (align.php, 92K)
This is the file of alignment calculations referenced in Chapter 32, "Olmec Site Alignments" above.

Appendix D: Change in the Axis. (axis.php, 35K)
Contents: A 25-degree inclination; megalithic construction in response to disturbances in 2000 BC by Mars.

Appendix E: Polar Relocations. (flip.php, 62K)
Contents: The source of the problem; Earth as a gyroscope; flipping the pole; frozen mammoths; other polar relocations.

Appendix F: The Palette of Narmer. (narmer.php, 34K)
Contents: Reading the Egyptian Palette of Narmer.

Appendix G: Deep Impact. (deep.php, 32K)
Comet Tempel 1; Deep Impact; predictions; the fireworks; the aftershocks; weeks later; months later; years later.

Appendix H: Other Cosmologies. (other.php, 57K)
Sitchin; de Grazia; Patten and Windsor; Ackerman; Gilligan; Clube and Napier.

Appendix I: The Canopus Decree. (can.php, 31K)

Contents: The Canopus Decree; Sothic dating; Venus rising; Sirius rising; implications; further notes.

Appendix J: Expanding Earth. (exp.php, 16K)
Contents: Pterodactyls; expansion; S. Warren Carey; questions.

Appendix K: Venus and Epidemics. (epi.php, 18K)
Contents: Spanish flu; Lockyer Observatory; diseases from space.

Appendix L: Long-Range Chronology. (long.php, 17K)
Contents: From 4.6 billion years ago.

Appendix M: The Red Sirius. (sir.php, 16K)
Contents: Ptolemy; the Maya; Gregory of Tours; Al-Sufi; Sima Qian and Yu Ji-cai.

Appendix N: Age of the Universe. (age.php, 6K)
Contents: The Milky Way; the local group; the Virgo supercluster; the visible universe.

Appendix O: List of Books. (books.php, 47K)
Contents: Relevant books on allied topics.

Appendix P: List of Links. (links.php, 16K)
Links pertaining to the Saturnian theories.

Revision: 42.24 (sun.php)
Contents of this chapter: [The Midnight Sun] [The Temple Cultures]
[Something Is Missing] [Consciousness] [Bicameral Kingdoms]
[The Flood of Noah] [A Second Strike] [Endnotes]

The Midnight Sun

This chapter will cover the 24th century BC: the advent of the midnight Sun, the temple cultures, and the event of 2349 BC which was misnamed "the flood of Noah" in the Bible. This is a popular chapter, for the flood of Noah would seem to everyone to explain all of the strangely destroyed and overturned landscape forms that we see. But actually it explains very little. Destruction of the landscape of Earth had been going on for millions of years. All the same, the flood of Noah is addressed below, after first establishing something of the social and political environment of the era.

The event of 2349 BC was probably the most impressive event ever -- and the most frightening. The next two chapters will expand on this and demonstrate that the "flood" never happened on Earth.

After the visits of Horus had ceased, and as the pyramids at Giza were under construction or shortly before (about 2600 BC), Jupiter again became the most spectacular object in the sky. The planet had at that time completed its movement through the main portion of the asteroid belt in receding from the Sun, and again developed a coma, as comets do today when changing their distance from the Sun. It sported a gigantic coma, much larger than the diameter of the Moon, and a massive mountainous plasma plume from its south pole, which extended down to the Earth's horizon (as seen in Egypt and Mesopotamia). Saturn, on the other hand, had probably distanced even further, and may already have become just a mere speck in the sky.

[Image: Jupiter with a banded headdress on a throne of a temple glyph. From the stele of Hammurabi. After printablecolouringpages.co.uk.]

The "collision" between Saturn and Jupiter had changed the orbital speed and direction of both (actually for a total of four planets) and as a result assigned them to orbits much further away from the Sun. In effect, the movement of Jupiter and Saturn were outward bound spirals, only slowed by their travels through the asteroid belt. I suspect that Jupiter took about 890 to 990 years to finalize its orbit. The movement of Jupiter through the Solar System is detailed in the next chapter.

The title of "Sun" was transferred from Saturn to Jupiter everywhere in the world. The Egyptians simply relocated their original creator God, Ra ("sun"), from the North Pole to the ecliptic. The title "Sun" for Jupiter was deserved, for after Jupiter left the asteroid belt, it would have lit up the night sky brighter than the Moon. Plutarch suggested, in circa AD 200 (in *Isis and Osiris*), that Jupiter was seen at first as a globe three times the diameter of the Moon. That's big.

The tail of Jupiter, a plasma in glow mode, might have extended a half billion miles (800,000,000 km) away from its south pole. Because Jupiter has a very strong, but reversed, magnetic field (unlike comets which have no magnetic field), most of the plasma expulsion would leave the planet at the location of its north magnetic pole -- at the bottom. This tail is the mountain that Marduk rose on, "in the center of the sky," or, as the Egyptians describe, "in the primordial waters" -- the Duat. The few depictions we have show the plasma as a very steep mountain.

[*Image: Left, carved ivory Amulet, Anatolia, circa 3100 BC. Right, carved petroglyph, China, circa 3000 BC. The "owl-eyed" petroglyphs occur throughout the world by the thousands.*]

A lesser portion of the plasma discharge would impinge at the south magnetic pole, located at the north geographic pole (and thus at the top), and would broaden like plumes away from the planet. This is shown in Mesopotamian images as rays emanating from the shoulders in depictions of Marduk (Jupiter). The identification of Jupiter in Akkadian depictions is certain from the banded headdress he wears, which represents the banded atmosphere of the planet.

Jupiter would indeed have blazed like a sun once it left the asteroid belt. In historic times the comas of comets have managed to light the night sky to the point of blotting out the stars. Comets are only a few miles in diameter; Jupiter is 89,000 miles (140,000 km) in diameter. The Maya of classical times (AD 400 to AD 900) still called Jupiter "the Midnight Sun," as did many other peoples in historical times.

The planet with its circular coma traveled on the ecliptic, where all planets travel. The mountain tail, however, would extend far below the ecliptic and seem to shine into the "water" of the sea of the southern sky, the

Duat. How much of the circular coma or the mountain tail would be seen under that condition would depend on the time of year. During more than half the year the ecliptic rises above the upper limit of the Absu.

Where the ecliptic dipped below the limit of the Absu, the coma of Jupiter would illuminate the Absu from behind. The central coma certainly would be bright enough to be seen shining right through the dust of the Absu. We also have later graphical images of the large red disk of Ra placed between twin mountains overgrown with reeds. The twin mountains are the Absu at the time of the equinox.

When Jupiter was seen in the sky, which happened for only a part of each year, it would first be seen in the northeast or somewhere in the east, depending on the time of the year and the location of the observer. Initially it would be of a small size and would move west during the course of the night. Over the following few months Jupiter would loom larger when first seen at night, and closer to the south, and following this it would expand to its full size in the south. It would then diminish in size again, moving toward the west, and disappear for perhaps 5 or 7 months. As an exterior planet, Jupiter was not normally seen by day. Gudea of Lagash, however, claims seeing Jupiter as if during the day.

Cylinder B of Gudea, governor of Lagash in the 22nd century BC (circa 2141-2122 BC), reads that Ningirsu "rose in overwhelming splendor," "in the land it became day," and "he changes darkness into light." Ningirsu has been identified as Shamash ("sun") and is thought by some mythologists to be Saturn, but Saturn had disappeared long ago. This is a description of Jupiter, although perhaps a recollection (the archaeologically assigned date of Gudea's Cylinder B is a decade late). The very fact that we have these accolades almost certainly determines that the "overwhelming splendor" was not a regular phenomenon. Perhaps Gudea's acclamation resulted from seeing the additional brightness of Jupiter when it appeared above the Absu. That would happen only periodically, that is, every dozen years or so.

Shamash, held by archaeologists to represent the Sun (it means "Sun"), is Jupiter. E. A. Budge, in *Babylonian Life and History* (1925) quotes a Babylonian (Akkadian?) hymn to Shamash, as:

"[O Shamash,] thou stridest over the wide and deep sea. ... Thy beams of light go down into the Ocean, and the vast mass thereof seest thy light."

Here is a sun which lights up the depths of the "ocean" and walks across the sea, as could be seen in observing the Absu. And, as shown below, travels an undetermined or irregular course, and shines by night and, in fact, both by day and by night. It becomes even more amazing when Jupiter was periodically seen during part of the night and during part of the day.

"Never by day dost thou cast gloom, they face never becometh dark, thou fillest thyself all the night long, and lettest light stream forth from there."

This is not the Sun. This is not the Moon.

"Thou dost hasten over an unknown and remote course, leagues uncountably long. O Shamash, thou journeyest by day and turnest not back by night."

This is certainly not our current sun.

Jupiter became the reigning god of Heaven. How long the coma condition lasted I am not at all certain. I suspect that Jupiter continued to blaze in the night skies for only a few hundred years. In the following chapter, I will suggest that the display ended completely (after one interruption) in 2150 BC.

The descendants of the pharaoh Khufu, builder of the first giant pyramid at Giza, added "Re" to their names after circa 2550 BC, as did all the pharaohs of the following dynasties. "Re" is Jupiter, but "Re" is identified by modern archaeologists with the daytime Sun. ("Re" or "Ra" translates as "sun.") The first pharaohs of the following dynasty (the fifth dynasty, after 2490 BC) construct "sun-temples" on the west bank of the Nile, in addition to their own burial pyramids. The sun-temples consisted of a steep obelisk mounted on a platform, looking like the outpouring of plasma from below Jupiter. The obelisk became the symbol for Re. Only six such temples were built by successive rulers of the fifth dynasty. The sun-temples stop being built, we can suspect, after the display disappeared.

The sun-temples are an indication that, during the period of the fifth dynasty (after 2494 BC), Jupiter stood in the sky as a large blazing globe. After some 50 years of these constructions (ending by 2445 BC), no additional sun-temples were ever built. We can assume that the coma of Jupiter had disappeared again. Eventually the blazing of Jupiter would have come to an end as the planet slowed its retreat from the Sun and its charge balance (electric potential) started to match the electric field of the Sun at its remote location. The next chapter will suggest a sudden final extinction of Jupiter and a blazing fire. That happened in circa 2150 BC. By that time Jupiter had stood as the Midnight Sun, except for two interruptions, one long and one short, for a 1000 years.

In both Mesopotamia and Egypt, the planetary Gods (which still included Venus, Mars, and Mercury) were now understood to travel along the river of the ecliptic and across the ocean of the Absu (Duat) by ship. How else could one travel over a sea? Since the rings of the Absu consisted only of thin layers of dust and gases, a bright object behind the Absu, like a planet, would cause a glare to spread in the horizontal direction. It would at least have looked as if the planet was being transported on a raft with sharply upturned stern and bow. After the fall of the Absu (in 2349 BC) only a single upper ring remained, so that planets would still be seen on a raft where the ecliptic crossed (fell below) the ring. Even in Roman times, all the Gods of Egypt were still shown in ships. It had become the proper way to depict gods. It is very likely that the last ring of the Absu remained in view through the Middle Ages of our era. It is the Uoroboros of medieval alchemists.

For 3000 years the Gods were depicted in ships in Egypt. There are pottery depictions of celestial ships from before 3147 BC, but these portray the ship seen in navigation around the globe of Saturn as its bright crescent (as Talbott has suggested). During the time of the three Kingdoms of Egypt, statues of the Gods were ferried up and down the Nile to visit Gods at other temples and carried in processions in boats. The deceased also had to cross the sea of the southern sky, a concept already well established before the first Egyptian dynasty. Complete ships were interred adjacent to pyramids; two have been found next to the pyramid of Khufu (Cheops) at Giza.

The later *Book of the Dead*, which promises that the dead pharaoh will ride in the "barque of the Sun," is referring to the ship of Jupiter, Re, the Midnight Sun. This was not just an Egyptian fantasy; the form of this celestial ship was seen worldwide. [note 1]

> *"Virtually every mythical form of the sun god's dwelling -- be it mother-womb or world wheel, city, temple or kingdom, egg, throne, or circular serpent -- was declared to be a 'ship' sailing on the cosmic waters."*
>
> *"It is not surprising, then, to find Scandinavian rock carvings showing the wheel of the sun resting in the cosmic boat, or to discover that -- from Assyria to Britain and from India to Polynesia -- images of cosmic ships either contained wheels or were set on wheels and conveyed around dry land in the rites. As symbols of the sun god's enclosure, ship and wheel merge as one."*
>
> -- David Talbott, "The Ship of Heaven" *Aeon (1988)*

Talbott ends up relating the disk (wheel) and ship to the crescent seen rotating along the edge of Saturn during the "Era of the Gods." But the ship with a disk or globe was also an image seen in the sky after the close of the "Era of the Gods." To the ancients the Absu or Duat was a "sea" without question and seeing the planet Gods traveling through this sea on a flat skid or in a boat was real.

The flat skid shape is the natural result of the radial spokes in the rings of the Absu, which result in reflective marks perpendicular to the spokes, and a quarter wavelength removed, as any photographer will verify. Because the Absu thinned out above the brightness of a planet there would be a lesser reflective mark above the image of the planet. This explains the long persistence of the "ship" imagery.

Note also that the "disk" or "wheel" representing the Sun God is always depicted as very large. Thousands of years of Egyptian illustrations never relinquishes in depicting the image of the "sun-disk" of Re as disproportionately over-sized. We are not being shown an object with a diameter of the Moon or Sun, but something vastly and impressively larger. The same can be said for the depictions of the "sun" in his boat in other lands in antiquity. This simply is not the Sun, but an immensely larger globe. If seen as three times the diameter of the Moon before reaching its final orbit, the coma of Jupiter would have had an actual diameter of three million miles. That is more than three times larger than the Sun. No other planet ever showed so spectacularly. The inner planets, Venus, Mars, and Mercury, might have been brighter, but never as large, except when Mars or Mercury cruised close to Earth. The inner planets are peanuts compared to the pumpkin size of Jupiter -- both in actual diameter but especially when seen with a coma. [note 2]

The disk of Jupiter was red, as clearly seen in Egyptian depictions. It was no longer green, as Osiris had been depicted earlier. I do not know when this changed. There are Vedic documents which claim that Jupiter had a green body but was dressed in a red mantle. In Egypt all the renderings of Re consist of a large red disk (this has thrown off the archaeologists). The *Chilam Balam* books of the Maya also claim Jupiter turned red:

"Red was the mat on which Bolon-ti-ku [Jupiter] sat. His buttock is rounded [shaped] *like a hat, as he sits on his mat."*

Other passages of the *Chilam Balam* claim that the whole world became red during the rulership of Bolon-ti-ku. [note 3]

After an annual disappearance of some months, Jupiter would first be seen again in the east. Many people watched for the appearance of the red star of the east. The Saturnian researchers have had problems with the identity of a Red Morning Star, and have all but suggested that Mars at one time might have been on an orbit between the Earth and the Sun, similar to Venus. North American Indians (the Pawnee) paid tribute to a morning star which was red, for which neither Venus nor Mars would properly qualify: Venus was not red and Mars was not an inner planet, even if it overran the Earth's orbit. Jupiter, however, had a massive red coma.

In the early 20th century it was suggested that Mars would have been the red star. The appearance of Mars in the east was checked against Pawnee festivities for the period of AD 1800 to AD 1900, but the festivities happened only at 9 or 10 year intervals. Mars is overtaken by Earth (making Mars appear in the east) every two years.

The original "red star" was Jupiter, which was overtaken by Earth every 12 years (today), but at a reduced interval at an earlier time, when Jupiter additionally would have been very large and very red.

The progress of Jupiter across the heavens is so slow that Earth catches up with a sighting of Jupiter in the sky. During a portion of its travels it might appear during the day or part of the day. Jupiter was certainly bright enough to be seen in daylight. Each following day (or night) would bring Jupiter higher up into the sky, since the Earth traverses a zodiac house (30 degrees) in a month whereas Jupiter would require a year to do the same.

Jupiter had a calming influence. Over 3000 years he never lost his status as chief God. He also never showed unexpected behavior, unlike the inner planets -- the other Gods. These secondary Gods visited Jupiter frequently, that is, they were seen in the same sector of the sky, but Jupiter only slowly moved from one zodiac house to the next over the course of a year. And he remained on his mountain.

The Temple Culture

The "Era of Kings" started with a legacy from the immediately preceding "Era of the Gods" and we can therefore assume that these times started with the initial expectations of the resumption of a good life, order and purpose, and a working economy. However, none of these were initially forthcoming because of the interruption of the flood followed by the absence of guidance from the Gods. Only the temple culture, which had been in charge of the economy in the previous age, provided a unifying direction. The priests were called upon to explain what the Gods had done, why they had left, and what could be done in their absence.

The solution to the void left by the departure of the Gods was the installation of a king as the steward of God or as the God himself. This happened simultaneously in Egypt and Mesopotamia. It cannot be stressed enough what a radical change was made in 3100 BC when civilizations with no apparent leadership became kingdoms and theocracies. The need for authentication and authority must have been intense.

The solution in both locations was also to foster a civilization which attempted to recapture the past. The building of cities, city walls, temples, and graves, the construction of canals, production of grain, and the waging of wars, writing, the assignment of kings as the stewards of God, and a hundred other implementations were all believed to have been instituted by the Gods above the north horizon of the previous age. [note 4]

Simplistic as this might seem, all indications are that this was sincerely believed by the people and by the priesthood and the kings. Both Sumer and Egypt used languages with a grammatical structure which looked only to the past and which in effect held that the future was something one backed into. And with such a reversed sense of time and the inability to imagine alternatives, the mandates of the Gods and their earthly representatives were inarguable, and answered questions for the masses, at the same time providing justification for the governing elite.

This mindset induced a strong conservatism. It also removed the possibility of mankind claiming for its own the advances made in the past. Despite the extensions in trade and commerce and the growth of cities, civilization remains but an imitation of the original "Earth," and virtually nothing new is introduced for the next 2000 years. Everything was, by design, a reflection of "how things were at the beginning," and was supported by the languages used throughout Mesopotamia and Egypt, which did not have a future tense. A slave-state mentality had been introduced which would control societies for the next three millennia. [note 5]

Something Is Missing

Is this the legacy of the "Era of the Gods," during which humans had learned to manage large farming and trading concerns, and had invented the wheel, bronze metallurgy, irrigation, and writing? You would expect a continuation of new ideas and advances. And, in fact, there are some. For one thing, the politics of the city-states continued to evolve. Larger and much more complex irrigation projects were instituted. In Sumer, trade was expanded to include the import of metals from the region beyond the Zagros mountains, wood, stone, and obsidian from Anatolia, and other products from India and East Africa. Egypt expanded its territory to control copper mines in the Sinai, transport of basalt blocks from as far south as Aswan, import honey from Crete, and lumber from Lebanon. There were changes and large improvements in ceramics and in bronze metallurgy.

However, there were no changes which did not proceed directly from a previously known process. There was a lack of imagination compounded by the turn to conservatism in the solidification of social structures, reinforced by the rapid rise of a privileged elite and the ever-expanding religious rites and superstitions.

It is this last, the overwhelming obsession with the multiple Gods, spells, ceremonies, and religious practices, which remains foreign to us today. And, as Julian Jaynes notes in his book *The Origin of Consciousness in the Breakdown of the Bicameral Mind* (1976), it is completely at odds with the expectation one would have for a people descended from Paleolithic hunters with their ever-expanding production of art and tools, or the ingenious farmers and villagers of the Neolithic who developed fishing, herding, and farming. Yet, the preoccupation with the demands of the Gods remains the central issue of the later civilizations for over 3000 years.

Is Jaynes on track? Something certainly was missing in Mesopotamia.

"From its beginnings in Sumer before the middle of the 3rd millennium BC, Mesopotamian science was characterized by endless, meticulous enumeration and ordering into columns and series, with the ultimate ideal of including all things in the world but without the wish or ability to synthesize and reduce the material to a system. Not a single general scientific law has been found, and only rarely has the use of analogy been found."
   -- Encyclopaedia Britannica, 15th edition

We do have a few examples of analogies. One is the Mesopotamian use of tokens since 8500 BC to represent products, and the use of bottle seals as signatures. Both of these are metaphorical displacements. But what is astounding is that it took 5000 years to take the next step -- that is, to map these three-dimensional objects to a flat plane and produce a script. The first step was to pictorially inscribe the content on the outside of sealed clay jars containing the tokens. These were used as bills of lading by trade caravans and ships. The conversion of these pictorial inscriptions to a usable script took much less time, and its development was predictable as an extension of the first efforts. The tokens were eventually discontinued. [note 6]

Describing a similar lack of the ability to conceptualize, I.E. Edwards's book *The Pyramids of Egypt* (1985) reads like a comedy of errors when it comes to the details of the construction of the pyramids of the Old Kingdom (Dynasty 4 through 6, 2700 BC through 2200 BC). One structure after another was obviously interrupted by changes in the plans. What the book describes, over and over again, and over a span of hundreds of years, are obvious changes in construction after considerable work has been completed. Subterranean tombs and access Tunnels are frequently re-excavated or moved to a different location. This happened with the exterior buildings as well (the valley building and mortuary temple). Walls and building extensions were added and subtracted almost arbitrarily.

I am not talking about the inferior completion of a pyramid, or failure to complete the pyramid of a predecessor, or the theft of materials from an existing pyramid in order to complete a later structure. And it is not that the Egyptians could not measure accurately. The pharaohs oversaw the work on their graves closely, often relocating to the site of the construction. The crews could locate a tomb room exactly under the apex of a pyramid when required to do so. However, rarely are the first efforts at digging the subterranean structure correct. Everywhere we see changes in direction, blind corridors, abandoned rooms (and not just for the purpose of foiling potential grave robbers). Although inconceivable to us, it seems that the overseers lacked the imagination to incorporate the details of a structure into a single unit, and frequently could not coordinate the excavation crew with the pyramid crew (although, overall, an enormous amount of work was completed).

Developing Consciousness

This failure of a complete overview, the inability to simultaneously see the details and the complete picture, extends to art as well. It is apparent in the images of Sumer and also in the standardized Egyptian depiction of the human body on flat surfaces showing a frontal trunk but with the head and legs in profile. This was noted by Jaynes, who adds that this is also especially to be noted among early Greek two-dimensional figures, which are often shown as curiously disarticulated groupings of arms, legs, trunks, and heads. This does not extend to three-dimensional art. Even the earliest Egyptian sculptures in the round were totally realistic, even if somewhat idealized.

The failure in imagination is a lack of subjective consciousness and this shows also in the languages of Mesopotamia and Egypt. Julian Jaynes notes that the Sumerian, Akkadian, and Egyptian languages were "concrete from first to last." The languages had no room for analogies or metaphors. The speakers could not imagine alternatives, perhaps could not imagine themselves. To *imagine*, one has to take a leap from the concrete. It requires the mental construction of imagined action beyond the exigency of the moment and the needs of the everyday. [note 7]

The method of overcoming this failure in imagination, Jaynes proposes, is through an extended use of metaphors. The primary trope is analogy, a space in the mind which is mapped to the equivalent space in the real world. With the addition of an imagined self inhabiting this imagined space, we are suddenly presented with ever-expanding possibilities of imagined actions in these places, interpretations of the effects of the imagined actions, and even the design of tools imagined as solutions to problems. We, in our age, do this sort of mapping to a mental space with past, present, and future experiences, testing the efficacy of possible actions by stepping through them in our mind. We also lay out time and mathematical concepts as viewable "spaces" in our mind.

Jaynes's concept (in brief) of consciousness -- more precisely, *subjective consciousness* -- is exactly this placement of an "imagined I" into imagined spaces in the mind. It is not actually "you," but a substitute, an analog. You can look through the "eyes" of this "substitute I" or even observe yourself from afar in your mind. If something in real space and time requires your attention, the "I" will shift to be located directly behind your real eyes. Note that, as so defined, "memories" (as we imagine recollections) and "self-awareness" are not part of "subjective consciousness." These are biologically determined and are common to all animals. Jaynes suggests that historically, subjective consciousness was a late and learned acquisition for humans. Subjective consciousness is learned, and is culturally transmitted. Some people never learn it, yet they will appear fully functional.

The stupendous advantage of subjective consciousness is the ability of the mind (actually the speech areas in the left rear brain) to be able to analyze the outcomes of multiple alternative actions, to guess what others might think and do, and to understand how others see us. Our subjective consciousness is responsible for all our analytical abilities. We use this with such facility that it is almost impossible to recognize the part of us which does things without "thinking," things which include all rote activities. [note 8]

Just as language is learned by children from their parents, so is subjective consciousness. You can watch parents proposing "what if" situations to small children. Learning subjective consciousness requires language as a base, the ability to use metaphors as a means, and the examples of others. Jaynes places the maturing of subjective consciousness by individuals at about age 7 or 8. Subjective consciousness involves the ability to recognize yourself as seen by others, as an "analog I" which is internalized and placed into the space of the imagination, and which enables you to vault through time. [note 9]

And, if not from parents, how is such subjective consciousness learned? It is also learned from meeting strangers (not friends and familiar faces), an experience which forces upon you the idea that others see you, and thus suggests a narratized space in the mind where you can see yourself being looked at by others. This reflected "analog I" becomes the first spark to light up the enormity of possible analogical mind-spaces which compose subjective consciousness.

Subjective consciousness can be learned quickly. The same Inca army which, on November 16, 1532, walked into the trap set by 110 Spanish soldiers and lost 8000 men because there was no Divine Guidance on how to respond to the novelty of metal-clad men on horses, became engaged in guerrilla warfare and laid ambushes for the Spanish within months after the death of the Emperor. [note 10]

Jaynes claims that in the Middle East subjective consciousness didn't develop until after 1500 BC. In the immediate 2000-year period after the "Era of the Gods," which had still looked with certainty towards the beginnings, subjective consciousness simply was not needed. As long as nothing changed, life was predictable and safe. It took a number of worldwide catastrophes, which Jaynes did not address and was not even aware of, to force a change.

According to Jaynes, the Middle East started to wake up to consciousness with the arrival of "strangers." For Mesopotamia the strangers are the Indo-European invaders from the steppes of Russia and from India and Persia -- the Hittites (1600 to 1200 BC), who settled in Anatolia, but especially the later Medes and Persian invaders of Assyria in 500 BC, followed by Alexander's conquest of Persia somewhat later. Many of the Greeks, in fact, had already passed the consciousness horizon with their wide trade contacts with other peoples, and their near-wholesale rejection of the authority of kings. In contrast, Sparta, a Greek state which remained a kingdom through the Classical era, never produced anything of note except mindless warriors. [note 11]

> *Their constitution has stood them well for 400 years.*
> -- concerning Sparta, paraphrased from Herodotus, *The Histories* (circa 400 BC)

We also have to wonder at the *myths* and *legends* which have come down to us, since the lack of subjective consciousness precludes detailed memories. We can all verify this for ourselves, for we remember little or nothing from the first few years of life -- when we lack language -- and little from before the age of seven or eight -- when we lack the imagination to embroider remembered experiences, unless these were outstanding or later retold to us.

This suggests that mankind would not be able to recall its early history except for unusual experiences, and further might suggest that the *myths* and *legends* are fabrications of a later age. But, just as we remember some events from childhood if they are retold to us (or to ourselves), so humans would also have been able to recall stupendous past events if these were retold or replayed.

Retold as *myths* from generation to generation and acted out in ceremonies, these past events would have become concrete tribal memories. The accuracy of the retelling would then have been carefully protected. Note how small children will correct you if you diverge from the telling (or reading) of a story that they already know. Ancient festivals reenacted the events, preserved the memories, and, at the same time, fleshed out the stories to fill those memories with details. [note 12]

The stories ("myths" to us) and festivals spoke of the deeds of the Gods, copied their actions, and illustrated their appearance. Mexicans today still play a football game with a flaming ball called "Purepucha," recreating the creation events described in Michoacan myths. Through this dramatization everything displayed in the heavens becomes part of the earthly domain and localizes the Gods to specific temples and cities. When mythologists today suggest that the Gods of mythology are only human heroes elevated to godly status, they have it backwards. We are seeing the celestial Gods made human. Which is also exactly how most of mythology reads today. [note 13]

Bicameral Kingdoms

The adoption of subjective consciousness seen in the Middle East beginning after 1500 BC is also accomplished in India and China at about the same time, and likely due to similar causes. Did anything like it happen in the Americas before AD 1500? The problem with finding an answer to that question is that we only know the story from the invaders.

On the one hand, for Mesoamerica, we have a record of the dialog between Aztec philosophers of the Valley of Mexico and Spanish theologians, recorded by the 16th-century historian Sahagún, which certainly attests to a well-developed subjective consciousness. These theological discussions are only now being published. [note 14]

Jaynes noted the striking similarities between the Middle East of 1500 BC and the Incas of South America of AD 1500. The parallels between the Inca emperors of AD 1500 and the pharaohs of third millennium BC Egypt are astounding, despite a separation of 3000 years. For the Inca emperor, as for the pharaoh, the purpose of life was union with the Gods. When the Spanish threaten one of the Inca cities, the Incas flee, leaving behind their gold, belongings, and food, taking only the mummies of their past god-kings to hide them in the mountains. We see the same in Egypt where the priests frequently remove mummies and hide them elsewhere when threatened by grave robbers at times of unrest.

Julian Jaynes proposes a generalized model of theocratic city-states and empires, and calls these civilizations "bicameral kingdoms." "Bicameral" refers to the separation of volition and consciousness in the speech centers of the brain. The start of any human activity is initiated almost exclusively by the right rear brain. This area of the brain is also responsible for generating speech which was not consciously thought out beforehand. Because of this, the right brain seems to be the location of the will. [note 15]

Consciousness, on the other hand, is located almost entirely in the left rear brain, as is also the ability to understand the speech of others and the ability to produce grammatically correct responses. The left brain is not aware of the right. This is, in fact, extensible to all right cerebral activities, most notably to mental dysfunctions. Oliver Sacks details this in case studies, in *The Man who Mistook his Wife for his Hat* (1970). We live in our consciousness, unaware of the input from the right hemisphere.

Bicameral kingdoms have a number of features in common, including the following.

- First, there was either a city God, with the city and surrounding area operated as a theocracy, or a king, who was held to be the God or the Son of the God and was revered as such, even after his death. Theocracies included Sumer and, later, Akkad (in fact, all Mesopotamia remained as theocracies up to Persian times), India, China, and all of Mesoamerica. Societies under the direct rule of God or the Son of God included Egypt, Japan, and the Inca empire.

- Second, the dead in these societies were considered alive in some way, and in need of material goods, especially foods, to accompany them in their graves. This practice actually extends far back into more remote antiquity, but becomes obsessive with the bicameral kingdoms. The new kingdoms initially buried their kings complete with their retinue. This practice seldom lasted more than a few generations in Egypt, but continued for 700 years under the Shang dynasty of China (and was only prohibited by the Chou after circa 1000 BC). The 200-year-old Inca kingdom still practiced it in AD 1532 when the Spanish arrived. In bicameral kingdoms throughout the world, people (and certainly the elite) were believed to become Gods on their death. The enormous ceremonial center of Teotihuacan in Mexico (200 BC to AD 700), at one time supporting 200,000 inhabitants, was known as "the Place Where Men Become Gods." [note 16]

- Third, the kingdoms of the "God on Earth" were jealous of any competing Gods, including those which had come before, and would destroy all signs of the preceding Gods, just as the cities of Sumer and Akkad would readily attack their contemporaries and haul off the God statues from the temples of nearby cities. The destruction of all previous records by edict of the Emperor of China in 213 BC is an example. The Aztecs destroyed all the manuscripts of their predecessors in the Valley of Mexico shortly after AD 1400. The priests who followed the Spanish invaders into the Yucatan in the following century burned all the books of the Maya.

- Fourth, the citizens were incapable of deceit, or more fundamentally, incapable of imagining the deceit of others. Not that these people could not lie or steal, but they were incapable of mentally "narratizing" a complex series of deceptive actions either by others or by themselves. This is vividly illustrated with the Inca empire, which had subdued half the South American continent, only to fall to the deceit of a handful of Spanish soldiers.

As a corollary it should also be noted that these people had no morals -- there was no such thing as good or bad. Actions were ordered and the humans responded like robots. The heroes of the *Iliad* were motivated by glory and shame, without regard for their own life, as were the Spartans who held off the Persian army at Thermopylae in 480 BC. In the vacuum left by the departure of the Gods, religion had substituted prescribed duties for individual judgment and assumed the absolutist attitudes understood as the prerogative of the earlier Gods. What is absolutely astounding is that these attitudes lasted over 4500 years after the collapse of the "Era of the Gods" -- as in the case of the Incas, for example.

What we have in these civilizations are people desperately holding on to the past. They considered themselves "slaves of the Gods," only now it was the local God in residence at each temple who needed to be housed, fed, and adorned. Everyone was employed in the service of the Gods, and surplus produce and products from the countryside surrounding a temple were collected (as a tax) for the upkeep of the temple God, for redistribution to temple craftsmen, and for long-distance trade for building materials and more exotic materials. All humans were as deeply invested in their assigned tasks as the worker bees of a hive. [note 17]

Population explosions are certainly the mark of each of these empires, including those which did not appear until long after the departure of the Gods, and Jaynes proposes that the elements of the bicameral kingdoms arise out of the need to control these large populations. But I question this. There is ample evidence that these kingdoms were voluntary societies where massive public works, whether digging irrigation canals or monumental building construction, were accomplished without coercion. This last becomes obvious with a closer look at the histories of Maya ceremonial centers. These were built with volunteer labor which depended only on the citizens' confidence in the leaders' connection with the spirit world. [note 18]

Jaynes suggests that these early civilizations were pre-conscious -- that is, not subjectively conscious. He suggests societies in which control was effected through auditory commands from the "Gods" -- actually the remembered admonitions of the governing class. This kept everyone to their task, and kept all things in order. Jaynes's use of "hearing the commands of the Gods" is a shorthand for the admonishing voice (which we still hear today) generated by the right hemisphere of the brain. In essence, these people, and perhaps especially the ruling class, were hallucinating. This description has turned some people away from a careful consideration of Jaynes's theories even though it is an accepted fact that the speech center of the right hemisphere acts as a separate but unconscious entity. [note 19]

But pre-subjective people are entirely functional humans. They can learn anything, including any skill, reading, and mathematics, they have the same sense of humor as the rest of us, they experience and express emotions, and they can converse with others in intricate details. It is difficult to distinguish bicameral humans from subjectively conscious humans. You will find yourself persuaded by each of the long soliloquies of the war chiefs of the *Iliad* when they meet in council -- yet no one among them takes action without receiving a command from a God. Bicameral humans seem normal. However, they rely heavily on the learned admonitions of parents and authority figures (blurting things out without any forethought, invariably in the context of "ought" or "should") and have great difficulty with novel situations. New situations require the ability to imagine a number of alternative actions which might be taken and then to make a selection based on the imagined results. A pre-conscious human does not have the ability to imagine the thinking of others, especially reflectively; that is, how others might imagine them as thinking.

The Flood of Noah

There is a disturbance in 2349 BC, 800 years after the flood of 3147 BC. There are changes in climate, noted by many researchers, perhaps to a limited extent in the Middle East, but apparently also in China. This is followed about 150 years later by an extended period of drought and dust storms, starting in 2193 BC.

From the interval of 156 years between these two climatic events, we would conclude that Earth was four times involved in an encounter with Venus, on a cycle of 52-year intervals. The interval of 52 years between events becomes a clear hallmark of disturbances by Venus and both 52-year and 104-year intervals between certain events are remembered by other nations at a later date. The 52-year cycle is assured, even for remote antiquity and even though the Earth's orbit would be different. See Appendix B, "The Celestial Mechanics," for how the interval can be derived for various periods in the past.

I would suggest, as others have also, that the planet Venus was the agent of the disturbances in 2349 and 2193 BC. In fact, we can be certain that Venus appeared a total of four times during this period. [note 20]

The first appearance of 2349 BC was absolutely spectacular and, at the same time, so psychologically disturbing to people the world over that this single event is frequently recorded as the very start of history -- often as a retelling of the flood of 3147 BC (as in the "flood of Noah"), coupled with the first appearance of the Moon. The most frightening aspect of 2349 BC was what looked like the collapse of the ocean in the south sky, the Absu. It was thought to have fallen onto the Earth like a flood, for the commotion in the sky was accompanied by endless rains and storms. The other disturbance was that the sky turned blood red. [note 21]

Claude Schaeffer, in *Stratigraphie comparée et chronologie de l'Asie occidentale* (1948), wrote:

> *"The great perturbations which left their traces in the stratigraphy of the principal sites of the Bronze Age of Western Asia are six in number. The oldest among them shook, between 2400 and 2300, all of the land extending from the Caucasus in the north down to the valley of the Nile, where it became one of the causes, if not the principal cause, of the fall of the Egyptian Old Kingdom after the death of Pepi II."*

Schaeffer's estimate brackets 2349 BC, the first strike by Venus. The "traces" of 2400 BC to 2300 BC extended over a very wide area in the Middle East, from Persia to Greece, and included "violent earthquakes and tidal waves, and other signs of a natural disaster" (paraphrased by Velikovsky). But it becomes obvious that what we are seeing is a swath of destruction only extending over part of Northern Iran, Anatolia, part of the Levant, and Greece, with little or no evidence in Mesopotamia or Egypt (despite what Schaeffer wrote about "the Nile valley").

It would seem that the event of this era caused an expanding circle of destruction throughout South Central Asia (the location of Indian civilization), the Eastern Mediterranean, throughout Southern Europe and parts of North Africa, plus China. Other areas we are not aware of, because they were not built up with cities. There is little indication that the seismic shock crossed the Atlantic to make contact with America. Worldwide, the destruction in this instance seems to have been limited to earthquakes.

At the first instant the crust of the Earth would have been subjected to a severe compressive force due to the electric repulsion between Earth and Venus -- but only for a period of a half hour or less. The compressive forces would have been followed by lifting forces as a result of an induced charge of opposite polarity. (More on the sequence in Appendix B, "The Celestial Mechanics.") Areas adjacent to the "impact area" would have experienced an uplift initially. Areas outside of the region of the initial "contact" would have been subjected to lateral seismic forces (earthquakes) as seismic shock waves spread around the Earth.

The destruction described by Schaeffer apparently pertains mostly to the end of this period, 2193 BC, when agriculture fails worldwide.

There seems to be no evidence of large-scale fires at the earlier date of 2349 BC. The damages noted by Schaeffer (he only presents information for the region west of the Himalayas) were due to seismic waves resulting from the initial compressive force to the part of the Earth that faced Venus, followed by somewhat later lifting forces. The earthquakes would have been astounding.

The contact with the plasmasphere of Venus would have resulted in an attempted charge equalization through the delivery of lightning bolts. At a closer distance between the two planets, such massive lightning strikes would have been capable of melting mountaintops, ripping out and incinerating forests, and lifting boulders and hilltops into the vortex of a fiery hurricane which would have moved west at over 500 miles per hour (800 km per hr), which is the linear speed of rotation of Earth at 30 to 40 degrees latitude. Traveling lightning bolts would have incinerated forests and grasslands, resulting in placing nanometer carbon dust in the stratosphere, with a resulting shadow extending over all of the Earth for centuries.

But in 2349 BC, there was nothing like that, as far as we can tell. This was not a traveling lightning strike, for there was no close electric connection to Venus. The planet was 20,000,000 miles (32,000,000 km) away (probably 17.5 million at a minimum, see later calculations).

In 2349 BC there was no follow-up lightning strike. This was an unusual condition and unexpected, but kept the Earth from experiencing the massive forest fires resulting from a traveling arc, and the darkness which could have followed the fires for hundreds of years. But, as mythological sources in India, Canaan, Mesoamerica, and China have it, the charge equalization consisted of a plasmoid arriving from 20,000,000 miles away. The event of 2349 BC did not result in a darkening of the skies as would be indicated by a failure of agriculture worldwide. We would also have to assume that the plasmoid dissipated at the Van Allen Belts or the ionosphere. The charge which held the dust of the Absu in suspension may have saved the Earth from being incinerated.

In this case, where the plasmoids had to travel a very large distance, the charge equalization (the thunderbolt) would have arrived late. The first plasmoid from Venus took six hours to arrive (in my estimate). See the chapter "The Day of the Dead," for details of travel time and speed. Also, from descriptions we have, it looks as if the initial gigantic plasmoid was followed by 9 smaller ones. This too, is expected for such a very remote interaction.

However, there was of course a "flood" thought to be associated with this electric contact, for it looked as if the Absu fell and drained onto the Earth -- although actually discharging to the upper atmosphere and causing severe rain storms. The disappearance of the "sea" of the Absu would have been enough to convince everyone of where the rain and storm water came from. The event was understood everywhere as a "flood" from the sky -- in the Eastern Mediterranean, in China, in the Americas.

From the damage done in the Eastern Mediterranean north of about 33 degrees latitude we know that the initial repulsive blow from Venus was delivered north of the equator, and the Earth's rotational axis would have undergone a gyroscopic reaction as the northern hemisphere was shoved away from the Sun. Thus the path of potential destruction (as an arc was delivered) would have traveled at an angle inclined to the equator, so that Western North Africa could have fallen on the path. By the time Central America faced Venus the gyroscopic reaction would have started to carry the equator back "down" to where it belonged, so that the remaining path of destruction angled up again. I'll develop more details in the next chapter.

The second appearance of Venus in 2297 BC and the third in 2245 BC seem to have left no record that we are aware of. Yet it is certain that these happened. People took no note in myths and histories because the results were not spectacular or religiously significant. The last event in 2193 BC will be discussed separately below. Again, as with the previous two, the contact in 2193 BC was not noted in any records. But in this case we have substantial secondary data available.

The first event, of 2349 BC, marks the traditional Noachian flood. It involved an electric contact with Venus which increased the orbit of the Earth, bringing Earth close to the established location of the Moon. It also resulted in a sudden dispersal of the equatorial rings of the Earth, accompanied by storms, rains, and hurricanes, which became known in the Bible as the "flood of Noah," or, as the Sumerians and Akkadians called it, the "flood after the flood." [note 22]

The story of Noah and the flood is well known from the Bible. But, as I pointed out in a previous chapter, flood stories are ubiquitous. People in all regions of the world have flood stories. Most of these stories show no signs of having been borrowed from other people, yet they all involve the same elements -- a worldwide inundation, survival of a few people with their animals in an ark, a boat, or a canoe, and anchorage at a mountain while waiting for the waters to subside.

When the Sumerian *Epic of Gilgamesh* became available in translation in Europe in the 19th century, it astounded everyone -- for it contained a clear description of the events of the flood of Noah, including the ark, the animals, and sending out birds to test for dry land. However, both the flood of Gilgamesh and the flood of Noah are the conflation of the Black Sea flood of 5600 BC and the worldwide flood in 3147 BC.

In 5600 BC, Noah didn't build an ark. As a Black Sea fisherman, he had a boat. He didn't collect all the animals in the world, only his family and farm animals, and as much seed and fodder as possible. He didn't moor at a mountain in Northern Iran, but landed at the river Halys or rounded the Anatolian plateau to land in the depression between the Pontic Mountains (bordering the Black Sea in the south) and the Caucasus Mountains (to the east of the Black Sea). From there, his "survival story" spread south into Iran and Anatolia, eventually to reach the plains of Mesopotamia and the Levant. After another flood and the passage of nearly two thousand years, the ark was the Sun-lit crescent on Jupiter, and the mountaintop of the anchorage was the lower plasma tail of Jupiter, decked in green. But they had been seen by all.

To the Hebrew priests who compiled the books of the Bible after 536 BC, the flood was an actual event experienced in 2349 BC. It was, for them, the only flood ever and the centerpoint of their people's history. However, the date, although widely accepted among Christians since Bible chronologies were established in the 17th century (Ussher and Newton), is backed up by very little physical evidence. (I will return to this in the next chapter.) Some think it may have been a local event. We are not even certain where in the Middle East Noah was to be found in 2400 BC. It might have been Anatolia, Mesopotamia, or the Levant, or even Arabia (with some scholars suggesting India).

The chronology of Mesopotamia (Akkadia) is only firmly established after the putative "flood of Noah," but there is no mention of a flood. The only strong coincidence is from China, where in 200 BC, long before Christian influences, the catastrophic flooding of China was dated to 2350 BC. The people of Mesoamerica also date one of the "creations of the world" to this time. I will return to this also in a later chapter. [note 23]

The Jewish world history (the Bible) was compiled sometime after 536 BC, when Cyrus allowed the Jews to leave their Babylonian captivity and return to their homeland with orders to rebuild the temple of their God. Cyrus financed the rebuilding and returned to them the "vessels of the temple." We could presume that their books and records were returned with these. The earliest of these books, Genesis, which includes the story of the flood of Noah, was held by tradition to have been written by Moses a thousand years earlier, after 1490 BC.

The priests subsequently edited and collated their books into a history of the world -- a creation epic. The editors must certainly have been familiar with the thousand-year-old Babylonian *Enuma Elish* creation epic, which at that time constituted the only other recorded history of the world from creation onward. (The *Enuma Elish* retells the flood stories found in earlier Sumerian epics.) But the *Enuma Elish* dealt with multiple Gods, and the Hebrews were monotheistic. I would also assume the editors knew the epic literature of Akkad and the *King List* of Sumer. We would have to assume that the Bible editors knew that the list of the "Kings before the Flood" was recorded in days, not years. And it would have been known by the editors that in a previous era the year was shorter (having all but witnessed the change in the year's length which happened in 747 BC), and that it was even shorter in earlier times -- or, in another way of understanding, that people lived longer lives. Their sacred book would certainly conform to these oldest known histories of the world, but would be populated with their own patriarchs and informed by their own records.

It is generally assumed that the Bible is derived from Mesopotamian records and legends. I do not think this is likely. I think it is a parallel record, perhaps partially oral, which was brought into conformity to known records at this late date. The flood of Noah is, in fact, only one of the world's more than 500 parallel flood stories. It is also sufficiently different from the Mesopotamian flood legend to be considered as standing on its own. [note 24]

The history of the world as presented in the Bible is, at any rate, unique. It presents a record of creation which parallels the Mesopotamian creation epics (and those of many other people) but conceives of a God outside of the visible domain of this world. This last is the result of a change in humanity's point of view on the Gods seen throughout the world after 650 or 600 BC, which will be discussed in a later chapter.

The Bible thus dispenses with the multiplicity of Gods of the other nearby cultures and remains consistently monotheistic. In itself, this is not unique. The Chinese were monotheistic, at least to the point of acknowledging a single supreme God, as were the Persians. But the book of Genesis, for example, takes the signs in the sky, which the other cultures had equated to distinct Gods, and treats them as humans. One description especially, the creation of Eve, stands out, as follows:

Adam is the lonely globe of Saturn in the sky. God -- the God outside of creation -- takes pity on him and creates a woman for him by extracting a rib and subsequently healing the wound. This is clearly the image of the expulsion of Venus from the side of Saturn, still connected with a rib-like plasma appendage. The image was common to the experience of all the tribes of the Eastern Mediterranean, but the interpretation by Moses was unique.

The Bible gives no date for the flood of Noah, but notes other events after the flood which can be matched to known dates. A correlation of Biblical events to known dates was attempted by James Bishop Ussher in AD 1650 and still stands as a classic work. Ussher dates the start of the "Universal Flood of Noah" at 2349 BC and the end at 2348 BC. [note 25]

The "flood of Noah" happened as the Earth's orbit increased and Earth joined the Moon at the Moon's established orbit. The result was that the Moon revolves around the Earth in a plane tilted up at about 5 degrees (as seen from Earth) -- not on the Earth's equator, but otherwise at the same average distance from the Sun. I suspect (from the records presented as sculptures at Maya Palenque) that the Moon did not fall into a regular orbit until 2283 BC, some 50 years after it first appeared. The Chinese *Shu King* claims it took 30 years.

The appearance of the Moon probably marks the "sign in the heavens" after the flood of the Bible. It is the end of the "time before the Moon" noted by Aristotle and others in antiquity. "Sin" ("Moon") becomes popular as a personal name in Akkadian Mesopotamia after 2350 BC. Sargon of Akkad, who conquered Sumer shortly after "Noah's flood," appoints his daughter as priestess of the Moon god ("Nanna" in Sumerian) of the Sumerian city of Ur. His granddaughter held the same position.

A Second Strike

The event of 2349 BC is followed by another worldwide disturbance in 2193 BC (three times 52 years, 156 years later). Again Venus makes an electric contact with Earth, the fourth in this era. With this event climatic changes are recorded worldwide, with social upheavals and abandonment of settlements spanning two hundred years. With this second event the Old Kingdom in Egypt comes to a sudden end, not to recover for more than 185 years. [note 26]

At the same time the Mesopotamian empire of Akkad collapses. Sumer had been conquered by Sargon of Akkad in 2335 BC, part of an empire of conquest which stretched from Elam on the Persian gulf to the Mediterranean. But his dynasty's brief hold is lost in 2193, coincident with the second disturbance. The empire fails economically and the barbarian tribes of the Zagros mountains descend into the Akkadian plain. Even a hundred years later the land of Akkad laments:

> *"The large fields and acres produced no grain*
> *The flooded fields produced no fish*
> *The watered gardens produced no honey and wine*
> *The heavy clouds did not rain"*
>   -- City of Akkad, circa 2100 BC.

Some climatologists have assumed that Mesopotamia and Egypt lacked rains during this 200-year period following 2193 BC. But the laments from Akkad, quoted above, do not speak of a lack of water, but of a lack of growth. This speaks of a downturn in temperature and, most likely, a lack of sunlight. It is very similar to the darkness which will envelop the world 700 years later, after 1492 BC, when the Hebrews "walked in darkness" and Mesoamerican recollections claim that a generation of people grew up in darkness. An oceanic strike of an arc from Venus traveling partway around the world would not have produced a cloud cover lasting for years. But an arc traveling across the land of Earth would cause extensive fires. This is probably the most likely cause for the 200 years of darkness.

There is other data from this 156-year era. The endless reconstruction of Stonehenge is interrupted for 200 years after circa 2400 BC. Malta, with its temples and worship of the Fat Lady, is vacant after 2200 BC. Two hundred years of wind-blown dust and volcanic ash show up in the Eastern Mediterranean after 2200 BC. The Indus river fails to produce enough water for agriculture and the parallel Sarasvati river dries up. The Harappan culture along the Indus (of over 250 cities and villages) declines slowly and disappears by 1900 BC. The Indus river region (lower Pakistan) turns into a desert. China's culture nearly falters. European construction of grave barrows ends for the most part by circa 2000 BC. [note 27]

The strange specificity of the area of destruction in the Middle East has suggested an air blast to some researchers, perhaps a Tunguska-like meteoric event -- an exploding bolide arriving from space. But most likely the two disturbances of 2349 and 2193 BC, the flood of Noah, the later demise of the Old Kingdom of Egypt along with the collapse of Akkad, were caused by the electric interactions of Venus. The restricted path of destruction, the damage caused by fires (also localized), the tilting (gyroscopic swing) of the axis (which is recorded in legend in China and as history in Mesoamerica), and then the later blockage of sunlight for an extended period of time, are all the marks of an alignment with a large planet and its electric field interaction with Earth. I will offer some additional details in the next chapter.

The two disturbances were 156 years apart, three times 52 years. The period of 52 years will remain as the mark of Venus's interactions with Earth: an 800-year span where nothing significant happens, then two or more contacts at 52 year intervals (or some variation of 52 years). In both 2349 BC and in 2193 BC the orbit of Earth changed. The year changed to 260 days in 2349 BC, and (I suspect) to 273 days in 2193 BC. [note 28]

After a few hundred years, Egypt will reorganize as the Middle Kingdom and start in again to build pyramids as grave markers and will do so for another thousand years, spreading ever further south along the Nile. Akkad and China also recover. The Harappan cultivation of the Indus valley is abandoned as its people move into the Ganges region.

In the next era, Mercury will become a prominent God while Venus will continue to lurk in the background. In the next chapter I will turn to some additional important considerations of the events surrounding the "flood of Noah."

Endnotes

Note 1 --

A similar condition with respect to the southern sky as a destination for the dead, occurs in the central Valley of Mexico, as related by the Spanish historian Sahagún in the 16th century AD, and quoted by Javier Urcid in *Zapotec Writing, Knowledge, Power, and Memory in Ancient Oaxaca* (2005). We have the following:

"And also they caused him [the deceased] *to carry a little dog, a yellow one; they fixed about its neck a loose cotton cord. It was said that* [the dog] *bore* [the dead one] *across the place of the nine rivers in the land of the dead ... And when the four years had ended, thereupon* [the dead one] *went to the nine lands of the dead,* [where] *lay a broad river. There the dogs carried one across."*

As I have already pointed out in previous chapters, the "nine rivers" are the Mesoamerican equivalent of the Duat, called the "House of Nine Bushes" in the *Chilam Balam*. The "broad river" is the ecliptic, which was noted as appearing about "2 or 3 degrees wide" in the early 19th century of the current era. In the 16th century AD the river of the ecliptic was still visible.

Note 2 --

As I have pointed out earlier, for Jupiter to have looked the same diameter as the Moon, at the eventual location at 5.2 AU from the Sun, with the Earth at 1 AU from the Sun, the coma would have been nearly 3.5 million miles in diameter (using the tangent of 1/2 degree for the size of the Moon). The dark mode plasmasphere of Jupiter today is still 3.5 million miles wide (5.6 million km). A coma of this size would have encompassed the Earth if it had developed before Jupiter entered the asteroid belt -- but without ill effects to Earth.

Because the asteroid belt provided multiple targets for plasma discharges, I do not think a large coma was needed as Jupiter traveled to the end of the belt at a distance of about 4 AU from the Sun.

If Plutarch's Zarathustrian sources are correct, and Jupiter initially looked to be three times the diameter of the Moon, then when Jupiter first exited the last clump of the asteroid belt at about 4.7 AU, the coma would at that time have had a diameter of 10 million miles (16 million km).

Note 3 --

"Rounded like a hat" can also be read as "sharply pointed" or could mean "shaped." The 16th century AD *Chilam Balam* dealing with ancient celestial phenomena apparently copied from illustrated glyphic bark books of great antiquity. We are here encountering a verbal description of an image for which the physical basis had been lost to memory. The "pointed hat buttocks" is probably a reasonable description of a depiction of the coma extending from the bottom of Jupiter.

"Sitting on his mat," however, is normally considered as a metaphor for rulership.

Note 4 --

City walls are not necessarily for defense. The first use of walls around compounds of buildings was probably to protect cattle or sheep from predators, like the "kraal" of 19th century Zulu villages, or as flood control. Lions roamed Persia well into Roman times, and would probably make excursions into the Mesopotamian lowlands for a kill.

But it must have become obvious before long that walls would also keep people from neighboring cities out. The walls around Jericho are a curious exception if seen as protection, as is the Jericho tower, since they were built much too early (6000 BC). It could be suggested that the tower was built to observe the southern ball plasmoid. In that case Jericho is no longer a cattle-trading town, but a religious center.

One might question the genesis of the planned cities arising in Mesopotamia and the Indus valley which seem to spring into being with no previous examples. The beginnings of the Harappan culture has not been dated, since earliest levels are below ground water. But I would suspect them to date to after 3000 or 2700 BC. This culture had examples of earlier cities -- in Iran and Baluchistan. The first cities in Southern Mesopotamia appear after 2700 BC, maybe earlier. They follow on earlier small villages and individual housing. Mesopotamian cities may have been derived from Iran, and certainly from the cities in Anatolia.

We should distinguish between villages and cities. Villages are a function of the availability of resources. If you live in a river valley where there is water, where you can plant, and surrounded by forests where you can hunt and cut lumber, it makes sense to settle a village near the water and farm land even if there are no more than a few families. People only live together when it makes sense to do so. Villages in forested Central Europe after 5600 BC are all located along river valleys.

Cities, on the other hand, are by and large based at a central temple, which soon become the centers for the manufacture of goods for trade. The temple compounds often precede the city, as for Uruk in Mesopotamia which is built adjacent to the earlier temple E-ana. Similarly in Egypt, and in Mesoamerica, it is the ceremonial centers which precede cities.

In Mesopotamia the cities were built by an immigrant people who had already lived in grouped houses (perhaps in Iran) for over a thousand years, or who may have come from Anatolia which boasts numerous cities much older than the Sumerian culture in Southern Mesopotamia. They moved into the flatlands of the Euphrates and Tigris because of the potential productivity (discovered earlier by local people). Much the same happens with the Indus valley Harappan civilization. These people had moved out from Baluchistan and probably also from the foothills near the source of the Indus and Ganges.

It looks like there was a sudden increase in population after 3100 BC in the agricultural centers of the world. As the climate became drier and colder, there were mass migrations of people from lands where the archaeology suggests more primitive conditions for housing, but not with respect to agriculture and animal husbandry. When groups strike out to new lands they are organized and naturally would plan their "new" cities with some reasonable order.

Having lived elsewhere in cities which had grown in helter-skelter fashion, it can be understood why the new cities were carefully planned in a grid fashion, and, as for example in the Indus valley, which were built from the start with sewers and running water.

This is not a case of foragers suddenly settling down. The foragers were probably largely killed in 3147 BC when coastal regions and lowlands flooded. Even if people survived, the game probably did not. The survivors of the flood are to be found in mountainous regions and far inland away from seas, coasts, and low areas. The farmers who suddenly appear after 3100 all come from the slopes and foothills of mountains. The survivors are those who had already learned to plant in addition to "gathering." In the lowlands of India or Pakistan there is no evidence of a prior foraging (hunter/ gatherer) population before 3100 BC.

Note 5 --

"... for nothing is older in human history than seeing the past as exemplary (the 'Golden Age'), the present as deficient, and then trying to restore conditions as they used to be. Few Egyptian Pharaohs came to the throne without undertaking to restore things 'as they were in the beginning.' That is, of course, the hallmark of the conservatism of traditional cultures. All traditional human societies justify their practices either by saying, 'that is the way things have always been,' or,

if origins are in issue, by saying that the gods established things that way. Mythic accounts may or may not have been offered, briefly or elaborately, to explain how or why the gods did establish things in the proper way. Eventually the explanation becomes the thing itself, and the historical dimension is simply eliminated, as religions like Judaism, Christianity, and Islam directly present the founding commands of God in revelatory literature."

    -- Kelley L. Ross, 1996 [www.friesian.com/conserv.htm]

Note 6 --

    Denise Schmandt-Besserat writes, in *Before Writing, From Counting to Cuneiform* (1992):

"The tokens were an entirely new medium for conveying information. Compared to the previous tallies, the conceptual leap was to endow each token shape, such as the cone, sphere, or disk, with a specific meaning. ... The token system was, in fact, the first code -- the earliest system of signs used for transmitting information."

    The use of ideograms or pictograms, pictures which stood for short nouns and eventually sounds, was in use from circa 3200 BC in Mesopotamia. Cuneiform is a more rapid "longhand" abbreviation of the "pictures." The cuneiform script eventually expanded to some 600 glyphs, representing short words or sounds, and was firmly established probably by circa 2800 BC in Mesopotamia.

[Image: Mesopotamian tokens. After Schmandt-Besserat.]

The use of pictograms, some identical to the original Mesopotamian, continued in Egypt, but were soon reduced to the sounds of syllables. It took 1500 years before an alphabetical script was introduced. Perhaps the reason the cuneiform never moved directly to an alphabet (the cuneiform was abandoned) is because the concept of an alphabet requires something entirely different. It requires sounds -- not words -- to be mapped to a flat space. This space, where sounds have a one-to-one (analogical) relationship to marks, has to be imagined and recognized. The alphabet probably derived from the sounds of Egyptian hieroglyphs.

Egypt, China, and Mesoamerica all developed mixtures of phoneme-based syllabaries, but none of them developed alphabets. The syllabary scripts of China and Mesoamerica had the advantage of being able to be read over a wide range of languages, since sounds were not strictly represented. The scripts were like magic.

On the other hand, it is not at all obvious that speech consists of finite units like consonants and vowels, as is easily demonstrated from the first writing efforts of the young. The leap to representing individual sounds first shows in the prefixes used with the signs of cuneiform, as it does in the word-sound signs added to both the Maya glyphs and the Chinese script -- but they did not move beyond the specific functional addition made to the syllabaries.

The first alphabet was a vowel-less set of signs introduced in Canaan circa 1500 BC, generally attributed to the Phoenicians, but probably based on the Egyptian demotic (longhand) which was already reduced to assigning sounds to glyphs. Once demonstrated, it spread like wildfire. It was quickly adopted by traders of the Levant (and by Moses). The Greeks added vowels needed for their vocalization in about 700 BC. Alphabets eventually spread even to barbarian Northern Europe where one form, known as the "Futhorc," is obviously based on Roman letters. But the ciphers of many other European barbarian alphabets show no relationship to known letter forms at all, demonstrating that it was the idea that was transmitted rather than the letters.

See especially H. W. F. Saggs, *Civilization before Greece and Rome* (1989), who lucidly describes writing (plus other topics) in Egypt, Mesopotamia, and Canaan.

Note 7 --

"Ideas such as objectified conceptions of a mind, or even the notion of something spiritual being manifested, are of much later development. It is generally agreed that the ancient Egyptian language, like the Sumerian, was concrete from first to last. To maintain that it is expressing abstract thoughts would seem to me an intrusion of the modern idea that men have always been the same."

-- Julian Jaynes *The Origins of Consciousness in the Breakdown of the Bicameral Mind* (1976)

Note 8 --

There are disadvantages also. We are so easily convinced of the validity of our metaphorical thinking, that we end up fooling ourselves.

*"It is one of the lessons of logic, dutifully repeated in its textbooks, that 'analogy is not proof.' But to humans of all times, analogy **must be** proof. The most marvelous sense of power, intellectually and behaviorally, comes from the association of the tiniest events and observations with the nature and conduct of the great universe."*
    -- Alfred de Grazia, *Homo Schizo, Human and Cultural Hologenesis* (1983?)

Another failing of speakers of Indo-European languages, and perhaps some other cultures who are similarly inclined, is to jump to conclusions about causal connections simply because two events follow each other in time.

Note 9 --

See the chapter "Language and Causality," where this is more fully developed.

Note 10 --

I would suspect that the delay in subjective consciousness in this instance might largely be due to the limited exposure to new people. The Eastern Mediterranean, in contrast, was constantly overrun by foreign tribes seeking better environments, especially after both 1500 BC and 800 BC. The same was true of China.

Consciousness also insinuated itself for totally different reasons, dating from after 2000 BC (Jaynes suggests), as writing came into greater use. Trade would have been an immense influence (meeting different people), as would the increased use of scripts for state administration. Jaynes, in fact, claims that the use of the scripts of the "talking tablets" displaced the voice of a person to an object, driving spoken commands into silence, and requiring the reader to listen to the tablet, rather than imagining a person dictating the text. The communications of Hammurabi (circa 1700 BC) to his distant government officials were addressed not to them, but to the tablets he wrote (in his own hand!)

Note 11 --

I wonder how much of a lack of *subjective consciousness* existed among the world's foraging populations, or if it had already developed. Hunters are required to be smarter than farmers. They need to previsualize their quarry, understand their habits, walk their territory, and plot a catch. That requires a lot more mental space than the rote repetition of wielding a hoe. This would suggest, in turn, that the God-obsessed farming populations were more prone to remain pre-conscious. However, in a previous chapter I have applied a pre-conscious condition to the Western European Cro-Magnon cave painters (and hunters) as a reasonable explanation of why nothing changed in their depiction technique for 30,000 years.

Note 12 --

We do remember the physical spaces that we learn to navigate as a child, the people we deal with, and thousands of other details which become assigned to near-automatic behavior. This is mainly a right brain function.

Note 13 --

"This process by which the early gods reappear in later legends under human or semihuman form ... can be observed in many parts of the world, notably in India and Scandinavia. There is no question of historical characters being invested with divinity. A detailed examination of all ancient religions, not to mention new ones, ... shows that the Gods were originally more abstract and general forces which gradually degenerated and became anthropomorphic or zoomorphic"
    -- Jean Markale *The Celts, Uncovering the Mythic and Historic Origins of Western Culture* (1978)

I would argue against the "abstract and general forces" and insist that the gods were instantly recognized as giant supernatural beings (and thus in a manner anthropomorphized), and only assumed human dimensions at a later date after they disappeared from view.

It seems likely that the predilection of our ancestors (and "primitives") for colorful decorations of bright bird feathers and oversized or outlandish headdresses reflects the colorful auroral plasma displays surrounding Saturn when he stood above the pole, as well as the plume-like headgear worn by planets in glow mode plasma displays. The same would be true of the crowns of kings and the halos of saints.

Note 14 --

The note about Sahagún is from Charles Mann, *1491, New Revelations of the Americas before Columbus* (2006). Mann uses this to demonstrate that the Aztec were hardly "savages." The Aztec philosophers, by the way, seem to have bested the Spanish in the discussions. Admittedly, a complex theology is not sufficient to suggest subjective consciousness, for we see the same in Egypt of the Old Kingdom and Middle Kingdom before 1500 BC. The status of consciousness ought to be sought in the accommodation of the Aztec to the religious environment of the Central Mexican region, which they invaded 200 years before the Spanish arrived, and their subsequent relationship to the Spanish. This should be considered, despite the fact that their relationship to the Gods was one of control (which reflected also in their relationship with other tribes) rather than the Mediterranean concept of having to placate the Gods.

Linda Schele and David Freidel, in *Maya Cosmos* (1993) attribute the collapse of the Maya in AD 900 to internecine warfare, not to a religious collapse (which would be an index of the lack of subjective consciousness), as Jaynes suggested 30 years ago, based on limited information available to Jaynes at that time. Similarly the destruction of ceremonial sites in the Valley of Mexico was not always accomplished for religious reasons. Many centers were destroyed by marauding invaders.

However, it is important to emphasize that pre-conscious people are almost indistinguishable from subjectively conscious people, and the only real hint pointing to a lack of subjective consciousness is the inability to deal with new situations. This was not true of the Maya and the Mexicans at the time of the Spanish invasion, but I will go with Jaynes's opinion in the case of the Inca empire, although this is influenced by my lack of knowledge of the specifics of the change in South America from indigenous religions to Christianity. The Maya and Mexica, on the other hand, seem to have integrated local traditions (or, more importantly, their philosophy) and Christianity very rapidly.

Note 15 --

See Julian Jaynes, *The Origin of Consciousness in the Breakdown of the Bicameral Mind* (1976), for additional details.

Note 16 --

The belief by Mesoamerican cultures in an afterlife at the time of the invasion is now disputed. See Charles Mann, *1491, New Revelations of the*

Americas before Columbus (2006). The ceremonial centers serviced the elite and the states. Instead of benefiting the population by supplying promises of an afterlife, the benefit was reaped in earthly terms -- good harvests, long life, many children -- through the intervention with the Gods by the ceremonial chiefs. When these were not forthcoming, the population would abandon the ceremonial centers at the drop of a hat.

Note 17 --

It is amazing that in Mesopotamia kingship and trade remained secular in most respects. The Kings were only infrequently promoted to the status of Gods, unlike Egypt, and the relationship of traders to the temple enterprises is not clear at all. The trade also supplied the elite with luxury materials. This condition arose from the fact that Sumer has no natural resources outside of agricultural products.

We have no clear indication of "temple economies" in China, since there are no accounting records on clay as in Mesopotamia or testimonials carved in stone as in Egypt. But there was an economy based on supplying the elite of the very large imperial court, the provincial governors and their staff, as well as the armies, with food and luxury goods.

Note 18 --

The Maya never supported standing armies, or a police force.

I disagree with Jaynes's contention that "authority" was needed to "control" groups of people through leadership, especially large groups. A look at the Plains Indians shows this is not so. See, for instance, Robert Utley, *The Lance and the Shield, The life and Times of Sitting Bull* (1993) or see Linda Schele and David Freidel, *A Forest of Kings* (1990) on the Maya. The need for authority is necessary to gregarious species, like us humans. But it need not be a matter of imposed control, and all indications from graves and houses before 3100 BC in Egypt and the Near East is that there was no leadership elite.

Note 19 --

Jaynes admits that perhaps people whose role was closest to the upper levels of leadership would be most under the influence of the hallucinating voices of the Gods.

It should be remembered that the concept of "free will" does not develop philosophically until the Classical Age of Greece and the concept of "chance" remains forbidden well past the Middle Ages of Europe.

Even today we see, as an example, that "moral development" -- a term designating the ability to make independent ethical judgments -- correlates inversely with religiosity, a belief in the importance of law, and in general with conservative beliefs. See Lee Wilkins *The Moral Media: How Journalists Reason About Ethics* (2005).

Note 20 --

Among the conditions for a plasma contact between Venus and Earth is the geometry of a transit of the Sun. Today the transits of Venus (when it moves across the face of the Sun) happen 4 times on a cycle of 243 years, in two sets of two transits, which are 8 years apart. The interval between the sets of pairs alternates between 121.5 and 105.5 years.

The use of a 52-year period (and the date of 2193 BC) is from Timo Niroma (at [personal.eunet.fi/pp/tilmari], which fits well with a number of other suppositions. It is perhaps a lucky guess, but it works out well.

As I will show in Appendix B, "Celestial Mechanics," the 52-year period was in effect at this time, but not at a later date, even though invoked by Velikovsky and by some other catastrophists for other time periods. This certainty about a 52-year interval is largely derived from the continued observance in Mesoamerica of 52-year intervals, but these intervals are based on the Maya calendar system based on "Tun" years, not solar years.

Book 10 of the Maya *Chilam Balam* infers seven approaches by Venus since 3147 BC. I can easily locate four of these to 2349 BC, 1492 BC, 1440 BC, and an appearance which looked like a "close approach" in 776 BC. Considering the 156-year span of time between the "flood of Noah" in 2349 BC and the 2193 BC agricultural failure of Akkad, Egypt, China, and probably Harappa, the remaining three approaches by Venus could then be placed after 2349 BC at 2297, 2245, and 2193 BC with some confidence.

Note 21 --

Venus would seem to approach Earth every 52 years during this period, but was unlikely to have looked all that large except for its coma. For an electric interaction Venus would have to line up with the Sun on the day side of Earth, but likely never got closer than 10,000,000 or 20,000,000 miles. I'll provide estimates in the next chapter.

Note 22 --

More and more climatological and archaeological data has come forward over the years to establish a flood event, or some catastrophe, circa 2350 BC, as global in scope. This is influenced by Western Christian traditions, which hold to "the flood" as dated by Ussher to 2349 BC. The climatological decline after 2200 BC (2193 BC) is actually much better established, and the greater political consequences of this later event can be verified from Egyptian and Mesopotamian sources.

"... Most sites in Greece (circa 260), Anatolia (circa 350), the Levant (circa 200), Mesopotamia (circa 30), the Indian subcontinent (circa 230), China (circa 20), Persia/Afghanistan (circa 50), Iberia (circa 70) which collapsed at around 2200 +-200 BC, exhibit unambiguous signs of natural calamities and/or rapid abandonment. The proxy data detected in the marine, terrestrial, biological and archaeological records point to sudden ecological, climatic and social upheavals which appear to coincide with simultaneous sea- and lake-level changes, increased levels of seismic activity and widespread flood/tsunami disasters. The main problem in interconnecting this vast amount of data chronologically is the application of incoherent and imprecise dating methods in different areas of geological and climatological research."
-- Benny Peiser, *SIS Cambridge Conference* (1997).

Peiser is hedging his bets here to cover both 2349 BC and 2193 BC by suggesting a range of from 2400 to 2000 BC. A few others have been more courageous and defined separate events for 2349 BC (the date is from Ussher) and the event 156 years later which resulted in a 200-year worldwide hiatus in agricultural production and abandonment of sites, apparently due to a notable lack of light.

We don't really know what happened, but the clues point to an alignment with Venus. On the other hand, Timo Niroma seems to think that the first flood was very localized, suggesting that a bolide fell in the region of the Dead Sea in 2349 BC. That might have devastated lower Mesopotamia, leaving Northern Mesopotamia intact, and allowed for the takeover of those lands by the Akkadians shortly after 2349 BC. But I doubt the local nature for this event.

I think the date and the cause are both incorrect. The cause for the devastation of the Dead Sea region (Sodom and Gomorrah) is a close contact by Mars. The date is 1936 BC and after. This information is developed in another chapter.

A book by Moe Mandelkehr, *The 2300 BC Event* (2006), in three volumes, similarly presents archaeological data spanning the continents, but, again, with peculiar absences of a record from Egypt and Mesopotamia. Mandelkehr also lumps data to a single date, 2300 BC. Mandelkehr blames the destruction on a massive meteor strike. More on this in the next chapter.

Note 23 --

The first Chinese chronicles recall the efforts of two early Emperors (or gods), Yao (Yâo) and Shun, in undoing the damage of a massive flood. This is the only flood reference in Chinese literature or later "legends." Chinese scholars circa 200 BC date these two legendary figures, which represent the last two in a series of ten "legendary emperors" (or Gods) to circa 2350 to 2200 BC.

James Legge, in his introduction to the translation of *The Shu King* (1879), absolutely insists that "Ti" (Tî), as in "Yao Ti," be translated as "God," not as "Emperor." He also reviews the slim literary threads which place the start of the reigns of Yao and Shun in circa 2350 BC.

Note 24 --

The parallels between the ten generations after Adam and the twenty early Sumerian and Egyptian kings and pharaohs (which can be equated with the ten appearances of Mars at approximate 30-year intervals) is a clear indication that we are not dealing with derivative sources. A notable parallel is that the 10 patriarchs born between Noah and Abraham are all (except the first and last) sired when their father was 29, 30, 32, or 35 years old. See Appendix A, "Chronology" for further considerations.

Other Middle Eastern influences have been noted in the composition of the Bible, especially the literature of the Canaanite city of Ugarit after 1500 BC. Additionally, there are very clear Egyptian influences, especially in Genesis.

Note 25 --

The other notable compiler of ancient history is Isaac Newton. The Saturnian people (of Thunderbolts.info) have steadfastly avoided bringing the Bible into discussion. I find this a remarkable omission.

Note 26 --

The Egyptian "Intermediate Period" between the Old Kingdom and the Middle Kingdom, is variously estimated at 185 years by Manetho (circa 300 BC), 315 years by Breasted (1905), 141 years by Clayton (1994), and 110 years by Lehner (1997). It is obvious from these disparate estimates that the dates are not well established. Today the start of the Intermediate Period is dated to 2160 BC with some confidence. This is 33 years after the event of 2193 BC.

Note 27 --

Mohenjo-Daro and hundreds of other cities in the Pakistan plain of the Indus river and the parallel dried-up river Sarasvati are totally abandoned after 1900 BC as the region had turned into a desert. It is suspected, however, that the Sarasvati river may be "mythical," that is, that it represented the "river" descending from Saturn during the "Era of the Gods."

The *Oera Linda*, a medieval book claiming to be the history of the Friesian people, calculates 2194 BC as the date of the sudden sinking of Atland -- the area between England and Holland. At the 7000 square miles of the Dogger Banks, off the coast of England, the stumps of trees are still dredged up from a depth of 50 to 100 feet (15 to 30 meters), along with mammoth tusks. The sinking of the area probably resulted from the uplift of Norway as the Ice Age glaciers melted, resulting in a sinking of adjacent regions, including the North Sea, which had been lifted up as the ice had depressed Norway. Geologically this event is located late in the Upper Paleolithic, but a subsidence at a much later date is also plausible.

The *Oera Linda* is suspected of being a hoax in the service of Frisian nationalism, revisionist history of antiquity, and promoting a species of feminism. Arguments against its authenticity are primarily linguistically based, but at times are as arcane as the accusation that the year tallies ignore a "year zero" and thus the sinking of Atland is off by one year from 2193 BC. Of course "At-land" is readily equated by others with Plato's didactic exemplary land of "Atlantis."

The date of 2193 or 2194 BC is not listed as significant by Ussher in AD 1650 or even encoded among other accepted but erroneous biblical dates by Josephus in AD 100. Dates like this did not come forward in the 18th through most of the 20th century, when Egyptian dynasties were still equated with the temporally dislocated Mycenaean occupation of Greece.

Although there were archaeological papers earlier in the 20th century. As far as I can tell, the first to settle on this date was Timo Niroma at his site [personal.eunet.fi/pp/tilmari]. He quotes H. Weiss, *The Sciences* (May/June 1996), about the Akkadian empire of Sargon:

"Then, abruptly, things fell apart. Sometime around 2200 BC seasonal rains became scarce, and withering storms replaced them."

A number of people writing in documents published by the SIS [www.knowledge.co.uk/sis] came to the same conclusions in the 1990s. But all of them retained tentative dates, like "around 2200 BC."

On the other hand, what I did was to apply Velikovsky's suggestion of a 52-year period for Venus (although he never reached as far back as 2200 BC), assumed the actual date was 2193 BC, and validated this with an arcane reference from Maya calendar information. I then applied the date also to the fall of Egypt after the 6th dynasty (the Old Kingdom). I should point out that this date also easily fits alterations in the Mesoamerican calendar.

My adopted date of 2193 BC is thus based almost entirely on common sense rather than documents and ancient testimony, and thus one of my least well supported.

Niroma also extended the start of the worldwide drought to the Indus Valley and the cessation of the Harappan civilization. And applied it to the fall of the Old Kingdom. This was a very large step for Niroma to take, far beyond the endless pussy-footing of Egyptologists and archaeologists (or SIS people), but once taken, it makes perfect sense and fits worldwide data. Niroma concludes:

> *"My hypothesis is that there were two events, the first one around 2350 BC (2345 BC?), and the second one around 2200 BC (2193-2194 BC?), of similar cause, but possibly independent of each other."*

How did the *Oera Linda* arrive at a date of 2193 BC? Wikipedia reports:

> *"It [the Oera Linda] also mentions Atland (the name given to Atlantis by the 17th century scholar Olof Rudbeck), which was supposedly submerged in 2193 BC, the same year as 19th century Dutch and Frisian almanacs, following traditional Biblical chronology, gave for Noah's flood."*

Wikipedia might be in error here. Why this almanac date is off by 156 years from the date published by Ussher in AD 1650 for the flood of Noah, I do not know. As a fake document, the *Oera Linda* dates from the middle of the 19th century AD.

Note 28 --

The Chinese *Annals of Shu* hold that Shun, the Moon, dies in 2205 BC, that is, he "dies and goes on high." The date was estimated by chroniclers of the Han dynasty (200 BC) and should probably be 2193 BC, applying a uniform correction to the Han dates (see later text). The action is an increase in the period of the Moon which would have accompanied an increase in the orbit of the Earth also. I'll expand on this in a later chapter.

Revision: 42.31 (noah.php)
Contents of this chapter: [The Flood Reconsidered] [The Fall of the Absu]
[The Moon on Fire] [The Flood from the Sky] [The Lifetime of Abraham]
[The Extinction of Jupiter] [The Career of Jupiter] [Endnotes]

The Flood Reconsidered

The shock of the disturbance of 2349 BC was entirely equivalent to the shock of 10,500 BC in North America, except that it was on a smaller scale. So I will not repeat the order of events involved here, details of which are, at any rate, to be found in Appendix B, "The Celestial Mechanics." There were differences. A different planet was involved, the latitude of the impact was lower in 2349 BC, the tilt of the earth was less, the direction of the leading edge of the impact area was different, and the high plateau where the mountains were removed was wider.

Most significant was the fact that there was no lightning strike to the Earth's surface, but instead a plasmoid traveling from Venus impacted the Absu, rather than the Earth's surface. No massive forest fires were started, and no nanometer dust levitated into the stratosphere to cause hundreds or a thousand years of shadow.

I think the "flood of Noah" never happened. At least, not on Earth as a flood, although certainly Earth sustained water damage from rain, storms, and hurricanes. I suspect that what was thought to be the "flood" by everyone was, in fact, the disintegration of the Absu, the rings surrounding the Earth -- which in antiquity was universally understood to be an ocean.

That the Absu (or the Egyptian Duat, or the Maya "House of Nine Bushes") was real, I have no doubt. The rings of Saturn had been seen since the invention of the telescope. Then, in the 1990s, as space probes approached Jupiter, rings were found, like the rings of Saturn, but fainter. Then rings were discovered for Uranus and Neptune also. All four planets have magnetic fields. So does the Earth.

Venus, the Moon, and Mars do not have magnetic fields and do not have rings. Mercury also does not have rings, probably because it has only a very weak magnetic field. Astronomers think that the rings of Jupiter, Uranus, and Neptune are fading and that the rings of Saturn will also fade over time. Saturn, which has the brightest and most extensive rings, is, however, a very electrically active planet. At closer distances, as reported by NASA in the 1980s, the rings of Saturn were seen to be composed of "spokes, braids, waves ... and spiral shapes." Twenty years later, in AD 2000 to 2008, during a less active period of the Sun, they have smoothed out. [note 1]

When the Mesopotamians start mapping the sky, they name the southern section of the sky, below the equatorial, "the path of Ea." Ea is the Babylonian God of the waters, the Akkadian god of the Absu. He is the Sumerian Enki, also God of the Absu. In Akkadian "Ea" is written with the Sumerian glyphs "EN.KI" -- "water house." "En" translates as "home," "house," or "temple." Houses in Sumer were initially constructed of reeds and with semi-circular (domed) roofs. This is what was seen in the south, a dome of reeds extending from the east to the west, located somewhat below the level of the equatorial in the sky, but with all the rings or sections of rings coming together at the east and west cardinal compass point. There is no question about the location of the Absu. [note 2]

It is certain that the Earth had rings, that they were clearly visible in the southern hemisphere of the sky (from a northern vantage point), and that the rings included constantly moving "spokes, braids, waves, and spiral shapes." The Egyptians also called the Duat "a field of rushes." It might have looked to them like marshland.

It certainly would also have looked like a sea, especially to people who lived some distance from the world's real oceans. In the Yucatan, closely surrounded on three sides by real oceans, the Maya were not fooled, however. The rings also stood 10 degrees higher in the sky as seen from the Yucatan, reaching to about 60 degrees up from the southern horizon. It was a celestial house instead, a "house of bushes" created by the Gods.

China, at about 35 to 40 degrees latitude, would have seen the rings stand about 50 degrees up from the southern horizon. China, like most locations further north than Egypt and Sumer, reported 9 rings. [note 3]

The Earth's clouds, rising from rivers and forests at dawn, could be seen passing in front of the Absu. That alone would be enough to make the Absu look like a real and solid object and as an extension of the land at the horizon. When the clouds passed, the Absu was still there.

Because of the way the rings merged at the horizon in the east and west, they are often represented as a 7-headed or 9-headed serpent. The heads of this snake were caused by the shadow of the Earth extending completely from the southern horizon to beyond the highest rings. This only happened at the time of the equinoxes. The penumbra of the Earth's shadow would make the gap wider at the top.

There are similar notions from Mesoamerica, where the rings stood considerably higher in the sky, that "the world" constituted a flat plane (a gap) between two giant step-pyramids. This was the view at the time of the year near the equinoxes. At or near the equinoxes, the view of the separate rings, each higher one in the sky ending at a distance further from the center of the gap, would certainly have made it look like the gap was bordered by two step-pyramids or inclines. Mesoamerican ballcourts almost always are built as 6 steps, but also as just a sloped plane.

It is obvious that many of the spells from the Egyptian *Book of the Dead* (first recorded as tomb texts in 2345 BC), which guaranteed entry to the afterlife for the dead, are better explained if referenced to the image of the Egyptian Duat rather than the Saturnian polar apparition before 3147 BC.

Most obvious are many spells dealing with travel in the ship of Ra. The spells were written and augmented over a period of more than 3000 years (and the imagery certainly dates back as far as 8347 BC). Some of the earliest spells speak of a crescent ship traveling around the "river" at the edge of the globe of Saturn in the north sky. But after the breakup of the Polar Configuration in 3147 BC, the planet Gods were seen to travel along the river of the southern sky. Ships were still required.

The gods and planets identified with the Egyptians continue to travel by boat for the next 3000 years, as they do nearly everywhere in the world. In Egypt the temple Gods are ferried up and down the Nile to visit Gods at other temples. Statues were carried in ships to be dragged in processions. The spells still speak of ships, but after 3147 BC the journey is no longer along the blazing circular river at the circumference of Saturn, but along the river of the ecliptic and the edge of the sea in the southern sky.

One phenomenon which is clearly difficult to associate with the polar apparition in the north is the "door to the underworld." But it is readily explained by the shadow of the Earth moving from east to west across the Duat every night. The Earth is illuminated by the Sun at an angle to the equatorial which varies with the time of the year. During most of the year, except at the time of the equinoxes, the shadow would have looked like an arched doorway (referred to in one spell from the *Book of the Dead* as a cave). In between the times of summer and winter, the shadow would have progressively lengthened to become infinite at the time of the equinoxes. [note 4]

When the shadow fell all the way across the rings and formed a gap, it would have been more or less shaped like an inverted trapezoid. The gap at the top would widen with the distance from Earth, since the penumbra of the

Earth's shadow widens with distance. The "half shadow" of the penumbra would have considerable density since it is located relatively close to Earth (unlike in a lunar eclipse, where the penumbra is markedly faint). But it would also decrease in darkness with distance, so that at a considerable distance above the Earth it would have fallen off noticeably.

During the day the Sun would have lighted the Absu from behind. The Sun would travel above the equatorial circles during most of the year, but would shine through the Absu in the winter months. I have no idea what the effect would be exactly. It might not have looked different from today's Sun located behind a haze. In that the Sun is the largest and brightest object in the sky, it would be certain that during the winter months the image of the Sun would be preceded and followed by other amorphous forms, which would show local motion because they were imbedded in the equatorial rings which moved incessantly. Today, during dusty atmospheric conditions, these show up and are called sun dogs. In antiquity they were held to be the horses of the Sun. In the 13th-century Icelandic *Prose Edda* the forms which follow are held to be wolves chasing the Sun. Even nearly 2000 years after the Absu had disappeared, the horses of the Sun remain in place: in 685 BC it is Phaethon who loses control of the horses of the Sun.

[Image: Sun dog images, Fargo North Dakota.
After Wikipedia. Note the start of a circular form.]

Seen from the southern hemisphere, the Absu would have looked the same as in the lands of the Eastern Mediterranean, Mesoamerica, North America, and Asia, except that the rings would have been placed above the north horizon. In Peru (for example, at Lima) the rings would have stood up at an angle of 60 or 70 degrees from the north horizon. The existence of the Earth's shadow on the rings might be acknowledged in the U-shaped ceremonial centers which dot the countryside in the deserts, and which date back to circa 2500 BC.

To recap: every night a gap appeared in which the rings were not visible, and which moved from the east to the west. The Egyptians called it "Naarutf." *"The meaning of the word is 'it never sprouteth',"* wrote E. A. Budge (1895), *"and is defined as 'a section or door of the Duat which lies to the north of Re-stau.'"*

"It never sprouteth" indicates the missing image of spokes and "rushes" which "grew" everywhere else where the shadow did not fall. "Re-stau" originally was the cemetery at Abydos, and came to mean, wrote E. A. Budge, *"the passages in the tomb which lead from this to the other world".* The phrase in the paragraph above, "north of Re-stau (Abydos)," might also be rendered as "Abydos lies south of the Duat," and thus the "other world" was located beyond the doorway of the Duat. The view through this doorway was obscured, for although some bright stars (and planets) would have shimmered through the unlit portion of the rings, the dust and gases of the ring would have blocked most starlight from passing through. (Sirius and Canopus, the two brightest stars were noted exceptions. See a later chapter on the effect of seeing both of these stars, one above the other.)

The concept of a doorway is completed when it is realized that when the shadow took on its longest shape at the equinoxes, and extended beyond the end of the rings, the shadowed gap would be capped by a lintel -- a beam -- stretching across the shadowed portions of the Duat and extending beyond it to the east and the west (although at an angle). This is the bright "path of the Gods" -- the ecliptic -- so far removed from Earth that the shadow could not reach it. This might be reflected in the post and beam gates seen as freestanding structures in China and Japan. But of course to the people of Earth the ecliptic was no further away than the edge of the rings. [note 5]

Near the time of the equinoxes, the east and west edges of the shadow, the penumbra, the partially lighted area surrounding the dark full shadow of the Earth, would have fallen on the rings. This would be an area which widened with the distance from the Earth, and became fainter further from Earth. Seen from Earth this would constitute an edge which bent away from the center, thus making all of the Duat look more like two mountains with a valley in between. [note 6]

There is a lack of early Egyptian visual references to the Duat or the doorway to the Duat. Perhaps this is because the spectacle in the sky never varied or showed any activity and came to a sudden end in 2349 BC. Later depictions of the sun god Re, however, frequently show disembodied arms extending up from a baseline (representing the horizon) to the red disk representing Re. These might be representations of the penumbra seen at the edges of the "doorway" shadow (although I doubt that). Two arms extending up from a baseline is the hieroglyphic for "ka" also, the meaning of which might be translated as "soul."

Late depictions in the New Kingdom show Ra as a huge red ball suspended in a valley between two mountains (or what looks like mountains). Tomb texts place the uplifted arms in the south, in the Duat, "The Aten [the globe of Re] is in the Tuat [Duat]. The arms of the Mysterious Face come out and lift it up." I have wondered if this last is a reference to the smiling face formed by the first ball plasmoid, where the arms would be two of the lines of electrons. This was something which could only have been seen two thousand years earlier by people close enough to the equator to get an unobscured view beyond the equatorial rings. (The snake-haired smiling face shows up regularly in Australia and South America where a clear view would be had. The Egyptians originated from Ethiopia, where the face of the southern ball plasmoid might have been seen clearly.)

Since the doorway moved from the east to the west, it was the west which became the location of the underworld, as Budge explained, about the Duat:

"... it must be distinctly understood that the Egyptian word does not imply that it was situated under our world, and that this rendering is only adopted because the exact significance of the name Duat is unknown. The word is a very old one, and expresses a conception which was originated by the primitive Egyptians, and was probably known to their later descendants, who used the word without troubling to define its exact meaning"

One of the spells of the "Book of the Dead" is titled:

- Chapter XCIII. The Chapter of not sailing to the east in the underworld.

Sailing to the east over the sea of the Duat (or possibly the river of the ecliptic) would result in missing the entrance to the "Land of Life," which was in the west. Almost uniformly all the Egyptian graves were located west of the Nile in the western desert.

If the shadow on the rings was understood as a doorway, then we would also expect references to a doorway among the spells of the "Book of the Dead," and as a matter of fact, these exist, as in the following examples (I have only listed their titles):

- Chapter LXVII. The Chapter of opening the doors of the tuat [Duat] and of coming forth by day.
- Chapter CVII. The Chapter of going into, and of coming forth from, the gate of the gods of the west among the followers of the god, and of knowing the souls of Amentet.
- Chapter CLXI. The Chapter of the opening of the doors of heaven by

Thoth, etc.

- Chapter CLXXIV. The Chapter of causing the khu to come forth from the great gate of heaven.

And, from the *Papyrus Ani*, a hymn pointing to the travels of Re through the skies:

- Chapter XV. A hymn of praise to Ra when he riseth in the eastern sky, and when he setteth in the [land of] life.

This again points out that Ra (Re), the chief God whose worship had started sometime after the close of the "Era of the Gods," was always first seen in the east after an absence from the south skies of many months. This is Jupiter with a lower coma tail, it is not Ra as Saturn when he stood still at the North Pole, nor is it the Sun. Jupiter would, after the course of some months, disappear again (or reduce in size) in the west. The "land of life" was located in the west, the location to which the rings, the doorway, and Re moved. [note 7]

The Fall of the Absu

What happened to the Sumerian Absu, the sweetwater ocean which had spanned all of the southern skies? There seems to be no unequivocal notice about its disappearance. That may be because it was so gradual as to be unremarkable, or to have transformed into something altogether different. As likely, we cannot read the references to it, couched, as they are, in language not at all familiar to us. The Absu is obviously gone by 2200 BC. In the Babylonian *Enuma Elish*, written somewhat later (probably after 1800 BC), the Absu has become deified as a God to become an actor in a narrative of the creation of the world.

Let me suggest that the Absu disappeared suddenly, in 2349 BC, perhaps in a matter of days, because of an electric interaction with Venus and a temporary change in the tilt of the Earth's axis. At the same time the Earth moved further away from the Sun and to the established orbital path of the Moon.

Moved further from the Sun, to a new location of lower potential in the electric field of the Sun, the Earth would have started discharging to the surrounding space. Such a discharge would normally be very slow, in dark mode (except at the poles), and lasting hundreds of years. However, the disruption caused by Venus was rapid, with the nearby Moon perhaps providing an additional electrical path into the space facing away from the Sun.

If we can give any credence to some of the "flood stories," the Absu fell in a few days. The fall was also probably rapid because the contact by Venus caused radical changes in the electric field which kept the rings suspended. The electric repulsive impulse force from Venus seems to have struck in the northern hemisphere in Asia north of India -- north of the Himalayas in Tibet.

The Himalayas at the edge of the northern border of India (Kashmir, Nepal, Bhutan) form a circular arc some 1,600 miles long (2,500 km), which has all the looks of a compression shock. Similar semicircular arcs of compressed mountains exist in Mongolia, Iran, and the continental USA.

Typical of the fact that the Earth would have kept rotating (while tilting away from the Sun), the opposite arc is missing. This is unlike the Moon's Orientale basin, or the Caloris basin of Mercury, which are also clearly compression shock sites, but of planets which rotated only slowly. [note 8]

[Image: Himalayan Mountains between India and China. After imgarcade.com.]

As a result of the sudden repulsive shock, the axis of the Earth went into a swing, with the northern part initially moving away from the direction of the Sun. The equatorial rings would have swung up at a steep angle to the Earth's orbital plane, placing them directly between Venus and Earth (as the Earth kept rotating).

The main disturbance of the rings came with the arrival of a plasmoid thunderbolt -- a disconnected electric arc -- from Venus. The particles, gases, and ionized atoms held in suspension in the Absu were disturbed or neutralized and departed when the plasmoid from Venus arrived and slammed into the Absu.

The Absu turned red and then disappeared except for one remaining ring. It looked like the arrival of a dragon which smashed into the rings. The untold billions of electrons arriving and smashing into the rings of the Absu would have neutralized most of the ionized gases and particulate matter. The dragon bled for three days. The "blood" seen in the sky could have been constituted by the ionization of any number of diffuse common atmospheric gases.

Much of the coulomb charge of the Earth is normally tied up in the toroidal belts of the magnetosphere at the equator. This is the source of hurricanes -- when this belt arcs over to the atmosphere in the tropics. I would expect the "discharge" of the Earth to have happened in both directions, towards Earth from the rings and out to space via the Moon. The arrival of the plasmoid would disrupt the rings by neutralizing the electrostatically suspended particulate matter and also by altering the electric field of the Earth which held the particles suspended above the equator.

The loss of the electric charge of the Earth might have been sufficient to have destroyed the Absu. The particulate matter could no longer be suspended in rings around the Earth. It fell in or moved out to space. We can assume that much of the particulate matter simply drifted down to Earth, and that larger rock-sized chunks (if any) started to move away from Earth. This reflects the current thinking of NASA concerning what they foresee as the ultimate dispersal of the rings of Saturn (http://photojournal.jpl.nasa.gov/ February 12, 2002).

... the snake Apep

As the gases and particulate matter moved away from Earth they would visually approach the equatorial, a plane directly above the Earth's equator, the far edge of which is seen as a circle in the sky located from directly east to directly west but set at an angle equal to the complement of the latitude (90 degrees less the viewing latitude). Visually, even as the dust and rocks kept moving ever further from Earth, it would never seem to move higher into the sky than the far location of the equatorial. Over time, as the distance from Earth continued to increase, it would simply disappear.

There remained, however, a last ring, at a considerable distance above the equator. This last ring might be equated with the lapis lazuli necklace of the Goddess Inanna, mounted up in the sky as a sign from the Gods to never again bring such a flood, except that the ring was red, not blue. It is the Uoroboros. It would, however, match the effect suggested in the Maya *Chilam Balam* which describes that, after the flood, the "roof beams" of the sky became visible -- the ecliptic and the last ring of the Absu below the equatorial, crossing each other at an angle. The ecliptic had not been seen earlier when it was behind the Absu.

The two rings rose in the night sky, surrounding the Earth. In the Yucatan the last ring of the Absu would be seen as standing very high up in the southern sky, stretching from directly east to directly west (but at an angle). The ecliptic consisted of a hoop which intersected the red equatorial ring at the two locations of the equinoxes. At that time the Pleiades stood above the intersection at the vernal equinox.

[*Image: Bunyip, Australian water monster.*
After "Illustrated Australian News " (circa 1890)]

The Earth still cast a shadow on the last upper ring of the Absu, but because of the increasing distance (the dust and particles of the red ring seem to have been located at about 6000 miles, 9,600 km, from Earth), the shadow would only show as the Earth approached the equinoxes. Then the shadow of the Earth, of the same width as previously at this location, would fall across the ring. The ring with this gap would look like a giant snake whose head moved up from the east and slid across the southern sky to the west each night, closely following its own tail. At other times of the year only the long body of the snake would be seen, since the shadow of Earth would not reach out far enough. [note 9]

The glowing band of the ecliptic would also be seen. The ecliptic crosses the equatorial at the location of the equinoxes. Since the Earth's shadow would not reach or be seen on the ecliptic, it would remain lighted where the shadow of Earth fell on the equatorial at the time of the equinoxes. The ecliptic thus looked like it passed in front of the red band below the equatorial -- certainly a confusing visual presentation, since we know that just the opposite is true.

In Maya iconography the crossing of the two sky bands is used in representing the sky or the sky band (the ecliptic), with a symbol known as the Saint Andrew's cross. This symbol is not simply an "X" figure, but always has one of the bars cross in front of the other. (The vernal equinox is designated by having the bar which starts at the top left pass in front of the other; the autumnal equinox reverses this.)

This last outer ring of the Absu lasted a long time, well into the current era. This last equatorial ring has entered mythologies worldwide as a celestial snake -- called Apep by the Egyptians and Apophis by the Greeks. It adds to the utter confusion of monsters, dragons, and serpents.

"Comparative investigation confirms that every well-documented culture possessed its own names and images of the serpent or dragon of chaos -- the monster whom the Babylonians called Tiamat, the Greeks knew as Typhon, and the Hindus called Vritra or Ahi. In Australia it was the Bunyip-monster, sometimes identified as the 'Rainbow Serpent,' that once decimated the earth. And in North America remarkably similar stories were told of the 'Great Horned Serpent.'"
-- David Talbott, *Thoth newsletter* (2002), draft text for the book *Thunderbolt of the Gods* (2005)

I cannot speak to the Australian Bunyip-monster, although it is said to lurk in swamps and waterholes -- an association, I presume, with the Absu. I find "Rainbow Serpent" quite revealing, not because of the implied coloration, but for the form of an arch across the sky. This would seem to be Apep of the Egyptians, except that the serpent has horns. This last feature would equate the Rainbow Serpent with a polar plume.

With the background of the historical sequence of events presented in this text, it will be recognized that the Babylonian Tiamat is Venus in 2349 BC, and the Greek Typhon is Venus in 1492 BC. Then, not included above, there is Phaethon, which can be placed in 685 BC as Mercury. These last three will be presented in later chapters. The "Great Horned Serpent" is distinct from all three of these. It is probably the north polar plasma plume which appeared each time the orbit of the Earth increased, complete with horns, as I have illustrated previously. Apep, on the other hand, is the last remaining ring of the Absu, also to be placed after 2349 BC, and remained in the sky into the current era, probably as late (I suspect) as AD 600.

Apep, in fact, does not appear in Egyptian mythology or depictions until after 2200 BC. It did not exist earlier, and since then was seldom noted because the red ring, like the Absu, never did anything significant except to color some bright stars. Spells to ward off the evils of Apep are only added to the *Book of the Dead* very late, as a matter of impressing the Greek (Ptolemaic) overlords after 300 BC. A chapter of spells in a papyrus dating from these times, called the *Book of overthrowing Apep, the Enemy of Ra, the Enemy of Un-Nefer* (Un-Nefer is Osiris), gives directions for:

"preventing storms, and dispersing rain-clouds, and removing any obstacle, animate or inanimate, which could prevent the rising of the sun in the morning, or obscure his light during the day," -- paraphrased by E. A. Budge, in *Legends of the Gods* (1912)

The Egyptians were at this time, after 300 BC, transferring the title of "Ra" to the daytime Sun. (It was about time!) The Egyptians had also run out of visible celestial monsters, and thus promoted the Apep ring to the status of a vicious snake. He was depicted in Egyptian illustrations as pierced with knives to color him red with blood. This is quite alike to the Maya depiction, where the celestial snake has patches of flayed skin.

Near the dates of the equinoxes, the head of the snake would be seen nightly rising in the east as its tail disappeared in the sky in the west. It seemed to be chasing its own tail. As the year moved away from the time of the equinoxes, Apep would catch up to its tail and swallow it. The image of a snake swallowing its own tail, called the Uoroboros, still appears among medieval alchemical documents. Of course it did not have a distinct head -- snakes do not have distinct heads. Among the later Maya it was merely a cord in the sky. [note 10]

In Ireland, St. Patrick, active to about AD 500, in legend drives Ireland's snakes into the sea. There never were any snakes in Ireland. But there was the celestial Apep which disappeared about that time.

Another story (legend) concerning St. Patrick and a snake is retold by

Philip Coppens:

"The legend states that Patrick was drawn here [to Station Island] *by the triple goddess Corra, a pagan goddess who apparently tried to reclaim Ireland to the pagan gods after Patrick's recent success at Croagh Patrick."*

Croagh Patrick is a sacred mountain in Ireland, where St. Patrick stayed 40 days to prove the superiority of Christianity. You will recognize the "triple goddess" as the southern ball plasmoids appearing between 10,900 BC and 8347 BC, especially when she turns into a snake.

"On his flight - indeed - from Croagh Patrick, he looked down, and saw that she had taken the form of a serpent, lying in the water of Lough Derg - the Red Lake, though some recent authorities prefer to read Derg as a form of the Irish deirc, "the lake of the cave". Descending to investigate, she swallowed him whole. It took Patrick two days and two nights to cut himself free, killing her in the process. The water turned red with her blood and her body turned to stone, forming the islands in the lake."
-- from http://www.philipcoppens.com/croaghpatrick.html

The action retells the event of 2349 BC -- 2800 years later for Patrick, 4300 years later for Coppens. It includes the "two days and two nights" common to all the retellings, plus the "water" turning red with blood. The "Red Lake" is as appropriate to the event of 2349 BC as the "lake of the cave" is in signifying the Absu with its doorway.

The *Younger Edda* of circa AD 1200 relates, as one of the subjects (constructs) of bardic epic poetry, the disposition of one of Loki's evil children, Jormungand the Midgard-serpent, which Odin the Alfather threw into the ocean:

"When they came to him he threw the serpent into the deep sea which surrounds all lands. There waxed the serpent so that he lies in the midst of the ocean, surrounds all the earth, and bites his own tail."

The snake swallowing its own tail is Apep again.

From Alfred Tozzer, *A Comparative Study of the Mayas and the Lacandones* (1907), from verbal sources, we have the following:

"... there was a road suspended in the sky, stretching from Tuloom and Coba [that is, the east] *to Chich'en Itza* [which is only halfway] *and Uxmal* [that is, the far west]. *It was in the nature of a large rope*

*supposed to be living and in the middle flowed blood. For some reason
this rope vanished forever. This first epoch was separated from the
second by a flood."*

The above account is quoted by Schele and Freidel in *Maya Cosmos*
(1993). This is a recollection of the lowland Maya (the Northern Yucatan).
The road in the sky will be recognized as the last remaining ring of the Absu.
The flowing blood, also, is an aspect of the last ring of the Absu, for it can be
determined to be red from the look of Sirius before AD 950, among other
things. The "flood" (the flood of 2349 BC) separating two eras, as mentioned
in the quote above, is actually misplaced. There is no causal connection with
the disappearance of the red rope, which happened at a much later date. But it
was at the time of this celestial flood that the red rope first appeared.

The story also reflects on the Maya road which was built in AD 800 to
850, between the city of Coba in the east and Yaxuna directly west of Coba,
62 miles long (84 km), and representing the largest construction project ever
undertaken in the Yucatan. This is less than halfway the total distance from
Coba to Uxmal. The industry and enthusiasm with which this project was
undertaken may reflect the fact that the red road in the sky had recently
disappeared. There are a number of other, much shorter, causeways like this,
also running east-west (some are processional roads to outlying shrines).
Schele and Freidel (in *A Forest of Kings*) think that this road, too, functioned
as a processional way.

... the Falling Rings

As I have mentioned, the Moon was thought to have been seen since the
remotest period in antiquity, but this was most likely the planet Jupiter seen at
close quarters when fully lighted by the Sun. Thus, as presented with the
sculptures of the Maya site of Palenque (AD 700), as well as in Hesiod's
Theogony (circa 650 BC), the Moon precedes any of the Gods. She is the
mother of all the gods.

The sudden clear appearance after 2349 BC probably made it look as if
the Moon swept the Absu clean. But the Moon, although given credit for the
cleanup after the flood (as the Chinese Legendary Emperor, or God, Shun),
could not have dispersed the rings physically, for the Moon today is 250,000
miles (400,000 km) away from Earth, and probably has always been on an
orbit of 250,000 mile radius. The rings probably only reached, at most, about
8500 miles out.

Both the initial as well as the eventual dispersal of the equatorial rings
was electrical. An outward dispersal, however, could have happened via the

plasma tail of the Earth, which, even today, reaches well beyond the orbit of the Moon. But probably most of the contents of the Absu drifted down to the atmosphere below, and fell to Earth.

Charles Raspil, in an article "Spatters and Planetary Iconography" (*The Velikovskian*, 1994), details the recording of "spatters" from the middle of the second millennium BC through the 18th century AD. The spatters look like raindrops and rosettes, placed in artworks almost randomly surrounding depictions of gods or humans in any scenery.

Raspil identifies the spatters as astrological iconography, rather than to think of them as representing physical phenomena. But the spatters maker more sense if understood as representations of minute dust particles drifting to Earth, carrying an electric charge from the far upper region of Earth. On nearing the surface of the Earth, the spatters would disintegrate electrically. This would suggest that dust from the Absu rained down for nearly 4000 years. If, as Raspil claims, the depiction of random spatters only started in the second millennium BC, then perhaps it was the change in the Earth's electric field after 1492 BC which made a difference. There is, however, little if any artwork from before even the first millennium BC to inspect.

[Image: Spatters. After Raspil.]

Raspil has made a career of finding strange anomalous forms interspersed with pictorial forms in artworks dating from antiquity to the 18th century AD. The spatters seem like fillers of graphical space, but at the same time look as if they were objects regularly seen in the sky, or near ground level. He writes:

> *"In their portrayal of the spatter, artists distribute it randomly within the confines of any particular artwork. It is small, taking up little space within the borders of any particular opus, and is multiple, appearing in pluralities. Its random distribution and appearance, along with its nonuniform configuration, suggest that it is a natural phenomenon and not an artistic symbol."*
>
> *"The basic spatter configuration consists of one large ringlet surrounded by many smaller ringlets (eight, usually). Variations exist: small square- or diamond-shaped ringlets may surround the central ringlet. On occasion, only a few nascent dots, not ringlets, will arrange themselves in significant spatterns (patterns of spatters)."*

Raspil illustrates a Rhodian plate (above) which highlights action from the Trojan War, and comments:

> *"Both the basic and more sophisticated spatters appear: the former to the immediate right of the first soldier's nose and between his legs, as well as above and on the second soldier's shield; the latter on the extreme right and left of each opponent, and in the centre of the diagram, between their two shields."*
>
> *"The sophisticated spatters appear to be 'petaled.' Two of these spatters are cut off by the borders of the plate. If these spatters were symbolic, not natural, why would the artist cut them off and treat them as if they were mere background, like clouds in a photograph?"*

This suggests dust particles falling to Earth, and igniting briefly in the blaze of plasma (a switch to glow mode or arc mode), as suddenly as firecrackers and perhaps with an explosive sound.

As Raspil points out, the spatters occur on all continents and with the graphics of all civilizations. Raspil traces the spatters into the 18th century AD, whereas I claim that the "snake" Apep disappeared before AD 800. But even though Apep was not seen, it is possible that the dispersal of dust to Earth's surface continued for another 1000 years.

... the Moon on Fire

Let me propose that the Moon, which joined Earth in 2349 BC, initially had an atmosphere, which caught fire a hundred and fifty years later in 2193 BC.

There are some disconnected Australian legends of the Moon alternately growing hair and trimming it. That would be the sight of the Moon's plasma tail seen from an angle from Earth, and shortening as the angle between the Moon and the ecliptic changed throughout the year. There are also Greek and other references to a bearded Moon, which is the same image.

If the Moon initially had an atmosphere, it would likely have consisted of hydrogen, methane, carbon dioxide, and oxygen -- if it was at all like any of the other planets. That represents a condition which could ignite massive fires if any impinging plasma changed to arc mode on contact with the Moon. We will see this condition for Jupiter in 2150 BC, and for Mercury in 686 BC.

The Moon may have been very active electrically after it joined the Earth in a nearly equal orbit. But I would also suggest that if the Moon initially had an atmosphere then plasma strikes from Earth impacted in glow mode at the Moon -- which means that nothing of particular note was seen, and few scars remained behind.

I am proposing this because at some point, there is a spectacular fire at the Moon. Everyone noticed, and all peoples incorporated the fire into their tales and legends.

When might a fire have happened, and in what order? Probably not initially after 2349 BC (Noah's flood), because the Earth only moved further from the Sun, and thus had to increase its own negative charge. However, this was not the case for the Moon. Then in 2193 both the Earth and the Moon moved to a new location, and both would have been subjected to an influx of electrons. For the Earth this would have shown as polar plumes (at each pole), but nothing like that would have resulted for the Moon, which has no magnetic field.

The glow mode display might have stopped after 2283 BC (Palenque, corrected from 2305 BC) or 2285 BC (according to the Annals of Shu). The texts would suggest a sudden change from glow mode to arc mode, and therefore noticed by humans, which would account for the assigned dates.

At Palenque the Moon becomes ruler in 2283 BC; in China, Shun joins Yao on the throne in 2285 BC. These dates may reflect another electric contact with Venus, which would most likely have happened in 2297 BC. But 2297 BC falls 14 years short of 2283 BC.

Interestingly, the two clear "legends" of a fire at the Moon indicate that an event happened on a mountain. The mountain image associated with Mars between 3067 and 2750 BC consisted of a plasma stream extending from the Earth's ionosphere to the surface of Mars. The mountain of Jupiter was the plasma plume extending from below the lower hemisphere into space. The tower (rather than a mountain) associated with Mercury in 686 BC was plasma streaming from Earth to Mercury (to be presented in the next chapter).

A streaming of plasma from Earth to the Moon (like for Mars and Mercury) would be unlikely, since the electric conditions would not have existed. For a long time, like today, Earth and the Moon have been at nearly the same electric potential for the region exterior to the Sun where they both travel. It is more likely that the mountain shape is a plasma tail of the Moon in glow mode, which it certainly would have had if an atmosphere still existed. The reason this was seen (and understood as a mountain) is because the nighttime Moon rises 5 degrees above the ecliptic, and thus the extension of its plasmasphere away from the Sun would have been visible from Earth.

After a fire on the Moon the plasma in glow mode would never again have been experienced. It has to be presumed that the remaining atmosphere would have disappeared over the course of the following thousands of years. Very little atmosphere is left today on Mercury after the planet fire of 686 BC. That was only 2600 years ago. Thus is it would be unlikely that the Moon would show any atmosphere at all, because the fire happened 4300 years ago.

A planetwide fire would explain the Bible tale of Abraham who is told by God to sacrifice his son Isaac as a burnt offering on a mountaintop. His hand is stayed by God, and a ram is substituted. Isaac thus survived the fire; so did the Moon.

A parallel Chinese legend has it that Khwan, who was engaged by Yao to clear the inundation, was "sacrificed on a mountain" in a fire -- when he failed to accomplish his task of clearing away the waters of the flood. His son Yu rose from the ashes and completed the task. Han dynasty historians speculated that Yu was born in 2300 BC. Yu is assigned also as the first king of the Xia dynasty.

In both cases someone survived the fire. Actually, of course, it is the smaller bare Moon who is the survivor. That would also suggest that all the electric scars of the Moon date to after 2200 or 2100 BC.

The Moon possibly rotated when it first joined Earth, although the very circular look of Mare Orientale basin suggests this was not so. Ralph Juergens, in "Of the Moon and Mars," has suggested that the basins (on the front side) could have happened in a contact with Mars in the 8th century BC. It is possible that the craters on the back of the Moon were formed in 685 BC, when, like Venus and Mercury, Earth and its satellite probably also exploded in flames -- from the stratosphere or ionosphere for Earth, from the surface for the Moon. During the 40 day nova event of 685 BC, the Moon circled the Earth one and a quarter times. So craters would appear on all sides.

Within a few decades after first meeting in 2349 BC, the Earth and the Moon would have started to revolve around each other on more or less the same orbit around the Sun, as they do today. The motion of the Moon actually describes a path today which starts some 20,000 miles (32,000 km) above Earth and over the course of six months spirals to a location an equal distance below Earth, after which it reverses again. (It actually describes the figure of a cycloid, not a series of loops.) Moon eclipses only happen at a six-month interval, at the time when the Moon is passing from above the Earth to below, or in the reverse direction.

We can now also clarify the contemporary quotation from a Columbian source in the previous chapter:

"When the Moon did not yet exist, a bearded old man named Botschika taught the arts of agriculture, clothing, worship and politics to the people. His beautiful but malevolent wife was Huythaca. She caused a flood in which most people perished. Botschika then turned her into the Moon."

Now we realize why the Moon was held responsible for the flood; the Moon's flood is here confused with the flood of 3147 BC. The bearded old man can still be identified as Saturn. If, however, this quotation actually recalls details from the "celestial flood" of 2349 BC, then the bearded old man is Jupiter, with his mountain perhaps identified as a beard.

At the end of Book 2 of the Maya *Chilam Balam,* there is a short disconnected section which obviously recalls the event of the "flood of Noah." It includes the line:

"And the face of the sun was corroded, and its face became darkened and was put out. And then, above, they became frightened. 'It has burned up! Our god has died!' their priests said. And they were beginning to think about making a picture of the figure of the sun, when the earth shook and they saw the moon."
-- Antonio Mediz Bolio, *Books of the Chilam Balam of Chumayel* (1930)

The Moon was noticed. The shock may have referred to the contact with Venus, or it may indeed have represented the first touching of the Earth's plasmasphere and the plasmasphere of the Moon. The shock might account for an alteration in the orbit of the Moon which would start it circling around the Earth. [note 11]

It is possible that all of this is conjecture -- that the Moon never had an atmosphere. But the concept of a planet-wide fire is reinforced by the fact that Jupiter caught fire soon after the supposed fire on the Moon. The fire of the Moon I have here dated to 2205 BC, although it could as likely be in 2193 BC.

The fire at Jupiter I am dating (further below) to 2150 BC. Rockenbach, in *De Cometis Tractatus Novus Methodicus* (AD 1602), places this event in 2060 BC, a hundred years later, and identifies it as the Tower of Babel incident. The Tower of Babel event which was actually well remembered was the flaming up of Mercury in 686 BC.

The Flood from the Sky

There was no "flood of Noah" in terrestrial terms. It all happened in the heavens, although the destruction of the Absu must have caused violent hurricanes, storms, rains, and thunder -- certainly for weeks or months. And, not to be neglected, we should recognize the flattening and raising of the Tibetan Plateau, and the subsequent path of earthquakes and seismic destruction traced through the Eastern Mediterranean into North Africa. [note 12]

The seismic disturbances were experienced in 2349 BC as Venus started to pass Earth on an inner orbit. As both Earth and Venus lined up with the Sun, the plasmaspheres would have touched, and suddenly the crust of the Earth would have experienced a repulsive force. The force would have been experienced on the hemisphere facing Venus, since the Earth's exterior surface distribution of electric charge in effect makes the interior of the Earth (and thus the other hemisphere) opaque to an electric field exterior to the Earth.

Because of the sudden onset, a stupendous seismic shock would have traveled around the world. At the location facing Venus, the crust would have been depressed, resulting in an uplift of the crust in adjacent areas. As the Earth continued to rotate, the region of the depression would have continued to move toward the southwest, although the force would very rapidly diminish as an opposing electric charge was induced at the facing sides of both planets.

The effect of the forces at the crust would be mechanically transmitted to the mass of the Earth, in a direction away from the Sun, thus relocating Earth to a different orbit.

Unlike gravitational forces, which act (equivalently) through the centerpoint of the Earth and therefore have no effect on the Earth's spin, if the electric forces were even slightly offset from the center, the Earth would have reacted like a gyroscope to the externally applied torque -- swinging the axis through a circle in response to a tilt the Earth's axis.

Venus, because of the extremely heavy atmosphere which carries its electric charge, would react very differently, absorbing and distributing the repulsive forces around the planet. Venus's orbit might not be significantly affected. (I have expanded on this and added some approximate calculations in Appendix B, "The Celestial Mechanics.")

There are indications of undetermined catastrophes in this era in many locations in the world. I think these can be attributed to the earthquakes due the initial electric repulsive shock (in central Asia) which traveled as a seismic wave around the Earth, plus a following attractive exterior force, applied as the Earth continued to rotate, which would have uplifted the surface in the next sector of Earth to come into alignment with Venus (Tibet). This was followed somewhat later by the arrival of a plasmoid lightning bolt from Venus (one large, nine smaller). It is this last which resulted in the hurricanes and torrential rains which have been identified as the Flood of Noah. [note 13]

But the crisis in religious concepts and the loss of a worldview was much more important and cannot be neglected. For a second time, the structure of the Universe had been radically altered. The removal of the Gods would be nearly complete when Jupiter, who had stood in the sky as the Midnight Sun, was permanently "taken away" 200 years later, in about 2150 BC.

As I noted in the previous chapter, sometime after about 2400 BC construction stopped on barrow graves and (mostly) on henges. Only the single-inhumation Round Barrows continued in use. The Long Barrow and Passage Graves were discontinued. After the fall of the Absu it must have become obvious that the south sky was filled with stars, and there was no place for the mound or the island to where the dead were transported in the past. The southern sky was as empty as the northern sky.

The construction of Stonehenge was interrupted for 200 years after 2400 BC, a date which should probably be equated to 2349 BC. But there is no interruption of activity in Egypt or Mesopotamia -- not until 156 years later, after 2193 BC. [note 14]

For the date of "Noah's flood" political events in the Eastern Mediterranean region also do not seem to reflect a problem. It seems there was no apparent damage in Egypt or Sumer, despite the best efforts of chronographers to locate a "flood of Noah" at that time. What we know with certainty is that in 2193 BC, 156 years after the "flood of Noah," a worldwide catastrophe brought the civilizations of Egypt and Akkad to a halt and caused the eventual demise of the Harappan culture in the Indus valley by 1900 BC. The island of Malta was completely depopulated after circa 2200 BC. Malta may have fallen directly under the strike path of an arc from Venus in 2193 BC.

... the Conquests of Sargon

There is no evidence for a flood in 2349 BC in Mesopotamia. This is underscored by the conquest undertaken by Sargon of Akkad almost directly after the "flood event" of 2349 BC. His conquests produce the largest empire seen in the world to that time, comprising the subjugation of Elam in Persia, Sumer located south of Akkad, Southern Anatolia (Syria), and the coastal cities of the Northern Levant -- an empire extending from the Persian Gulf to the Mediterranean Sea.

Considering that the later event of 2193 BC caused the collapse of political systems worldwide, lasting 200 years, we could suggest that Sargon started his armies on the march almost directly after the "flood event" of 2349 BC. Had there been a worldwide flood or a similar catastrophe, would not Akkad, located directly north of Sumer, also have been affected? Instead, Sargon seems to have taken advantage of the jolt by Venus and the religious paralysis of Sumer. His patron Goddess was Ishtar, Venus.

We have no contemporaneous records of Sargon, only tales and legends recalled in Babylon a thousand years later. We do know, however, that he appointed his daughter and granddaughter as priestesses of the Moon god Nana of the Sumerian city of Ur. Hymns by one of the priestesses have been preserved.

... the Flood in China

The Chinese flood is mentioned in the first book of the *Annals of Shu*, the Chinese historical record dating to 2357 BC. It speaks of a flood which "stood above the mountains." This cannot be anything other than the Absu. What waters will stand up above the mountains? The rains and storms, however, were real. (Incidentally, Psalm 104:6 reads, "the waters stood above the mountain.")

A person named Khwan, during the reign of Yao (Yâo), spent 9 years on the project of draining the waters from the valleys. His son Yu was hired and in turn spends 9 years on drainage. Yu is possibly a real person, and is the first king of the Xia dynasty which started about 150 years later, in 2205 BC.

The second book of the *Annals of Shu* recalls the work of Yu. Among the records on his assigned task of gathering an inventory of the resources of the land, is the following note:

"Being sent to the great plains at the foot of the mountains, notwithstanding the tempests of wind, thunder, and rain, he did not go astray."

Chinese history does not deal with the weather. It is unusual to find this anecdote.

Yao existed, it was estimated in circa 200 BC, from 2357 BC to 2255 BC, for some 100 years spanning what would be the date of Noah's flood in 2349 BC. Yao is Jupiter, and his initial date of first showing should be set at 2349

BC. Yao shared the throne with Shun during his last 30 years. His "death" in 2255 seems to be off by 100 years from better Bible, Mesopotamian, and Mesoamerican chronology. His reign should be around 200 years, not 100 years.

Shun clearly is the Moon, spending all of his time on monthly inspection trips, as described in the *Annals of Shu,* which even records that his inspection tours all start on the first day of the month.

The ending date for the reign of Shun, the Moon, is 2205 BC. This is 110 years after the Moon's birth, 144 years after the "flood of Noah." When Shun (the Moon) "dies" in 2205 BC, Yu, who had been employed by him in the administration of the land, becomes the first king of the Xia dynasty -- in time for the dry spell starting in 2193 BC. [note 15]

The much earlier flood of 3147 BC, which had come from the South Pole and the South Pacific, was not recalled by the Chinese, perhaps because of the width of the Pacific adjacent to China. Siberians remember a flood, but it came from the north, spread over the land, and then rolled back to the polar sea. This it may have been a rebounding wave.

For China it is the "flood" of 2349 BC which stood out, and although this "flood" was celestial in nature, it would have been accompanied by severe wet weather and heavy rains. Chinese history started with the aftermath of this "flood" when organized reclamation (needed because of the rains) was initiated by Khwan and later by Yu.

... the Temple Inscriptions at Palenque

The Maya temple inscriptions at Palenque in the Yucatan (circa AD 700) are one of only three Maya references to world history. The inscriptions place the birth of Venus, Mars, and Jupiter in 2360 BC. The Moon, "Lady Beastie," is their mother. The implication is that these planets became clearly visible when half of the ecliptic no longer dipped into the Absu to be obscured by the rings. Or so I would think. There is another, more elegant, solution also.

The date of 2360 BC (based on the Long Count) is earlier than the start of the "flood of Noah" in 2349 BC. It has been presumed that the dates of the carved texts for the birth dates of the three planets (November 8, October 21, and October 25) were selected to have a congruence of qualities so that they "matched" later dates used to argue the legitimacy of the ruler who erected the temples. They are not to be considered as dead accurate. However, the era (Baktun) and double-decade (Katun) were most likely completely correct. The dates were retrocalculated in AD 700 based on the Long Count and on a year of 365.24 days.

To correspond to a true solar year (which is the "calendar" used throughout these pages), rather than a Gregorian calendar year, the Long Count dates of Palenque should be moved forward in time by 22 years. Thus 2360 BC of the inscriptions, which precedes the flood of Noah, becomes 2337 BC which follows the flood of Noah by 13 years. [note 16]

Another hint that the events of 2360 BC have reference to the flood of Noah, is the transcription of the glyphs of one of the temples, the Temple of the Cross, which transliterates as:

"753 years and 12 months after
[that is, after February 5, 3112 BC]
GI-prime [Saturn] *had set the wac chan*
[the World Tree house of the north,
mentioned in detail earlier]
and then the matawil person was born."
    "On October 21, 2360 BC, the matawil,
the blood of Lady Beastie,
touched the earth."

The first paragraph follows the detail of the displacement of Saturn from the north polar region to the ecliptic of the south. "The World Tree house of the north" is likely the northern polar plume after 3147 BC. The retrocalculated date of February 5, 3112 BC, for the appearance of Saturn in the ecliptic of the south sky, is about right. (It is a year a half after the end of the era of the Gods, retrocalculated by Palenque as 3114 BC.) And then the "matawil person" was born.

Who or what is *the matawil*? Freidel and Schele have determined that Lady Beastie is the Moon, or the "First Mother" and this is generally accepted. They have *the matawil* as Venus. I'm not so sure. They translate the last line into readable English as:

"On October 21, 2360 BC, GI [Venus]
the child of Lady Beastie, was born."

It is a reasonable guess, considering that Freidel and Schele, like all archaeologists, have absolutely no clue as to what is really going on, and just assume the Maya were making up Gods to fill out a creation epic of sorts. Others have suggested that *the matawil* is a place. Some assume it is the dark space at the center of the Milky Way. Yet others hold that it might be closely associated with Palenque, in being a toponym for Palenque (the Spanish called the site *Palenque*, fortress).

I would think that *the matawil* might represent the doorway or gap in the "House of Bushes," as the *Chilam Balam* calls the Absu. Alternately I would suggest that it may represent all of the Absu. Then "the blood of Lady Beastie touched the earth" represents the fall of the Absu rather than meaning "the child of Lady Beastie" although "touched the earth" commonly is a phrase meaning "was born" in Chol.

Text at the doorways of the three temples reads as follows:

"On October 21, 2360 BC,
GI [Venus], the matawil, touched the earth;"
"On November 8, 2360 BC,
GII [Mars], the matawil, touched the earth;"
"On October 25, 2360 BC,
GIII [Jupiter], the matawil, touched the earth."

GI, GII, and GIII represent Venus, Mars, and Jupiter, following their dates of birth. This does not resolve what "the matawil" is. "The matawil" also follows the naming of Lady Beastie. In fact, we do not know if it should be presented as an ellipsis as in this translation, or if it should be understood as an adjective, a noun, or some other word form. If Lady Beastie is then the Moon, why was she born in the previous era, that is, before 3114 BC?

The Moon certainly would have been visible before 3114 BC, although only periodically, and seen at a considerable distance, often looking more like a star. But, considering that the temple inscriptions at Palenque also place the birth of Saturn, as a pure fiction, in 3122 BC and, like the birth of Lady Beastie, also before 3114 BC, it might be suggested that these two births and the implied marriage are just made up to suit the situation.

Also we cannot neglect that the Greeks, starting with Hesiod, held that the Moon preceded the births of all the other planets. We know that this isn't true. But what would have looked very much like the Moon at the earliest times would have been the lighted face of Jupiter, which was at a distance from Earth to make it look about the size of the later real Moon, or, as I have also pointed out, as an egg (and as recorded in pottery by Neolithic Mediterranean cultures since remotest times, as presented by Marija Gimbutas).

The Moon, as Lady Beastie, "lets blood" in 2325 BC (corrected to 2302.3 BC), a date separate from the 2360 BC event, when her "blood touched the Earth." Bloodletting is a trance ceremony of the Maya, used to commune with ancestors. Is this a plasma display of the Moon?

The Palenque inscriptions next claim that in 2305 BC (corrected to 2282.6 BC) the Moon crowns herself ruler. The inscriptions at Palenque were used to establish the legitimacy of the claim to rule by the Ahau of Palenque, who had attained his position through a matriarchal line. The inscriptions were meant to show that there was ancient precedent for this, for the celestial Gods also trace their ancestry through a woman ruler, the Moon. Frankly, I do not know how the concept of "rulership" might relate to the Moon in physical terms. The *Annals of Shu* claim 2287 BC as the year in which Shun (the Moon) joins Yao on the throne. At least it is an interesting near coincidence. [note 17]

The date of the Palenque inscriptions can be compared against the estimates listed in the *Annals of Shu*, as shown in the table below, where corrected dates for Palenque are shown against uncorrected dates from the Shu.

```
         Palenque inscriptions              Annals of Shu
      event       inscribed corrected      event          dated
   Moon shows      2360 BC  2336.8 BC   birth of Shun    2318 BC
   Moon bleeds     2325 BC  2302.3 BC
   Moon rules      2305 BC  2282.6 BC   Shun employed    2287 BC
                                        Yao dies         2257 BC
                                        Shun dies        2205 BC
```

... the *Chilam Balam*

There are also two mentions of the arrival of the Moon in the 16th century AD Maya *Books of the Chilam Balam of Chumayel*. The texts were transcribed from much older glyphic bark books. In Book 10 there is mention of the fall of the Absu, as the water which fell from the "center of the sky." Mention is made of the establishment of the intersection of the ecliptic and the last ring of the Absu, and that the Pleiades first showed above this intersection. Importantly, the arrival of the Moon is mentioned, although obliquely, in Book 10. I will elucidate the Chilam Balam in the chapters "The Chilam Balam" and "The Olmec Record of the Past."

The events of the *Chilam Balam* are listed by the names of Katuns, thus dating events to spans of 20 years. We have to supply the corresponding Baktun, that is, we have to guess the longer era of 400-Tun periods that a Katun falls in. All except one of the Katun dates of the *Chilam Balam* match the records from other sources -- or span the dates of these other sources outside of Mesoamerica. The dates need to be corrected in a different manner than the dates from Palenque. The text clearly recounts (among other celestial events) the 24th century BC, although listed wildly out of order. [note 18]

The Lifetime of Abraham

Abraham is variously dated anywhere from 2026 BC (534 years before the Exodus of 1492 BC) to 1271 BC (1876 years after the flood of 3147 BC).

Traditional Bible chronology dates Abraham from 1812 BC to 1637 BC. In Appendix A, "Chronology Notes" I equate Abraham with Gilgamesh, but it would be more correct to equate Abraham with Jupiter. Some scholars have also equated Abraham with the Moon, or Moon-worship. Actually, I would suggest that the first orbiting of the Moon might have been used by the Bible editors to establish a 175-year life-span for Abraham. The first showing of the Moon might be 2325 BC. The demise of Jupiter is 2150 BC. This is 175 years, although here the date of 2325 BC is an estimate.

Most Bible chronologists placed the birth of Abraham in 1900 or 1800 so that Abraham could have forefathers between himself and Noah, in fact, ten generations. As I mentioned earlier, all except the first and last of these 10 generations (in the Bible) were sired when their father was 29, 30, 32, or 35 years old. These are also my estimates of the intervals between appearances of Mars during the earlier period of 3147 to 2750 BC. The forebears of the Sumerian Gilgamesh (the kings of Kish in pairs) are spaced likewise. The Bible is a mix of events from different eras, which holds the "flood" of 2349 BC as the world flood, but derives all its other information from earlier eras.

It makes most sense to equate Abraham with Jupiter. The birth of Abraham then is in 2349 BC. His death is 199 years later, in 2150 BC. I have used these two dates as anchor points in developing the chronology of Jupiter.

The Assyriologists P.J. Wiseman, in *New Discoveries in Babylonia about Genesis* (1936), and D.J. Wiseman, in *Ancient Records and the Structure of Genesis* (1958), proposed that Genesis is a series of separate records, copied and collated by Moses, each ending in a colophonic phrase, like "these are the generations of Noah," called "Toledoth" in Hebrew. These recap what has been written up to that point (this happens 15 times) like a signature by the person who is supplying the record. At each of the 15 colophons, the writer is still alive, but nothing more is heard of him in the following text, except his age at death, which is related by the next writer. There is one notable exception: Abraham.

> *Who would doubt, however, that the most "prominent" individual in the Book of Genesis is Abraham? He, more than all the other great Patriarchs, would be entitled to be named in a Toledoth. ... "Yet", as Wiseman had observed, "it is remarkable that while lesser persons such as Ishmael and Esau are mentioned, there is no such Toledoth phrase as `These are the generations of Abraham'"*
> -- from *California Institute for Ancient Studies*

That would present a problem for Bible chronologists, for Abraham needed parentage, being ten generations from Noah and the Noachian flood. The ten generations after the flood is correct, if the flood is understood as the worldwide flood of 3147 BC. The ten generations are the recalled ten appearances of Mars between 3067 BC and circa 2750 BC.

Bible chronologists, using a "flood" set at 2349 BC by Ussher, were thus forced to make Abraham first appear some 300 years later, variously in 1900 BC to 1800 BC. Ussher uses 1976 BC to 1801 BC, 175 years.

The Extinction of Jupiter

I estimate that Jupiter extinguished sometime in the era after the "flood of Noah," possibly in 2259 BC, as the *Annals of Shu* claims, although I am more comfortable with a date of 2150 BC, the end of the 199-year life span of Abraham (as Jupiter) since 2349 BC. The large coma of Jupiter would, at any rate, have come to an end as the planet slowed its retreat from the Sun on reaching its final orbital destination and, once at that destination, its electric potential started to match the electric field of the Sun at that remote distance. At first the glow mode discharge would have simply diminished as the flow of plasma decreased. Then Jupiter would have experienced a sudden change from glow mode to dark mode plasma discharge, as plasma flows do when switching between modes.

There is a planet fire recorded in the *Chilam Balam*. The text of Book 10 reads, as a concluding line to a description of Jupiter:

"Suddenly on high fire flamed up. The face of the sun was snatched away, taken from earth."
"This was his garment in his reign. This was the reason for mourning his power, at that time there was too much vigor."

The "face of the sun" is Jupiter, the Midnight Sun -- "Lord Sun" of the Maya. The "excess vigor" might be translated as "commotion" as if to suggest that the effects were experienced on Earth. They were not, except for the religious changes -- the sense that their god had been removed from near Earth to a far off distance, as it diminished to the size of a star.

The *Chilam Balam* seems to date the extinction of Jupiter to a Katun 8-Ahau (as seems most likely), placing this event in 2167 to 2147 BC, which matches the extra-Biblical date 2150 BC which I am using from other sources.

Of the other sources, the first is the portion of the *Annals of Shu* compiled during the Xia dynasty. The Xia dynasty has other records of events noted to be contemporary with the events, that is, not "mythological" (the "mythological" records read, "Looking into antiquity, we find...").

Under the Xia we are getting descriptions from sensible Chinese humans, who could care less of stars and planets, writing, however, that there was "a celestial phenomenon" in about 2153 BC. This is recorded in Book IV, "The Punitive Expedition of Yin," of Part III, "The Books of the Hsia [Xia]." James Legge records that, *"This Book is another of the 'Speeches' of the Shu, belonging to the reign of Kung Khang, a brother of Thai Khang, the fourth of the kings of Shang (B.C. 2159-2147)."*

The second source is a cuneiform tablet of Gudea (as discussed earlier), governor of the Sumerian city of Lagash in 2144 BC to 2124 BC, concerning a brightening -- the "overwhelming splendor" of Ningirsu, who "changes darkness into light" -- dated to the mid-2100's.

Ningirsu is Jupiter (although the name is also assigned to Saturn). Gudea was dedicated to Ningirsu, building him a temple and supplying weapons of war for the temple (Ningirsu is understood as a war-god, which is not characteristic of Saturn or of Jupiter). The building and dedication activities are probably an indication that Jupiter had disappeared altogether from the skies, and that Lagash was in trouble. The social reforms, return to traditions, and fervor of religiosity initiated by Gudea must reflect attempts to keep Lagash alive under the adverse condition of a disappeared God. This was also 50 years after the start of the agricultural failures of 2193 BC.

Having established that something spectacular happened around 2150 BC, the question next becomes, What happened?

Most likely Jupiter experienced a sudden change from glow mode to dark mode plasma discharge, which is how plasma flows behave. Since this involves a marked decrease in current flow, the driving voltage would have risen suddenly and could have resulted in a brief return to a much higher current rate -- a brief change to arc mode. After the sudden change to arc mode, Jupiter would again have dropped to dark mode, and been reduced to the size of a star.

This is regularly seen elsewhere in the Universe where stars repeatedly explode into brilliance and subside as they switch from arc mode to glow mode or dark mode (a loss of the coma). After the extinction, Jupiter would have all but disappeared from view, for in the final dark mode nothing would be seen of a coma.

The Midnight Sun had stood in the sky for nearly 1000 years, and with a huge coma for much of that time, and certainly the last 200 years. And for all that time there were no interactions with the Earth, except to disappear after some months and return again.

Then in 2150 BC it suddenly brightened and died, while in view of Earth. The Midnight Sun would have suddenly shrunk from a Moon-sized brilliant globe set on a mountain which lit up the night skies to just a bright star (still the brightest planet in the sky today, next to Venus). Since in the text above I have suggested that the burning of Jupiter could have been a switch from a failing glow mode plasma briefly to arc mode, there is certainly a good possibility that it did indeed involve a planetary fire. A single location of an impinging plasma in arc mode could have set off the ignition of an absolutely massive fire as methane and hydrogen burned, engulfing the largest planet in the Solar System. It would have been spectacular. There are problems, of course, with the temperatures near absolute zero. But the striking of an electric arc raises the temperature locally by thousands of degrees.

The fact that the coma of Jupiter was red since leaving the asteroid belt could be indicative of low-level oxygen in an excited state, but it could also be hydrogen or methane. This would be an explosive combination, although not normally at utterly low temperatures. That might explain why this had not happened earlier. Perhaps the statement in the *Chilam Balam*, that "suddenly on high fire flamed up," should be taken at face value. This was not a coma in arc mode, it was flames. The same, of course, was said for the Tower of Babel.

The Career of Jupiter

The story of the flood of Noah is the story of the death and resurrection of the primary God of antiquity. It is a story which will be repeated and re-represented for the next 4,500 years -- to today. Let me present, then, the career of Jupiter in narrative form, and follow it with some background information.

At this point we can describe the complete career of Jupiter from before 3147 BC to its last flaming and extinction in about 2150 BC. The complete career of Jupiter, from the first time he was noticed in the skies is as follows:

- Before the end of the "Era of the Gods," 3147 BC, Jupiter was certainly seen, alternately as a moon-sized egg shape when Earth and Saturn were inside the orbit of Jupiter, and as an up-turned crescent shape when Earth and Saturn were outside Jupiter's orbit. The distortions in both instances were due to the fact that Earth was some three million miles (4.8 million km) below Saturn, and thus Jupiter was seen from a much lower perspective (Saturn's orbit additionally dipped 1.3 million miles, 2 million km, below Jupiter's orbit at times.)
- The egg-shape shows up in pottery decorations during this period (the European Neolithic); the crescents less so. As I have pointed out previously, a painted pot of the Classical Maya era, depicted in *Maya Cosmos* by Freidel and Schele, presents the imagery of six Gods in council with a seventh and elder God. They are advising the seventh god to start creation.
- The seventh and elder God (God L) is easily identified as Jupiter as

well as the Maya "First Father." The six Gods have various names, of which some are easily identified. God "Three Born Together" is obviously the three plasmoids of the south and God "Nine Footsteps" is Mars. Subtracting God "Three Born Together" of the south leaves the five Gods all associated with the polar configuration of the north as described in the *Popol Vuh*.

- The image on the pot illustrates, in somewhat different form, the conferences between the three gods of the south and the five gods of the north which are related extensively in the *Popol Vuh*. What is different here is that a seventh god is invoked, the old God L, who is without a doubt Jupiter, as can be derived from Classical Era iconography. What is amazing about this also is that the Maya, from their own sources, or from books derived from the Olmecs, would recall the primacy of Jupiter, dating back to the time before 10,900 BC.
- In the sculptures at Palenque (AD 700) Jupiter is also identified as one of the old-man gods holding up the "bleeding dragon" bar in the Temple of the Sun (a sculptured panel also called "the War Stack"). The Maya of Palenque were certainly aware of Jupiter as well as Saturn -- as specks in the sky -- as shown by the inscribed text (at Palenque) of a close conjunction on July 23, AD 690, of Jupiter, Saturn, Mars, and the Moon.
- In 3147 BC, Saturn and its companion planets passed by Jupiter, so that Jupiter was between Saturn and the Sun. Jupiter, on a smaller and faster orbit, caught up with Saturn and its companion planets. Once the plasmaspheres touched, electric interactions caused a massive electric shock, followed by electric arcing. The small planets Earth and Venus, were not involved in the interactions, probably because the reformed combined plasmasphere of the giant planets locked them out. [note 19]
- Certainly this involved the flow of plasma as gigantic interplanetary lightning bolts spanning millions of miles, but the most violent interaction would have been the electric attraction initiated as soon as the planets could first sense each other's electric fields. I am suggesting "attraction" here because Saturn and its companion planets would most likely still have been at a charge level (voltage) representing the far region of space outside of the Sun's plasmasphere. Only a condition of attractive forces could account for the relocation of all the large planets to the far reaches of the Solar System.
- The pulse would not have lasted long, for after receiving an impulse which disturbed the orbits of the four large planets, the planets separated and individual plasmaspheres would have formed again, in effect isolating them from each other. Jupiter must have been diverted from its normal orbit path, attracted to the Saturnian set on an outer

orbit.

- The change in forward speed would normally have cast Jupiter completely out of solar system. But since Jupiter at some point does reach a stable orbital location, it has to be suggested that Jupiter's forward speed was modified by the planet's passage through the asteroid belt.

- Saturn, Neptune, and Uranus would have been yanked backwards from their normal orbital path. The initial attractive force must have been almost at right angles to their orbits, resulting in a greatly reduced forward (orbital) speed. The orbits which the Saturnian planets eventually settled into is related to their mass and to their distance from Jupiter at the first moments of electric contact. Their orbital speeds also were modified by passage through the asteroid belt.

- Jupiter, now under electric stresses because it was moving away from its former location near the Sun, produced a coma and a gigantic tail. Unlike comets, Jupiter's giant plasma flow appeared at the south geographic pole (the location of the north magnetic pole), with lesser plumes at the north pole. Jupiter's magnetic field is reversed from that of any of the other planets and is also ten times stronger than any other planet.

- The lower plasma tail became the mountain to which the people of Earth see Noah's ark moored. As we know from Egyptian sources and the Mesoamerican *Popol Vuh*, the mountain of Jupiter was colored green initially.

- The first view of Jupiter after the flood is recorded in Sumerian flood stories, in the Bible, and in hundreds of other "flood" myths. The vertical separation of the planets can easily be found from current orbital data. The initial vertical locations are discussed in Appendix B, "The Celestial Mechanics."

The view of Jupiter seen from Earth initially was of a bright crescent on the bottom of the globe. This was the view seen from far below Jupiter, seen about 45 degrees up from Earth. Only a crescent was seen, even though all of Jupiter's face was lighted by the Sun.

Humans at this time had no concept of the extended space away from the Earth. The concept of Earth and all the surrounding space was that of a land mass enclosed by an "ocean" in the south (the equatorial rings), and another region in the north where the river from paradise (the "real Earth") had been seen to flow toward the land of Middle Earth. It was like living at the bottom of a bowl.

A widening (green) plasma discharge in glow mode extended down from the crescent (from the south pole of Jupiter). From the perspective of Earth the crescent looked like the ship of Noah placed on the mountain where he had landed. Both the "ship" and the "mountain" which were seen at the end of the flood are ubiquitous elements of the 500 or more flood legends throughout the world.

The huge horned shape which had been seen approaching (or seen earlier and known about) was also identified in Egypt as the celestial bull who wrecked the city of the Gods -- he is shown as such on the Palette of Narmer, and one other palette from the same predynastic period, but, significantly, not on earlier cosmetic palettes. Jupiter also appears as the "bull of heaven" in the Mesopotamian *Epic of Gilgamesh*.

- As the Earth traveled further along its new orbit, the view of the battling planets (Jupiter, Saturn, Neptune, and Uranus) changed from an initial view from below to a side view of the same planets in the southern skies. Immediately after being released from the electric field of Saturn, the Earth would have changed its orbit so as to have the Sun again as one focus. The new orbital inclination to the equatorial of the Sun would be at a steep angle -- 7 degrees to the equator of the Sun. Within a half year the Earth would pass to above the equator of the Sun, and the people of Earth would get a new point of view on the receding giant planets, now seen in the south sky at night. The rings of Saturn were now seen edge-on as Earth's orbit lifted past the equatorial of the Sun.

- The Maya *Chilam Balam* reads that Saturn was thrown on his back by Jupiter. This was the new view which saw the rings of Saturn edge-on. The first "pyramid texts" of Egypt state the same thing: that Osiris (Saturn) fell on his side and died -- at the riverbank. The riverbank is understood by later Egyptians as the bank of the Nile, but obviously the riverbank originally was the edge of the ecliptic.

- Both the Bible and the Sumerian flood legend record birds being released to test the abatement of the floodwaters. In the Sumerian version, the first two birds return. These were the bright Venus (the dove), and what would seem to be Mercury (identified in Sumer as a swallow) but more likely is the Moon (when it still had an atmosphere). Because Venus returned (being on an inner orbit), it was assumed that the Earth had not dried up yet. The third bird to be released is Uranus, as a dark raven. On an outer orbit, Uranus did not return.

- The Sumerian interpretation is different from the Bible story, where the raven is released first, but only the later return of the dove with an olive branch signifies that the Earth had dried up. (The earlier release of the raven in the Bible is much more correct to the celestial mechanics.) To Utnapishtim (the "Sumerian Noah"), it is actually the travels back and forth of the raven (Uranus) that signals that the waters had ebbed. Noah is not convinced until the dove (Venus) returns with an olive branch -- the green tail it had developed in taking its first turn around the Sun.

- Note that, in both flood stories, it is only a matter of weeks before the Earth has dried up and Noah and Utnapishtim would exit their arks (fourteen days in the Sumerian version, forty days in the Bible.) The flood from the south polar seas of the Earth was a singular event, sweeping across the land like a tsunami, and rolling back at once, but then sending secondary waves north.

The duration of the flood, as presented in the legends, is in agreement with the fact that Jupiter would soon be seen from a much greater distance (half way across the orbit of Earth, rather than only a few million miles), frontally lighted by the Sun, but now looking much smaller. To both Noah and Utnapishtim this sight is a fire lighted for a sacrifice to the Gods. Seen from upward to one AU (93,000,000 miles, 150,000,000 km) away from the scene of the "collision," the planet Jupiter with its coma would have looked about the size of today's Moon, with the actual globe within the coma lighted by the Sun, and all of this still standing on its mountain, with wisps of plasma extending above the upper part of the coma -- seen as smoke of a sacrificial fire lit by Noah or Utnapishtim. The satellites of Jupiter orbited the fire.

"I made an offering on the peak of the mountain:
The gods smelled a savor,
The gods smelled a sweet savor,
The gods gathered like flies over the sacrificer."
      -- Theophilus Pinches, translator, *The Religion of Babylonia and Assyria* (1890)

- Over the next few years Jupiter and Saturn, traveling at different orbital speeds, would be seen to pass each other as both planets receded from the Sun. It is unlikely that Saturn developed a plasma tail. Later Egyptian legends speak of the casket of Osiris (here Saturn) drifting out to sea (the Duat again). An image of a casket is possible if Saturn had a plasma tail, but I seriously doubt if this was ever so. The casket thus more likely is Jupiter.

Osiris in his casket drifted out to sea, and north to Biblos (which was an Egyptian port of trade in Lebanon), and became lodged in a tree -- the north polar plasma column -- after which not much more of Saturn is seen at all in the sky, having by this time perhaps distanced itself considerably. There are, of course, later tales of Isis removing Osiris from the trunk of this tree.

- The engagement of Jupiter and Saturn could certainly not have lasted all that long, as they would soon become separated by their new spiraling orbits. We do know from some early depictions and late literary sources that there were frequent plasmoid thunderbolts between Jupiter and Saturn and the other Titans (and even originating from Venus), launched like missiles which landed with explosive effects. This may have lasted 80 years, although it is uncertain how much of this time period (assigned by the Egyptians) was occupied with "battle" and how much with "negotiations."
- The "negotiations" were the constant ranging of planets around the ecliptic followed by regrouping every few years near the slowest planets, Jupiter and Saturn, something never seen before by humans. To the Egyptians, the planets, as Gods, were having meetings. For the Egyptians it was most important to again have a celestial king assigned as ruler of the lands, and thus they describe the "negotiations" in detail. The claims between Seth and Horus are described in details encompassing the plasma interactions of the planets and possibly the asteroid belt, but all of it described by the Egyptians as taking place in a swamp, the Duat. [note 20]

The remaining career of Jupiter can be followed with some confidence. This is not true of Saturn. Saturn must have been unremarkable looking, except when its rings were still seen, and now known to go also behind the planet. Saturn just seems to disappear from active mythology, although the planet was watched and tracked throughout all of antiquity, everywhere. Saturn soon would have been a tiny speck of light among the stars (and moving very slowly). [note 21]

The Asteroid Belt

Jupiter took on the role of Osiris after Saturn disappeared from view. He is understood as mummified, standing up in the sky, with his mantle reaching down to the horizon. The toroidal equatorial plasma form produced what looked like two eyes staring back to Earth. Jupiter would have looked gigantic until it reached the first objects of the asteroid belt at about 2 AU. That would have taken perhaps 300 years after 3147 BC. A period of 288 years is a calculation based on a linear regression of Jupiter from the Sun (see the chart further below).

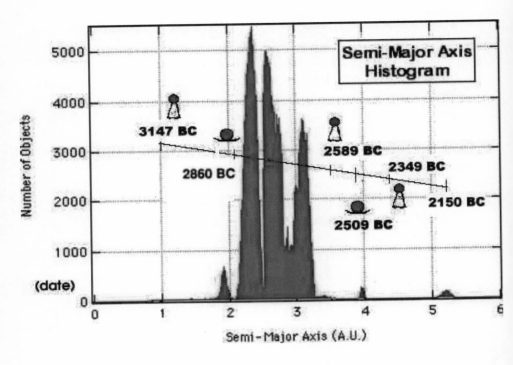

[*Image: "Histogram of the semi-major axis of asteroid objects; and path of Jupiter between 3147 BC and 2150 BC. The left ordinate represents both the number of asteroids and also the date, as BC, in the previous era." (Data: ftp.lowell.edu/pub/elgb/astorb.html. Plotted at case.edu/sjr16/; Information for 336,341 asteroids. Additional graphics for Jupiter added.)*]

- On reaching the asteroid belt the coma did not need to be particularly large and its lower mountain form would have shrunk to a plasma pouring sideways from the bottom of the globe, since electric contact could be made to the 300,000 or more asteroids (some suggest millions) which occupy the belt between 2 and 3.5 AU, plus all the dust already in place because of the passage of three other giant planets.
- Jupiter may have dimmed and then brightened again in passing through the leading clump of asteroids. By chance, my calculated date of the disappearance of Jupiter into the asteroid belt (2860 BC) is nearly the same (2890 BC) as the date of the end of the first dynasty of Egypt. Egyptologists cannot find a cause for the change between Dynasty I and Dynasty II. If my suggested dates are even reasonably accurate, then I could suggest that the change in dynasties was due to a religious crisis of immeasurable proportions: the mummy of Osiris had disappeared.

Jupiter eventually was displaced to 5.2 AU from the Sun. If Jupiter had started its recession at 0.7 AU (as I will suggest later), it would have moved at a rate of 221.5 years per AU. This is plotted on the chart below.

```
                    The career of Jupiter

      Note: the locations and dates are approximate, based on
       date = 3147 - (location - 0.7 AU) * rate of recession
             Note: dates revised about 15 percent 2/2011

      event, location          event date        concurrent look    period of time
      --------------------     -----------       ---------------    --------------
      starting location          3147 BC           mountain form      ~288 yrs
        from 0.7 AU

      start of asteroid
        belt, ~2.0 AU            2859 BC            shen form          ~332

      end of main asteroid
        belt, ~3.5 AU            2527 BC            mountain form      ~89

      last set of asteroids
        at ~3.9 - 4 AU         ca 2438 BC          return of shen     ~89

      fall of the Absu
        at 4.3 AU **             2349 BC            mountain form

      another interruption ?
                              ca 2337 BC          extinguished? Moon shows?
                              ca 2283 BC          Moon in orbit, mountain form?

      at 5.2 AU location ca 2150 BC              end of travel, extinguished

      The linear rate of recession is based on
      (3147 - 2150)/(5.2 AU - 0.7 AU) = 221.5 years per AU.
             ** location calculated
```

In the above chart the date of 2349 BC was set, and the location for this was calculated. The return of the mountain form in 2349 BC was due to the giant plasmoid from Venus. There may be a progressive error in this chart as Jupiter recedes further from the Sun because I have used a constant rate of radial recession. This may not be justified.

The date of 2150 BC, when Jupiter reached 5.2 AU in this linear model, is fairly well supported from a number of sources. The distribution of the semi-major axis of the asteroid objects shown in the graph above represents today's conditions. There is no reason to believe that most of the asteroids were not in approximately the same location from the Sun 5000 years ago as they are today.

The exception certainly are the two sets of asteroids (the Trojans and the Greeks) which are today located at 5.2 AU, in the orbit of Jupiter, and displaced about 60 degrees from the planet. These are thought to have been distributed to these Lagrangian points (gravitational minimums) of Jupiter's orbit through gravitational interactions with Jupiter over the last 4 billion years. Nothing explains why these asteroids are still there and are as widely distributed about these locations, except that they have only recently arrived at these locations.

Their location far removed from the main mass of the other asteroids is also peculiar. It certainly suggests that these are remnants of asteroids from the asteroid belt which were gravitationally removed by the movement of Jupiter through the Asteroid belt. That might also explain the paucity of asteroids near the end of the Asteroid Belt at about 3.9 to 4 AU, for on the basis of "historical" evidence, there should have been considerably more asteroids at the location of 3.9 to 4 AU, since Jupiter seemed to have again lost its coma and tail at this location, corresponding to a time 100 years before the "flood" of Noah in 2349 BC.

Surprisingly, some "Trojan" asteroids have been found for the transjovian planets, suggesting that these also were removed from the asteroid belt with the movement of these planets through the belt. These Trojans are far fewer than the 1500 or more which follow Jupiter. But then, Jupiter has more mass than Saturn, Neptune, and Uranus combined. Six Trojans have also been found to follow Mars, and Trojans are suspected for Earth. (The first Trojan to be associated with Earth was announced in 2011.)

- The peculiar gaps in the Asteroid belt are due entirely to the action of gravitational forces of Jupiter over the span of 5000 years, but the same gaps would also result if Jupiter had been on an inner orbit since the breakup of most of the asteroids about 3.2 million years ago. This is discussed in more detail in Appendix B, "The Celestial Mechanics."
- The asteroids represent an estimated total mass of 1×10^{22} kg. This is very little -- about 12 percent of the mass of the Moon. The majority of asteroids are of the chondrite variety, that is, they are rocky, and have a break-up date of 3.2 million years ago. The rocky composition suggests a smaller planet rather than a planet large enough to have had a metallic core. But this also suggests that, at the time Saturn and Jupiter passed through the asteroid belt, there might have been much more material than what remains today.
- Additionally, every plasma contact with the asteroids would have generated additional positively charged fine dust to be electrically repelled and launched into the space between the asteroids. The fireworks must have been spectacular. It should be apparent that the fine dust would have supported a continuous plasma flow from Jupiter.
- The asteroids represent planets which were part of the original Solar System. As the remnants of exploded Moon-sized planets there might have been fewer asteroids in number and the fragments might have been larger. Much of the debris could have dated back millions of

years, as can be ascertained from the break-up ages of meteorites ("meteorites" are asteroids which have fallen to Earth) -- 3.2 million years for the Chondrite meteorites, 100 and 700 million years for the iron meteorites. The various meteorites have a creation date (as opposed to their "breakup" age) of 4.4 and 4.6 billion years ago. As planets these may have orbited the Sun since the remotest times.

- Jupiter was not likely the cause of the breakup, first of all because (as developed here) the asteroids were in their location long before Jupiter passed through them after 3147 BC, and secondly because the pre-asteroid planets would have been at a charge level appropriate for their location from the Sun if they had been orbiting the Sun since their creation 4.4 to 4.6 billion years ago. Saturn, however, when repeatedly entering the Solar System at the potential (charge level) of deep space, would have been quite capable of electrically causing the breakups.

- But because Saturn would initially have traveled on a steep trajectory (I am assuming), the 20 entries into the Solar System would have done considerably less damage than the movement of the four planets away from the Sun after 3147 BC, which were on spiral paths -- resulting in much greater contact with the asteroid belt at that time. As noted above, the most recent breakup age for asteroids is 3.2 mya. This corresponds to what I have assumed to be the last entry of Saturn into the Solar System.

- Although it is here suggested that the breakup ages of many meteorites should be on the order of 5000 years, it should be understood that the mainstream Establishment researchers would delete any such data as measurement errors. Recent breakup ages would not likely be admitted.

- Initially, on reaching the asteroid belt, Jupiter would have discharged via plasmoid thunderbolts. This is the second battle of Zeus described by Hesiod, where various monsters are attacked. The plasmoids are visually described in the name tags of the predynastic king Narmer of Egypt (circa 3050 BC). "Narmer" translates as "catfish-drill." Plasmoids have all the looks of catfish, and a drill is a stone-working tool which stirs up clouds of dust in its application.

- The asteroid belt initially consisted mostly of rock fragments with some dust intermingled. Only after considerable additional dust had been created by the first massive plasmoids lightning bolts of Jupiter, would this activity subside to a more continuous stream of plasma. In the meantime, the dust and the asteroid objects must have taken on monstrous shapes. The dust remained for some 4900 years, lit by the Sun, and defined the ecliptic as the road of the Gods until very recent times.

- Jupiter would have entered the asteroid belt at an estimated date of

2860 BC. Once inside the asteroid belt, the electric discharges moved "sideways" from Jupiter -- from the north magnetic pole at the bottom of the planet, to the nearby asteroids and the clouds of particulate matter created in earlier discharges (and from the other planets which passed through). The plasma in glow mode would follow the magnetic field lines and be directed to the dust of the asteroid belt from the south geographic pole. (This would have primarily been an inflow of electrons directed to Jupiter, but also an outflow of protons and other disassociated ions.)

- Seen from Earth, Jupiter thus would have looked like a red disk seated on a plane below its coma while within the asteroid belt. A symbol for this, first dated from the third dynasty (after circa 2850 BC), is the "shen," a circle placed on a line, often made to look like a rope, that is, with a set of knots at the bottom. The same symbol is used from the end of the same third dynasty as the "cartouche" used to write the names of pharaohs.

[*Left Image: Shamash holding a shen; Mesopotamian seal. After Wikipedia; Right Image: Egyptian carved shen symbol. After globalegyptianmuseum.org.*]

- Images similar to the "shen" are found in Babylonia (above). Some Egyptian variations of the "shen" have "hairs" at the top and bottom of the circle. This completes the look of a plasma discharge from the magnetic poles, with the north geographic pole supporting a much lesser amount.

- The Egyptian crown of Re (Jupiter) and Amun-Ra (Jupiter as "the hidden sun"), is depicted as a red globe above nearly horizontal twisted ram's horns. A frequent depiction of the "shen" is with the circle filled in solid red, which would represent the mostly spherical coma of the planet. The *Chilam Balam* states that Bolon-ti-ku (Jupiter) was red when he "sat" in rulership.

> *"Red was the mat on which Bolon-ti-ku* [Jupiter] *sat. His buttock is sharply rounded, as he sits on his mat."*

• Notice that Jupiter has changed color after exiting from the asteroid belt. He was green originally (or the tail was) when he moved into the south skies after 3147 BC, which is how the mummified body of Osiris is always depicted. But on entering the asteroid belt and later, Jupiter lost its green mantle and the coma turned red.

Special thanks to J Brookes for suggestions on the cratered back of the Moon.

Endnotes

Note 1 --

Since there is no record from antiquity for rings of Jupiter or the Titans, it is likely that the current rings of these planets were acquired from dust in the asteroid belt. This might also explain why Mercury has no rings, since I do not think Mercury ever entered very far into the asteroid belt. The original orbit extended to the edge.

Thornhill suspects that the minor magnetic field of Mercury is induced in its travels between perihelion and aphelion, which doubles its orbital radius in each 88-day circuit around the Sun. This would move it alternately into two considerably different regions of the electric field of the Sun.

Note 2 --

There was a doorway, caused by the Earth's shadow on the rings.

To have the rings come close together at the east and west cardinal direction would depend on having an unobstructed view of the horizon at sea level. Of course the rings were seen to move differentially with respect to each other. This would certainly take away from the image of the house of a God as a stable object.

Note 3 --

That the number of rings should increase with high latitudes is a discrepancy I cannot explain. Nine rings are also noted for some Northern European locations, and possibly in India (where the latitude of the observations is not at all clear).

Note 4 --

In summer, at the solstice, with the Earth tilted at 23.5 degrees toward the Sun, the shadow will be found to extend 6000 miles (9600 km) onto the disk of the rings from the equator, **4000/sin(23.5) - 4000 = 6031 mi**, using 4000 miles as the radius of the Earth, and be shaped as a semicircle. In winter the shadow is actually cast on the bottom of the rings, but visually the results would be the same.

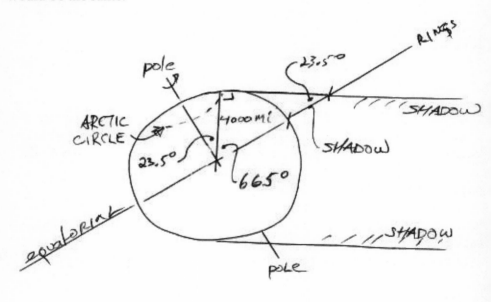

[Image: Earth's shadow on the equatorial rings at summer solstice. Illustration by J. Cook.]

This is the minimum dimension for the portal. As the spring or fall equinox approached the shadow would lengthen to become infinite. If the rings extended less than 6000 miles (9600 km) from the surface of the Earth at the equator, there would always be a gap (rather than an oval shadow). However, I have shown in an earlier chapter that I would expect the rings to extend about 8500 miles (13,600 km) above the Earth's equator.

In a later chapter I develop the idea that the Earth's axial inclination (to the normal of the orbital plane) was 30 degrees before 685 BC. I should note the results here. With an axial inclination of 30 degrees, the shadow will be found to extend only 4000 miles (6,400 km) onto the disk of the equatorial rings, **4000/sin(30) - 4000 = 4000 mi** in mid-summer and mid-winter. Again, the shadow would extend infinitely at the time of the equinoxes.

Note 5 --

The beam of the ecliptic would connect the left and right edges of the Absu or Duat only at the time of year near the equinoxes. The ecliptic would dip into the rings at the autumnal equinox and rise out of the rings at the vernal equinox. The portion of the ecliptic behind the shadowed rings would be obscured, except for bright planets. In summer (at night) the ecliptic would disappear behind the Absu, and in winter be placed above the Absu -- as with the Moon and planets today, which travel high in the winter night sky and low in the summer. The post and beam "gates" in China are said to be imported with Buddhism after AD 200.

Note 6 --

The construction of a ballcourt -- a flat plane between stepped pyramids or inclined embankments -- is derived in Mesoamerica from descriptions recorded in ancient glyphic books, not from directly remembered experiences. It is a view of the trapezoidal gap in the Absu at the time of the equinoxes, which disregards the fact that the left and right embankments were probably not visible at the same time. The central playing field of the horizontal space between the embankments is accurately rendered, but notice that the ballcourts vary tremendously in size, as does the slope of the walls, although somewhat less. This suggests that the ballcourts are not modeled on a physical object which could be used as a model for the builders.

Teotihuacan, one of the three largest cities in the world in about AD 700, did not have a ballcourt. But the orientation of the main street and the Pyramid of the Sun with the horizon in effect turned the whole city into a giant ballcourt, using the Sun as the ball. More on this in a later chapter.

Note 7 --

The name "Ra" or "Re" was probably transferred to Jupiter without hesitation by some of the Egyptians temple domains after 3147 BC, for the apparition of the globe of Jupiter in the south sky was nearly identical in size and in other aspects to the earlier view of Saturn at the north horizon. Only the fact that Jupiter soon (after about 200 years) reached the edge of the asteroid belt and lost much of its coma and all of its tail, at a time when Horus had been appearing regularly in the skies above Earth, kept Jupiter from being accepted universally as chief of the Gods at that time.

Note 8 --

The Himalayas today are held to be very young, having "reached" their current height after the ice age, and often suggested to have done so in historical times. The mechanics are discussed in Appendix B, "The Celestial Mechanics".

Note 9 --

In the second century AD Ptolemy reports the star Sirius as red, as do others in late antiquity. However, Sirius is listed as white by the Arab (Persian) astronomer Al-Sufi in the *Book of fixed Stars*, published in AD 964. Both Ptolemy and Al-Sufi were very competent astronomers. Details of how Sirius disappeared behind the last red band are presented in the Appendix "The Red Sirius."

Note 10 --

The outer red ring may have lasted a long time after the fall of the Absu, and along with the bright ecliptic become known as one of the roads or rivers of the sky. In the *Popol Vuh*, Hunahpu and Xbalanque reach the domain of the underworld by crossing the river of blood (the last equatorial ring) and the river of pus (the ecliptic).

The Classic Era Maya (AD 400 to AD 700) graphic of the Wakah-Chan Tree consists of an upright tree (identified by others as the Milky Way) with a cross bar and with a serpent (called the "square-nosed dragon") draped over a cross bar. I would identify the draped serpent as the ecliptic and the cross bar as the equatorial, although this identification may be reversed. The cross bar (at times the ecliptic serpent) has heads at both ends of its body, one identified as the Sun, the other as Venus. I think the double-headed bar likely represents the plasmoid lightning bolt directed at the Sun by Jupiter in 685 BC, and seen worldwide, which will be discussed in the chapter "The Tablets of Ammizaduga."

Note 11 --

If the Moon changed its orbit, the force that altered its course might show as the Orientale basin compression scar located at the extreme lower left edge of the Moon as seen from Earth. The Orientale Basin is overlaid with younger craters, and is thought itself to be one of the "youngest" craters or basins. It is (of course) held to be 3.9 billion years old. The outer ring of displaced mountains is 200 miles (320 km) in diameter.

The Moon retained its original path around the Sun, which has an inclination to the Sun's equatorial which is slightly different from that of the Earth.

[Image: Orientale basin of the Moon. After NASA.]

Note 12 --

John Anthony West in *Serpent in the Sky* (1979) claimed that the excess erosion of the Sphinx is due to rainfalls thousands of years before the construction dates of the Pyramids (2600 to 2500 BC). He wrote, *"The last time Egypt experienced a rainy period capable of producing such weathering effects was the Neolithic Subpluvial, between 5000 and 7000 BC."*

However, Colin Reader, in "Giza Before the Fourth Dynasty" *JACF* (2002), writes that wetter conditions existed in general in Egypt "as late as the end of the 5th Dynasty" (circa 2500 BC). The Giza pyramids were built during the 5th dynasty. He also suggests that most of the weathering of the Sphinx took place before the building of the pyramids, but he dates the Sphinx to the first or second dynasty. The first dynasty ended in 2850 BC. He also suggests that additional weathering is due to seepage from the adjacent areas of the plateau where limestone was removed during construction of the pyramids and the quarries backfilled with rubble.

Let me add to the rains proposed here the following two: first, the incessant rains during the fall of the Absu at the end of the 5th dynasty (2349

BC), and second, the initial rains of the years of darkness after the Exodus (1492 BC).

Note 13 --

In this instance, 2349 BC, the interplanetary lightning strikes consisted of a series of 9 plasmoids following an initial much larger plasmoid. Some of these may have landed in Central Asia on the second day.

Note 14 --

See the website of Timo Niroma for a detailed overview of the 2349 BC and 2193 BC events, at [personal.eunet.fi/pp/tilmari]

Note 15 --

It would seem to be difficult to disassociate the first showing of the Moon from the events of 2349 BC, with the exception of the life span given to the Moon in the *Annals of Shu*, which is only 110 years.

The "death" of Shun, the Moon, when "he went on high," is likely to be a change in the orbital path of the Moon, coinciding with an increase in the Earth's orbit in 2193 BC. Thus the 110 years since the "birth of Shun" should probably be lengthened to 156 years, if we assume that the Moon showed up at the earlier increase of the Earth's orbit.

Note 16 --

The date correction is based on the assumption that the backward extension of the Long Count by the Olmecs in 747 BC was based on a 360-day year. This is clear from the 20-day Uinal "months" which add up to a Tun ("year"). There are 18 of these months to make up a Tun. All other measures rotate at a value of 20 -- Kins, Tuns, and Katuns. (Baktuns rotate at 13.)

This was done by adding 6 Baktuns to the count of 0.0.0.0. The history of past events was probably a listing of Katuns and Baktuns (where a Baktun is a double-decade of Tun years). But when the Maya retrocalculated in AD 700 they would have used a 365.24-day year to arrive at a predetermined Baktun and Katun. Our calculation based on the Long Count is also based on the assumption of Gregorian years (365.24 days) in the remote past, and thus also places events too far into the past by 5.24 days per year. Thus to recalculate the inscribed Long Count dates to the correct chronography, a value of ({date} - 747) * 5.24/365.24 years needs to be subtracted from the Mesoamerican dates. See the chapter "The Maya Calendar."

A date from the Palenque sculpture which falls in the 7th century AD (a conjunction of Saturn, Jupiter, and Mars on July 23, AD 690, in Libra) needs no correction, and is dead accurate. This date falls after 747 BC.

Note 17 --

The Egyptians never recognize the Moon. There is a total absence of the crescent of the Moon in depictions. Upturned crescents, as, for example, part of the headdresses of Gods and Goddesses, are based on symbols dating to before 3147 BC, and on graphic simplifications of cattle or ram horns, they are not based on the Moon, since the Moon never produces an upturned crescent at the latitudes of Egypt.

Note 18 --

Since the Katuns (and the implied Baktuns) were retrieved from ancient records, they were not retrocalculated, as at Palenque. The Katuns (and Baktuns) were most likely based on Tun years which were equivalent to solar years. A Baktun would thus be equal to 400 solar years, and a Katun would be 20 solar years, without regard to the actual length of the year. Thus the correction formula (below) is based first on subtracting 6 Baktuns (2400 years) from 747 BC to arrive at 3147 BC as the year of the end of the "Era of the Gods." Other corrections are thus found numerically as **3147 - 400*Baktuns - 20*Katuns**.

Note 19 --

Venus was probably orbiting the mass centroid of Saturn, Neptune, and Uranus, and thus somewhere at the level of Neptune. Venus could easily have been locked out of the reformed combined plasmasphere if its location managed to avoid the extension of the new plasmasphere in the direction away from the Sun, or, alternately, if it passed through this space in revolving around the Saturnian planets, and subsequently passed out of the combined plasmasphere. That would place it behind Jupiter from the slightly later point of view from Earth, after 3147 BC. This conforms to the notion of the Greeks (and only the Greeks) that Venus had been born from the head of Jupiter (Zeus), because it was first seen passing from behind Jupiter.

It might easily be suggested that the original diameter of the "gravitational sphere of influence" of Saturn shrank in the presence of the mass of Jupiter (which is three times that of Saturn). Shrinking a gravitational sphere of influence released the somewhat distant planets Earth and Venus from being carried along as satellites of Saturn. Away from other large masses, a sphere of influence is generally about 100 times the diameter of the parent planet -- 7 million miles (11 million km) for Saturn.

Mercury and Mars must have continued to travel with Saturn, for they show up near Earth about 80 years late. The Sumerian *King List* places Mars near Saturn in 3147 BC by virtue of the fact that only 80 years had passed since the last lowering of Mars. That time span is half of the earlier periods between lowering -- thus placing Mars closer to Saturn than to Earth.

With the following appearances after 3147 BC, Mars is accompanied by many asteroids, suggesting an aphelion in the asteroid belt. The movement of Mars and Mercury -- why they returned to the region of the inner planets from the asteroid belt -- was governed by the gravitational attraction of the Sun, expressed as soon as Mercury and Mars fell away from the enclosing plasmasphere of Saturn. It can only be suggested that, like what we will see Jupiter do also, the plasmasphere of Saturn would have shrunk on reaching the asteroid belt. It can thus be suggested that these planets were released when Saturn's gravitational sphere of influence shrank as it entered the asteroid belt.

Note 20 --

The "tree" at Biblos of the *Isis and Osiris* story (by Plutarch in AD 100), is the plume of plasma impinging at the north magnetic pole of the Earth, after the change in the Earth's orbit in 3147 BC. The lodging of the coffin of Osiris in the tree is likely a ball plasmoid at the end of the plume. The polar plumes were presented in the text of a previous chapter.

Isis, in the shape of a swallow, flew around the tree which entrapped the coffin of Osiris. The swallow is possibly Mercury, which had polar plumes, because of an atmosphere (partially extant today). It had a split tail which additionally make it look like a swallow. The split plasma tail is typical of a body with only a limited magnetic field. Split tails have regularly been observed for comets over the last 400 years. The visual impression that a swallow was "circling" the tree of the north likely reflects Mercury's close passage to the Sun or the circling of the first northern polar plume.

This does not measure up to my other, later claim that Mercury only appeared with Mars at the end of the 80-year period. So, rather than the swallow being Mercury, it more likely is the planet Venus, who is Isis.

The fire lighted by Isis, where she roasted the baby of the Queen of Biblos, was seen also in antiquity, and is likely the lower portion of the plasma plume in arc mode. At a later date the Egyptians would identify the plumes as the braziers of the four cardinal points.

Note 21 --

I have only found one reference to a possible plasma discharge associated with Saturn after 3147 BC in the Maya *Chilam Balam* books, but I think it is a transcription error.

Calculations are in Unix bc notation, where ∧ denotes exponentiation; the functions a(rctangent), s(ine), and c(osine) use radians; angle conversions to radians or degrees by the divisors rad=.017+ and deg=57.2+; other functions are shown as f( ); tan( )=s( )/c( )
units: million == 1,000,000; billion == 1,000,000,000;
AU == 93,000,000 miles.

Revision: 42.59 (jup.php)
Contents of this chapter: [Blood and Alcohol] [The Ten Suns]
[The Day of the Dead] [The Twin Peaks] [the *Enuma Elish*]
[the *Book of the Dead*] [24th and 23rd Century BC] [Recap and Reactions]
[The Moon Dies] [Return of the Axis Mundi] [The Tower of Babel]
[The First Histories] [The Return of Mars] [Sodom and Gomorrah]
[The Return of Mercury] [Endnotes]

Blood and Alcohol

At this point I want to add some elements from the event of 2349 BC: the bloodbath by Kali, Hathor, and others, the intervention by Jupiter, and the worldwide celebration of the Day of the Dead.

... Kali

The Hindu Goddess Kali (Venus) goes on a blood-soaked killing rampage. Another God (Shiva) has to intervene to stop her. Kali is portrayed as black with black hair and black garments, if any. The same occasional hag-like appearances can be found among other descriptions of Venus as a raging madwoman, a witch, in Mesopotamia as well as in Mesoamerica. Venus would be a dark shape if the planet passed in front of the Sun during the daytime. The rotation of the Earth (plus the movement of a gyroscopic reaction) would make it look as if Venus raged across the sky a number of days.

Kali is black because she (Venus) was backlighted by the Sun as it moved into a position of having the Sun, Venus, and Earth all in a line. The plasma tail directed away from the Sun would then point at the Earth. In that Venus has no magnetic field, the tail probably consisted of separate spikes diverging from the centerline of the Sun-Venus axis, as is also seen in cometary tails. If

these streams moved about in adjusting to the Earth's plasmasphere that they were passing through, Kali would be seen with flailing arms and legs -- in effect Kali was dancing.

I suspect the compressive contact with Venus was made in a region north of India. This would have tipped the equatorial rings up to move Kali into the midst of the blood-red rings (although the red color may have developed the next day). This was followed within a half day or less by a disconnected plasmoid from Venus (followed by 9 lesser plasmoids over the next day).

The gyroscopic reaction torque to the initial compressive shock (and the tipping back of the Earth's axis) would have rotated the Earth's axis counterclockwise, so as to move Eastern Asia (Russia) to face the Sun and shorten the day in India and Southern Asia. This probably accounts for the fact that the plasmoid "dragon" from Venus was seen in the Middle East, but not noted in India. That suggests perhaps six hours of travel for the plasmoid. That would place Venus at a distance of 12 million miles (19 million km) from Earth during this incident, if the plasmoid traveled, similar to the solar wind, at a rate of about 2 million miles per hour. [note 2]

... Ku-Bau

From the Sumerian *King List* we have:

"After kingship was brought back to Kish again, Ku-Bau, the innkeeper, she who made firm the foundations of Kish, ruled for 100 years as `king' before Kish was defeated."

Her occupation is also translated as "prostitute" or "barmaid" -- the last as yet another association with alcohol. She is probably Venus, but cannot be dated with certainty to the destructive appearance of the planet in 2349 BC, although her "reign" predates Sargon's conquest of Mesopotamia, which is

listed somewhat later in the *King List.*

"In Kish, Puzur-Sin, son of Ku-Bau, reigned 25 years as king; Ur-Zababa, the son of Puzur-Sin, reigned 400 years."

Archaeologists date the barkeep Ku-Bau at circa 2400 BC (how amazing!). Puzur-Sin ("Moon"), her son, is estimated by archaeologists at circa 2360-2340 BC, and Ur-Zababa, the grandson at circa 2340 BC. Here is Venus as the barmaid, Puzur-Sin as the Moon, but I don't know who the grandson is (I suspect it may be the electrically active Moon stripped of its atmosphere). There was no 500-year delay before Sargon's conquest of Sumer, however, as presumably indicated in the King List. It happened at the same time as Ku-Bau's appearance. Individual dynasties listed in the Sumerian King List often run simultaneously, or more likely list the extent of the lifetimes of the individual kings.

The association of what would be the smell of alcohol (or wild dancing) with some of the legends, and the association of the color red with all three of these tales (there are many more), might suggest an analysis of the possible chemistry of the gases and particulate matter of the Absu. It may have been a smell associated with brewing or fermentation. There will be similar suggestions of worldwide odors at much later dates, but these are recognized as sweet smells like the scents of flowers, or, as I would suggest, like diesel exhaust, and thus the burning of hydrocarbons like crude oil.

Ka-Bau (Kubaba) eventually is recognized as Kybebe (or Cybele) in Anatolia, and is adopted by the Romans as a goddess 2000 years later.

... Anath

Continuing further west, in the Levant the Goddess Anath of Ugarit goes on a "drunken rampage" extending from the location of sunrise to the Mediterranean sea. Here, too, the local chief God (Baal) has to intervene. Baal, of course, is Jupiter. Here, as in other tales, the dragon or goddess (now the plasmoid, rather than Venus) is described as "wading" in blood or gore

(and in other descriptions as slapping her tail through the "waters").

The people of the Eastern Mediterranean saw the approach of the plasmoid from Venus. This lightning strike was not instantaneous; this took time to travel. Leonard King wrote:

"We have long possessed part of another local version of the Dragon myth, which describes the conquest of a dragon by some deity other than Marduk; and the fight is there described as taking place, not before Creation, but at a time when men existed and cities had been built. Men and gods were equally terrified at the monster's appearance, and it was to deliver the land from his clutches that one of the gods went out and slew him."

"Tradition delighted to dwell on the dragon's enormous size and terrible appearance. In this version he is described as fifty beru (bêru) in length and one in height; his mouth measured six cubits and the circuit of his ears twelve; he dragged himself along in the water, which he lashed with his tail; and, when slain, his blood flowed for three years, three months, a day and a night. From this description we can see he was given the body of an enormous serpent."

-- Leonard King, *Legends of Babylon and Egypt* (1918)

The "beru," a footnote mentions, was the space that could be covered in two hours' traveling. The apparition is thus held to be 400 miles (640 km) long (assuming 8 miles are covered in two hour's walking), and 8 miles (13 km) in width. The head of the plasmoid may have looked larger, in that it was closer to the observers. The size of the object in the sky might have been estimated by comparison to distant mountains.

The Goddess Anath of Ugarit is described as extending in size from the location of sunrise to the sea. This is similar to what is suggested above for the dragon.

The dragon apparition was not Venus, since Venus would have (or might have) blocked the Sun, being in a direct line with the Sun. This dragon with its enormous head was a plasmoid launched from Venus, an object lighted by its own arc mode plasma. As the Earth rotated toward the east the "head" of the dragon, a round ball of plasma with what looked like tentacles hanging from the mouth (the classical depiction of a dragon in China and in Mesoamerica), would first be seen in the south and then pass by, headed toward the west with the "tail" following behind it in the east.

... Leviathan

One of the beasts of the Bible which Yahweh conquered is Leviathan, mentioned in Job 41, and referred to in Psalm 68:30, as "the beast of the reeds." The reeds, again, describe the Duat.

The whole apparition, being brilliant enough to shine through the dust and particles of the Absu, had the appearance of being within the rings, "in the sea." It would have happened in the course of a half a day, for the travel time of the plasmoid would not have lasted more than 6 hours. The Earth shock happened east of the region of the Eastern Mediterranean from which we have reports (and likely north of India). The contact with Venus would have been made as the Sun, Venus, and Earth were all in a line -- at noon local time. The plasmoid would have been launched very soon after the Earth shock, and was seen arriving by the people of the Eastern Mediterranean before night fell -- about 6 hours or sooner.

This was a time near the equinox, so that the day would normally have been about 12 hours long, but the reaction torque would have reduced the length of the day, moving the west part of the Earth faster toward the east, because of the swing made by the Earth's rotational axis. If the plasmoid traveled at a rate of two million miles per hour (3.2 million km per hr), which is the speed of the solar wind after leaving the Sun, then Venus would have been at a distance of about 12 million miles (19 million km) from Earth at the time the plasmoid was launched. At a higher speed of travel (as I will propose), Venus would have been separated from Earth at a greater distance.

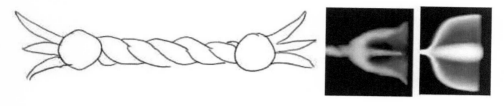

[*Images: Left: Plasmoid lightning bolt shown in its full extent. Illustration by J. Cook. Right: The end form is based on viewing the denser edge of the cup-like form and a dense central core. After David Talbott and Wallace Thornhill,* Thunderbolts of the Gods *(2005).*]

The tail would have grown in size as the plasmoid was viewed at an increasing angle. As it closed in on Earth, the rear tines of the plasmoid would become distinct and look as if they were wading through the rings of the Absu like the legs of a giant animal. The slashing tail is the collapse of the main body of the plasmoid delivered almost broadside onto the rings of the Absu, and exploding on reaching the electric field surrounding the Earth. For this reason Chinese dragons are depicted as contorted and twisted snakes with legs.

The dragon, as Tiamat, opened its mouth and swallowed the winds, whereupon she burst. So reads the Babylonian *Enuma Elish*, which I'll address further below. The winds were real; but resulted from the heat of the expanding air mass originally centered on Asia. Additionally, the explosive blast, followed later by additional plasmoids, would have sent scorching waves of heat to the Earth's surface. This too added to the winds.

... Hathor

Associated with the fall of the Absu in 2349 BC is the notion of blood everywhere. The blood-red condition shows up in tales of the destruction of mankind recorded in Egyptian New Kingdom tombs (Tutankhamen, 1327 BC; Seti I, 1279 BC; plus others down to 1136 BC, although these dates are held by Velikovsky to fall in the 10th to 9th century BC), where Hathor (Venus), as the lion-headed Goddess Sekhmet, wades in the blood of men and in red beer.

These New Kingdom texts replicate the written style of the Middle Kingdom, that is, the era in Egyptian history after the demise of the Old Kingdom in 2193 BC, and would thus date from long before the time when they were recorded. Most likely the tales date from 2349 BC, the same event

(the "flood of Noah" and the fall of the Absu) which was also replayed shortly after 2349 BC by Unas in his Pyramid Texts, where he threatens to cut the throats of the celestial gods and disembowel them.

In 2349 BC, when Hathor (representing the plasmoid of Venus) starts to destroy humans and drink their blood, Ra (Jupiter), who had ordered the destruction, managed to stop Hathor when she went out of control, by ordering the manufacture of 6000 jars of beer, dyed red with hematite (red iron oxide), to be poured out over the land. The Goddess drinks the beer, gets drunk, and ceases the killings. Ra retires soon after (which actually would have been 200 years later in about 2150 BC).

The story is recorded as the *Legend of the Celestial Cow,* so called because Ra also orders the creation of a celestial cow on whose back he then sits and leaves Earth. I have introduced the Hathor-cow earlier, in the chapter "The Gods Leave," related to the change in the electric field of the Sun. I suggested that the Van Allen belts would change to a glow mode display from the excess electrons spiraling back and forth along the magnetic field lines. After creating the cow's back, Ra next orders the creation of the cow's legs. (Is that a strange detail?) All this happens on the third day after Hathor's bloodbath. In this last detail the *Legend of the Celestial Cow* parallels other descriptions of the same events, as also in the detail that Ra then creates the southern stars. [note 1]

... Grendel's mother

In the Anglo-Saxon epic *Beowulf,* the hero Beowulf battles the mother of

the monster Grendel in a cave under the sea (or a lake) over the course of three days. The mother of Grendel is yet another version of Kali, Tiamat, Anath, Sekhmet, and Ku-Bau. The "sea" (again) is the Absu. The cave is the Earth's shadow on the Absu. Beowulf rises out of the blood and gore of the lake at the ninth hour (3 PM) of the third day. It is strange that the poem actually mentions the time of day. This closely matches estimates elsewhere in the world of how soon after the earth-shock of 2349 BC Jupiter "rose from the dead."

The three-part epic recounts events of 3147 BC (Grendel's arm is torn off at his shoulder), 2349 BC (a bloody fight with a monster under water), and 685 BC (a battle with a fire dragon), aided in the last instance by one of his young cohorts, Wiglaf. Beowulf is played by Jupiter throughout, except perhaps in the last instance. The protagonists in all three parts are Venus or an associated plasmoid. Beowulf's display of the hilt of the sword which slew Grendel's mother is the southern polar plume seen from 55 degrees north latitude. Grendel's loss of his arm recalls the same detail as presented in the Maya *Popol Vuh*, where Hunahpu (Venus) has his arm torn off "at the shoulder" by Seven-Macaw -- the loss of the plasma connection of Venus with Saturn.

The alcohol seems to be missing from the Beowulf epic, perhaps because the tale was composed some 3000 to 4000 years after the events, although the central event, the attack by Grendel's mother, occurs after heavy feasting and drinking at Heorot Hall. For the more contemporaneous generation of the tales of Hathor, Kali, Anath, and Ku-Bau, there is a close association between the arrival of Venus in 2349 BC and alcohol, as well as intervention by the chief God. The Babylonian *Enuma Elish* records this last also. It could therefore be suggested that Jupiter again assumed its giant coma and tail within 2 and a half days after September 6, 2349 BC (the date of the equinox at that time) to be reestablished and remain as chief God for the next 199 years.

I should also note that the 400 Lost Boys, recorded in the *Popol Vuh*, who become the Pleiades (at the time of the "flood of Noah"), are also "dead drunk" at the time they are blasted into the heavens by Zipacna, the mountain giant Jupiter.

Where did the plasmoid land? I suspect that it never reached the surface of the Earth. I think that it dissipated at the equatorial rings, but not without massive return strokes of lightning from the Earth's toroidal belts (the Van Allen belts, located above the atmosphere at the equator) into the equatorial ring system. The *Chilam Balam* mentions the return lightning strokes, as does the Chinese legend of the archer Li.

The Ten Suns

Having been introduced at this point to the black Kali of India, Anath of Ugarit, and Hathor of Egypt (Tiamat of the Babylonian *Enuma Elish* will be discussed later) -- all wading in the blood of slaughtered humans -- it is perhaps appropriate to tie together these "legends" and attempt to establish a sequence of events for the days of the 2349 BC event which are otherwise known as the "flood of Noah." Details are scant, but the following sequence seems reasonable.

India saw the approach of Venus, initially as a black mass occluding the Sun. The initial compressive Earth shock in Asia north of the Himalayas, due to the electric fields of the planets, was instantaneous. The seismic aftershocks to the repulsive electric force north of the Himalayas would have made Kali dance. The details of a bloodbath were only added the next day when the Absu had broken up into a red bath.

The seismic shockwave traveled in all directions, causing great damage, noted mainly southwest and west of the shock impact site, among sites from the Caucasus through Anatolia and across Greece. This condition would have been aggravated if there had been attempts at charge equalization through lightning bolts reaching the surface of the Earth. There was a lightning bolt, but it took 6 hours to arrive, and then apparently dissipated at the Earth's Van Allen belts or the ionosphere. This was, on the one hand, a peculiar interaction, and on the other, a grace for the Earth. We were spared the incineration of forests and prairies, and the loss of light for thousands of years. It is possible also, that the initial plasmoid landed in the Pacific. Water vapor in the atmosphere will not cool the Earth by blocking sunlight for hundreds or thousands of years. If the plasmoid was mostly absorbed by the ionosphere, it would have resulted in massive lightning strikes from the ionosphere or upper atmosphere to Earth's surface (under the condition of the upper atmosphere or ionosphere inducing an opposite voltage at ground level).

The surface lightning strikes to Earth were thus not from Venus. From Venus came one very large plasmoid, and some nine additional smaller ones.

Except for the damage done to the Absu by the first plasmoid, it is difficult to determine where these bolts landed and what the damage would look like. More on this further below.

The date of the shock can be established as occurring on the day of the autumnal equinox. This will be discussed in a following section. At the fall equinox the axis of the Earth would have been inclined forward -- in the direction of travel of Earth along its orbit. As mentioned earlier, the jolt to the Earth, above the equator, would have caused the spin axis to tilt away from the Sun, followed immediately by a reaction torque twisting the axis back toward the leading position of Earth's orbit, but in a counterclockwise direction (as seen from above). The effect would have been to bring the equatorial rings up to face Venus and the Sun, a condition probably accomplished within a few hours. The travel of the Earth's axis in this loop would have kept the broadside of the rings of the Absu facing Venus for about a half a day or a day.

This action is important, because the twisting of the axis may have kept the Earth from being incinerated, for the very next event after the initial shock was the release of the plasmoid thunderbolt by Venus. But it took time to reach earth.

The people of the Eastern Mediterranean saw the explosion, which, if my sense of timing is mostly correct, most likely happened over North Africa or the Atlantic or even further west. At this time the Eastern Mediterranean was turning away from the Sun and Venus at a faster rate than normal (the result of the gyroscopic reaction), and it was in Central America where the next phase of the spectacle was clearly witnessed.

As the day dawned in Mesoamerica, the arrival of secondary plasmoids was witnessed and recorded by the Olmecs, to be transcribed to garbled narrative texts some 3900 years later on separate pages of the *Books of the Chilam Balam*. The last page of Book 2 reads:

"'Our gods have grown!' their priests said (those from [of] *the Sun). And then days of the year were introduced."*

"'Behold abundant suns come,' they said. And the hoofs of the animals burned and the edge of the sea burned."

"'This is the sea of bitterness!' they said."

"And the face of the sun was corroded, and its face became darkened and was put out. And then, above, they became frightened. 'It has burned up! Our god has died!' their priests said. And they were beginning to think about making a picture of the figure of the sun, when the earth shook and they saw the moon."

-- Antonio Mediz Bolio, *Books of the Chilam Balam of Chumayel* (1930) [note 3]

This single page of the *Chilam Balam* obviously refers to 2349 BC, with its reference to a new calendar ("days of the year were introduced" -- the Tzolkin), the disturbance of the Absu ("the edge of the sea burned"), and the arrival of the Moon ("the earth shook and they saw the moon"). The first line may refer to the initial plasmoid from Venus, seen in the east, but the phrase, "behold abundant suns come," describes secondary plasmoids of lesser intensity which followed on the heels of the initial dragon-sized bolt. [note 4]

The darkening of the face of the Sun can be attributed to the fact that the Sun would have sunk toward the south horizon as the Earth's axis tilted away (up) from the direction of the Sun. On the remainder of this page of the *Chilam Balam* a war ensues, with whole armies being shot down with arrows. This likely represents the lightning bolts traveling up through the Absu on the same or following days. China records the same. [note 5]

Except for the clear reference to 2349 BC, some of this text would have remained inexplicable if it were not for the fact that an almost identical description exists in China, as the legend of the "Ten Suns" which are shot down with the arrows of the celestial archer Li and which is placed "after the time of Yao." Both the Mesoamerican text and the Chinese text mention the multiple Suns, the heat felt on Earth, and the arrows directed up through the Absu. Li might be the Moon or a narrative fiction.

In China, daylight would normally arrive nearly a half day after it was daylight in Mesoamerica. But as the Earth's axis spun away from the direction of the Sun and simultaneously started to lean in the lagging direction of the Earth's orbit (initially), daylight and the secondary plasmoids, would have appeared hours earlier than normal. Otherwise it would be difficult to maintain that secondary plasmoids from Venus continued for as much as a day. The many suns were seen as rising, that is, in the east, and likely followed each other. The lightning bolts were launched individually. Nine were shot down. The last, the real Sun, remained.

And then it stopped, except for the bleeding of the sky. In India black Kali was now wading in blood. It stopped, observers noted, because a God had interfered. A sudden reappearance of the coma of Jupiter, on the second night after the day of the event, was the sign that this had happened. The timing of this is not entirely clear, though. In Babylon, in the *Enuma Elish*, written hundreds of years later, the rescue of Earth is attributed to a complete plan devised by Marduk before the onset of the plasma contact. But in India, the Levant, and Egypt, the God who quells the raging goddess acts shortly after the start of the killings. If the plasma expulsion of Venus (the plasmoid) also traveled past Earth, down the extended tail of the Earth's plasmasphere facing away from the Sun, it would have reached Jupiter (with Jupiter in line with Earth) in about 6 days and caused it to switch to a glow mode coma. This assumes a speed of about two million miles per hour (3.2 million km per hr).

It could have been sooner, however, for coronal mass expulsions (a dense plasma) from the Sun have been known, in recent times, to travel on occasion at a rate of 200 million miles per hour (320 million km per hr), rather than 2 million miles per hour. At a somewhat higher speed of six million miles per hour, it would have reached Jupiter (at that time located at 4.5 AU from the Sun, and thus about 3.5 AU from the location of Earth) in two and a half days. The worldwide celebrations of the "Day of the Dead," which will be introduced below, almost uniformly last two and a half days. [note 6]

If Jupiter blazed, suddenly, two and a half days after the Earth shock, as the tremors from the shock lessened and the sweeping hurricanes abated, and after experiencing the plasmoids from Venus, Jupiter would have been understood as the savior of the Earth. Only the blood in the "ocean" remained.

The bleeding of the dragon lasted, one of the above sources notes, for 3 years, 3 months, one day and one night. The time for the complete fall of the Absu can be compared to the various times that flood survivors spent floating in their various boats and arks, which, of course, is nowhere near three years. In most myths the extent of the flood is much shorter, although these tales represent references to the flood of 3147 BC. Noah, in the Biblical story spends a much longer time afloat, but not three years.

I also do not know if the Absu was originally colored red, although it could be suspected that at least part of the rings may have been. Some low-density gases will glow in red when ionized and under electric discharge, as is seen today in the Aurora (and in the rings of Saturn). If the Absu had always been red, we would never have heard anything about it. More likely, it was a condition of 2349 BC due to a continual plasma discharge via the equatorial rings. The *Chilam Balam* claims that the whole world turned red at this time, and attributes the condition to Jupiter. Another page of the *Chilam Balam* claims that the condition only lasted past the ending of one Katun, and partway into the next -- 18 or 20 years.

Blood would have been everywhere in the sky. It was near the fall equinox, and at night the Absu would have been divided by the long shadow of Earth. Based on Maya iconography it appears that by coincidence Jupiter appeared in the very center of the gap of the Absu as it expanded into a giant form. As the rotation of the sky, due to the gyroscopic reaction, neared completion at about this time, then Jupiter would have been seen as rising from within the gap. Actually, the Absu lifted up again against the background of the stars as the Earth resumed its normal tilt -- at the same time that Jupiter suddenly developed a large glow mode coma and a giant expulsion of plasma below the coma, its mountain.

With the initial gyroscopic condition of the Earth tilted away from the Sun, the gap created by the shadow of the Earth would have closed to become a cave or doorway to a cave. Returning the Absu, or what was left of it, to its normal position against the backdrop of the stars, would also move the shadow of the Earth up against the rings. This would make it look as if the cave exploded open as Jupiter moved up and out.

This is confirmed from a number of Mesopotamian seals, dated to shortly afterwards, which depict Jupiter rising from between two mountains. This is correct for an alignment of the Sun, Venus, Earth and Jupiter. But there is much more that confirms this condition from throughout the world.

The Day of the Dead

Moe Mandelkehr, in *The 2300 BC Event* (2006), assumes that the events of 2349 BC and 2193 BC can be represented as a single incident of a fall of meteorites in about 2300 BC and the subsequent creation of a series of circumpolar rings which lasted some months. The book, in three volumes, includes a wealth of information, of which the details of a worldwide celebration of a "Day of the Dead," centering on the culmination of the Pleiades in the south sky, is the most interesting and bears directly on the topic of this chapter. (A culmination is when a star reaches the highest point in the sky directly above the south cardinal direction at midnight.) He opens with a quotation from W. T. Olcot which effectively sums up the information he presents. [note 7]

> *"Memorial services to the dead at the season of the year when the Pleiades occupied a conspicuous position in the heavens are found to have taken place, and to have been a feature in the history of almost every nation of the earth, from remote antiquity to the present day."*
>
> *"The universality of this custom may well be considered one of the most remarkable facts that astronomical history records. ... A great cataclysm ... is in some way associated with the Pleiades, and some reference to such an event can be traced in many of the legends and myths surrounding these stars that have come down to us from nations far removed from each other."*
>
> -- W. T. Olcott *Star Lore of All Ages* (1911)

Mandelkehr provides details spanning all continents and both hemispheres. He records the festivals worldwide as celebrating new-year, fire-lighting, and commemorating the dead. He lists details for Britain, Scandinavia, continental Europe, Greece, the Middle East, Israel, Africa, Egypt, Iran, India, Central Asia, China, Japan, the Pacific islands, North America, Mexico (Aztecs), Central America, South America, and Peru. Not all the references are solid and convincing, and some have nothing to do with the topic at hand, but there are certainly more than enough to build a case for a "Day of the Dead" celebration worldwide which had its genesis in remote antiquity. Today this festival is institutionalized in the Christian world as "All Saints Day" and "All Souls Day," and celebrated in other forms, as "Halloween," for example, and as the "Day of the Dead" in Mexico. [note 8]

Mandelkehr associates the Pleiades with the autumnal equinox in 2300 BC, based on a retrocalculation from the current constitution of the heavens. As the Sun sets in the west, the Pleiades would have risen in the east. Six hours later, at midnight (sidereal time), the Pleiades would have stood at their highest point in the south sky, a culmination.

The same information is found in Book 10 of the *Chilam Balam*, which mentions that after the fall of the Absu ("the baptism from the center of heaven") the ecliptic and equatorial became visible (as "the crossroads") with the Pleiades ("precious things," as seed corn is called) above these. Details in the chapter "The Chilam Balam."

The fact that an ephemeris will show the Pleiades culminating in the south skies at the autumnal equinox in 2300 BC, is actually a nagging coincidence, for my supposition (developed in later chapters) is that the skies were different and invariant before 685 BC. As it happens, the condition of the sky before 685 BC can be simulated (except for the zero longitudinal line and the horizon) by selecting the year 2000 BC with an ephemeris. This is very close to the retrocalculated conditions for 2300 BC, so that the Pleiades indeed stand at their highest point in the south skies on our equivalent date of September 21 on an equivalent Gregorian calendar -- the autumnal equinox by our accounting. [note 9]

The shift of 15 days experienced in 685 BC almost entirely accounts for the coincidence of the Pleiades appearing at the autumnal equinox in 2300 BC by retrocalculation.

The festivals noted by Mandelkehr for earlier ages occur near the expected culmination of the Pleiades in the sky at midnight in late October or early November. These dates have drifted away from the equinox because the culmination of the Pleiades moved later into the fall of the year after 685 BC due to the precession of the equinoxes (after 747 BC). The dates for many of the "Day of the Dead" celebrations do not recognize the equinox, but only the dates at which the Pleiades stand highest in the sky.

Yet it is also curious (as related by Olcott) that many of these festivals, where they are still celebrated today, start about 15 days early -- 15 days before the Pleiades reach their highest location in the sky. This agrees with what I will develop in the chapter "Modern History": that the equinoxes moved 15 days into the future after 685 BC. Before 685 BC the fall equinox fell on the equivalent calendar date of September 6th. (This also agrees with the earliest Mesopotamian records which inexplicably place the equinoxes in the constellations Taurus and Scorpio.)

This probably accounts for the 15-day discrepancy between when many of the "Day of the Dead" festivals are observed today and the actual calendar date of the culmination of the Pleiades. But whereas some people used calendar dates for the celebrations (15 days early), others followed the changing dates of the culmination of the Pleiades, and yet others kept the celebration at the date of the equinox, and in some cases, apparently, returned to the earlier date of September 6 of the equinox (noted by Mandelkehr). [note 10]

The information to be gleaned from Mandelkehr's book is unfortunately insufficient to make any determination of how these various dates for the celebrations may have developed historically, except in a few instances. Although he points to festival dates "around the end of October and beginning of November," he almost never makes note of when in the past these were celebrated. At best this might suggest that festivals seemed to have kept pace with the changing date of the culmination of the Pleiades over the last 2600 years.

It is, however, clear that at various times in the past some of the festivals were codified, that is, tied to a certain calendar date rather than continuing to follow the changing date of the culmination of the Pleiades. We see this in the Christian "All Saints" and "All Souls" days. These were set as a church feast day in about the year AD 700 or AD 1000, purposely coinciding with the "Day of the Dead" celebrations of the European tribes, celebrated, at that time, at the culmination of the Pleiades on October 31, Gregorian. Once tied to the church calendar, this feastday remained locked to October 31 and November 1, with allowances made by the church to continue the celebrations over two days. The pagan Halloween evening festival also kept pace with the church calendar.

A similar codification can be seen in Mesoamerica before the Spanish arrived. Mandelkehr, quoting Bernadino de Sahagún from a secondary source, notes that a "Day of the Dead" celebration occurred on October 20 in the 16th century AD. [note 11]

Interestingly, the primary God of the Aztecs, Huitzilopochtli, celebrated his "birthday" on November 9 (Gregorian), when the Spanish arrived in the 16th century AD, which was the actual day of the culmination of the Pleiades at that time. Huitzilopochtli is generally equated to the planet Mars, but the coincidence with the date of the culmination of the Pleiades would suggest that Huitzilopochtli may need to be equated with Jupiter, or that he was originally equated with Jupiter -- who, 3900 years earlier had reappeared from death on the day of the culmination of the Pleiades.

All the festivals honor the dead, light fires, and include torchlight parades. Many at one time marked new-year day. Invariably the celebrations last three days, or two days preceded by an evening festivity, even in Mexico of the 16th century AD. I think this is important in pointing to a series of closely related events, and I would suggest that the fall of the Absu, which was an absolutely terrifying event, would have been closely followed -- in fact, by two days and a night -- by the reappearance of Jupiter in his full mountain-sized form. "After three days he rose from the dead." [note 12]

"Who died?" As I have suggested above, it may have been only Jupiter who died and rose from the dead. The giant coma of Jupiter had disappeared from the sky, as noted in the *Chilam Balam*, sometime before 2349 BC. Although Mandelkehr assumes millions died from comet fragments (ice cubes?) falling from the sky, I think few people died, excepting those in the regions struck by the electric repulsive shock and the traveling seismic disturbances which devastated the landscape -- possibly affecting a large portion of the Earth. Sodom and Gomorrah suffered their initial destruction in the collapse of buildings at this time (which were rebuilt). Some regions of Earth would have been absolutely devastated, as Claude Schaeffer has pointed out. But it was the "blood" seen in the "ocean" which would have convinced the rest of the world that indeed millions of people had died.

The Twin Peaks

The appearance of Jupiter three days after the dragon had arrived and turned the sky to blood, formed an image which entered Christianity and is retained to this day.

The image is one of Jupiter suddenly appearing, when he had been held as dead at an earlier time. He appeared in the center of the gap of the Absu, two days after the fall equinox. Jupiter's coma was at this time three times the diameter of the Moon (so says Plutarch), with plumes spreading out from the top of the coma, and an absolutely gigantic plasma outpouring below, as the three leaves of a flower, but much denser so as to look like a solid mountain. The Olmecs, with a view of the ecliptic much higher in the sky, depict Jupiter's body as the open mouth of a cayman or alligator (which have short tongues).

Because it was the time near the fall equinox, the Absu at this point had opened up and split into two mountains. The umbra of the Earth's shadow extended across the rings, becoming less wide further from Earth. But the penumbra widened with distance from Earth, in effect rounding the left and right halves of the Absu from the center. The result was to have two mountains -- twin peaks -- next to each other, with Jupiter centered on the valley between the mountains for some hours on the night of September 8th. Since this was the time of the fall equinox, Jupiter (on the ecliptic) would rise above the equatorial in the following weeks and months anyway, reinforcing the concept of rising up out of a depression.

[*Image: Shamash rises from between the two mountains. Dawn and dusk, or east and west, are shown as flag standards. After E. A. Wallis Budge.*]

In the print of an Akkadian cylinder seal, shown above, dated to slightly after 2349 BC, an absolutely giant Shamash (Jupiter) is seen stepping out of the gap between twin mountains, the left and right halves of the Absu. The symbols on both sides of Shamash are partially schematic and partially in script. The right symbol of a star, meaning "heaven" or "holy," is placed on a pole rising out of the glyph for "mountain." Schematically it represents the earlier polar configuration. The left symbol I do not know.

Cylinder seals are small cylindrical stones carved in intaglio, used to roll across a clay slab to be used as a marker of ownership on trade materials. These appear after 2350 BC, although there are also seals dating to shortly after 3000 BC.

The rays rising from the upper arms of Shamash represent the upper plasma of Jupiter as three separate plumes. At other times this resulted visually when the planet dipped below the top level of the Absu and its light was diffracted by the structure of the rings. It thus signified the brilliance of the planet. The same rays show in depictions of Venus, for the same reason.

[*Image: Ishtar (Venus) and Ea (Sumerian Enki) aid in the resurrection of Shamash (Jupiter); circa 2308 BC. After crystalinks.com*]

Flanking the twin mountains are flag standards (with small lions on top), held in place by two gods. The two flags are what was seen of the equatorial plasma toroid surrounding the Earth (the Van Allen belt), which showed up whenever it was energized to glow mode. This was thus a temporary phenomenon, and represents two of the four posts holding up the heavens. These would rise up from the east and west cardinal directions of the horizon, follow the curvature of the equatorial and be truncated by the shadow of the Earth at the time of the equinoxes. It thus reached considerably above the rings of the Absu, which everywhere appeared below the equatorial. These two forms did not move significantly, except that they may have fluctuated in density so that they seemed to waver. This would cause them to be represented as flags, just like in Mesoamerica they are held to be trees.

The lion shown on top is an interpretation (I suspect) of the cross-section of the toroid where the Earth's shadow fell across it. At later instances a circle is shown, which is closer to being correct, because the equatorial toroid would be densest at its outer edges. Because of this ring at the top, these forms are also identified as doorposts (the ring forming the upper "hinge"), and texts describing the appearance of Shamash refer to "the doors of heaven opening."

The above impression of a somewhat later cylinder seal (2300 BC) shows what really happened. Here the Goddess Ishtar (Venus) and Ea (Mercury) attend the resurrection of Shamash. The script at the left reads "place of purification." That puts a different twist on the event of 2349 BC, as if Jupiter is being baptized. The seal still represents the event of 2349 BC, although at this time the Absu has long since disappeared. The flag standards are gone also.

Within the next few hundred years the Babylonians will spin a new theology with the writing of the *Enuma Elish*, which will bring Jupiter forward as the main character in the event of 2349 BC, under the name of Marduk. The *Enuma Elish* retains the attack by the dragon (Tiamat) and the blood in the skies, but removes the resurrection of Jupiter. Despite the importance of this new retelling of the drama, the fact that Jupiter (Shamash, Zeus, Jove), the most important God of antiquity, had returned from the dead in three days was long remembered -- parts of this tale are replayed a thousand years later in the telling of the Exodus story (the mountain, the sea split open), the resurrection of God is retold many times in many differing religions, and even 2300 years later it entered the Gospels.

[*Image: The Corn God (the First Father, Jupiter) rises from a crack in a turtle carapace, attended by Xbalanque and Hunahpu. After Freidel and Schele, "Maya Cosmos" (1993)*] [note 13]

In Egypt Ra, Jupiter as the midnight Sun, is always shown as a giant red globe, at times depicted in the saddle between two mountains, or hovering in a valley between two mountains. The mountains, in turn, are shown covered by what looks like rows of reeds. Such depictions are quite late, during the New Kingdom (after 1500 BC), and thus a thousand years removed from 2349 BC. At that time Ra is shown without his lower mantle or the three-pronged plumes at the top -- just a red sphere.

Although in Mesoamerica the depictions are 3000 years removed from the actual event, the sculptures and engravings are based on very old records extant at the time of the Classical Era (AD 400 to 900), and at times uncannily accurate. The image above is of the resurrection of Jupiter from a crack in a turtle shell. It represents a mixture of events separated by thousands of years. Here Jupiter is shown as the Corn God or as the First Father.

The "image of the turtle" had first appeared in 10,900 BC. The nearest of the three plasmoids likely gave rise to the second and third ball plasmoid of remote antiquity, as if rising out of the nearest ball plasmoid. What is depicted here is the first appearance of Jupiter as the new ruling god in 3147 BC, and additionally his resurrection in 2349 BC. Hunahpu and Xbalanque are assisting him, even though their actions date from shortly before 685 BC. But in effect they are the same two gods in attendance as in the cylinder seal shown earlier -- Ishtar and Ea. The two monster heads below Hunahpu and Xbalanque represent the two-headed plasmoid from Jupiter of 685 BC.

A portion of many Maya commemorative stelae have reference to the completion of a previous creation. They read, "... on 4-Ahau 8-Cumku was (first) seen the image of the turtle." This is a reference to a ending of the first creation, which included the 2500 years of appearances of the ball plasmoids of the south, ending in 8347 BC. The appearance of First Father ("Hun-Nal-Ye," Jupiter) is dated (here) to the beginning of the current calendar round in 3147 BC, when Bolon-ti-ku, Jupiter, seized the reign from Oxlahun-ti-ku, Saturn, as told in the *Chilam Balam*.

Other references to the creation on the date 4-Ahau 8-Cumku point instead to the placing of the three hearthstones in the sky. These are held (with certainty) by archaeologists to be three stars in the constellation Orion (one belt star and his two feet, enclosing M-42 as the fire). I would suggest that the reference actually is to the start of the "first creation" of 10,900 BC when the three ball plasmoids first appeared in the southern sky.

Hunahpu and Xbalanque, on the other hand, show up in the 120 years between 806 BC and 687 BC, as the twins Mars and Mercury, except in the last instance when they are Venus and Mercury. Since the celestial twins, as told in the *Popol Vuh*, attempt to raise their father from the dead (although without success), an association is had here to the resurrection of First Father. The *Popol Vuh* does not allow success in the efforts of the twins to revive their father, but the theology of other Maya centers speak differently, as is shown by this imagery.

Marduk and the *Enuma Elish*

Jupiter had lost its tail and coma (had died) some time before the "flood of Noah." There is a passage in the Babylonian *Enuma Elish* which tells of this. The express purpose of the *Enuma Elish* was to establish Jupiter (Marduk) as the chief God and to resolve a religious crisis in Babylonia. In the *Enuma Elish* Marduk is installed by the other Gods and invested with power in order to fight common enemies of the Gods, among them Tiamat ("chaos") and Absu ("the abyss"). Marduk asks only that,

> *"... an 'unchangeable command' might be given to him -- that whatever he ordained should without fail come to pass, in order that he might destroy the common enemy. ... The testing of his newly acquired power followed. A garment was placed in their midst:"*

> *"He spake with his mouth, and the garment was destroyed,*
> *He spake to it again, and the garment was reproduced."*

> -- Theophilus Pinches, "The Religion of Babylonia and Assyria (1890)

The Akkadians (and Babylonians) changed their dress after circa 2500 or 2400 BC from skirts to shoulder-hung robes. The climate had become colder. The century marked the end of the Hypsithermal. (Or we are seeing a change in fashion, which is unlikely.) The Babylonian priests did not spin tales out of whole cloth. The reference to the disappearing and reappearing garment -- it was Marduk's own -- was remembered by everyone, or talked about by their grandfathers. "Mountain" and "skirt" are the same word in Akkadian. The reappearance of Marduk's mountainous plasma tail skirt coincided in time with the arrival of the plasmoid of Venus, the fall of the Absu, and the later arrival of the Moon.

The exploits of Marduk are briefly related as follows:

> *"Neither An nor his son Ea knew words of power strong enough to subdue Tiamat, but Ea's son Marduk, the patron god of the city Babylon, took on the task of fighting Tiamat in return for his being proclaimed king of the other gods."*

Tiamat, whom Marduk is to battle, is the plasmoid of Venus.

> *"They gave him power to destroy things with a word and made him their king."*

"He, in turn, took his bow, the rainbow [actually, the polar plasma plume] *that arches across the sky, and his lightning arrows and made a great net to ensnare Tiamat, and riding the winds of seven great storms he went to do battle with her. When he threw his great net upon her, she opened her jaws to swallow him, and the winds that Marduk controlled rushed into her mouth and swelled her belly until it burst."*

"Then Marduk cut Tiamat's body in half and raised up one half to make the sky, leaving the other half as the restless oceans."

-- quoted by L.C. Geerts at http://Earth-history.com

Tiamat is not an Akkadian or Sumerian Goddess -- but she is female. Tiamat is an invention of the Babylonians, but identified as a dragon. What a sight, to have Tiamat distend and blow up! Here Tiamat is the first plasmoid from Venus in 2349 BC. The Absu, of which nothing more is heard of in all of the *Enuma Elish* after initial mention, becomes one of Marduk's weapons, "the net," along with another, called "the flood." Obviously the *Enuma Elish* was written well after the actual facts had started to fade.

Marduk at this telling of the *Enuma Elish* has become a creator God. The relationship of the *Enuma Elish* to the time period of 2349 BC, however, is clearly indicated by the tasks undertaken by Marduk after defeating Tiamat. Theophilus Pinches, in *The Religion of Babylonia and Assyria* (1890), writes:

"Then came the ordering of the universe anew. Having made a covering for the heavens with half the body of the defeated Dragon of Chaos [Tiamat, the Venus plasmoid], *Merodach* [Marduk, Jupiter] *set the Abyss* [the Absu], *the abode of Nudimmud* [Ea], *in front, and made a corresponding edifice above --the heavens -- where he founded stations for the gods Anu, Bel, and Ae."*

"Stations for the great gods in the likeness of constellations, together with what is regarded as the Zodiac, were his next work."

"He then designated the year, setting three constellations for each month [an Egyptian decan, and thus 30 degrees], *and made a station for Nibiru* [Venus] *-- Merodach's* [Marduk] *own star -- as the overseer of all the lights in the firmament."*

"He then caused the new moon, Nannaru, to shine, and made him the ruler of the night, indicating his phases, one of which was on the seventh day, and the other, a /abattu/, or day of rest, in the middle of the month."

China

These activities duplicate what the Chinese Legendary Emperor Yao accomplishes in the same era: adjusting the calendar, revealing the planets and stars (now that the equatorial rings had fallen), and setting the Moon in place.

The Chinese *Annals of Shu* were subjected to chronography by the Han between 200 BC and AD 200, and possibly earlier by the Taoists (and there are also comments about estimates by Confucius's disciples). But many of the names on the lists of kings had missing reign lengths, so that averages were used. Dynastic lengths seem to have been better established.

The story of the mortals Khwan and his son Yu forms a parallel to the story of the gods Yao (Jupiter) and Shun (the Moon). We are told that Khwan started drainage of blocked waters on a commission by Yao. The *Annals of Shu* record that in failing to accomplish this, he was kept prisoner on a mountain until his death. His son likewise was hired by Shun for the same purpose and additional tasks; he was appointed to the throne by Shun and survives him to become the first king of the Xia.

Unas and the *Book of the Dead*

Unas, at the end of the 5th dynasty, 2345 BC, is the first pharaoh to add text of the *Book of the Dead* to the interior of his pyramid (as do all the following pharaohs), perhaps being no longer convinced that the recitation by the priests will suffice. If the dates for Unas are correct, then he witnessed the fall of the Absu in 2349 BC. [note 14]

Much Later, in 2193 BC the Old Kingdom will end because of the failure of agriculture. When it is finally reconstituted as the Middle Kingdom 200 years later, it is as if nothing had happened. Egyptian religious practices continue with the old traditions of Horus, Ra, and Osiris. It was Unas who introduced the full-fledged theology of Osiris with his pyramid inscriptions. The worship of Osiris was new at the time of Unas.

There are no literary references to Osiris before the time of Unas. It suggests that the texts of the pyramid of Unas were meant to promote Osiris. As Jane Sellers, in *The Death of Gods in Ancient Egypt* (1992), writes:

> *"At the beginning of the Sixth Dynasty another change took place. The religious fervor honoring the sun god* [Re] *which had marked almost all the efforts of the Fifth Dynasty, shifts its emphasis to the worship of Osiris. It is in the pyramid of Unas, last ruler of the Fifth and in the pyramids of rulers of the Sixth Dynasty, that texts were now inscribed, and it is in these Pyramid Texts that the role of Osiris is predominant."*
>
> *"Sir Alan Gardiner has written that the Pyramid Texts had the sole aim of insuring the deceased ruler's identity with Osiris and insuring that the king would fare as Osiris had."*

The reference is to Sir Alan Gardiner, *Egypt of the Pharaohs* (1961). There are references in the pyramid texts of Unas to the bloodbath of Hathor of 2349 BC, although not directly, but displaced as actions by the dead pharaoh.

Sellers again:

"In the Fifth Dynasty some of the kings began a use of a name compounded with that of Re [Note: this actually started during the Fourth Dynasty], *and the nomen was now used less often on the monuments; concurrently the building activities now centered on sun temples. By the end of the Fifth Dynasty, however, the worship of Osiris (as evidenced in the Pyramid Texts* [of Unas]*), appear to rival the worship of Re. From these changes Egyptologists have concluded that competing groups worshiped Re and Osiris."*

Sellers quotes J. Gwynn Griffits, from *The Origins of Osiris and His Cult* (1960), as:

"While there is every likelihood that the Osirian material in the Pyramid Texts derives in part from a much earlier date, so far it has proved not possible to track down the god or his symbols tangibly to the First or Second Dynasty."

Let me: Osiris is always shown as a mummy, and consistently colored green. Although depicted as a green mummy in the middle kingdom, the actual green color dates from after 3147 BC to about 2914 BC. This is the green mummified creation-god Ptah of Memphis. He lived forever and is first king of Egypt. Why have the experts not noticed this? He is equated with Hephestus (who is Venus) by the Greeks and married to Sekhmet (who also is Venus), and wears the Osiris crown. I could add more aspects identifying him with Osiris. How could Sellers have missed this?

This is the same green that describes the mountain form of Jupiter in the *Popol Vuh* -- where he is simply known as "Mountain" (and as the "green tree of the center" in the *Chilam Balam*). Osiris thus is Jupiter, but in a form only recalled or recorded by one or more of the Egyptian temple domains. It is the form assumed by the planet Jupiter until it entered the asteroid belt in circa 2914. The mummy form of Osiris also recalls (or is) Min, the delta God from circa 3100 BC. Both are shown as ithyphallic. Min is thought to be the first pharaoh of the first dynasty, Menes -- "mn" in Egyptian, "he who endures" -- and thus also most likely Jupiter.

I am pointing out the sudden interest in Osiris because it was not new at all, and interestingly, the recollection from an earlier time is correct. The

Osiris tale can certainly be tied to the reappearance of Jupiter directly after the arrival of the plasmoid from Venus. Additionally, at a later time, a day in the calendar is designated as the commemoration of the death of Osiris, with a day three days later as the date Isis brought him back from the dead, although temporarily. There is an inversion of sorts of closely related events, as is not untypical of a number instances in antiquity. But here again is the interval of three days (two days and a night) between the sky turning blood red and the sudden reappearance of Jupiter with a lower plasma mountain.

Jupiter probably had lost its coma before 2349 BC, that is, had "died" earlier. Thus in the narrative "legend" of Osiris there is a temporal connection for which there is only a tenuous claim in reality, based on what we know or have been told. All the same, this particular claim -- the death of God followed by his resurrection after three days -- will resound in other legends and in religious claims throughout the ages. The God Marduk of Babylon and Ashur of the Assyrians each also die and are resurrected.

As I mentioned above, Unas, whose tomb walls were inscribed with the texts and spells of the *Book of the Dead*, most likely witnessed the fall of the Absu and the blood in the sky. This is almost certain from consideration of the following engraved Pyramid text. E. A. Budge, in his introduction to the translation of *The Egyptian Book of the Dead* (1895) notes a section of the Pyramid Text from the tomb of Unas which is totally out of character with the other texts dealing with the material and spiritual enjoyments of the deceased. He writes:

> "... the most remarkable passage in this connection is one in the pyramid of Unas. Here all creation is represented as being in terror when they see the deceased king rise up as a soul [ba] in the form of a god who devours 'his fathers and mothers'; he feeds upon men and also upon gods. He hunts the gods in the fields and snares them; and when they are tied up for slaughter he cuts their throats and disembowels them. He roasts and eats the best of them, but the old gods and goddesses are used for fuel. By eating them he imbibes both their magical powers, and their 'khu's.'"

Budge quotes the actual passage, of which I will only reproduce the opening line:

> "The heavens drop water, the stars throb, the archers go round about, the bones of Akeru [mythological guardians of sunrise and sunset] tremble, and those who are in bondage to them take to flight when they see Unas rise up as a soul [ba], in the form of the god who liveth upon his fathers and who makes food of his mothers."

Unas has here been transformed into the plasmoid of Venus at the fall of the Absu, just as, in other retellings, Hathor had appeared as the lion-headed Goddess Sekhmet in the form of the eye of Horus. Unas here also wades in blood and gore, while the sky fills with water and fire, and arrows are launched, as also on a page on the "third creation" of the *Chilam Balam.* There is little doubt that the priests took advantage of the event of 2349 BC to offer an additional spell to be added to the texts (these were carved before the pharaoh died). It is also certain that the sudden change in religious emphasis -- especially in the worship of Osiris -- was initiated by this absolutely stupendous cataclysm.

Chronology of the 24th and 23rd Century BC

At this point we can collate some dates. The dates below concern four events:

- the fall of the Absu,
- the first appearance of the Moon,
- the "death" of the Moon or the time when it settled into a regular orbit around the Earth, and
- the extinction of Jupiter.

We have these dates from the following sources:

- the *Annals of Shu,*
- the *Chilam Balam,*
- Ussher's chronology, and
- the inscriptions at Palenque.

I have added the four suspected passes of Venus, assuming an interval of 52 solar years. (See Appendix B, "Celestial Mechanics" for the validity of the 52-year cycle during this era.) In the following, read "sb" as "should be."

Fall of the Absu, appearance of Jupiter (Yao)

- 2349 BC - first contact with Venus
- 2349 BC - Ussher: flood of Noah
- 2286-2266 BC - Chilam Balam: The second baptism (see comments)
- 2357 BC - Annals of Shu: Yao takes the throne
- 2357 BC - Annals of Shu: Khwan on the inundation
- 2360 BC - Palenque: the three planets born (sb 2336.8 BC)

The Moon (Shun) appears in orbit

- 2297 BC - second approach of Venus
- 2325 BC - Palenque: Moon lets blood (sb 2302.3 BC)
- 2318 BC - Annals of Shu: Birth of Shun (Moon)
- 2305 BC - Palenque: Moon becomes ruler (sb 2282.6 BC)
- 2287 BC - Annals of Shu: Shun joins Yao on throne

The Extinction of Jupiter (Yao)

- 2245 BC - third approach of Venus
- after 2247 BC - Ussher: "Tower of Babel" (may be 2150 BC)
- 2257 BC - Annals of Shu: Yao dies

Fall of Akkad and the Old Kingdom

- 2193 BC - fourth approach of Venus (electric contact)
- 2207 BC - Annals of Shu: Shun (Moon) dies
- 2205 BC - Annals of Shu: start of the Xia dynasty
- 2193 BC - fall of Akkad and the Old Kingdom
- 2128 - 2108 BC - Chilam Balam: "fire on high" (sb 2167-2147 BC)
- 2155 BC - Annals of Shu: Celestial Phenomena
- ca 2150 - Cylinder of Gudea: splendor of Ningirsu
- 2150 BC - extent of Abraham's lifetime
- 2150 BC - likely "Tower of Babel" event

The records of Mesoamerica as reflected in the *Chilam Balam* accurately record dates, which in deep antiquity probably consisted of Baktuns (periods of 400 solar years) and Katuns (periods of 20 solar years). These can be converted to solar years, if we can guess the Baktun associated with any recorded Katun. Unfortunately, some dates around 2349 BC seem to be in purposeful disorder.

The dates from the sculptures at Palenque of AD 700 will require conversion to solar years (equivalent Gregorian years) on a somewhat different basis, for the Maya at this time calculated in Long Count measures identical to how we use these today, that is, by assuming that the year was 365.24 days long. [note 15]

The Chinese *Annals of Shu* record estimated reign lengths, because many were missing when these records were compiled. Dates were estimated in about 200 BC by Chinese historians. If we equate the date of 2357 BC from the Chinese *Annals of Shu,* the date Yao takes the throne, to the date of 2349

BC (the "flood of Noah"), then the first few dates of the Chinese *Annals of Shu* should be moved 8 years into the future. Dates concurrent with the Xia dynasty can probably be taken as correct.

There may be better concordances of the dates than what I have presented here. One of the really suspect dates is Ussher's Tower of Babel event, which he casually places a hundred years after the completion of the "flood of Noah" at "after 2247 BC" -- it should be set in 2150 BC.

To adjust the dates derived from the records of various peoples, I am using Ussher's date of 2349 BC for the "flood of Noah" as an anchor. This is the fall of the Absu which happened because of the electric contact by Venus and which caused a change of the Earth's orbit to near the Moon. The change of the orbit of the Earth is even noted in the Bible when it is suggested that men's lives were shortened after the flood -- the year had become longer. In the *Annals of Shu* Yao takes on the task of calendar reform at this time. In the Babylonian *Enuma Elish*, Marduk (Jupiter) also establishes a calendar after battling Tiamat. Book 11 of the *Chilam Balam* claims *"and then days of the year were introduced"* as an aspect of the Third Creation. The Third Creation is the event of 2349 BC. [note 16]

The date for the fall of Akkad is archaeologically well-established as 2193 BC, 156 years after the "flood." The period of 156 years is three times the 52-year interval between approaches by Venus -- an interval still seriously observed by Mesoamerica in AD 1500, but in Tun years instead of solar years. I have calculated estimates of the changing intervals in the appendix "Celestial Mechanics." [note 17]

Recap and Reactions

The 24th century BC was important. The second break with the elder Gods took place during this time, and it happened in the course of a hundred and fifty years. To recap:

- Before the first pyramid was completed at Giza, after circa 2527 BC, Jupiter had cleared the asteroid belt and again developed a coma and tail. "Re" was added to the pharaohs's names. The first six pharaohs of the following dynasty, the 5th (2490 to 2350 BC), built separate sun-temples dedicated to Re -- modeled on the mountainous lower plasma outpouring of Jupiter (the shape of which is called a Benben).
- Before 2349 BC Jupiter seems to have lost its coma tail, perhaps on entering the last outlying clump of asteroids. The Egyptian pharaohs lost interest in monuments to Re. This was followed in 2349 BC by an electric contact with Venus which brought the Earth to a larger orbit,

near the existing orbit of the Moon. The *Chilam Balam* claims that Jupiter did not have its lower plasma form ("he was not crying"), when the Moon showed up. This suggests that the Moon showed up later than 2349 BC, although by the content of the *Enuma Elish* this could be questioned

- In 2349 BC the Absu fell, causing a period of extensive rains and storms on Earth (Noah's flood). The *Chilam Balam* places the "second baptism" (the "descent of water from the center of heaven") a hundred years later, but the text clearly deals with the fall of the Absu in 2349 BC. The date selected in the *Chilam Balam* was retrocalculated at a late date to match a unique Mesoamerican calendrical consideration: it had to fall on July 25th.
- The Palenque inscriptions of AD 700 claim that the three planets, Venus, Jupiter, and Mars were "born" in the newly cleared skies (corrected to 2337 BC), that is, they were clearly seen on the ecliptic, no longer obscured by the rings of the Absu. This is 10 years after the fall of the Absu.
- The plasma mountain of Jupiter returned very soon -- within three days -- after the fall of the Absu. The *Annals of Shu* claims that Jupiter, as Yao, took the throne in 2349 BC (corrected from 2357 BC). Yao will reign as supreme God (emperor of all the world) for another hundred years in China (it should be 199 years). One of Yao's first acts is to correct the calendar, since the length of the year had changed.
- The Palenque inscriptions record that the Moon crowns herself as ruler in 2305 BC, which should be corrected to 2282.6 BC. It is possible that the "crowning" does not mean anything. In the *Annals of Shu* Yao selects Shun, the Moon, to join him on the throne in 2287 BC.

Humans are now ruled by two large globes in the sky, Jupiter and the Moon, possibly of equal size. One is steady and slow, the other is forever busy on a survey of the land (as said in the *Annals of Shu*). The *Chilam Balam* reads, "the entire world was proclaimed by Uuc-yol-zip." Watching the daily changes in the movement of the Moon will convince anyone that the Moon spends considerable time above other parts of the land.

- The *Annals of Shu*, state that Yao dies after a long rule. The Chinese scholars of the second century AD estimate the date as 2257 BC, but it should probably be a hundred years later, in 2150 BC -- matching the death of Abraham. (It is uncertain as to what was actually seen.) Ussher places the Tower of Babel incident after 2247 BC. But it was Jupiter which went up in flames in 2150 BC and not Mercury. The *Chilam Balam* places the "fire on high" in the (corrected) double decade dates of 2167 to 2147 BC. The *Chilam Balam* also ties the event directly to Jupiter.

[*Image: a victory stele of Naram-Sin, the great grandson of Sargon. He is named after the Moon, Sin. Erected after 2250 BC. The two gods shown at the top as stars are the Moon and Jupiter. Jupiter is shown on his mountain. Collection of Louvre Museum.*]

- There was an additional intersection of Earth's plasmasphere with the tail of the plasmasphere of Venus in 2193 BC, causing another Earth shock, a change in the orbit, and a loss of sunlight lasting 200 years. The Second Kingdom of Egypt collapses, as does the Akkadian

Empire. The flaming of Jupiter in 2150 might not have been noticed at the latitude of Mesopotamia and Northern Egypt. It is suspected that the shading of Earth by nano-sized carbon particles in the stratosphere may have differing effects at different latitudes.

From the mix of these four records -- the *Annals of Shu*, the Bible chronology of Bishop Ussher, the inscriptions at Palenque, and the *Books of the Chilam Balam* -- it is clear that there is little agreement on when the Moon first showed near Earth, or when it was considered to be established on a regular orbit. There is closer agreement on a date for the fall of the Absu, although the *Chilam Balam* places the event much later, but on purpose. There is more agreement on the date of the last event, the "burning tower." This concludes a century busy with celestial events.

Different people interpreted the events differently, but all of them needed stories and histories to reflect what they had experienced and how things had changed. Most of the "legends" came forth in the years following 2200 BC, although some were further delayed by the 200-year drought which followed immediately.

... Egypt

The Egyptians remained faithful to the elder gods, although they no longer confused celestial apparitions with rulership of their lands as they had a thousand years earlier after 3147 BC. The pharaohs of the 5th and 6th dynasty institute a worship of Re, then seem to change it after 2349 BC (for Osiris), to be picked up again later. After Jupiter extinguishes two hundred years later, a new supreme God is added in Egypt, or rather, named. It is Amun-Ra -- "Hidden Ra" or "the hidden sun," as archeaologists have it.

Amun-Ra is also spelled "Amen-Ra" and "Amon-Ra," and is also known simply as "Amun." Amun is almost universally identified with the Sun by archaeologists, even though there is not a single indication of this in all of Egyptian writings and inscriptions. The Moon is never seriously added as a God, although today the Moon is almost universally confused (by archaeologists) with Thoth, who is Mercury. In the Ptolemaic era (after 300 BC) the Moon seems to have taken over the identity of Thoth, although the Greeks of that period still equated Thoth with their Hermes. So do I. The Moon also goes by the name of Aphrodite ("foam born" according to Hesiod, meaning the foam of the sea), and is female. [note 18]

... Babylon

The priests of the city of Babylon, under the dynasty which might have included Hammurabi, and probably after 2100 BC (but possibly a lot later), wrote the *Enuma Elish*, a creation account which raises Marduk (Jupiter) to the status of chief God, by agreement (says the text) of the elder Gods of Akkad and Sumer. The text relates events which had been witnessed (but not recently) as proof of the change: the disappearance of Marduk's garment and its reappearance at his command, the battle with the dragon Tiamat (the plasmoid of Venus), the removal of the Absu (the net), the clearing of the skies in the south, the sighting of the southern stars, the delineation of the zodiac, the placement of the Moon, and the revision of the calendar.

For the Babylonians, and for the older land of Akkad and Sumer, to recognize Marduk as chief of the Gods resolved a crisis in faith, and gave proof that the large red globe in the south, previously standing on a mountain of plasma, along with the Moon which had now appeared, was there by destiny and in agreement with older traditions. Marduk became the most widely recognized God in Mesopotamia, from Assyria to Elam, and retained his status as chief God for two thousand years. Not a little of his status was due to the central political position assumed by Babylon after 2200 BC -- but also because he could be seen yet at that time in the skies.

Because it was probably written 500 years after 2349 BC, the text of the *Enuma Elish* is out of order, even though all the individual elements of the event of 2349 BC are included.

... Bible texts

In the Bible texts Jupiter has become Abraham, who receives a son, the Moon, only in old age, and then nearly sacrifices him on a burning mountain. Similarly to the *Annals of Shu*, Jupiter is held up as the model of good behavior. [note 19]

... Mayan texts

The *Chilam Balam* certainly is the most strangely different from the other texts mentioned above. Even though relating events from 4000 years earlier, it is also consistently the most accurate. It is mostly different in not having an obvious didactic agenda. We are presented instead almost solely with natural history, and a few complaints about the kings and leaders of the past. In the face of the new Christian religion, the *Chilam Balam* only seeks to prove that the older worship of "these stones" might simply have been a mistake.

"Very rightly they worshiped as true gods these precious stones."

"These stones" were volcanic concretions, noted in the *Popol Vuh*, which were held to be the spirit containers of the earlier Gods which had roamed the skies. One section of the *Chilam Balam* even equates the planetary Gods before "creation" as stones inhabited by the spirit of the Christian God.

... China

The Chinese would recall Yao and Shun as exemplary figures who instituted good government. Nothing is said of the burning of Jupiter. The Xia dynasty, which followed the reign of Yao and Shun (after 2205 BC), took control of the land and the people, and made it through the period of bad weather.

China turned secular, although it remained nominally monotheistic, but never again concerned itself with signs in the sky. All the subsequent rulers were "kings." The title of "emperor" -- a ruler over all the Earth -- was not used again in China for the next 2000 years.

The Moon Dies

In 2193 BC Venus made electric contact with Earth again, the last time in this era. As I noted in the previous chapter, both Akkad and the Old Kingdom of Egypt come to a close. There is very little else we hear from the Eastern Mediterranean region, or nearly anywhere else, about this event, except for the failure of agriculture.

We have only very slim chronological data which point to what actually happened. The contact by Venus was not accompanied by impressive celestial events, and nothing was recorded in legends and stories, unlike the earlier contact of 2349 BC. What I believe most likely happened in 2193 BC, is that Venus, in this instance being considerably closer to Earth, made a compressive contact to land, followed quickly by lightning strikes to land which resulted in large blazing forest fires which in turn lofted ashes and particulate matter into the stratosphere, blocking sunlight for the next 200 years.

The Earth's orbit again increased, to 270 or 280 days (I suspect 273 days). At the same time the Moon relocated further from Earth, taking 28 days to complete one rotation (month) around the Earth. The recorders of the Xia dynasty tell of the removal of the Moon (Shun) from nearer to Earth to higher up at the conclusion of his tasks, suggesting that he died.

"In the thirtieth year of his age, Shun was called to employment. Thirty years he was on the throne (with Yâo). Fifty years afterwards he went on high and died."

"Going on high" is not likely to be the sudden disappearance of the coma of the Moon, although this should be kept in mind as a possibility. The Moon may have had an atmosphere at an earlier time, before meeting up with Earth. But I do not think the Moon ever supported much of a coma, being a small rocky planet without a magnetic field, and having spent perhaps millions of years at the same distance from the Sun. (The Moon is older than the Earth.)

If, in effect, the Moon became smaller, it would be because it moved further up into the sky. Adding the 30 plus 50 years to the date when Shun was called to employment, 2277 BC (corrected from 2287 BC), places the "going on high" of the Moon in 2197 BC. This is four years before 2193 BC, but, given the guesswork at chronology by the Han dynasty (and me), it is close enough to suggest that this can be linked to the fourth approach by Venus in this era.

The reason for suggesting a year of 270 or 280 days with ten months of 28 days, is that a ten-month year and a 28-day month start to show up in this era. The Shang dynasty of China (although after circa 1700 BC) records 28-day months and 27-day months. I suspect from this, that the year may have been at some value in between, and suggest it may have been 273 days (which also solves some problems with the Olmec calendar). Ten lunar months would likely have been in use.

We have little information on the ten-month year, except that even today some people count only ten months in the year, stretching the last month of each year to 90 days. Additionally, a few calendars kept counts of 10-month cycles, even when there were 12 lunar months in the year. In India the sky was mapped to 28 "lunar mansions" a concept still in use today. (For additional information see Appendix A, "Chronology.")

In the following years the southern stars were mapped, calendars were adjusted, commerce and trade were expanded, and histories were created. Politics changed and developed as they always had, but the relationships with the Gods remained stable.

The Return of the Axis Mundi

Since in 2349 BC the Earth increased its orbit, it would again have to equalize its charge to match the new orbital location. And do so again in 2193

BC. Again this would be accomplished through an influx of electrons at the magnetic poles. The plume of plasma in glow mode which had appeared directly after 3147 BC, would return, and probably at both poles.

After the battle with Tiamat, Marduk sets his bow (classically identified as "a rainbow") up in the heavens as a sign of triumph. The bow is the south polar plasma plume. It is a bow standing up, not hung horizontally across the sky from pegs like a rainbow.

[*Image: Shamash (Jupiter) with his banded head wrap, seated on his temple seat and holding a "shen." The "shen" dates the iconography to after 2914 BC. The south polar plume rises above Jupiter (and thus the ecliptic), dating the image to after 2349 BC. A small figure at the end of the plume controls the rotation of the southern stars. The terminating ball or ring of the plume is here interpreted as a manikin. The end of the plume moved with the rotation of stars. The table and pillar likely are architectural details, like the God's seat, which latter reads "temple." The humans are identified and place this Babylonian cylinder seal in the 9th century BC. Collection of the British Museum.*]

The Maya *Chilam Balam*, which lists the four trees which hold up the heavens in each instance after a recreation of the world (a change in the orbit), speaks directly to the tree of the south as part of the event of 2349 BC (the "flood of Noah," and the Maya "third creation").

"The planted timber was set up. Perishable things are assembled at that time. The timber of the grave-digger is set up at the crossroads, at the four resting places."
  -- Ralph L Roys *The Book Of Chilam Balam Of Chumayel* (1933)

The text is not exactly lucid, but see the chapter "The Chilam Balam" where this is further explicated. The first "planted timber" may be the plasma plume at the north magnetic pole. The second one, set up at the "crossroads" is the plume of the south (viewed from north of the equator).

The "crossroads" is the intersection of the ecliptic and the equatorial, both of which were visible, and thus the equinox. The "perishable things" are the Pleiades, held to be celestial seed corn by the Maya. The "grave-digger," Roys notes, can also be understood as "hider," someone who hides objects. I would suggest this as applicable to the Absu. Note the phrase "at that time." A new condition is being described. From the further context of the *Chilam Balam*, it is, without a doubt, the event of 2349 BC.

It is further of some interest to recall that this event, the sudden appearance of a southern plasma plume, is described in the *Popol Vuh* as the attempt by the Four Hundred Boys to impale the mountain giant Zipacna in a grave he has inadvertently dug to hold the center post to their house. Zipacna is Jupiter. He appeared in the depression of the Absu on about September 8th (two nights after the fall equinox). Once the Four Hundred Boys are thoroughly drunk, Zipacna enlarges himself and "blows up the house."

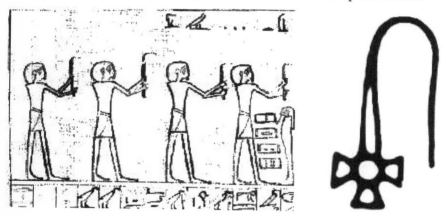

[*Image: Egyptian: Flames of the four cardinal directions; brazier glyph detail.*]

The "house" shape of the Absu would result because the Earth's axis had initially bent away from the direction of the Sun when the shock was received from Venus. This should be remembered, it is integral to any recollection of the 3-day event. The image of the Absu would thus have been rounded again like a hut, with the Earth's shadow creating what looked like an arched doorway to this hut. On the third day, with the axis of the Earth sufficiently recovered from the application of the gyroscopic reaction torque, this imagery would have changed back to a gap -- as if the house had exploded. The Four Hundred Boys become the Pleiades, now seen among the stars directly above the gap of the exploded house and above Jupiter which is seen to rise from the gap also. See the chapter "The Popol Vuh." The rising or resurrection of Jupiter from a cleft in the Earth -- the old Absu at the time of the equinox -- reappears in Maya iconography, as Jupiter rising from a crack in a turtle carapace.

References to the polar plasma plumes show up also among the spells of the Egyptian *Book of the Dead*.

> *"Who then is it?"*
> *"Those above their braziers -- it is,*
> *the image of the Eye of Re, together*
> *with the image of the Eye of Horus."*
> *"Others say:*
> *It is the two mighty and great cobras*
> *on the brow of thy father Atum."*
> *"Others say:*
> *It is his two eyes which are lacking in his head."*
> *"Who then is he?*
> *It is Horus with the Two Eyes."*
> -- E. A. Budge, *The Egyptian Book of the Dead* (1895)

This describes the two ball plasmoids (as eyes), which existed at the ends of the polar plumes. Sycamore trees seem to have been used for the "plumes" of the east and west cardinal points, at times as dual trees. The guardians of the east and west, the Akeru, are depicted as lions (not only in Egypt, but also in Akkad). The implication of these texts is that the chief God of the Egyptians is absolutely gigantic in size; he spans all of the heavens.

"Lacking from his head," refers to Jupiter in his later form, when the "eyes," originally formed by the equatorial toroid are no longer visible at the much greater distance after leaving the asteroid belt.

The flaming braziers, with smoke which curves back to point down, are usually presented as four in number, but at times as six. There are also depictions of six braziers at the edges of a rectangular "lake of fire." This last, the lake of fire, remains as an obstacle to reaching the underworld throughout all of the Book of the Dead. There is no physical analog for the "lake of fire."

In Southern Mesopotamia depictions of the east and west plumes appear on cylinder seals as flags (vertical banners), mounted to poles which are bent back somewhat, with a circle at the top (called "ring-topped standards" by archaeologists). These forms appear regularly, and have also been called "doorposts" both in original Akkadian texts and by archaeologists.

On one cylinder seal the plumes are depicted adjacent (left and right) with a reed hut with rays emanating from its roof. They are "associated" with

Inanna (Venus) in that the cuneiform symbol for "Inanna" has been added. The house is likely the Absu, so that in this case the "circle plumes" represent the plumes of the east and west cardinal directions.

[Image: Mesopotamian circle plumes, depicted on a vase. After H. W. F. Saggs, "Babylonians" (2000).]

The Tower of Babel

An incident, and possibly this very incident, following about 200 years after the fall of the Absu, generated the initial version of the "Tower of Babel" stories throughout the world. The Tower of Babel story is interesting because it occurs everywhere in the world. A "Tower of Babel story" was told to the invading Spanish in Central America in AD 1500. It was known also among North American tribes. Around the world, the stories all have the same three elements: a burning (or collapsed) tower whose construction is attributed to humans, a confusion of languages or loss of memory, and the dispersal of peoples. It seems almost certain that the Tower of Babel event was the last spasm of Jupiter before diminishing to just a star-like pinpoint of light.

However, quite a few of the stories attribute the burning tower to the planet Mercury. This might be correct and I'll discuss this below, even though the incident involving Mercury happens 2000 years later. There are, however, only hints in mythology that it might have been Mercury. Surely the *Chilam Balam* would have had reference to Mercury, since the story is widespread. The Chilam Balam says nothing. It only reports that "the face of the sun" -- the midnight sun -- was "taken from earth." "The Sun" is Jupiter. The Maya or Olmecs would not have made a mistake in identifying this planet.

Ussher dates the Tower of Babel event to "after 2247 BC." According to

Velikovsky, the medieval chronographer Abraham Rockenbach, in *De Cometis Tractatus Novus Methodicus* (1602), places it in 2060 BC, but attributes it to a comet seen over Egypt.

> *"In the year of the world one thousand nine hundred and forty-four* [2060 BC], *two hundred and eighty-eight* [288] *years after the Deluge,* [which calculates to 2348 BC] *a comet was seen in Egypt of the nature of Saturn, in the vicinity of Cairo, in the constellation of Capricorn, and within the space of sixty-five days it traversed three signs in the sky. Confusions of languages and dispersals of peoples followed. On this the text of the eleventh chapter of Genesis speaks in more detail."*
> -- Abraham Rockenbach *De Cometis Tractatus Novus Methodicus*, in Velikovsky, unpublished documents, at [www.varchive.org]

The Tower might have been a comet, but it is not Jupiter. Jupiter does not traverse three zodiac signs in 65 days. The date of 1944 AM is based on starting a count in 4004 BC. The date 288 years earlier is the Deluge of 2349 BC or 2348 BC, the classical date of the flood of Noah. Both of these match Ussher's chronology.

Velikovsky, in a footnote to an unpublished document ("Mercury"), quotes from the *Bhagavatamrita* that "Buddha [Mercury] became visible the 1002nd year of the Cali yug." The Kali era (Cali yug) started in 3102 BC, as retrocalculated as a conjunction of planets. The 1002nd year is 2100 BC. This is likely the second showing of Mars and Mercury (to be detailed in a later chapter) in 1936 BC, which caused the destruction of Sodom and Gomorrah.

Rockenbach's date of 2060 BC does not match Ussher's estimate of "after 2247 BC" for the Tower of Babel incident, nor a Mesoamerican date for the "fire on high" which I have placed with some confidence in 2150 BC -- in Katun 8-Ahau (2.10.0.0.0) dated 2167 to 2147 BC (corrected dates). This last date, however, together with the Kali yug date, correspond to additional dates for the extinction of Jupiter: the mention by Gudea in a tablet or prism of the "brightness of Ningursu," dated to circa 2150 BC, and the historical notice in the *Annals of Shu* written during the Xia dynasty of a celestial event in about 2155 BC. Details of the mention in the *Annals of Shu* follow.

Of the four records of the Xia dynasty in China (2205 to 1767 BC) listed in the "The Books of the Hsia [Xia]" (of the *Annals of Shu*), there is one, the last, dated to 2155 BC, which mentions a "celestial phenomenon." We should ask why, from among the hundreds of eclipses which (may have) happened in China during this long period of history, only this single event, "a celestial phenomenon," was deemed noteworthy enough to record and transmit to the future. [note 20]

Although Mesoamerican and Chinese sources speak to a crisis of Jupiter, almost all sources on the "burning tower" speak of an incident involving the planet Mercury. In the Americas, at first contact with Europeans, stories of a "Tower of Babel" event were extant. Elsewhere, in Mesopotamia, Greece, and Egypt, there are dozens of documents in antiquity, plus additional tales and legends spanning four continents, which all relate the loss of memory or changes in languages to Mercury -- the Gods Hermes, Thoth, Nebo, Odin. In fact, the status of Mercury as an important God dates from remote antiquity (around 2100 by the estimate of de Grazia).

Velikovsky placed the event "after the flood which ends the age of Jupiter" -- by which he would likely mean the Noachian flood. In the late legends of Egypt, which recall the flood of Noah as the bloodbath (and beer bath) of Hathor, when the God Ra abdicates he turns his duties over to Thoth. That would have been, as best I would guess, after 2150 BC. That date agrees with the first appearance of Mercury as a God to which attention needed to be paid -- in the 1002nd year of the Kali era, 2100 BC, and certainly coming close to Earth starting in 1936 BC. The "first appearance" is thus likely to be the coincidence with the flaming and extinction of Jupiter, when Jupiter's duties are turned over to another planetary God.

Let me point out the obvious: Velikovsky's choice of a date was influenced by Ussher's chronology. Ussher's pick of a date was in consideration of the Bible story of the Tower of Babel. The Bible in turn could not admit that Abraham had gone up in flames 199 years after the flood, or, for that matter, that Abraham was born two days after the flood of Noah, so that the Tower of Babel text as presented in the Bible ended up being based on a much later event: the real Tower of Babel event which is dated to 686 BC.

Why was the Tower of Babel story included in the Bible at all? Mainly because it was part of the sacred history of the world, of which the Hebrews were the recognized keepers. But, perhaps more importantly, everyone (at the time of the final composition of the Bible) knew it had happened: a tower to heaven was built, it caught on fire, and it burned. Other people and other tribes would hold the Jews accountable for an accurate history of the world, especially with their claim that only their God was the true God of all history. In antiquity the books of the Torah were used as valid sources about the past by a number of other nations.

Mercury

I will now turn to Mercury, and introduce some facets of this planet. Although only somewhat larger in diameter than the Moon, it has 4.5 times the mass. Mercury is half the mass of Mars. We know that Mars in 747 BC budged the Earth to a larger orbit and longer year, by 930 thousand miles (1500 thousand km) and 5.24 days. It is quite possible that Mercury, with half that mass, never "hit" the Earth with a repulsive electric shock serious enough to move Earth in its orbit. At least, we have no calendrical record. But it could have involved a change in eccentricity. This would change the kinetic energy of the Earth without changing the orbital period.

It seems certain, also, that Mercury overran the orbit of Earth since remote antiquity. That Mercury was seen on a wildly eccentric course is almost certain for several reasons. First of all, Mercury still has the most eccentric of all planetary orbits. Mercury is the one planet which nearly doubles its distance from the Sun over the course of its 88-day orbit. No other planet comes close to having such an eccentric orbit, and we could be assured that, if Mercury had been seen in both the northern and the southern skies 3000 years ago, when the orbit of Earth was still 30 percent less than it is today, Mercury would have regularly reached beyond the orbit of Earth. This corresponds to the fact that Mercury was assigned in antiquity, almost universally, the duty of messenger of the distant Gods Saturn and Jupiter -- the planets remaining on the ecliptic of the southern sky.

Secondly, the God Mercury had the "wings" and "snake tail" of the "caduceus" -- an indication that it moved on a highly elliptical path, behaving like a comet which loses and regains a surplus of electric charge with each turn around the Sun. The disk with wings and the extrusion at the end was a glow mode plasma discharge generated as Mercury traversed the electric field of the Sun. But, whereas Venus sported an immense tail (30 million miles, 48 million km, today in dark mode discharge), Mercury, which is much smaller (only 40 percent larger in diameter than the Earth's Moon), would most likely have had a relatively short plasma tail but with wings as the north and south plasma plumes at the poles (which, by the way, were seen sideways as Mercury passed close to Earth: one above, one below).

The "disk" of the caduceus is likely to be its spherical coma, which could be supported by Mercury since it had a substantial atmosphere (it still has a remnant atmosphere today). Mercury has only a very weak magnetic field, but apparently it was enough in the past to allow the part of its plasmasphere facing the Sun to light up in glow mode. It looked like a musical instrument, and music is attributed to Mercury. It also looked like a bow strung with an arrow. Mercury was identified by the Greeks as Apollo, "the archer God who shoots from afar." The name Apollo was transferred to the Sun after Classical times. [note 21]

And lastly, again, we have the many descriptions from antiquity that Mercury was the messenger of the Gods -- swinging from aphelion beyond Earth's orbit to perihelion with the Sun after passing by Earth. If Mercury were on an orbit which reached from the Sun to a location beyond the Earth, it would look as if he were visiting the departed Gods in the far reaches of space. It would have been logical to assign Mercury the role of messenger. As such, Mercury was charged with the task of caretaker of mankind.

As I will suggest in the chapter "Exodus," when it was certain that all the Gods had left, Mercury as the caretaker God was acknowledged as the intermediary between the distant Gods and mankind, a God who was charged with all the arcana of magic, special materials, writing, and language. That God was the Egyptian Thoth, Sumerian Enlil, Greek Hermes (originally Apollo), Roman Mercury, and the Norse Odin -- each of which can be identified with the planet Mercury.

In Roman times, some Northern European tribes declare Odin as their primary God. That is really strange if Mercury had always behaved as today -- only seen infrequently for a few minutes per night above the east or west horizon near the rising or setting Sun. Mercury was the last planetary God, except for Mars and Venus, who still visited long after the other Gods had retreated. But, unlike Venus, he seemed immensely busy, crossing Earth's orbit every year and a half. But when Mars was still active in coming close to Earth, the destructions by Mars (especially in the Eastern Mediterranean) completely eclipsed notice of Mercury when both showed at the same time.

The Burning Tower

Since there are universal memories of the Tower of Babel event, it was either an absolutely stupendous event, or a recent event. The blood in the sky and the fall of the Absu in 2349 BC was a stupendous event and was universally remembered for 4300 years. The Tower of Babel, if assigned to Mercury, could not have been at all remarkable by comparison. I would therefore suggest instead that the event was recent and, in fact, much more recent than Ussher's estimate of "after 2247 BC" -- it happened on March 23, 686 BC. The basis for this date will be developed in a later chapter.

In identifying a plasmasphere contact in 686 BC, I am continuing my claim that every catastrophic event of the past should be able to be clearly identified, graphically visualized, mechanically reconstructed, dated, and located by a consideration of orbital parameters. This is not to say that tales, stories, and myths were not recycled, so that the extinction of Jupiter in 2150 BC became a foretelling of the event of 686 BC, and the fire on Mercury in 686 BC provided the details for the Bible's description of a similar event 2000 years earlier.

Where does the "burning tower" enter into the picture? It was likely a plasma discharge between Earth and Mercury. I would assume that, after the plasmaspheres touched, and a shock was exchanged, a charge imbalance between the planets induced a stream of plasma in glow mode to reach from the ionosphere of Earth to the cloud cover or surface of Mercury -- in effect a lightning strike. (The southwestern prairies of the US burned up directly after the shock.)

The shock between Earth and Mercury happened as Mercury passed in front of Earth between Earth and the Sun. The distance between the planets was likely equal to the distance between Earth and the current aphelion of the orbit of Mercury. That represents a distance of 48,000,000 miles (77,000,000 km). That is the location that Mercury returns to today with each orbit around the Sun.

There would have been physical effects, an Earth shock and earthquakes and fire falling from heaven, but not nearly to the extremes of what was experienced when Venus made electric contact in 2349 or 1492 BC. Since the mass of the Earth is 20 times the mass of Mercury, it is unlikely that the Earth's orbit would be significantly affected. And, in fact, we have no record of a change in the length of the year.

Mercury, however, would likely have received a shock which might have thrust it far away from Earth. The shock location of 686 BC on Mercury can be identified; it has been known since the first spacecraft flyby in 1970. The contact location on the Earth is on the North American continent. The chapter "Destruction by Mars" will pinpoint the contact location.

The plasma charge exchange would have been limited because Earth had been in its present location from the Sun for a thousand years, except for the minor change in orbit of 747 BC. Mercury similarly had moved on a course from near the Sun to the asteroid belt for nearly 3000 years. In the case of Mercury, its charge would have been normalized to a value close to what was held by the Earth, since Earth was located about halfway along the elongated orbit of Mercury.

The plasma contact (exchange of charge) might have involved arc mode exchange, but Mercury would quickly have distanced from Earth and the plasma exchange would have switched to glow mode. At that stage it probably would have assumed the shape of a steep triangular mountain -- similar to the pyramid-shaped "mountain" of plasma between Earth and Mars at the time of Horus after 3100 BC -- but at this time the mountain was understood as a man-made tower that could be seen as being constructed over a period of time (perhaps only a day or so) as it extended upward.

The tower would eventually have reached to the aphelion location of Mercury's orbit, 48 million miles (77 million km) from Earth. The tower could be seen to grow from Earth as the plasma stream changed from dark mode near Earth to glow mode further away. Possibly the "tower" was constructed in the reverse direction (that is, constructed from Mercury to Earth). The stream of plasma would increase in density on approaching

Mercury -- an increase in electric current -- so that the mode changed to arc mode on reaching the surface of Mercury. There was the start of the fire.

During the earlier visits of Horus, no man-made pyramids or ziggurats had been built yet, and the very similar phenomenon at that time was described as the mountain built by the god Horus -- "who rises on *his* mountain." But towers or pyramids and ziggurats had already been erected by the time of the approach of Mercury and the idea that this was a tower constructed by humans was well within the imagination of those who were watching. In Mesopotamia the destruction of the tower had precedent in ziggurats which had been destroyed by massive lightning strikes.

The tower burned and collapsed. The tenuous atmosphere of Mercury still holds vast amounts of hydrogen and helium, as well as oxygen and sodium (which, because of its small size, would not be the case if Mercury were billions of years old). Hydrogen gases might have burned when the plasma stream connection from Earth turned to arc mode at the strike points on Mercury. The burning might have extended long past the time of the initial plasma contact.

The burning tower legends worldwide hold that people everywhere lost their memory or changed their language or both. The ubiquity of this detail suggests that it was fact. If we take this universal story at face value, it would suggest short-term amnesia, perhaps due to some sort of electro-shock, induced by the sudden change in the electric potential of the Earth's surface. Perhaps the plasma contact with Mercury fried our brains.

Mercury also is the only planet with a (slight) magnetic field to have made a close approach with Earth (even though its magnetic field is weak, and should not exist at all). This fact may explain why this incident was physiologically different from earlier and later approaches and plasma contacts with Venus and Mars, neither of which have a magnetic field. The effect of an imposed planetary magnetic field will not be felt, because planetary magnetic fields are weak. But the flow of electricity toward the Earth's crust creates a magnetic field also.

The electric contact with Mercury was (possibly) at a closer distance to Earth than any of the half dozen contacts by other planets, with the exception of Mars. Mars completely entered the Earth's plasmasphere, and came so close that the devastating effects were local, extending perhaps only a few hundred miles north and south of its path. Mercury's contact, by comparison was global.

It is perhaps also likely, however, that during the plasma contact with Mercury, a time-varying electric or magnetic field was experienced. A varying magnetic field is known to have physiological effects. (See the endnotes to the chapter "The Start of Time.") This would also suggest another possibility for the "loss of memory" or "loss of speech." The plasma contact with Earth may not have been an event which took away memory, but which instead caused speech and memory to falter, thus bringing these to awareness in people worldwide. Perhaps this also brought an awareness that other people speak differently. [note 22]

The experience with the failure of speech may have forced people to write down their stories which previously had been passed along by word of mouth. The stories could thus be rendered correctly with future retellings. They might have also become aware that "old stories" could be "placed" in an imagined "earlier time." With books of recounted stories we immediately jump to the matter of primacy -- there are earlier and later events. That forces a new consideration of historical time.

It is also interesting to consider that shortly after the event of March 23, 686 BC, the output of the Sun changed radically after June of 685 BC. Within two or three generations after 685 BC we start to see the first attempts -- worldwide -- of a separation from a mythological past. This happens in physics, in philosophy, and in religions.

The dispersal of people in the Tower of Babel stories may or may not have happened. A few stories (as with some from North American Indians) do not include the details of a dispersal. It may have been that, instead of a dispersal, people were suddenly able, for the first time, to imagine the whereabouts of others.

The dates of 2060 BC or 2247 BC for the Tower of Babel event are incorrect. The date of 2150 BC represents the extinction of Jupiter, and became only a pre-telling of the Mercury event of 686 BC.

The First Histories

The suggestion made above follows from consideration of the onset of the development of subjective consciousness, nominally placed in circa 2000 BC or 1500 BC.

It is from Egyptian, Mesopotamian, Indian, and early Greek and Roman sources that we can extract the most details about the celestial dramas and the corresponding human activities. Egyptian sources are primarily from tombs, since texts on papyrus have not lasted (although we have some papyrus texts dating back to 2400 BC). Egyptian sources have a continuity over more than 3000 years -- a continuity unequaled anywhere else. This is so because Egypt was the least affected by the worldwide floods which accompanied the three major catastrophes, and its land has retained productivity in the face of permanent climatic changes elsewhere.

Mesopotamian texts were inscribed on clay tables, more stable than papyrus (or bamboo slivers, as in China) and even more permanent when inadvertently fired to baked clay due to the burning of a palace or town. The clay tablets date back to 2700 BC and earlier.

The remaining sources elsewhere are textual recollections made after 700 to 500 BC from earlier verbal retellings. Indian sources are plentiful but are poetic representations of past events, recorded for their exemplary religious value and not transcribed to texts until very late. For China almost identical conditions are true. Greek and Roman sources also date exclusively from the period after 650 BC.

Inca sources in South America are silent. There is some evidence suggesting that literature may have been suppressed before the arrival of the Spanish.

Mesoamerican sources at one time graphically recounted the complete history of the world dating back 40 thousand years, including the birth of the Gods and their abandonment of Earth, but the records are clouded by a displacement of thousands of years, awaiting the invention of a script by the Olmecs and its full development by the Maya. The texts are now lost, destroyed by the Spanish invaders. Only recopied snippets survive. Yet the *Popol Vuh*, written circa AD 1500 in Central America, and thus 13,000 years after the "first creation," frequently recounts events with an unrivaled clarity.

For the rest of the world, however, many of the specifics of the genesis of the Gods and their abandonment of Earth are forgotten and today, thousands of years after the Gods left, we are presented with a confused set of oral histories offered as creation myths and tales of the stupendous deeds of forebears from hundreds of separate and isolated societies throughout the world. The actors in these dramas are varied, and the actions seldom make sense and offer no lessons, but they all involve the same themes, and the consensus in the remaining details, even after the passage of thousands of years, is astounding.

Almost everywhere the legends and records of the past date from after the fall of the Absu (2349 BC), and after the extinction of Jupiter (2150 BC). It may have been the loss of these last images of the "Era of the Gods" which created the impetus to start an historic literature. These events fall at a watershed in historical consciousness for it is followed soon by a profusion in the composition of legends and records everywhere. At least, this is true of Mesopotamia, but also of India and China.

In Egypt, vernacular narratives about previous earth-shaking events appeared much later. These narratives only show up in texts on tomb walls during the New Kingdom (1327 BC through 1136 BC), rendered as fashionably "old," that is, in the style of the Middle Kingdom, 2000 to 1500 BC -- the period following the events of the fall of the Absu. They are stories of previous destructions of mankind, not unlike the epics being written in Sumer, but unlike any text ever created in Egypt up to that time.

The composition of the earliest Hindu scripture, the Rig-Veda, can be placed before 1900 BC from geographic references to a location in Northwestern India adjacent to the Sarasvati river, which is said to have dried up over a period of 300 years after 2200 BC. The Sarasvati is held as the center of civilization in the Rig-Veda, although it may have been a mythological river.

The records of China were collated circa 550 BC as the *Annals of Shu*, transcribed from older sources. Only the first two sections of the *Annals of Shu* are recollections, dating back to 2357 BC. All the remaining sections of the *Annals of Shu* were written contemporaneously with the events they describe, and all these date to after 2200 BC. The first record is "The Speech at Kan" which can be dated to the period of 2188 to 2160 BC.

The script of Sumer, which had been used only for the most mundane record-keeping for 5000 years, was suddenly, after 2200 BC, used to record older extant stories like the *Epic of Gilgamesh*, to compose in Akkad (almost out of thin air) the *Enuma Elish* creation myth, and to write lengthy declaratory texts like the Code of Hammurabi (circa 1700 BC, in revised chronology). Although the texts of the narratives are often attributed to much earlier times because of their contents, they all date from within a few hundred years of 2200 BC to 2000 BC.

With the composition, in about 1750 BC, of the Babylonian *Enuma Elish*, Jupiter became the first conceptual -- philosophical -- God. Except, of course, that he could still be seen, and remained the brightest star-like object in the sky. This is still so today. [note 23]

The Return of Mars

The Early Bronze Age is a generic name for the period of about circa 2000 years BC, but the date varies from one region to another because the "Early Bronze Age" depends on what people were manufacturing. For our purposes, we can take it to mean approximately 2000 BC to 1800 BC, for the region of the Middle East which includes Canaan, Anatolia, Syria, and Mesopotamia. Dates this far back are not well established.

My interest in this period stems from the suspicion that perhaps Mars had again cruised close to Earth and caused extensive destruction, like it had between 3067 BC and circa 2750 BC. This is, in fact, testified to, and not only in the Middle East, but apparently worldwide.

"... almost every one of the flourishing Palestinian cities was destroyed at the end of the Early Bronze III period. The succeeding era, Middle Bronze Age I, ... was characterized by a non-urban pastoral society."

-- Damien Mackey, in "The Old Kingdom From Abraham to Hezekiah, A historical and stratigraphical revision" (2002) http://www.specialtyinterests.net/old_kingdom.html

Damien Mackey is here pointing up information originally compiled by Claude Schaeffer in *Stratigraphie comparée et chronologie de l'Asie occidentale* (1948), a source mentioned earlier.

After mentioning 2400 to 2300 BC, Schaeffer records a date of 1700 BC when many urban centers in the Middle East were destroyed. The date of 1700 BC is one from his series of dates which cannot easily be moved to a later period by imposing our knowledge of the fictional Greek "Dark Ages."

To be included in Schaeffer's compilation the disturbing elements had to include earthquakes and firestorms. This would signify close contacts with Mars -- very close. This had been the case for a period of 300 years some 1100 years earlier starting in about 3070 BC. This would happen again for a period of (only) 120 years, some 1100 years later, starting in 806 BC during the time of the prophets of Israel (detailed in a later chapter).

Schaeffer's dates have been summarized, expanded upon, and corrected by a number of people. I will give examples, starting with Geoffrey Gammon, writing in "Bronze Age Destructions in the Near East" (*SIS Review*, 1980).

Gammon notes that for Ugarit, the first incident of destruction is dated to 2300 BC. Schaeffer claims for this, and many subsequent destructions, that earthquakes were at cause, despite the fact that earthquakes do not extend (as he even notes) over distances of 600 miles (1000 km) with equally destructive results. They do not extend even 100 miles. Gammon points out fire, too:

*"As Alfred de Grazia has argued in a highly original and challenging article published in **Kronos** a few years ago, the severity of the conflagration which destroyed Troy II, to which the thickness of the layer of calcined debris or burnt ash 15 to 20 feet thick [5 to 7 meters] bore eloquent witness, indicated that whatever natural disaster overwhelmed the city must have been of massive, even catastrophic, proportions."*

Gammon here references Alfred de Grazia in "Paleo-Calcinology: Destruction by Fire in Prehistoric and Ancient Times", *Kronos* I:4 and II:1 (1976). De Grazia has detailed this also in *The Burning of Troy* (1984).

De Grazia notes that the evidence of fire..

"... has sometimes, with less than complete evidence, been interpreted as the work of torch-bearing invaders. For example, James Melaart uses the convenient phrase 'whether by accident or by enemy action' to

describe the destructive combustion of Troy IIg. Earthquakes, too, are invoked with some frequency, although a determination that a fire is an effect of an earthquake is by no means simple."

Another who has expanded on Schaeffer's original data is Moe Mandelkehr, writing in "An Integrated Model for an Earthwide Event at 2300 BC" (*SIS Review* 1983), and three additional articles to 1999. Mandelkehr's first article is completely shrouded in caveats, one of which reads as:

"... there is no intent on my part to argue that all site destructions or cultural changes took place simultaneously at 2300 BC, or at any other specific point in time around 2300 BC. Even under conditions of wide area crustal stresses, earthquakes still occur fairly locally so that site destructions would be expected to be spread in time."

This last quote would have been added by anyone who considered the destructive Earth shock of 2349 BC, or would have been added as a warning to any other collection of similar data. Any sensible person would do this, and of course it would be phrased exactly as presented above -- that earthquakes might be many, but *certainly* would be expected to be distributed over time.

But that is completely wrong in this instance. In 2349 BC, the destruction everywhere was simultaneous.

The Earth shock of 2349 BC, which I have already presented, was so outstandingly frightful and impressive, that it was recorded in nearly identical "legends" worldwide, and long afterward, so that in AD 600 the Irish still weave it into their history of St Patrick, and the medieval epic poem *Beowulf* recounts the timing of the event with precision. The shock of 2349 BC and the following shock of 2193 BC were singular and instantaneous over a very large area, encompassing perhaps as much as half the circumference of the Earth. The initial shocks would have toppled cities and citadels, and would have been followed with lesser aftershocks for some time.

This was followed some 250 years later with additional nearly instantaneous events, probably at intervals of decades. These resulted from destructive sweeps of Mars close to Earth between 1936 BC and sometime in 1700 BC. (These dates will be developed below.) These were also nearly instantaneous over very large spans of territory. The cities where Mars passed close by -- perhaps a few hundred miles north or south of its path -- were given only minutes notice. Mars passed the Earth's surface at the speed of rotation of the Earth, which would be about 500 miles per hour (800 km per hour) at a mid-latitude. Along the path underneath Mars there would have been a gigantic moving fire storm, spreading flames left and right (north and south), which incinerated everything, even melting the very surface of the

Earth, and sucked the burning material up into a hurricane-sized tornado. The agent of the fire most likely consisted of ionized and electrified blazing dust from the surface of Mars.

The traveling electric arc of the tornado would have paused on high places, which is where citadels had been built. The pause would be caused by the fact that the next location after an elevated spot would represent a longer electric conduction path for the arc. In pausing the arc might have extinguished locally, to start up again further along. Where it stopped and extinguished, the suspended debris of burnt material and soil would dump. In the case of Troy, at a later date, this reached a depth of 15 feet (5 meters). To assign such fire evidence to marauding aliens is sheer lunacy.

What is instructive about Mandelkehr's articles is that he assigns the destruction primarily to fires. However, he relentlessly dates all of his destruction to 2300 BC. I'm certain that this is incorrect. It confuses the event of 2349 BC with other and later disturbances. I have discussed Mandelkehr's book *The 2300 BC Event* earlier in this chapter. [note 24]

Sodom and Gomorrah

Let me now introduce Sodom and Gomorrah with a quotation from E.J. Sweeney, "Abraham in Egypt" in *SIS Workshop* (1986):

"Genesis informs us that shortly after Abraham's expulsion from Egypt, the world witnessed a terrifying natural catastrophe. Fire and brimstone, it was said, fell on the Earth and consumed large areas of land in a general conflagration. The cities of Sodom and Gomorrah were obliterated from the face of the Earth; not one stone of them was left on top of another. Genesis imaginatively portrays the catastrophe as a punishment from God on the immoral inhabitants of these cities."

It was as bad as it sounds. Five cities were completely obliterated. There are only scant traces left today. These include an extensive cemetery of 500,000 graves at what is assumed to be Sodom, and others elsewhere. Archaeology has determined destruction by earthquake in 2350 BC, followed by a destruction by fire in circa 1700 BC.

"Paleoenthnobotanists found in Bab'edh-Dhra [Sodom] traces of wheat, barley, dates, plums, peaches, grapes, figs, pistachio nuts, almonds, olives, pine nuts, lentils, chick peas, pumpkin, flax seed, and watermelon. It was a gourmand's delight. The healthy diet manifested itself in the physique of the inhabitants: skeletal remains indicate that a height of 5'9"-6'4" was quite normal."

*"The date of the destruction of Sodom and Gomorrah according to
Biblical chronology was a year before the birth of Isaac, which was in
1712 B.C.E."*
-- Biblical Archeology (on line),
www.aish.com/ci/sam/48931527.html

Other causes have been voiced, of course. A press release of the
Cambridge Conference (a SIS event), headlined the following on March 30,
1997:

"Comet Destroyed Sodom And Gomorrah"
*"Sodom and Gomorrah may have been destroyed by debris from a
comet, startling new archaeological and astronomical research
suggests."*

The article places all the destructions in 2200 BC, 150 years after the
earth shock (and "day of the dead") of 2349 BC, and 250 years before the
more likely date of circa 1936 BC (by my calculation, shown below). The
press release was prepared by Benny Peiser, who is given to cometary causes,
and who added (http://abob.libs.uga.edu/bobk/ccc/cccmenu.html):

*"Previous explanations, like a massive earthquake or volcanic eruption,
could not account for destruction over such a vast area. The meteorites
would have exploded above the ground with the power of scores of
nuclear bombs: one devastated a vast area of Siberia in 1908."*

Peiser is here extending the explosive effects to the catastrophic ending of
the Egyptian Old Kingdom, the failure of the Akkadian Empire, the demise of
the Harappan civilization, and the end of the Xia Dynasty of China. Victor
Clube of the Clube and Napier team who wrote the unlikely *Cosmic Serpent*
(1982) joined the bandwagon and announced that (quoting the press release)
"He [Benny] has calculated that the Earth passed through a cloud of debris --
the Taurid meteorite stream -- thought to have resulted from the break-up of a
comet 40,000 years ago, between 2200 BC and 2000 BC." I don't know
where they get these dates, always conveniently placed at one catastrophe or
another. The meaning here is that Earth passed through debris in 2200 or
2000 BC. of a meteor which broke up in 40,000 BC.

I doubt almost all of this. But an earthquake which destroyed the five
"cities of the plain" in 2350 BC is certain. A BBC story, "The Destruction of
Sodom and Gomorrah" (February 17, 2011), reported an estimate of 6 on the
Richter scale. That is sufficient to topple a city of mud-brick buildings. The
epicenter, we know, was in Tibet. The second destruction is certain also -- the

evidence is in plain sight -- but it came 400 years later, in 1936 BC. This consisted of a fire which reduced the stones and walls to a powder.

Now for a determination of the most likely date. Adding the known starting date of 3067 BC for the earlier close passes of Mars, to the start of close passes in the 8th and 7th century BC, 806 BC, and dividing by two, results in a starting date of 1936 BC as a most likely start of a set of "contacts" by Mars at the close of the Early Bronze Age which resulted in the destruction of Sodom and Gomorrah. In an article in *Aeon*, Donald Patten writes that Talmudic source materials pinpoint the destruction to the day of Passover. [note 25]

The Return of Mercury

Standard Bible chronology places the destruction of Sodom and Gomorrah at one year before the birth of Isaac in 1712 BC. But this is likely to be incorrect since all of it is tied to the lifespan of Abraham, who is Jupiter, and who is badly misplaced in time for the sake of a coherent timetable which places Abraham after Noah, rather than before. I have detailed all this earlier.

We should look instead at other sources. First, it has been noted by others that the local name for the planet Mercury, which (I claim) was a constant companion to Mars, became a faddish personal name after about 2200 BC. De Grazia notes that Mercury "was assigned a period of heavy worship between 2200 and 1500 BC." He writes, in *The Disastrous Love Affair of Moon and Mars* (1984):

> *"M. Mandelkehr has more recently informed me of several additional authoritative sources who found Thoth* [which is Mercury] *active throughout the Old Kingdom of Egypt, and points out that his ibis symbol existed even before dynastic times."* [note 26]

It should also be pointed out that there is a progression of latitudes where Mars passes by Earth. I had supposed that the first set of close passes by Mars may have happened above the Earth, or at least away from Earth. Manetho, however, identifies some catastrophes in Egypt after 3067 BC, the first period of close approaches by Mars

The second contact involves the destruction of Sodom and Gomorrah. Schaeffer, on the other hand, identifies sites of destruction for this second time period at about 40 degrees latitude.

The third set of passes by Mars, to be discussed in a following chapter, happened at 35 degrees north latitude.

Last, the Bible story of Sodom and Gomorrah is not easy to read and is easy to misread. Two angels visit Lot, reads the King James bible, but the

Hebrew bible calls them kings. The very fact that there are two angels makes me suspect that they represent the twin planets Mars and Mercury. Too bad that descriptions are missing, unlike for Esau and Jacob. Jacob is smooth, Esau is red and hairy. What we do have is the stated fact that the angels blinded the Sodomites before destroying their city. This might be the magical abilities of angels, but I am more inclined to understand this as a celestial explosion, an explosion not unlike the blast at Tunguska.

The birth of Esau and Jacob is also most likely the reappearance of Mars and Mercury in time for the destruction of Sodom and Gomorrah, at their birth date or a decade and a half later. Esau and Jacob are sons of Isaac, who is the son of Abraham. Estimates of the destruction of Sodom and Gomorrah in about 1700 BC are thus probably correct.

Also not to be neglected is the curious condition of Lot sitting at the gate to the city when he encounters the two angels. Although this tale of Sodom and Gomorrah is 400 years after the fall of the Absu, here again we encounter a doorway to another place. It is the doorway of the Absu. If it can be told that Samson could tear out the city gates of Gaza 700 years later, and carry them off, then certainly the tale of Lot sitting at the city gates should be allowed at the same mythological level of retelling. Bible commentators, since antiquity, have attempted to make much of Lot sitting at the gate, assigning Lot the mayorship of Sodom, with the task of greeting all visitors. Similarly much is made of the licentiousness of the inhabitants.

It would seem that something ought to be made of the fact that the orbit of the Earth was different in each of these three cases -- 3067 BC, 1936 BC, and 806 BC. But the circular geometry has little effect on the interactions between the planetary orbits. It will change the calendar dates of the interference slightly, and it might affect how close Mars came. Only the rotation of the second nodal points of the two orbits would in each instance have brought the interactions to a halt to be continued again 1100 years later -- excepting the last, as I will show, which ended in an accident for Mercury.

Special thanks to J Brookes for questioning the red look of Sirius.
Special thanks to J West for interpretation of Sodom and Gomorrah.

Image credits: Kali after Richard Wikinson; Ku-Bau (Ku-baba), after Wikipedia, Georges Jansoone, public domain; Anath, after JBL Statues; Leviathan, after Gustave Doré; Grendel, after Lynd Ward.

Endnotes

Note 1 --

There is a 1000-year gap between the event of 2349 BC and its retelling in 1350 BC and after. But the appearance of Hathor as the Celestial Cow had happened again in 1492 BC and 1440 BC. The name of Marduk, the chief god of the Babylonian empire, is spelled in the Akkadian language with the Sumerian glyphs "AMAR.UTU" which reads "calf of the Sun."

Note 2 --

The reaction of the spin axis of the Earth to a torque applied off-center to the equator is discussed in Appendix B, "Celestial Mechanics" and illustrated with diagrams.

A better estimate of the travel time of the plasmoid from Venus would be based on a speed of 6 million miles per hour (9.5 million km per hr). This is detailed in the text.

Note 3 --

I am using the translation to English by Suzanne D. Fisher from the Spanish original made by Bolio in 1930. This text, along with a later translation of the Mayan original to English made in 1933 by Ralph Roys, is discussed in the chapter "The Chilam Balam." In this instance the text by Bolio makes a little more sense of the original than the more secular interpretation by Roys.

Note 4 --

The words "and" and "then" of the phrase "and then days of the year were introduced" are both from the same base Mayan word, and do not imply the time-order of words as in Indo-European languages, where "then" means "after" and "and" implies simultaneous. I hope this will hint at why quotations from the *Chilam Balam* are to be taken in with some caution, and why the translations are often so choppy.

Note 5 --

Warfare weapons in Mesoamerica included spears, halberds, and dart throwers, not arrows. Only game animals were hunted with arrows. This war, however, is described as using arrows.

Note 6 --

If the plasmoids from Venus traveled at 6 million miles per hour, Venus would have been within a distance of over 20 million miles (32 million km) from Earth in order for the arrival of the first plasmoid to have been delayed 6 hours. The travel delay to Jupiter, at 6 million miles per hour would be **(4.5-1)*AU/(6000000*24) = 2.26 days**. The switch to glow mode by Jupiter would have been seen on Earth about 30 minutes later -- **2.28 days.**

Although it is not at all certain how long "a day" was reckoned to be (most days during this period still started at sunset), the time delay could be counted as twice from midday to midday, plus 12 hours to midnight. At some locations the celebration of the "Day of the Dead" uses full daylight days and an evening, although in other locations it starts with a nightfall event.

The distance of 20 million miles may be an overstatement. If the eccentricities found by Lynn Rose and Raymond Vaughan for Venus and Earth for the 7th century BC, 0.15 and 0.10, can be applied to the era before 2349 BC, the difference between the perihelion of Venus and the aphelion of Earth is 17.5 million miles (28 million km) under the assumption that both orbits were 0.75 AU before 2349 BC;
0.75 * (1-0.10) = 0.825 AU, and
0.75 * (1-0.15) = 0.6375 AU, thus
(0.825 - 0.6375) * AU = 17,437,500 miles.

Note 7 --

I cannot agree with the circumpolar rings, for a number of reasons. First, a circumpolar ring of dust or ionized gases would be electrically unstable. Mandelkehr assumes that these would be ice particles, following the "snowball" notion of comet composition.

Second, there is the standing problem of needing to radically change the speed and direction of material (whether meteors, asteroids, or fragmented "icy comets") coming in from outside planet Earth in order to be "captured." In all of recorded history, while millions of meteor-like objects are intercepted by the Earth each year, not a single object has ever been "captured." The Moon was not captured; it is a planet sharing Earth's orbit. It would be more correct to say that the Moon captured the Earth.

Third, Mandelkehr suggests that the rings would only have lasted some months. I have no opinion on that. What strikes me as strange, however, is his compilation of some 450 gods and their attributes, gathered from mythological sources from around the world. All of them, even sets of a half dozen from a single culture, are "associated" (to use his phrasing) with rings, circles, fires, horns, bows, mountains, and streams and serpents surrounding the Earth. I find most of this severely decontextualized from the mythologies I am familiar with, and I would suggest that it is very unlikely for 450 gods and goddesses to align themselves with the iconography of a celestial phenomenon which lasted only a few months.

Fourth, although Mandelkehr's rings are nominally circumpolar, he places them at an angle of about 70 degrees to the equator, so that they pass between Ursa Major and Ursa Minor (as seen from Earth) near the Earth's North Pole. This conclusion was apparently reached on the basis of frequent references to Ursa Major in antiquity. But this location, between these two constellations, happens to be the location of the Earth's rotational axis if this is retrocalculated on the basis of today's conditions -- using the "precession of the polar axis" -- to 2300 BC. This condition would not define a set of rings at an angle of 70 degrees to the Earth's equator, but a set of rings at an exact circumpolar position, at right angles to the equator. This seems like an oversight.

The "rings" were seen and noted by the people of antiquity. But the rings had always been there, not circumpolar, but below the Earth's equatorial in the south sky. After 2349 BC, this was reduced to a single ring at a great distance from Earth but still below the equatorial in the sky -- which seems to have lasted to AD 400 or 600.

Note 8 --

Alfred de Grazia made note of the ubiquity of the Pleiades in mythology in *Chaos and Creation* (1984), writing:

"Many places around the world mark the beginning of November as the Day of the Dead; it is All Saints Day; Halloween; All Souls Day; etc. The time is associated with the Pleiades for reasons not clearly understood yet. The coincidences of time, mood, ceremony, and stellar assignation is so great as to exclude independent invention except in particulars and to insist upon a common experience of explicit quality."

De Grazia follows this by some comments on the possibility of diffusion, but diffusion is negated by the existence of a "Day of the Dead" festival in Mesoamerica before the invasion of the Spanish. De Grazia could not date or place the event.

Note 9 --

In addition to the invariant skies before 685 BC (actually, the lack of a precession of the equinoxes before 747 BC), I will develop in a later chapter that the equinox moved 15 days forward in 685 BC. Thus the equinoxes happened earlier. This is born out with data from the horizon setting angles of the Sun for Mesoamerican ceremonial centers, where 6 alignments out of 13 that were checked, point to an equivalent Gregorian calendar date of September 8th, two days after the earlier autumnal equinox date of September 6. See the chapter "Olmec Alignments."

The Pleiades were seen directly above Jupiter, because they are located about 6 degrees in elevation above Jupiter (which is on the ecliptic). Even if the coma of Jupiter was as large as Plutarch suggested in AD 200, "three times the diameter of the Moon" (and thus about 1.5 degrees in diameter), this would not have obscured stars located 6 degrees above the ecliptic. By the following year the Pleiades were used as the marker to celebrate the event. Jupiter would not return to this location against the background of stars for 9 years. The period of Jupiter at 4.3 AU is $\mathbf{sqrt((4.3\^3)*(12\^2)/(5.2\^3)) = 9.02}$ years, compared to the current 12 years at the location of 5.2 AU. On a retrocalculated ephemeris Jupiter will not appear in the night sky on September 21, 2300 BC.

Among 13 Mesoamerican ceremonial sites I investigated there are 20 alignments using horizon locations (to a mountain or volcano) for the setting of the Pleiades. See the chapter "Olmec Alignments."

Note 10 --

To return the "Day of the Dead" celebrations to September 6th, the old day of the equinox, is astounding!

Mandelkehr. by the way, notes that the Pleiades culminate on about November 1 today. They do not. Culmination happens on November 14th today.

Note 11 --

Bernadino de Sahagún recorded his observations of Aztec culture from native sources after AD 1527 in *Historia de las cosas de Nueva España* (translated in AD 1829). The culmination of the Pleiades for Mexico City, equivalent to the ceremonial center of Teotihuacan, is as follows.

I think that the date of the "Day of the Dead" may have been established by the priests at Teotihuacan at about AD 200, when the city was built. At that time the Pleiades culminated between October 20 and October 22, Gregorian (October 20 to 21, Julian). Teotihuacan was the undisputed primary religious center until circa AD 700, and set the standard for most of Mesoamerica. Its influence lasted into the Aztec era. The Aztecs still celebrated the "Day of the Dead" on October 20 or 21 in about AD 1550.

```
Culmination of the Pleiades -- Mexico City, 19.25 deg n latitude
                                 midnight     --westerly setting--
    year      Julian  Gregorian  culmination  azimuth   deg n of w

  original   Oct 9*   Sep 22*    76.1 deg     275.6 deg   5.6  <--
    685      Oct 15   Oct  8     83.5         283.3      13.3  <--
    600      Oct 16   Oct 10     83.8         284.6      13.6
    200      Oct 17   Oct 14     86.5         285.8      15.8
    100      Oct 18   Oct 16     86.2         286.7      16.7  <--
  AD 100     Oct 19   Oct 18     87.3         287.1      17.1
    200      Oct 20   Oct 20     87.7         288.1      18.1  <--
    400      Oct 21   Oct 22     88.1         288.7      18.7  <--
    700      Oct 23   Oct 27     89.5         290.7      20.7
   1000      Oct 25   Oct 31                  292.0      22.0
   1550      Oct 30   Nov 9                   294.2      24.2
   2008               Nov 14                  295.3      25.3

  * -- using the current location of the equinox.
  Frequent alignments are marked.
```

-- The entry "original" can be used for all years before 685 BC, where the dates should be reduced by 15 days to reflect the earlier location of the equinox.
-- The westerly settings of the Pleiades marked "<--" appear with great frequency among the significant alignments at Olmec and Valley of Mexico ceremonial sites. In all, for the 13 sites I looked at, there were 25 alignments with the setting location of the Pleiades. More details can be found in the chapter "Olmec Alignments."

Note 12 --

Ussher paraphrases from the New Testament as follows: *"He told them it was necessary for Christ to suffer and to rise from the dead the third day."* This is attributed by Jesus to "Moses and the prophets" and thus from very old sources. In Mark 12:26 Jesus speaks of the Books of Moses, and, speaking of God, says, "Yet it is of living men, not of dead men, that he is the God." This is in distinction to Osiris, the Egyptian God of the dead.

Note 13 --

The front of the turtle is on the left. Hunahpu and Xbalanque appear as headdresses of two monsters or gods peering out of both ends of the turtle, not unlike the heads showing out of the two mouths of the celestial serpent bar. The face on the side (center) of the turtle names the crack as "Precious Torch Death." A footnote (48 on pg. 465) in Freidel and Schele, *Maya*

Cosmos, suggests an extended name from another source of "Yellow Torch Death Skull." "Yellow" is the south directional color; the "torch" may be in reference to the "image of the first turtle" which appeared in 10,900 BC as a brilliant torch.

Note 14 --

The *Book of the Dead* is a collection of unrelated spells which never follow the same order, and are often unique. These include the spells engraved in pyramids from Unas's time on, spells painted on coffins, and later written scrolls included with coffins.

Note 15 --

If my estimate of the travel of Jupiter through the asteroid belt is correct, then Jupiter would have entered a separate "clump" of asteroids at about 4 AU, in about 2400 BC. After that a change in the plasma of Jupiter to dark mode could have existed for a period of 50 years, only to return to glow mode with the electric activity of Venus in 2349 BC. This would be almost coincidental, but it was held as very significant, religiously, worldwide.

From the dates recorded in the sculptures at Palenque, it could be suggested that the Moon arrived about a decade after 2349 BC, in 2337 BC.

However, the *Chilam Balam* states that Jupiter was not "weeping" when the Moon arrived. This could mean that Jupiter was located behind the Sun (on the other side of the ecliptic), so that the plasma tail could not be seen, or that there was no plasma outpouring.

Note 16 --

Although I would, at first thought, tie the first appearance of the Moon to 2349 BC, it seems almost certain that it would take some time before a regular orbit was established. In fact, from some sources it seems that the Moon did not show up until a decade later. With the Earth on an elliptical orbit, and the Moon on a different but nearly identical orbit, it would take time before the Moon's orbit stabilized. The Maya *Chilam Balam* takes note of an Earth shock and the first sight of the Moon, but no dates are even hinted at. It might simply be part of a panoply of associated events. That includes the first note on the establishment of a calendar, "days were added."

Note 17 --

Velikovsky originally established the 52-year interval. This interval has been confirmed by many researchers from other sources, at times as 104-year intervals. In Mesoamerica the interval is confirmed from the "52-year celebrations" recorded at the time of the Spanish invasion, although based on Tun years of 360 days, and specifically from the apparent intervals when the "primacy" of religious centers passed from one location to another after about 1400 BC.

But the actual interval of approaches of Venus did not remain the same after 2193 BC. It became shorter by a few years. Mesoamerica celebrated the "52 years" as an interval based on a Tun year of 360 days, not solar years. This has caused considerable confusion among researchers.

Note 18 --

Amun first appears at Thebes (in Egypt) after 1985 BC, in the Twelfth Dynasty during the Middle Kingdom. Amun appears to be a reconfiguration of Ra as the Midnight Sun, who had disappeared from view over 200 years earlier. Only after circa 1550 BC (at the beginning of the New Kingdom) does Amun become widely recognized in Egypt (as Amun-Ra). After this time he starts to assume the attributes of the older Gods. He was called, "the king of the Gods," by the Thebans.

Jupiter appears under a number of other names in Egypt at this time, which combine "hidden" with the original name for "sun," although the original "sun" designation universally referred earlier to Saturn at the North Pole. In Canaan Jupiter is known as Baal Tsaphon, the Hidden Lord. In 500 BC Herodotus claims that the Egyptian Amon is Zeus, that is, Jupiter.

Note 19 --

With the fall of the Absu the "gate to the other world" is removed. At a later date, both Hercules (Mars) and Samson (of the Bible) in legends carry away the gates of a city.

Note 20 --

See Book 2 of the Shu and the introduction by James Legge to *The Sacred Books of the East, Volume 3, The Shu* (1879).

Of the Books of the Xia, Legge notes:

"Of the still earlier dynasty of Hsiâ [Xia], there are only four documents, and we have no evidence that there were any more when the collection of the Shu was made in the times of Kâu. ... In the last of them a celestial phenomenon *is mentioned, which has always been understood to have been an eclipse of the sun in Fang, a space of about 5 1/2 degrees from pi to sigma of Scorpio, on the first day of the last month of autumn. P.*

Gaubil thought he had determined by calculation that such an eclipse really took place in the fifth year of Kung Khang, B.C. 2155. Doubts, however, have been cast ... on the accuracy of his calculation."

Others have demonstrated that the eclipse could not have been seen in China. Scorpio, however, is two houses over from Capricorn, although retrograde of normal planet travel in the ecliptic, where Rockenbach places the comet of 2060 BC, "in the constellation of Capricorn, and within the space of sixty-five days it traversed three signs in the sky." This suggests a comet outside the orbit of Earth, fairly close by, and seen in retrograde motion, as would happen since Earth would be traveling at a faster orbital speed (which is meaningful only if we assume that these two events are related).

Note 21 --

That Mercury had a substantial atmosphere can be surmised from two facts. First, that in remote antiquity, when Mercury stood between Saturn and Mars, it appeared as white, and looked much larger than Mars (which, however, was closer to Earth). In Mesoamerica it was misidentified as Venus from the perusal of ancient codexes. So in the *Popol Vuh's* recollections from the most ancient narratives (10,900 BC to 8347 BC) Mercury is called "Sovereign Plumed Serpent," a name otherwise reserved for Venus. Venus only came into existence after 4077 BC.

Second, in the earliest diagrams of the standing stones of the Neolithic Avebury monument in England, there are two interior circles of equal diameter, which most likely represent a large Mercury and much closer Mars. Since Avebury probably dates to after 3100 BC, the construction of these two smaller circles is probably schematic and from memories. This is duplicated at Stonehenge, and one other location that I was aware of (but cannot place). The small planets shown below Saturn are remembered, rather than actual. This would not have been Venus, which is twice the diameter of Mars.

The side view of Venus figurines of the late Upper Paleolithic also render two lumps offset from each other and located below Saturn -- depicted as if the figurine had large buttocks and was pregnant to boot.

The misidentification of Mercury as Venus has carried forward to the current era, where Talbott claims that the white globe between Saturn and Mars was Venus. The misidentification is partially due to the fact that Mercury simply has never been considered as part of the "Polar alignment."

Talbott claims multiple plasma streams in glow mode as impinging on "Venus" (Mercury) in a circular form, making the planet look like a petaled flower or a seashell. The form of multiple streams would be correct for a planet with a magnetosphere. The separation of the glow mode plasma stream from Saturn would not be expected to separate into distinct bundles (making it look like a petaled flower) unless the planet had a magnetic field. That eliminates Venus.

What is also clear, is that Mercury should, because of its atmosphere, be practically devoid of so-called "impact craters" -- as the Earth is also -- so that in losing most of its atmosphere (at a late date) this would show. And it does. The cratering of Mercury is noted by astronomers to have a look of freshness unlike the craters of the Moon or Mars. All of the cratering happened in June and July of 685 BC. This was a year after the atmospheric fire on Mercury.

Note 22 --

James E. Strickling, in "The Tower Of Babel And The Confusion Of Tongues" in *Kronos* volume 8, number 1 (1982), suggests interference of the faculty of speech, not in creating new languages, but in causing a garbling of speech so as to make it incoherent. He sources M. A. Persinger, *ELF and VLF Electromagnetic Field Effects* (1974).

Note 23 --

The *Enuma Elish* is completely new; it has no precedent among older Akkadian or Sumerian texts except for incorporating the Sumerian flood event.

Note 24 --

Mandelkehr blames the movement of people to a climatic downturn, which I blame on an increase in the orbit of the Earth. Mandelkehr blames it on dust generated by a comet of the Taurid complex, something, by the way, totally overlooked by the astronomers Victor Clube and Bill Napier, in their book *The Cosmic Serpent* (1982), or in any of their later talks. I will blame the 200 year climatic downturn after 2193 BC on nanometer dust in the stratosphere.

Note 25 --

"The 108-year Cyclicism of the Ancient Catastrophes" in *Aeon* (1990). I would expect such hard-and-fast dates because planetary orbits can be expected to remain the same. Planets do not leave their orbits. It is not as Stephen Jay Gould wrote, in *Ever since Darwin* (1977): "Mars then left its regular position and almost collided with the earth in about 700 BC." That's just nonsense.

An intruding planet would repeat an earlier appearance except to be perhaps a few hours earlier or late compared to the previous overflights. This is because the planetary orbits are first of all circular, and a path of a planet on an elliptical orbit drawn across these circles will not deviate by more than a day in crossing an orbit currently from the date of crossing an orbit at the same inclination to the equator of the Sun at an earlier time.

However, the orbit of an intruding planet which crosses the path of another planet is governed by apsidal precession. All the planetary orbits are ellipses, which thus have two nodal points: one at the Sun, and the other some distance away from the Sun. This second nodal point slowly revolves around the Sun, and thus the whole shape of the orbit revolves around the Sun -- counterclockwise as seen from above the north pole of the Sun. This rotation is called apsidal precession.

The Moon's period of apsidal precession around the Earth amounts to about 19 years. The Earth's orbit takes 112,000 years to rotate around the Sun today (estimates vary). What I have already suggested is that the orbits of Mars and Mercury were extremely elliptical. Perhaps because of this, the orbits of Mars and Mercury caught up with the orbit of Earth every 1150 years. The interference of overrunning the orbit of Earth would therefore only happen periodically.

Note 26 --

I doubt the use of the Ibis symbol as indicating Thoth before dynastic times. Mandelkehr may have reference to the Narmer Macehead of 3050 BC which shows an Ibis above a temple structure, thought to be the temple of Buto in the delta, which, however, was under water at that time. Buto may be a reference to Saturn in the northern "sea above" with the Ibis representing Uranus seen above Saturn at an earlier time.

De Grazia lists as his sources for Mercury the following: E. A. Budge *Osiris, The Egyptian Religion of Resurrection* (*Book of the Dead*) (1895, 1961); J. Bonwick *Egyptian Belief and Modern Thought* (1878, 1956), Theosophical literature, reviewed, however, as "tripe"; R.T.R. Clark: *Myth & Symbol in Ancient Egypt* (1959, 1991); D.B. Redford "The Sun-Disc in Akneton's Program: Its Worship & Antecedents I", *Journal of the American Research Center in Egypt* (1976); and *Cambridge Ancient History*, Third Edition, Vol. 1, Part 2 "Early History of the Middle East."

Calculations are in Unix bc notation, where ^ denotes exponentiation; the functions a(rctangent), s(ine), and c(osine) use radians; angle conversions to radians or degrees by the divisors rad=.017+ and deg=57.2+; other

functions are shown as f( ); tan( )=s( )/c( )
units: million == 1,000,000; billion == 1,000,000,000;
AU == 93,000,000 miles.

Recovering the Lost World, A Saturnian Cosmology -- Jno Cook
Chapter 22: The Exodus of Moses

Revision: 42.29 (moses.php)

Contents of this chapter: [The Terror of Venus] [The Messenger Gods] [Moses and Yahweh] [In The Desert] [The Moving Sky] [The Psychosis of Yahweh] [Return of the Axis Mundi] [Joshua and Jericho] [Abandoned by the Gods] [Endnotes]

The Terror of Venus

This chapter concentrates on the period surrounding the events of 1492 BC, including an electric contact by Venus, the Exodus of Moses, the fall of the Middle Kingdom of Egypt, and changes experienced worldwide.

"In the Bronze Age," reads a book on the prehistory of Crete, "Crete was the first center of naval power, where people lived in peace and plenty in unwalled cities. This lasted for over 1500 years."

"About 1400 BC a great catastrophe befell the island, a catastrophe of which we have no clear record in history, but one which is marked by destroyed and abandoned cities and villages, and from which the civilization as a whole never recovered."
-- R. W. Hutchinson, *Prehistoric Crete* (1962)

The same author notes in the next paragraph, however, that, after an interval of 400 years, "... a new life and culture arose in Crete. Even this revival of culture in Crete, however, did not survive the seventh century BC, and a new decline set in... ." [note 1]

The story of the sudden decline of civilization is repeated over and over, all following shortly after three dates -- 2400 BC, 1500 BC and 800 BC -- for one locality after another: in Greece, in the Middle East, in India, in China, in Mesoamerica, and in South America. This is especially true for the 8th and 7th century BC when some 300 cities in the Middle East were destroyed by earthquakes and fire. These incidents were better remembered. I will return to the 8th and 7th century BC later. The current topic is the era of 1500 to 1400 BC, when vast migrations of people are noted, apparently caused by natural disasters and worldwide changes in climate. [note 2]

We are now dealing with events not as remote as the flood of 3147 or the shock of 2349 BC. There are more records for this later period (although still pitifully few). The incident of circa 1500 BC was a worldwide catastrophe, in some ways larger in scope than the early flood events, for the Earth was moved considerably further from the Sun. Farmers and herders were affected; some civilizations never recovered. The later and much more frequent disruptions of the eighth and seventh century might be considered minor events in comparison. [note 3]

Whole nations of people migrated following 1500 BC. Others disappeared. It may be conjectured that Mesoamerica developed its bloodbath of controls over the spiritual world at this time. India disappeared into a Dark Age which did not lighten for 700 years. China, on the other hand, started its civilization in earnest. There were probably as many clever solutions to the catastrophes as there were desperate failures. Those who coped, those who found the imagination to handle unpredictable disasters, survived.

It was in 1492 BC that the dragon Venus "attacked" Earth. This is the planet which had been "expelled from Jupiter's skull" at the time of the confrontation with Saturn (3147 BC), had swung into an orbit nearly identical with Earth's orbit of that time. Venus would blaze through the sky for 2400 years with a coma and a 30 million mile (48 million km) long tail. Venus is the only deity which is almost universally recognized as having been "born" during historic times. The birth of Venus was seen by humans in 4077 BC (when Saturn went nova), or alternately seen as the separation from Saturn and Jupiter after 3147 BC.

I should point out also that the electric contact with Venus was the core of Velikovsky's book *Worlds in Collision*, where it is supposed that Venus traveled on a path that brought it close to Earth -- "nearly collided." This of course is nonsense, since planets do not alter their orbits to nearly collide with one another. If this had happened, we would not be here to tell the tale of Venus. But it is obvious that Mars after 800 BC did come very close, as it had at two earlier times, with an unbelievable amount of damage done to Earth by such a tiny planet. If this had been Venus, Earth would have been totally destroyed. The contact, the "near collision" with Venus in 1492 BC happened at a separation distance, I estimate, of some 10,000,000 miles (16,000,000 km).

In Mesoamerica, Venus appears as the feathered serpent Quetzalcoatl. In Greece, she was called Athena, sprung fully armed from the skull of Zeus (so say the Greeks). In Upper Egypt, she was Isis and in the south she was Hathor the celestial cow. In Lower Egypt and Libya, she was identified with the warrior Goddess Neith, who persisted to classical Greek times from 10,900 BC. Neith was held as the generatrix of mankind and the mother of the Gods. The Egyptian queens and mothers of the first dozen Horus-named pharaohs after 3150 BC took *Neith* as their name. Plato says that Neith is Athena. That is not true, but it will do. [note 4]

Venus lined up between the Sun and Earth at great intervals. As retold in the previous three chapters, starting in 2349 BC, Venus assumed the disastrous position between the Earth and the Sun four times, ending with the last electric contact of 2193 BC. Most likely the orbits of both Earth and Venus were eccentric, and Venus may have crossed over the orbit of Earth. But this last would not *per se* have resulted in an interaction. And as I mentioned in the previous chapter, when electric interactions did happen, the distance between Venus and Earth was probably on the order of 17- to 20,000,000 miles (27- to 32,000,000 km) in 2349 BC and 10- to 12,000,000 miles (16- to 19,000,000 km) in 1492 BC. The destruction of the Earth was electric, not gravitational. [note 5]

Since 2193 BC (the second "contact" in this era), and for 700 years afterward, Venus and Earth were never again in line with the Sun at the same time. Nothing more spectacular happened than the displays of the coma and tail of Venus as the planet ranged across the skies, approached and retreated over the span of the year, and periodically crossed Earth's path to move deep into the night skies of the south. Venus was discharging its birth legacy of surplus charge. It would continue to do so perhaps until sometime before the time of Aristotle who commented on the status of Venus as a planet -- the Babylonians, somewhat earlier, had not considered Venus to be a planet because of its strange behavior.

In 1492 BC Venus moved past the orbit of Earth on the Sun-side of Earth, and the plasmasphere tail of Venus touched the leading edge of Earth's plasmasphere. Both planets suddenly experienced a massive electric repulsive impulse -- affecting the orbits of both planets. This veered the Earth from its orbit to a path of greater radius around the Sun, and moved Venus also. Although the year became longer for Earth, it seems that Venus perhaps only changed the eccentricity of its orbit. [note 6]

The date of 1492 BC is listed by Velikovsky as minus 1492. A number of late medieval chronographers use 1495 BC instead. Johannes Hevelius (in AD 1668) offers 1495 BC, Abraham Rockenbach (AD 1602) uses 1493 BC. James Ussher (AD 1650) uses 1491 BC. Sethus Calvisius (ca AD 1600) uses 1495 BC. Josephus (ca AD 80) inadvertently also uses 1491 BC (my date of 3147 BC less 1656 years), but identifies it as the year of the flood of Noah (1656 years after creation, where I have used the true date of creation in the calculation). The tomb of Senmut, Vizier to Queen Hatshepsut of Egypt, was started in circa 1500 BC, in Thebes. The construction was halted in 1493 BC, the astronomical year -1492, and never completed. (But dated to circa 940 BC in Velikovsky's revised chronology.)

... a sequence of events

A sequence of events can be established. Venus passed on the day side of Earth, between Earth and the Sun. There is good evidence (from Olmec Mesoamerica) that a plasmasphere contact (an Earth shock) happened on the Gregorian equivalent calendar date of April 19th, 1492 BC. This date is developed in the chapter "Olmec Alignments." The book of Exodus says it happened on the 14th day of the first month of spring, held to be April.

There is evidence brought forward by other researchers that the Southeast Pacific experienced a gigantic impact between 1500 and 1400 BC, but of course the information has been attributed to a meteor impact. There was no gigantic "meteor impact" in the South Pacific, even though tsunami waves traveled (it is presumed) as far as the coasts of China and New Zealand. It was a compressive electric shock from Venus. Additionally, the most likely location of the compressive impact of 1492 BC would be just south of the equator. The impact would also have been four times as massive as the repulsive impact of 2349 BC which had shoved over the Himalayas, but the lever arm of the applied torque was much shorter. [note 7]

Velikovsky wrote the following, correctly associated with the 1492 BC event:

"In the manuscripts of Avila and Molina, who collected the traditions of the Indians of the New World, it is related that the sun did not appear for five days, a cosmic collision of stars preceded the cataclysm; people and animals tried to escape to mountain caves."

He quotes, for this, Brasseur de Bourbourg from *Sources de l'history de Mexique* (1860) as follows:

"Scarcely had they reached there, when the sea, breaking out of bounds following a terrifying shock, began the rise on the Pacific coast. But as the sea rose, filling the valleys and the plains around, the mountain of Ancasmarca rose too, like a ship on the waves. During the five days that this cataclysm lasted, the sun did not show its face and the earth remained in darkness."
-- Velikovsky, in *Worlds in Collision*, p.76

The use of this source is misleading, since the quoted paragraph is not about Mexico, despite the book's title. Francisco de Avila and Christoval de Molina documented Peru and the Inca. The mountains of Cerro Ancasmarca are in Peru at 11.5 degrees south latitude, and inland near Cusco.

The Andes might have lifted. Some geological researchers think the Andes were raised suddenly by as much as 10,000 feet (3300 meters), although 3000 feet (1000 meters) would be more realistic. Charles Darwin, writing in 1835 during his voyage on the Beagle, noted:

"... the Cordillera [the mountain chain of the Andes] *itself is absolutely modern as compared with many of the fossiliferous strata of Europe and America."*

It is quite possible that the Andes in fact moved up quickly, within a day or week or a year. At one time the marginal agricultural conditions surrounding Lake Titicaca, at an altitude of 12,500 feet (4000 meters), which is above the tree line, in the Alto Plano of Central Peru adjacent to Bolivia, were used to justify this. It was suggested that the monumental constructions of Tiahuanaco, south of the lake, dated to much earlier times. But the best archaeological evidence of changes in the region is that it was not settled until after 1400 BC. Construction commenced in about 800 BC. [note 8]

The impact was near the equator (because this was just after the vernal equinox), and the force would have passed through the Earth below its center. In response, the southern hemisphere tilted away from the Sun, and the Earth would have been subjected to an immediate gyroscopic reaction. A look at a globe will reveal that most of the Earth was spared from utter destruction because the 1500 mile (2400 km) diameter compressive Earth shock was experienced in the Pacific.

The shock, writes Velikovsky, was felt at midnight in Egypt. A location in the Pacific west of South America would have faced the Sun and is, in fact, 180 degrees removed from Egypt -- noon in the Central Pacific at 150 degrees west longitude, somewhat east of Hawaii but south of the equator. However, going by the complete lack of islands in the region of the Eastern Pacific north of Easter Island, a location of 120 degrees west longitude might be more appropriate

The impulse fell below the center of the Earth would first have tilted the upper half of the Earth's axis of rotation toward the Sun. Asia and Europe initially tilted in this direction, bringing India, Arabia, and the lower Eastern Mediterranean in direct line with Venus -- as the Earth rotated. This condition would have held for maybe a day, for the simultaneous gyroscopic reaction torque would move the spin axis to the forward direction of the Earth's travel on its orbit (the celestial east direction). Since the axis of the Earth would initially have pointed mostly to the rear portion of the Earth's orbit (it being early spring), the effect would have lasted some time. (See Appendix B, "The Celestial Mechanics" for the effect of a gyroscopic reaction torque.)

As the Earth's axis tilted and moved through a clockwise loop, the path of the subsequent electric arc would have angled up past the equator, past Australia, but might have crossed land in Southeast Asia, India, Arabia, and the Eastern Mediterranean. The arc traveled west, whereas the cloud of suspended water vapor over the Pacific, moving much slower, moved east, as all weather does.

At the point where the arc reached the Eastern Mediterranean, the axis would have completed about half of its sweep, and the northern hemisphere would have started to tilt away from the Sun again and angle toward the rear portion of the Earth's orbit (the celestial west direction). This would have caused the path of the arc from Venus to now angle back to the equator, so that North Africa might have been on the path, the Atlantic would have been crossed, and landfall would be made in Central America or upper South America. The water in the atmosphere could have caused the five days of darkness. This path and the atmospheric conditions might explain the difference between the date of the start on the 14th given by the Bible and the date of completion on the 17th of the equivalent same month used in Mesoamerica.

I cannot be certain of this path. And certainly the effects would have been felt away from this path also. The initial shock would have been felt worldwide. With the displacement of the air with the impact, the atmosphere would have reacted with hurricane force winds in the direction away from the impact location in the Pacific. It is also uncertain how long the electric repulsive force would have lasted -- to be replaced by an attractive force -- perhaps only minutes. It was not in effect by the time Southern Asia faced Venus.

Whereas in 2349 BC the year had lengthened by 20 days, and in 2193 BC the year had lengthened by 13 days, in 1492 BC the year lengthened by 87 days. This was recognized in remote antiquity. Ussher paraphrases the following, from sources I cannot place:

"... as the Israelites continued to die in the wilderness, Moses composed the 90th Psalm, 'Lord thou hast been our refuge.' He also showed that the normal age of men was reduced to 70 or 80 years. Therefore, the age of man was shortened to a third of what it was before 1490 BC."

This would be correct if we read this as "by a third" rather than "to a third," for an increase of 87 days represents a change of 30 percent in the length of the year (of 273 days). Ussher probably meant to make a comparison to the ages of Abraham, Isaac, Jacob, and Joseph which ranged from 100 to 200 years.

Venus had been positioned closer to Earth this time than it had in 2349 BC, on an orbit estimated to be 9,000,000 to 10,000,000 miles away from Earth. It would have taken some time for Venus to overtake and pass Earth on its parallel orbit. Actually, the movement past each other would be determined by the width of the two plasmaspheres: certainly 320,000 miles (515,000 km) (40 Earth diameters, 20 to 30 diameters today) for Earth, and a lesser width for Venus (since it has no magnetosphere), which would determine how long the electric arc might have lasted. At most it would have taken about six days for Venus and Earth to pass each other. [note 9]

This would account for the fact that an electric arc, initiated in the South Pacific, managed to travel across the Earth at least as far west as the Eastern Mediterranean -- over half the circumference of the Earth, representing a half day. It seems to have traveled through lower Asia and India or along the Indian Ocean, hit land in Arabia, continued through the Sinai and lower Egypt, and probably continued through the Mediterranean along the coast of North Africa, to cross the Atlantic and approach the Americas. Arabia's deserts are still marked with large areas of scorched stones.

The initial repulsive electric impact in the Pacific would have reversed itself (as an opposite charge was induced), and began to lift vast amounts of ocean water into the atmosphere and stratosphere -- which would have spread throughout all of the world within a few days or a week. The levitation of seawater would have ceased even before the electric arc was established. Thus, although I estimate that Venus and Earth were electrically visible to each other for a span of 6 days, the arcing might have dissipated at the water-soaked upper atmosphere after a single rotation of Earth. [note 10]

After the initial shock, Venus was seen later that day in the Middle East as a gigantic red glowing globe. We have a number of recollections and descriptions of this. The water vapor from the Pacific, traveling toward the east, had not reached the Middle East yet. If the red globe were the size of the Moon, it would have been twice as far away as the Moon is today, or about a half million miles (805,000 km). But it is more likely that Venus had a much more extensive coma, and would look huge even at far distances. We have to assume that it looked red because of local dust in the air, from arcing across India and Arabia. The globe in the sky was memorialized as the attacking demon or the God Typhon.

Because Venus must have carried a much lesser coulomb charge since the contact of 2349 BC, there were no disconnected plasmoids released. Instead there apparently was a continuous arc from Venus striking Earth, as recorded by Moses in the book of Exodus and recalled later by the Greeks as the legend of Typhon.

The major effect of the contact with Venus, in addition to the change in the Earth's orbit, was the addition of a massive amount of dust (from forest fires) to the stratosphere, and water vapor to the atmosphere (the result of the initial compressive contact to the waters of the Pacific and the subsequent attractive electric force).

The Earth dimmed, and agriculture failed. A people "walked in darkness" for 40 years (Bible) and "a generation grew up in darkness" (Mesoamerica). The Earth had been subjected to electric arcing earlier (in 2193 BC) with a corresponding 200-year downturn in climate. The electric exchange with Venus in 1492 BC was largely moderated by the amount of water vapor in the atmosphere. The rain clouds that hung above were darkened by the nanometer dust in the stratosphere. The gloom lasted 40 years.

... some details

Mesoamerican retellings mention the total destruction of buildings and villages. The coastal regions of South America must have become largely depopulated. People at latitudes further north from the strike point and the path of the arc were not directly affected, except for earthquakes, tsunamic ocean tides, and the aftermath of a "fallen sky" -- the result of massive amounts of oceanic waters vaporized and forced into the atmosphere, and held there by the failure of the Sun to break through the dust of the stratosphere. The clouds never warmed up to release their moisture and were perhaps also kept suspended by the increased electric charge of the Earth. Forty years in the desert, however, or "a generation," is a lot less than the 200 years of climatic downturn experienced in 2193 BC, or the 1500 years of shadow of 10,500 BC.

Velikovsky had suggested that the two planets may have closed to as little as 6 diameters in distance from each other (48,000 miles, 77,000 km) and may have circled each other. I seriously doubt both of these. This has become part of the "collision" scenario of Velikovsky for which he has been faulted. It is, in fact, one of the few valid objections stemming from a consideration of the physics involved.

> *"Because of the proximity of the earth, the comet* [Venus] *left its own orbit and for a while followed the orbit of Earth."*
> -- *Worlds in Collision*

That is just nonsense. A planet does not "leave its orbit for a while." At the time of Velikovsky's writing this was needed, despite the fact that a close approach of a planet as large as Venus was known to be completely untenable, for Velikovsky needed to account for a number of things which could only be achieved through gravitational interactions. One of these is the oceans and waters which stood up to the sky. Another is the vast destruction encountered by Earth and its people during this period -- to the point where some who recorded the event claimed that almost all humanity died.

Velikovsky has documented the interaction between Earth and Venus for this period in detail from Indian, Babylonian, Egyptian, Mesoamerican, and Biblical sources (including Bible commentaries), as well as from Roman and Greek recollections. There are tales of 6 or 10 days of darkness (Middle East) and days when the sun never set (China). The world was swept by fierce hurricanes and later versions of *The Epic of Gilgamesh* incorporate the hurricanes into its description of the earlier flood. Recollections that "ocean waters stood up and reached to the skies" are found in the Middle East, India, and in Mesoamerica. [note 11]

Considering the fact that humans only developed subjective consciousness during or after the time of Moses, we would expect there to have been a lack of descriptive memories of environmental catastrophes before this time. However, memories of stupendous doings of the Gods, which would be retold and replayed as dramas, would be remembered. And at this time, ca 1500 BC, we have already experienced 500 years of efforts at written histories -- at least as repeatedly retold "legends."

Even as late as the seventh century BC, these histories include very little of natural disasters. Exceptions are the writings of the prophets of Israel and the Chaldean astrological records. The Chinese pay almost no attention to the heavens. All this is not different from our lack of attention to natural events today. [note 12]

The electric arc swept across the Middle East. This was a Birkeland stream of plasma in arc mode seen as if at close quarters, identified as a monstrous twisted snake, with multiple heads in the upper sky -- the monster Typhon of legend. The Greeks insisted that the planet god Zeus came to save the world from this creature, mistaking the sphere of Venus seen above the dragon for Zeus (Jupiter). [note 13]

The battles of Marduk and the dragon Tiamat, the revenge of Horus on Seth, the battle of Krishna and the serpent, all describe similar details, although likely referring to 2349 BC rather than 1492 BC. Some people in antiquity correctly identified the large red globe at the apex of Typhon's multiple heads as Venus, and understood it to be the cause of the devastation. Some people called it a comet. To the Israelites leaving Egypt, the column of lightning was the arm of their God Yahweh, who spoke to them from the overhead globe. [note 14]

Velikovsky identifies a series of events as the ten plagues visited on Egypt by the God of the Israelites. The Egyptian Ipuwer Papyrus echoes the plagues of Exodus one for one. Velikovsky proposes causes for many of the plagues based on presumptions about the comet tail of Venus, which (he claims) would have swept into the Earth's path before the arrival of Venus. The "tail" of a comet or planet faces away from the Sun. The main tail is an extension of the planet's plasmasphere and is shaped by the shadow of the Sun's electric field in the direction away from the Sun.

There is a second tail of particulate matter, which curves, but it curves in a direction lagging the orbital movement of the planet Venus. This tail spreads out as the ionized particles repel each other. There is thus no tail which sweeps into the path of Earth prior to an electric field contact. There may, however, have been earlier contacts between the double layer of the plasmasphere tube of Venus and the Earth's plasmasphere.

Thus it is possible that before 1492 BC the tail of Venus had been experienced perhaps by having the edges of the plasmaspheres of Earth and Venus brush against each other, causing an interaction of the outer layers without establishing a clear sight-line between the two planets. Thus, as Venus was passing Earth on the Sun side the tail could have reached Earth from perhaps as far as 30,000,000 miles (48,000,000 km) away. The effects of this probably were noticed during a passage of Venus two years earlier. An electric interaction of the globes would only occur when the plasmaspheres of the two planets actually lined up. [note 15]

Velikovsky proposed that Venus approached Earth from the Sun side, and thus Earth at first intercepted the plasma tail of Venus. Actually, Venus likely caught up with Earth, with Venus moving faster than Earth because Venus was on an inner orbit. The edges of the plasma tail would certainly have "touched" the Earth's plasmasphere and transferred electric charges and gas ions constituting the boundary layers of the plasmaspheres. This might have resulted in changes in the weather during these earlier near alignments. Storms could have been a fact, and, as a result, Egypt would have been blanketed with dust, not from Venus, but from the Sahara.

I also disagree with Velikovsky's proposed makeup of the tail of Venus. He assumes a composition of fine ferrous dust at the far end of the tail, larger particles closer in toward Venus, and then hot cinders and rocks in the tail portion closest to Venus -- as if Venus was a tossed firebrand. Although I will (reluctantly) concede the presence of dust (ionized silicon compounds) or hydrogen and methane gases (which he identifies with petroleum), the tail of Venus was a plasma -- composed of electrons, protons, and ionized atoms. The outer edges of Venus's plasmasphere tail would have had a density approaching the classical notion of the vacuum of outer space. The tail of matter was composed of ionized particles.

It is thus not likely that the plasma tail would be composed of a hail of hot stones, despite the fact that the surface of Venus was at that time still incandescent. It is more likely that the grit and hot rocks were generated from the Earth's surface where the arc from Venus traveled over land surfaces and explosively launched dust, cinders, and rocks into the atmosphere. [note 16]

One would at first suggest that the electrical proximity of a large planet would have also severely stressed the Earth's crust, and there are many references to this sort of phenomena in antiquity -- mountains moved and the ground swelled underfoot the fleeing Israelites, who were in the process of leaving Egypt when this occurred. (The exodus will be discussed below.) Both the Bible and the records from the Americas speak of the ground opening up and of caves closing on fleeing humans. Lava flows and volcanoes burst forth. The Arabian Peninsula lifted and folded. Indian sources speak of mountaintops being lifted up, cast into the air, and ground into dust. The land west of the Zagros mountains rose, and the Euphrates river moved a hundred miles west. South American sources speak of the rising ocean tide and the simultaneous rise of the ground as if it floated on the waters. There is no written history for the period of 1500 to 1400 BC during the Shang dynasty in China. In 1400 BC, in response to some calamity, the capital had been moved and the Shang is renamed as the Yin for its new location.

The anecdotes which I have collected in the above paragraph from other sources are obviously primarily imagined to be caused by the gravitational forces of a large nearby planet, and assumed to be operating on the Earth's crust. Nearly nothing has been developed (or imagined) of the effects of the repulsive electric impulse forces operating in compressing rather than lifting the crust, followed by an attractive force, both from a great distance, and both of which far exceeded any forces which gravity could have produced at much closer distances (by a factor of billions on billions). This last would have operated on the facing crust, and cannot, like gravity, be assigned to operate on the bulk of the Earth. See Appendix B, "The Celestial Mechanics," which discusses the repulsive (and attractive) electric forces as the agent of destruction, and as the primary mechanism behind changes in orbits.

Another element of the destruction was the resistance of the Earth's crust to the compressive initial shock -- but not to the gyroscopic reaction, which would have been a smooth transition. Earthquakes, in fact, probably lasted for decades. Hurricane winds were probably due both to the traveling arc and the compressive shock, not to the gyroscopic motion of the Earth. I also feel that many of the geological disturbances attributed to this era might more properly be located in the span of time of 800 to 685 BC.

Last, let me assure the reader that an electric arc from 10,000,000 miles (16,000,000 km) is very possible, even if this seems like an absolutely impossible distance. First, the double layers of plasmaspheres are conductors in that they are composed of disassociated ions. It is like an electric cable.

Secondly, the interior of a plasmasphere and tail of a planet is consistently at about the same electric potential, so that it also is an effective conductor of electricity. The arc did not travel through empty space. Travel over this short distance might become easier to believe when we reach 685 BC, where we will meet up with a disconnected arc from Saturn to the Sun, traveling an absolutely unbelievable distance of 480,000,000 miles (773,000,000 km).

Yet Velikovsky, despite his initial claims for the electrical nature of the planets of the Solar System, was not ready to carry through with this concept. The best he could do was to produce a spark between Venus and Earth -- at which point the waters of the Red Sea, which had opened up a passage for the Israelites by standing up as a tide reaching to Venus (and imaginatively assigned to gravitational effects), fell again. The Israelites placed the climaxing event of their escape from Egypt on the night starting the 14th day of Aviv, in 1492 BC. Their day is counted from sunset. The "climaxing event" actually is not the opening of the "Red Sea" but the earlier earth shock of worldwide proportions. The opening of the "red sea" is clearly a descriptive recollection from 2349 BC, and may have had nothing to do with the ocean which today we call the Red Sea.

The 14th day of Aviv, where Aviv is the first month of the year after the spring equinox (Exodus 12:18), is marked with a sunset alignment of April 19 by the Olmec San Lorenzo site built around 1450 BC (see the chapter "Olmec Alignments"), and repeated at almost every later site.

The Earth was shrouded in low clouds for years, recalled in Biblical and Egyptian sources, and even more vividly in Mesoamerica, where sources claim that "the people grew up in darkness." However, the pillar of "cloud by day" and "fire by night" which the Israelites followed through 40 years of desert wandering was (possibly) from the electrostatic induction of the Ark of the Covenant -- not from a continued arc from Venus. It is even more likely that the pillar represents a plasma plume above the north magnetic pole of the Earth, the result of a relocation of Earth much further away from the Sun. I'll discuss this further below. [note 17]

The crust groaned endlessly. The Egyptian scribe Ipuwer writes, "Oh that the earth would cease from noise, and tumult be no more." As Moses met God on Mount Sinai, the Earth groaned, "Lo tirzah, lo tin'af, lo tignof..." -- the Ten Commandments, brief, to the point, "Kill not, Steal not... ." [note 18]

After the electric contact with Earth, the path of Venus was bent toward the Sun (or remained nearly the same, as suggested above) and the path of Earth was angled away. Velikovsky suggests that Venus reapproached Earth after six days and exchanged yet another traveling plasma discharge. Still attracted toward each other (presumably gravitationally), Venus, now hidden by the fallen skies on Earth, proceeded to yet another encounter six weeks later on the day of the Law Giving at Mount Sinai, says Velikovsky. The planets subsequently did not come close enough in their travels to cause any further interactions for the next 50 years. The first return of Venus after six days is quite likely, although it was not a return, it was probably just a contact with the trailing edge of the plasmasphere of Venus. The second return, after six weeks, is unlikely. [note 19]

Soon after the electric contact with Venus, with the Earth now much further away from the Sun, northern climates changed for the worse. The climate became cold. Grapes no longer grew in Scandinavia. The cloud cover affected agricultural production everywhere. During the first years, massive rainstorms stripped the Southern Balkans of soil and trees. Then a drought set in. The water table dropped precipitously and rivers dried up. Drought is a sure sign of a pervasive cloud cover without rain. The early European Bronze Age north of the Alps came to an end.

[*Image: the god Sharruma guiding his steward king Tudhaliya. The king has a kalmush in his left hand, the sign of sovereignty. Sharruma's pointed cap is adorned with god-ideograms. -- Rock carving at Yazilikaya, Turkey. Hittite, 1250 BC. After uned.es.*]

Tribes and peoples migrated to find better places to live. The Middle Kingdom of Egypt came to an end (probably soon after 1492 BC) when the Hyksos (the Amalekites met by the Israelites during their exodus) invaded from Arabia and held the delta for two hundred years or more, disrupting the political unity of Lower Egypt and ending the far-flung trade on which Egypt had depended during the period of the Middle Kingdom. The Hyksos established two dynasties in the delta. They established fortifications in

Southern Palestine, as at Avaris, from where they regularly raided Upper Egypt and the Levant as far north as Syria. Others have suggested that it was the Mitanni or Philistines who controlled the Hyksos. [note 20]

Under the Hyksos, a new calendar was introduced in Egypt. In Mesoamerica, the Olmec culture initiated a 360-day calendar by setting up 18 months of 20 days. It was, in fact, the first rational calendar, but was used simultaneously with the older 260-day calendar of 13 periods of 20 days. Moses was given a new calendar by Yahweh. The orbit of Earth had changed.

The Messenger God

When Jupiter lost its coma in 2150 BC, the last of the older Gods had been removed from the vicinity of Earth. Only the dragon -- Venus or Quetzalcoatl -- still followed an eccentric path through the skies, closing in on Earth's orbit at 50-year intervals. And Mercury (as well as Mars, although less visible) was still seen scurrying back and forth across the skies on errands for the distant Gods and in the administration of humans.

The planet Mercury was now the most active remaining celestial body. Mercury had a coma and tail which lit up; Mars did not. Mercury becomes identified as the emissary and messenger of the older Gods and was named Thoth (Egypt), Enki (Mesopotamia), Hermes (Greece, initially known as Apollo), and Mercury (Roman, but at a much later date). He became the special caretaker of humans, providing all the gifts of civilization and controlling the fate of humanity. In Egypt, Mesopotamia, and Greece, he is the God with the arcane knowledge of writing, music, mathematics, and magic. Thoth, and the others, represented those faculties which seemed unnatural to humans -- those which were not held by the Ka of the Egyptians. These faculties included the knowledge of spells and magic, and were responsible for the expansive application of writing and measurement after about 2100 BC.

Eventually the messenger God would be woven into earlier tales and even held as a creator God. The details of his assigned tasks, like the names of the messenger, vary widely, but they have a similar characteristic everywhere. They do not have power; they have cunning. [note 21]

After the previous electric contact with Venus, in 2193 BC, the static electricity of the atmosphere had probably steadily decreased, as it also had after 3100 BC. But the remaining atmospheric static electricity was still likely to show up just about anywhere: on mountains, pyramids, the tops of columns, and the horns of cattle -- as if it were delivering messages from the far-away Gods.

"Everything was in flames, the sky with lightning, the water with luminous particles, and even the very masts were painted with a blue flame."

-- Charles Darwin, writing about the voyage on the Beagle, circa 1856.

The blue flame experienced by Darwin was Saint Elmo's fire, a plasma exchange at glow level, which I have made note of in a previous chapter. It has been experienced since antiquity, especially by sailors, but today it occurs less frequently, and only under circumstances of impending electric storms at sea. The glow will show on ship masts, church steeples, and airplane wings. Saint Elmo's fire is a plasma flow between the crust of the Earth and the ionosphere. The plasma stream, which is normally at a low density and in "dark mode," will be concentrated to higher densities and "glow mode" by pointed objects which are electric conductors. The result is as eerie as it is spectacular. [note 22]

Shortly before 1500 BC, the atmospheric electric charge, which had declined for 700 years since the last contact with Venus, increased again as the plasmasphere tail of Venus swept past the Earth and possibly touched at intervals a few years apart. The Egyptian magicians noticed. Moses noticed. You could tell from the environment. Something was coming. [note 23]

Moses and Yahweh

In the Sinai desert, Moses sees God in a flaming bush. Specifically, a thorn bush. This is important, for he notes how Saint Elmo's fire issues from the thorns and how it assembles itself into a dense core where the thorns point together. He will construct the Ark of the Covenant in a similar form -- two gilded angels on a box with their wing tips covering the Ark and nearly touching, which will be the seat for Yahweh. Yahweh is one of the gods associated with the play of electricity, but he is no messenger. He is a God in his own right. "Who are you?" asks Moses, addressing the flaming bush. "I am who am," Yahweh answers. Another reading of the Bible text is, "I am who comes."

Plutarch says Athena (Venus) means, "I come from myself." Cicero states Venus is so named because, "she comes to all things." The *Vulgate Bible* translates "Yahweh" as "He who is," although "He who casts down" might be a better translation. The equivalence of the names is not a coincidence, for it was the approach of Venus which generated the electric conditions resulting in the display of Yahweh. [note 24]

Alfred de Grazia adds "God fights," as a variation on "Downcaster" for the name of Yahweh. The Israelites were, in fact, the most ferociously belligerent nation to enter the Middle East before the Assyrians rose to power a third time. They were an army forged in the Sinai Peninsula under the tyranny of Moses and his God Yahweh. They took the Ark of the Covenant into battle as a secret weapon, terrifying their enemies. The slaughter was enormous. Many centuries later, the Philistines capture the Ark. After moving it to three different cities, they beg the Israelites to take it back. It was uncontrollable and those who approached it became ill.

The *Book of Exodus*, as an account of these events, is not to be dismissed and needs to be read with an open mind. Take Alfred de Grazia as a guide.

"There myth is cozy with history. And the combination has been fiercely, obsessively retained, as if a purely historical recollection would be unbearably painful. Although the second of the five Books of Moses, the Exodus, is the best account that we have of that year, its most ancient lines were written down under stressful circumstances; to these lines, perhaps of Moses himself, a full oral tradition was added in the course of several centuries. The materials were sometimes lost; they were copied, rewritten, amended, translated and retranslated, time and time again."
-- Alfred de Grazia

I am indebted to Alfred de Grazia's *God's Fire* (1983) for what I will summarize in a few paragraphs. First off, to dispel a few inaccuracies: [note 25]

- Moses is a member of the court, probably the pharaoh's adopted brother. This is supported by the story of his birth and upbringing. Pharaohic succession was matriarchal, including by adoption. Nothing else explains the ready access of Moses to the court. As a member of the elite, he was fully Egyptian and, although nursed by his biological mother, he was raised as the adopted son of an Egyptian princess. [note 26]
- Moses spent a decade in exile in the Sinai peninsula (he had killed a member of the court), married into a local Midianite tribe of herdsmen, and tended flocks. As an exile, he received insights into other gods (the people outside Egypt had, of course, different Gods) and learned from the smiths of the Egyptian copper mines of the Sinai. As a court member, he read, he wrote, he knew materials, and he performed magic.
- The Jews were not slaves, except in the sense that all citizens of a nation were slaves of the Gods. When they leave Egypt, they carry

swords and other arms. Within the first month in Sinai, they spend a day fighting a rear-guard action against the Amalekites (Hyksos). Arms are not the hallmark of slaves.

- What Moses and his spokesperson, Aaron, sought of the Pharaoh was an "exit permit." The population of Israelites were an economic force and would have been pursued if they had just decided to leave Egypt *en masse* and without permission. Of course, at the last moment, the Pharaoh changed his mind and did pursue them.

- The exodus was well planned and organized. The Israelites left with the body of Joseph, and with their herds and ox-drawn carts and plenty of materials: provisions, tents, metals, forges, and lumber. They left with a mixed multitude of other squatter nationals and disaffected Egyptians. And they left with the Levites -- a cadre of Hebrew-Egyptian scribes, bureaucrats, and administrators, who would be assigned as the priests of Yahweh and the camp police.

- The passage through the standing waters was not through the Red Sea (the "Sea of Reeds"), but past the string of lakes between the Red Sea and the Mediterranean, between today's cities of Suez and Port Said. They were headed towards the Sinai Peninsula from the eastern margins of the delta because the way to Gaza was patrolled by Egyptian troops, whereas the route south to the Sinai was not. [note 27]

The Sea of Reeds

The wall of standing waters was indeed from the Red Sea and the lakes, but it stood on the land outside of the sea and the lakes. "The waters that confronted the Israelites were unexpected," writes de Grazia.

Before continuing with the physical aspects of Exodus, let me present the following:

Velikovsky, and thus de Grazia, followed the traditional notion that the crossing happened at Lake Sirbonis, or a similar location. James Hoffmeier, in *Israel in Egypt* (1997), presents various theories for a crossing of the "Red Sea," including the Gulf of Aqaba.

The derivation of the name "Red Sea" is very uncertain. There are no "red" aspects associated with the waters. The name for the Red Sea in Hebrew is "Yam Suph" which is translated as the Sea of Reeds. Velikovsky, however, offers:

"But the name of the Sea of the Passage -- Jam Suf -- is derived not from 'reed,' but from 'hurricane,' *suf, sufa* in Hebrew. In Egyptian the Red Sea is called *shari*, which signifies the sea of percussion (*mare percussionis*) or the sea of the stroke or of the disaster."

In line with the lack of evidence for an exodus, it might be noted that we are presented with the following image: "the Lord divided the sea with a wall on one side and on the other as well," plus, following the passage through the gap in the water, the Israelites camp "before the mountain of God."

This exactly recalls the event of 2349 BC, when the Absu -- the sea of reeds -- parted at the time of the fall equinox, followed by the appearance of Jupiter on his mountain, "the mountain of God." The "Sea of Reeds" is, of course, the Absu or Duat, referred to as filled with reeds in Egypt. In 2349 BC, during the most fearful period that humanity ever lived through, the Sea of Reeds turned red. Perhaps a rare coincidence, but such details added to Exodus, which obviously is a conglomeration of sources (as de Grazia also admits), point this particular text to legendary status.

The Quiche Maya will record in the *Popol Vuh* a similar passage through a gap in the sea: "a place called Great Hallow" and a mountain "called Place of Advice." Reading from their original sources, the 16th century AD transcribers write:

"Sandbanks was their name for the place where they crossed through the midst of the sea. Where the waters were divided, they crossed over."
   -- *Popol Vuh* translated by Dennis Tedlock (1996)

As narrated for our benefit: The arc of Venus moved the water into position to block the fleeing Israelites, then moved it aside for passage, only to have it fall back just as the Pharaoh and his army closed in. Exodus records that the pillar of fire stood before Israel, then moved behind them (to the west). The physical description of the changes in the winds, the movement of the water, and the movement of the pillar support the concept of an electric arc traveling west across the Sinai and part of the Nile delta.

The timing as recorded in Exodus may or may not be correct. It was just sheer luck, but a most monumental event, which would be played back to the Israelites by Moses for years, even though (Jewish legends have it) a hundred thousand Israelites also perished in the collapse of the standing waters.

"Then the Angel of God who went before the host of Israel moved and went behind them; and the pillar of cloud moved from before them and stood behind them, coming between the host of Egypt and the host of Israel. And there was the cloud and the darkness; and the night passed without one coming near the other all night." -- Exodus

The delay ("the night passed") is difficult to allow physically if this were an extra-terrestrial arc traveling west with a rotation of the Earth. And this certainly would not have happened at night. The arc from Venus could only happen during daytime. It is possible that the day had extended into the night hours, as a number of nations recall. This would be due to the gyroscopic reaction torque twisting the axis of the Earth in a circle to compensate for the initial shock from Venus. China complained of the Sun not setting for some 5 or 10 days.

It is interesting to consider where the axis of the torque of the gyroscopic reaction might have intersected the Earth's surface. This had to be near the equator to be at right angle to the rotational axis. Five days of sunlight in China can only mean that the Earth had tilted over so far that the North Pole faced the Sun. As the Earth rotated, large portions the northern hemisphere, including China, would have remained in daylight.

The Exodus narrative claims the arc appeared near northern Egypt and to have come to a standstill. This could have happened as the rotational axis of Earth started to move to an upright position again. It would have to be daylight, however, and the region would have faced the Sun in order to experience the arc. The arc could have been located in the Mediterranean, for a continuous arc on land would have bored gigantic holes, and been very destructive. Placing the arc in the Mediterranean also suggests the spectacle of water standing up to the heavens, except that it would have been steam rising thousands of miles up, not water. Except for the drowning of the Pharaoh's troops, there is no notice of a flood of cascading water.

So, despite what Exodus claims, it was daytime in Egypt when the arc appeared. The darkness may have been from dust electrically removed from the surface and whipped up by the tornado winds surrounding the arc, to be levitated electrically by the magnetic field surrounding the arc. Tornadoes operate exactly in this manner. But the length of days and night were in disorder, as Iranian myths also claim (notes Velikovsky).

We are thus presented with the spectacle in the Bible, probably with more drama than might be called for. The reported location of the arc could likely have been five hundred miles (800 km) "before" or "behind" but would still have been seen. But at one point it was "in between" the Israelites and the Egyptians. The arc is thus reported to have passed right between the two troops. What a frightful sight that would have been. De Grazia writes:

"Moses could hardly have imagined the horrible immensity of the natural catastrophe. A legend recites that the plague of hail in Egypt had [also] *brought great famine to Jethro's Midianites* [in the Sinai]. *Upon arriving in his 'promised land'* [Moses had not originally meant to move to the Sinai] *there was little left there but parched earth, dry water holes, flaming mountains, and, Thank God, Yahweh. By now Moses and the*

leaders must have known that they could go nowhere until they were in better shape all-around and the natural forces had become subdued."

"By that time, Moses must have been as fanatically possessed as any man could be, insane with the problems of a people clinging only to hope and staring wild-eyed and worshipfully at alternative hopes. Whatever he did had to be quite mad. But what he did was rational unto the occasion. He insisted upon his obsessions. He exercised his talents, and those of the Levites and Aaron, and all the capabilities of his instruments.

"He worked Yahweh, the Lord, furiously, wrenching from this Great Father Figure concession after concession, arrangement after arrangement, law upon law, giving up in the end only his right to cross the Jordan River into the Promised Land [Canaan]."
-- Alfred de Grazia

In the Desert

The actual crossing of the "sea of reeds" has been disputed endlessly by scholars and bible exegetes. It doesn't really matter if nearly all of this sea-crossing description in Exodus was taken from the event of 2349 BC. It probably has little bearing on the overall narrative which is about a people escaping from the servitude of one religious observance and adopting a new and more consistent alternative.

With the previous electric contact by Venus in 2193 BC, the atmosphere had been heavily charged with electricity, although steadily decreasing over time. All along priests had been taking advantage of the atmospheric electric charge as a sign of the presence and favor of the Gods. This was a real phenomenon. Recall that Abraham in his sacrifice of a ram discovered he had no way to light his fire, but God ignited the kindling for him. This practice dates far back into remote antiquity, although all we have are more recent descriptions which only hint at the fact that offerings on altars on high places would ignite themselves.

Aurochs horns had traditionally been used at altars to ignite the flame with electric arcing. But this is the Bronze Age and altars were now clad in bronze with bronze horns. This material conducted much better than cattle horns on stone platforms and overcame the mounting deficiency in the atmospheric electric charge.

After completing the Ark, the Israelites build an altar for offerings. It is made of wood sheathed in thin bronze, with bronze horns at the four corners, facing in towards each other. Yahweh provides the plans. Moses asks Yahweh, "Will it not melt?" There was difficulty getting it to light, but once a spark generated between the horns it stayed lit for over 100 years.

The *Midrashim* records that, when the building of the Ark was completed, the sky stopped moving. The contact with Venus had disturbed the axis of the Earth, causing the spin axis of Earth to sweep through a loop. The sky came to a complete rest a year and a month after the Israelites passed through the Red Sea (Ussher).

The Moving Sky

The "moving sky" relates only to how the dome of the stars was seen with respect to the horizon. Or it could have been determined by where the Sun rose and set -- one has to assume that even with a heavy overcast, at least the Sun was noticed.

The movement of the stars, on the other hand, would change only as the result of a change in the inclination of the axis of rotation to the orbit of Earth. No other change will make the stars look like they have moved (except, of course, the daily rotation of the Earth). Because of the immense distances to the stars, the stars will look the same no matter what orbit Earth takes around the Sun. It is possible, although unlikely, that the Earth's rotational axis kept up its corrective gyroscopic maneuver for a year and a month.

The repulsive impact was close to the equator, and resulted in the largest displacement of Earth that we have a record of. Venus was half as far away as in 2349 BC, which would have doubled the force of the impact. But the gyroscopic reaction torque was much slighter than usual, moving the arc contact up only 30 degrees in latitude and 180 degrees in longitude (from mid-Pacific to Egypt), in the time span of a half rotation of the Earth.

However, a number of anomalous circumstances might be explained if we assume that the gyroscopic reaction torque completely or almost completely inverted the Earth. Then it might take a considerable amount of time to rectify the location of the rotational axis of the Earth in space. But this was not likely to have happened. It only appeared to be such. We can blame the lack of light and the change in climate for people to have reached this conclusion.

One of the anomalies was the reports that winter followed spring, which would be true for an inversion, but also if the correction took a year. But an extensive cloud cover, and the relocation of the Earth to 30 percent more distant from the Sun would certainly result in the same impression.

The numerous citations by Velikovsky of the interchange of north and south, and especially east and west, in the support of an inversion of Earth, simply do not apply to whatever might actually have happened in 1492 BC. I have quoted many of these in the Appendix "Polar Relocations Disputed," with comments added to explain all of them. We are generally dealing either with exaggerations of a catastrophic condition, or a complete misreading of statements from the more remote past, like the following from *Worlds in Collision*:

The *Ipuwer* manuscript reads, "The land turned *over* like a potter's wheel."

But that makes no sense. Potter wheels do not turn over, and the quotation was altered by Velikovsky to include the word "over." Velikovsky also quotes a pyramid text as *"the luminary* [Velikovsky's words] *ceased to live in the occident, and shines, a new one, in the orient."* The pyramid texts date to after 2350 BC, so this is not concerned with the period of the Exodus. The text, in fact, describes the changes in 3147 BC -- typical of Egyptian spells, this is not a narrative concerned with the event of 2349 BC, only the remembered event from the remote past. The "new one" here is Jupiter, which rose in the east, replacing Saturn which had stood in the northwest, and brightened at nightfall in the northwest before traveling east below the polestar.

The extensive cloud cover is still a concern, for the notice of a generation "growing up in darkness" or the Bible complaint about "walking in the shadow of death," would presume that the stars could not be seen. However, the Sun and Moon might certainly be seen, and these would only indicate that the sky was moving in unexpected ways.

In any case, it could not be guaranteed that the Earth would return to its original inclination. Thus it is likely that the 30 degree inclination of the rotational axis dates from this event. My earlier suggestion in the Chapter "Pyramids and Henges" is that the Earth's initial axial inclination was 25.2 degrees.

Gyroscopic reactions are relatively gentle. Even an inversion would not be noticed by humans, except for the relocation of the Sun and Moon in the sky (and climatic changes), and no landmasses would be subjected to earthquakes or even tremors -- only those which absorbed the initial external impulse force. All the talk by any number of catastrophists (besides Warlow, de Grazia comes to mind) about splashing oceans, tsunamis, and crashing mountains is largely imagined. [note 28]

The Ark of Yahweh

Alfred de Grazia gives the following explanation of how the Ark worked, although he has it wrong:

"The ground ark, unlike the pyramid or mountain altar, makes its own divine fire. It does not depend upon a single point high up to provide the electrical discharge. In a small machine, grounded by one pole and pointed to the sky at the opposing pole, the two being insulated from each other, an opposing charge is accumulated at the poles and, when sufficiently charged, the poles exchange a spark, a light, a divine fire. Unlike the pyramid, or mountain, the Ark can be moved to where its sources of strength are greatest and its effects can be most affective for psychological or other purposes."
    -- Alfred de Grazia

However, the Ark operated as a device using static electricity, not as an electric circuit. There is no need to electrically isolate the two cherubim. They will arc between their wing tips even if electrically connected. Rather than using stone and an extremely high location, the Ark would have displayed Saint Elmo's fire because it was made of metal and set on a clear flat space. The Ark depended on being a highly conductive object set on a grounded flat plane and thus, in effect, a lightning arrester. When the ground was soaked with water, the minerals in the ground would turn the surrounding area into a conducting surface. When transported at a later date from Shiloh to Jerusalem, the Ark was temporarily located on a "threshing floor" to keep it operational. It was a matter of finding a location where the ground was flat and conductive.

Moreover, it can be suggested from the construction details that, in effect, the Ark was a Leyden jar, a large capacitor, which means that it could store enormous electric charges (at a potential of 10,000 or more volts). Not just a Leyden jar, but more like a *Van de Graaff* generator. A *Van de Graaff* generator is generally constructed as a metal sphere, where a trickle of static electric charges is introduced to the interior through an opening. The delivered charge accumulates at the interior of the sphere. This induces a charge of opposite polarity on the exterior, allowing the delivered charges to be continuously accepted. A *Van de Graaff* generator is able to hold large charges at very high voltages.

When current, in the form of Saint Elmo's fire, passed through the exterior of the Ark, an opposite charge would accumulate on the gold-plated interior of the box. This would build up a nearly unlimited interior charge which would make the exterior even more positively charged. In this manner the Ark must have attracted an unusual amount of static electricity as a stream of plasma from the upper atmosphere. Yahweh showed himself at the intersection of the wingtips of the hovering cherubim, sparking and hissing his name -- "Yahweh, Yahweh, Yahweh." [note 29]

The continuous arc would have generated ultraviolet radiation. There are many reported cases of UV burns, including Moses. The arc would also generate X-rays. The Ark was kept in an unroofed double tent, a curtained enclosure -- the Tabernacle. Yahweh could not be casually looked at. The attending priests shaved themselves and wore protective garments and face masks, "lest they die." A number of persons were electrocuted by touching the Ark, some accidentally and some on purpose. Both of Aaron's sons died by electrocution. De Grazia suggests that part of Moses's additional "magic" displays may have consisted of chemical censers used near the Ark, specifically sulfur and phosphorus, which could also lead to chemical burns. [note 30]

The Ark was often carried far ahead of the people in the desert. At night a visible stream of light would rise like a beacon from the Ark. During the day it would look like a diffuse cloud column. This was the column which went before the Israelites day and night. It was a function of the exceedingly high atmospheric electric charge, as might be expected since the Earth had received a recent electric discharge from Venus.

The pillar of fire at night was a visible column of plasma at glow level (not at arc level) connecting the ground plane to the upper atmosphere via the two angels on top of the Ark. During the day this would look more like a column of smoke -- an effect which may have been augmented by the censers of the Tabernacle. The smoke would ionize and outline the plasma, even at dark mode level. Only at the wing tips of the angels was the flow of electricity concentrated enough to go into arc mode. The Israelites followed a forty-year path of connected conductive regions in their wanderings. Rest periods would result when the humidity lowered and the column disappeared (and when cattle and sheep needed grazing). The column would reappear when the overhead conditions changed. (Further below I will suggest another source for the image of a column of light and smoke.) [note 31]

Other nations might very well not have noticed that, under these new conditions, a simple metal box with up-pointed spikes set on a grounded plane would do what in previous years had required tall stone structures. As a weapon of war, the Ark would have been seen by the enemy as the approach of the God of the Israelites -- frightening the inhabitants of besieged cities and the troops of opposing armies. The visible acts of Gods were undisputed in antiquity.

When the Ark was moved to the temple at Jerusalem in 900 BC, after having been outside in a tent on the plain of Shiloh for 512 years, the displays of static electricity had declined noticeably. The electric display may have started to falter. Josephus says the electric fire stopped in the first century BC -- after 1400 years.

The Psychosis of Yahweh

De Grazia dismisses the concepts of a developing subjective consciousness suggested by Julian Jaynes. De Grazia writes, "Jaynes was not able to cope with the historical materials, largely because he relied upon conventional chronology." De Grazia dismisses the whole concept of the bicameral mind. As he states:

"In reality it was the catastrophes of the world whose terrible stresses made hallucinatory leaders out of borderline cases and staunch believers out of normal people."
-- Alfred de Grazia [note 32]

This serves to support de Grazia's extensive analysis of the politics of the exodus and the psychology of Moses. But as Jaynes had warned, de Grazia is unable to distinguish a bicameral mind from a fully functional human and de Grazia's description of Yahweh reads almost exactly like a bicameral Moses. Yahweh *is* Moses, but as the separate right hemisphere of his mind. In effect Moses had a split personality. This is, in fact, how Jaynes defines the bicamerality of the mind -- the independence of the right hemisphere which can guide the verbal left hemisphere and which, in earlier times, would order the other half around verbally. Even today the right hemisphere imposes itself completely on schizophrenic individuals. The rest of us, having learned to silence the voices, still frequently hear the right hemisphere as the unvoiced utterings of *oughts* and *shoulds* -- "close the door," "turn off the light," "do you have your keys?" Moses, as a pre-conscious human, was guided in what he did by the right hemisphere of his mind and experienced this as a separate "being" who spoke to him.

When de Grazia writes, as above, "it was the catastrophes [which] made hallucinatory leaders out of borderline cases," he is entirely correct in that the events of the period were certainly stressful, but those are also the conditions which foster subjective consciousness. Jaynes has noted (without any reference to worldwide catastrophes) that this period saw the first light of subjective consciousness in individuals, first in bemoaning the failing presence of the Gods and their guidance, and then as a reaction to the press of strangers. These were only two facets in the series of unpredictable events and novel conditions which changed us as humans. The only "evolutionary" solution was to engender the ability to imagine what might happen in these new situations.

Moses certainly had the imagination and ability to organize the exodus from Egypt of a large group of people and keep it organized under exceedingly difficult conditions. (Josephus claimed, in the first century AD, that Moses had previously led a military expedition to Ethiopia.) The only thing that he failed to imagine, much later, was the actual entry into Canaan and the whole new set of problems and conditions to be dealt with in the conquest and settlement of this new land. Forty years earlier the voice of Yahweh had driven him; by the time he reached Canaan, Yahweh had gone silent. Moses dawdled endlessly, and eventually it cost him his life. [note 33]

Allow me to quote from de Grazia extensively, for his source document, the second book of Exodus, is important. The writing in Exodus is personal without being self-serving, and is a rare window on an age which changed humanity. The nexus of catastrophe and the human mind, desperately seeking to resolve the unpredictable, is key to understanding how we, within the next thousand years, became fully human -- that is, how we evolved subjective consciousness and started teaching this to our children, silencing the demanding and controlling right hemisphere, and, most importantly, how we came to rely upon the imagined spaces of consciousness in the left hemisphere to help us live in the changing world.

> "The abrupt commands of Yahweh, his great noises, curses, and marvelously clear consultative advice enrich the verses of the Books of Moses. The lack of explanation is typical of both hallucinatory voices and of Yahweh's words."
>
> "Yahweh says and Yahweh does. What he says consists of describing himself, expressing his emotions, relating what he has done, instructing as to what must be done, and foretelling what he will do."
>
> "All that Yahweh says is in an absolutely authoritative mode. This includes those expressions which comment upon behavior that is against his will or interests."
>
> "What Yahweh does, supplementing what he says, is to cause all things to happen, even expressions of disobedience coming out of 'free will,' in the sense that if he wished to do so, he could make people will what he wanted them to will."
>
> "He even asserts a power to be bad, to do evil. He is not bound by notions of good or evil. 'Who makes peace and creates evil, I Yahweh do all this.'"

These observations by de Grazia are completely archetypal and descriptive of the right hemisphere of the brain, and you will recognize them instantly if you are familiar with Jaynes's research on schizophrenia, hypnosis, talking in tongues, complex automatic activities, and the narratives of antiquity.

> "Yahweh writes; he organizes lists or rules; he keeps books; and

little else that is technical; he is the product, not the fountainhead of the science of Moses."

"Write this in your book," Yahweh commands Moses. The organization of lists and rules is also archetypal of schizophrenia, but the phrase "little else that is technical" is not quite fair. Typical of a right hemispherical presence -- the hallucinating voice -- Yahweh is quite accomplished technically. He explains to Moses the new calendar. Moses has to return to Yahweh with questions, for he does not understand. It is Yahweh who designs the Ark, and sets all the safety requirements for the attending priests, their clothes, the procedures, the curtained tents, and all the altar appurtenances.

However, it is certainly correct to say that Yahweh was "the product of the science of Moses." As with us, the right hemisphere of Moses's brain had access to all that he had learned, and as with us, the right hemisphere could draw together physical concepts and synthesize disparate parts into a working whole -- in short, solve problems -- and then deliver the solutions to the conscious left hemisphere, as if out of thin air. And Yahweh is quite well aware of what problems Moses is capable of solving without help. At one point Yahweh demands an Ark design with red, blue, black, and white fire. Moses asks how this might be done, and Yahweh, in a fashion absolutely typical of the annoyance often displayed by the right hemisphere today, answers, "I fabricate my glory; you make your own colors."

De Grazia took this anecdote from a secondary source which quoted some Midrash tradition. The Midrash is the collected Jewish commentary on the Bible, originally oral, but reduced to writing after the second century AD. It thus constitutes a comment some 1600 years after the Exodus.

The colors, except for blue, are the same directional colors as will be found in the Maya *Chilam Balam*, which suggest that these are the four fires of the cardinal directions, "the four ancient khu's who dwell in the hair of Horus," or, as the *Chilam Balam* has it, the four directional trees. As I have already suggested in previous chapters, these are likely to be the polar plasma plumes in the north and south, and the edges of Van Allen belts in the east and the west.

The colors here match the colors of the trees of the cardinal directions described by the Maya, except that blue is substituted for the Maya's yellow of the south. (I am assuming that the order of the colors follows the rotation among the compass points.) The assignment of colors to compass points also occurs in China, in Central Asia, and among North American and Central American tribes. No two sets of colors are assigned to cardinal points the same way, however.

As Jaynes points out, it is a transitional period. The attendant visual hallucinations have disappeared -- God no longer strolls with Adam in the cool of the evening. Yahweh has become a disembodied voice. Only one time does Moses speak face to face with Yahweh. Fifty years later Joshua is spoken at, rather than spoken to by Yahweh. "At times Joshua is so uncertain he has to cast lots." [note 34]

The Third Return of the Axis Mundi

As the Earth increased its orbit in 1492 BC, it would again have to adjust its electric charge to its new location. Again the *axis mundi* appeared in the north and in the south. Peculiar to the south was the fact that in 2349 BC the polar plume had risen directly (or nearly so) out of the gap in the Absu, standing next to the blazing image of Jupiter. I detailed this resurrection of Jupiter in a previous chapter. In the narrative of Exodus this imagery is understood as Moses holding up his staff to keep the waters of the Red Sea parted. (This is the shepard's crook of the pharaohs also.)

About the northern polar plasma plume, Milton Zysman suggested in 1994 (at a Velikovsky Symposium), that the pillar followed by the Israelites for 40 years was an extended aurora. He wrote, about Velikovsky's developing causal theory:

"Since meteoric showers, great and small, are understood to be debris entrained by comets, Velikovsky took the next logical step by gleaning the Bible and associated Talmudic sources for evidence of a comet during Exodus and Joshua."

"It was then that the 'mysterious pillar' became the tail of the protoplanet Venus."

So claims Zysman, and continues, quoting Velikovsky:

"Because of the proximity of the Earth, the comet left its own orbit and for a while followed the orbit of the Earth. The great ball of the comet retreated, then again approached the Earth, shrouded in a dark column of gases which looked like a pillar of smoke during the day and of fire by night and the Earth once more passed through the atmosphere of the comet, this time at its neck."

Zysman commented on this as follows:

"It has been for some time this author's opinion that this 'mysterious pillar' is not a comet's tail, but the Earth's north and south magnetic poles illuminated by the joint action of electric discharge and the commingling of Earthly and cometary gases. In other words, a giant

aurora."

A plume of plasma in glow mode at the magnetic poles would be a much more likely candidate. Auroras don't behave like polar pillars. I have already described the polar plume as extending 20 Earth diameters up into the plasmasphere (160,000 miles, 260,000 km), and thus visible from anywhere on Earth. Auroras do not extend more than 300 miles (500 km) above the surface of the Earth and do not assume the shape of pillars. The coloration of auroras is limited to the atmosphere and stratosphere, where Oxygen and Nitrogen are encountered. Zysman is correct, however, in locating this at the magnetic pole.

The pillar shows up in the mythology and legends of many people, although with some sparsity, for the column did not do anything. It was just there. The suggestion, today, that these recollected columns only refer to the Saturnian planetary polar configuration from prior to 3147 BC is an error, for the polar columns were seen again and again in antiquity. Only the terse history of the world recalled in the Maya *Chilam Balam* books is specific about how many times that occurred. The four trees which hold up the sky, and are said to commemorate the previous destructions of the world, appear three times, after 3147 BC, after 2349 BC, and after 1492 BC, each time after the massive "destruction of the world." The "destructions," as listed by the *Chilam Balam*, can be dated to match information from the Eastern Mediterranean region. (As mentioned earlier, ballcourt markers from Copan suggest nine appearances of the northern plume, seven for the southern plume.)

In addition, the *Chilam Balam*, in its severely abbreviated history of the world, categorizes the event of 1492 BC, from the translation by Ralph L. Roys, as follows:

> *"But it was (over) the whole world that Ah Uuc Cheknal* [he who fertilizes the maize seven times] *was set up. He came from the seventh stratum of the earth, when he came to fecundate Itzam-kab-ain,* [the Earth] *when he came with the vitality of the angle between earth (and) heaven."*

Roys suggests another translation of the last line ("when he came ...") which reads, "then he descended while the heavens rubbed against the earth." This looks like the sixth appearance of the "Celestial Cow" -- with the Van Allen belts in glow mode.

During Moses's 40-day absence, while he was communing with God on the Mountain of the Law Giving, Aaron manufactured the Golden Calf idol for the impatient Israelites. *"Here are thy gods, Israel, the gods that rescued thee from the land of Egypt"* -- Exodus 32:4. ("Elohim" for "gods".) The calf did not last long, for when Moses returned from the mountain, he destroyed the Golden Calf. This may be an indication of how long the Celestial Cow stood in the skies after first appearing sometime after 1492 BC.

The Golden Calf, as the Hathor Cow, was an Egyptian false Goddess to Moses. Which may also be why it did not last very long. When Moses came down from the Mountain, he carried the Ten Commandments, all the laws, and all the design details of the Ark of the Covenant which was to be the seat of the God of Israel. He destroyed the Golden Calf.

In the third year after leaving Egypt, God orders Moses to create a brass serpent mounted on a pole -- as a medical device to be used to cure snakebites. This brass snake lasted 800 hundred years. Hezekiah finally destroyed it after 700 BC. [note 35]

Of all likely possibilities, the snake as representing the north polar plume seems most likely. Inadvertent research by NASA have discovered the polar plumes to consist of dual (entwined) plasma columns. We can suggest from the three-year delay, that this hints at how long the polar plasma plumes may have lasted.

Zysman suggests that the "column" which lighted the night and marked the north for Israel during wanderings in the wilderness, was important enough to have been additionally venerated in the temple of Jerusalem 500 years later. He writes:

"It may have evaded the scrutiny of even the most assiduous Velikovskians that there is very little direct evidence for the appearance of a comet during both the Exodus and the Joshua stories. All the indicators of a great meteoric shower are in place and it can be argued that any well-informed tribal leader or court magician would have little trouble inferring its involvement, yet we have no specific mention of a comet being observed before or during the event."

Let me comment on that.

There is specific mention of a "comet," but only by those people who saw the display. Most of the world saw nothing, apparently even India, where the arc may have traveled partway through the Indian Ocean and produced vast amounts of steam and water vapor. The Greeks, not directly affected by the arc or needing to worry about their own survival, saw Typhon. (On the other hand, the later strike at the time of Joshua could have landed anywhere on Earth to produce the catapulted rocks and bolides.)

I doubt very much if this was an asteroid shower so extreme that people throughout the regions migrated *en masse* for that reason -- the Greeks (Ionians), Dorians, Phrygians, Carians, Lycians in the Eastern Mediterranean, the Mitanni, Hyksos, Hebrews, Kassites, Persians, in the Near East, and the Central Asiatics into Pakistan, India, and regions north of the Himalayas. What were all these people fleeing from? Ice cubes and snowballs falling from the sky? Such a shower never returned, yet the migrations continued for hundreds of years.

Primarily they were all attempting to escape from the dreadful climate which followed on 1492 BC. Over the next hundred years the grass of the steppes turned brown, the central lakes of Asia dried up and turned into deserts. They headed for what they knew to be the fruitful agricultural lands of the civilized nations which were largely unprotected. Joshua did the same.

Joshua and Jericho

As the cloud cover starts to lift, and after forty years of wandering with their herds throughout Arabia, the Israelites started the invasion of Canaan from the east. They crossed the Jordan on a dry bed, for an earthquake had just blocked the river with a fallen bank. It was seen as a display of the favor of their God. During this period earthquakes still occurred frequently.

The walls of Jericho also fell because of an earthquake. The Israelites had walked the Ark of the Covenant around the city for seven days. When the Ark lit up in response to the subsurface piezoelectric effects generated before the earthquake, they knew that the walls of Jericho would fall and the Israelites blew their trumpets as the shifting Earth also started to squeal. [note 36]

The Israelites proceeded with the invasion of Canaan, a war which would take 14 years. Near the end, in about the 12th year, Joshua orders the Sun to stand still in the heavens for the span of a day to allow completion of a battle. During the same battle stones fell from heaven.

> *"And the Lord cast down great stones from heaven upon* [the Canaanites]; *they were more which died from hail stones than they whom the children of Israel slew with the sword."*
> -- Joshua 10:11

This happened, it is estimated, in 1440 BC, 50 or 52 years after the exodus, and is the second time in this era that Venus made electric contact with Earth and exchanged a plasma discharge. We do not know where the strike connected to Earth. Explosively launched rocks from an arc striking on land, rather than the sea, can travel immense distances and even be ejected from Earth. The "great stones from heaven" may have come from anywhere on Earth. [note 37]

Eva Danelius, in "Did Thutmose III Despoil the Temple in Jerusalem?" in *Journal of the SIS* (1977/78), also retells her experiences at Gibeon:

According to the [Septuagint] version "the Lord struck them (the Amorites) with a panic, on account of the children of Israel, and the Lord routed them, with a great slaughter, at Gibeon. And they [the Israelites] pursued them by the way of the ascent of Oronim, and smote them. .. And as they were fleeing from before Israel, at the descent of Oronim, the Lord poured a storm of hailstones from heaven upon them... so that there were more who died by the hailstones, than the children of Israel slew with the sword in battle."

Josephus, in about AD 100, adds "the discharge of thunderbolts and the descent of hail of more than ordinary magnitude."

The Pharaoh [Thutmose III] obviously spent the night at Beth Horon the Nether (today: Beith 'Ur et-Tachta), right at the entrance to the dangerous part of the defile, which is already in the mountains. The next morning, according to the Annals [at Karnak] (lines 58/9), "My majesty proceeded northward carrying my father Amon [lacuna] before me...."

Danelius adds:

This is the only instance I know of in Egyptian records where we are told that statues or images of the gods were carried into battle, as the Hebrews carried the ark.

What kind of fear had gripped the Pharaoh that he felt it necessary to take this precaution? Why did he take it here, and only here, once in a lifetime? The objective difficulties of the way ahead of the army were considerably less than those which had confronted, and been overcome by, the Egyptian army in [Ethiopia], where mountains 10,000 feet (3000 meters) high rose sheer above narrow canyons filled by torrential streams.

Danelius had received a bolide of the type that apparently had fallen "at that time and place, according to the Biblical record" from H. H. Nininger, founder and director of the American Meteorite Museum.

She continues with:

When I showed the aerolite to the stonemasons working by the roadside at 'Ur et-Tachta (Beith Horon the Nether), they immediately recognised it: "Hajar min 'Allah!" ("A stone from Allah," i.e. from heaven), they exclaimed. According to them, the slope going down into the wadi, and the wadi itself "the going down to Beth-Horon" of the Bible, were full of stones like the one in my hand. The same answer I got from the teachers at the local schools.

Though this cannot be called conclusive, the amazing familiarity of the local Arabs with the phenomenon of meteorites seems to justify the conclusion that the Biblical story is based on reality. As Nininger [of the American Meteorite Museum] and other experts have abundantly proved, meteorite falls have been known and remembered for centuries among local populations, and more often than not considered intervention of the God(s) in human affairs. And here we meet with a second conception of those times: the understanding that there was a metaphysical connection between a God, His people, and His land.

Thutmose was not afraid of a human enemy but was reluctant to enter a road where "The God of the Land" had intervened, from heaven, to help His people; and Thutmose perfectly understood the motivation of his officers who preferred one of the other defiles, and neither blamed them nor punished them, but let them choose. And this fear, too, explains why he had the standard of "his father Amon" carried before him: Amon was a meteorite god, able to protect his children from a calamity similar to that suffered by the five Amorite kings.

Velikovsky, who estimated the date of 1440 BC, had some problems bridging the gap between the exodus and the order by Joshua for the Sun to stand still, feeling the need to span 52 years, which is a figure he derived from Mesoamerican sources. Celebrations of the renewal of creation in Mesoamerica were based on 52 "Tun" years, which varied with the calendar in use. But after 1492 BC the actual period between apparent close "approaches" of Venus was 50 or 51 solar years. The actual event of Joshua thus occurred in 1442 BC (1492 less 50). Details are given in Appendix B, "Celestial Mechanics."

I suspect that the arc may have traveled through mainland Asia and towards Europe, and may have touched Mesoamerica. Part of the travel must again have been through oceans, for the cloud cover again returned -- so say Mesoamerican sources. For a second time in quick succession, Mesoamerican culture suffered destruction. The Olmecs recognized the agent involved and took note of the interval since the previous catastrophe. The end of the world would now be expected every 52 Tun years on the Olmec calendar. A day was assigned in the 260-day Tzolkin calendar to correspond to a day in the new 360-day Haab calendar. This day combination would repeat only once every 52 calendar "years" and once every 52 years all of Mesoamerica trembled in fear awaiting sunrise or doom. In Mesoamerica the travels of Venus, as Quetzalcoatl, the feathered serpent, continued to be watched and recorded with great anxiety for the next 3000 years. Venus approached Earth numerous additional times during the coming centuries, but without striking. [note 38]

Abandoned by the Gods

It was a transitional period not only for the Israelites, who would continue to cling to their one God, but also for other peoples, who felt abandoned by their many Gods of old. Mercury seemed to have remained. Mars possibly was not seen since it had no magnetic field or atmosphere to support a coma. Mercury's duties (as Thoth of the Egyptians) were extended to include creation and guide for the dead.

The period after 1500 BC saw mass migrations of tribes in Southeastern Europe, Greece, Anatolia, Iran, and the Arabian peninsula. The volcano on the island of Thera in the Aegean explodes during this period, sending a tsunami 600 feet (200 meters) high towards the coast of Greece and Asia Minor. The harbors and quays of Crete, just south of Thera, sank below the level of the ocean.

As Jaynes suggested, this period also saw the first glimmer of subjective consciousness -- the effect of the widespread catastrophes, mass movement of peoples, and the loss of the familiar commands and admonitory voices of the Gods. It is also the start of our current religious beliefs. Like abandoned children, mankind took the blame for the leave-taking of the Gods and the silencing of the voices. Supplications to the Gods and pleadings for forgiveness first appear in extant documents at this time (that is, after 1200 BC), as do devils and evil spirits, and the search for significant omens. This attitude toward the Gods is conspicuously absent before this period. A superstition of spells and magic starts to envelop the Middle East. [note 39]

In Mesoamerica, pleading with the Gods includes the periodic destruction of temples and monuments and their rebuilding or overbuilding. This starts after about 1300 BC by the Olmecs and continues into the era just prior to the arrival of the Spanish in AD 1500. We have to presume that the bloodletting, which so characterized Mexico at the time of the Spanish arrival, also had its genesis at this time, although I will suggest later that this probably started after 685 BC.

Fifteen hundred years earlier, mankind had been cast from Paradise but had been sustained by the guiding voices of the Gods. As subjective consciousness bloomed in response to the catastrophes of 1500 BC, and especially to the disorder of wandering tribes, the voices disappeared. Laments for the loss of the personal Gods were added to the literature of the Middle East after 1300 and 1200 BC. They are echoed in the oldest book of the Bible, Job, as in the *Ludlul bel Nemegi*.

My God has forsaken me and disappeared,
My Goddess has failed me and keeps a distance,

The good angel who walked beside me has departed.
    -- Shubshi-Meshre-Shakkan in *Ludlul bel Nemegi*, Mesopotamia,
13th century BC

Endnotes

Note 1 --

Middle Eastern dating is based on comparison of pottery and other objects with Egyptian wares. This dating in turn is based on the various fragments we have of the list of dynasties and pharaohs prepared by Manetho in Ptolemaic Egypt. The original text is lost, but it is quoted partially by many authors in antiquity. The chronological sequence was set out in the 19th century, and is incorrect by about 400 to 600 years, mainly the period of 1200 to 700 BC. Thus the archaeological date of 1200 BC, when all cultural activity in the Middle East came to a sudden halt, is actually 800 BC.

This accounts for a gap in the archaeology of Greece called the "Dark Ages of Greece," after which material culture (of the Mycenaean Greeks) picks up in 700 BC exactly where it left off in 1200 BC. This missing era includes such quasi-mythological adventures as the Trojan War, the exploration of the Black Sea by Jason, and the Dorian invasion. The "Dark Ages of Greece" extends to all of the Middle East. The Greek and Roman historians of 2000 years ago disagree completely with this chronology.

As P. John Crowe, wrote in "The Revision of Ancient History" (*SIS Conference*, 1999):

"Archaeology, when interpreted with an open mind, has now actually proved beyond reasonable doubt that the Dark Ages did not exist, but the proof is ignored. Vested interest in the status quo has won the day. Huge amounts of public money are being spent on studying this Victorian invention, and hundreds of books written about them without resolving their historicity. Sadly, it seems no one in academia has had the courage publicly to question seriously the basic assumptions upon which Egyptian chronology, the progenitor of the Dark Ages, is founded."

Many archaeologists prefer pottery shard dating over Carbon-14 dating, especially because inspection of shards is much less expensive and Carbon-14 dating was entirely destructive until recently. If the dating by pottery shards is correct, it should also be more accurate (if the pottery dates don't hinge on a fictional chronology), for there is an almost complete year by year known sequence of, for example, amphora used in the wine trade by the cities of export.

I originally suggested that Hutchinson must have used Carbon-14 dating, so that the approximate dates of 1400 BC and 700 BC could be accepted. But this, I now realize, is a coincidental extension of the "Dark Ages of Greece," although the quoted dates of 1400 BC and 700 BC fit my narrative of the incident of circa 1500 BC. Alfred de Grazia, in *The Iron Age of Mars* (2nd ed. 2009), concurs that these dates may indeed reflect the devastation by Venus in circa 1492 BC and the later destruction by Mars starting in 806 BC.

Note 2 --

As an example of an 8th-century BC destruction, consider the excavation of Troy (Hisarlik). Four- to six-foot deep layers of burned material were found here, as in many other cities (citadels). No ashes from forest fires or from a volcanic eruption have ever exceeded six inches. This suggests simultaneous forest fires and hurricane winds. It suggests, in fact, the deposition of wind-carried burnt materials, including soils, specifically to hilltop locations.

Note 3 --

Using the kinetic energy of Earth based on the forward orbital speed (only), the change of 1500 BC amounted to four times the change (loss) in energy of either 3147 BC or 2349 BC. The disturbances of 747 BC, by comparison, represent a change of only 1/8th the magnitude of 3147 BC.

Note 4 --

I have probably overemphasized Quetzalcoatl for Mesoamerica, except as recognized from his properties. With the Mexica, at the time of the Spanish invasion, Quetzalcoatl did not have much standing. Not so, however, with the Maya.

Neith probably represents the southern ball plasmoid first seen in 10,900 BC. The crossed arrows (or shuttles) used as her identifying name represent the beams of electrons shooting like arrows past Earth.

Note 5 --

Seven approaches by Venus are noted in the Maya *Chilam Balam*, of which four can be assigned to the period of 2349 BC to 2193 BC. This is also the only period of time when the interval between approaches was actually 52 solar years.

There is good reason to believe that the orbit of Venus crossed the orbit of

Earth until 1492 BC, but not afterward. In 1994, Lynn Rose and Raymond Vaughan calculated, on the basis the Assyrian clay tablets known as the *Venus Tablets of Ammizaduga*, dating to the 7th century BC, that the eccentricities of the orbits of Venus and Earth were still 0.15 and 0.10 respectively before 670 BC (reported at the Kronia Conference, Portland, 1994). This suggests the possibility that in the 7th century these orbits did not cross.

A calculation can be made of the perihelion and the aphelion (the closest and furthest distance from the Sun) of the orbits of Venus and Earth for various estimates of orbits (based on calendar information) since 3147 BC. This reveals that the orbit of Venus could have overrun the orbit of Earth, although this would only happen if the orbits of Venus and Earth precessed (rotated about the Sun) to a relative location around the Sun where the perihelion of Earth coincided with the aphelion of Venus. See Appendix B, "The Celestial Mechanics" for estimates.

Thus in more remote antiquity, at long intervals, and probably for periods of hundreds of years, Venus would appear as a planet on an outer orbit. Rather than remaining within some 30 degrees of the Sun, Venus would move across the night sky from horizon to horizon (rather than to just show in the early evening and before morning), as other planets do. Normally, because of its brilliance, Venus would have been seen during the day also.

This infrequent appearance of Venus beyond the orbit of Earth explains the strange Sumerian legend where Inanna (Venus) visits hell or the netherworld (*Inanna's Descent to the Nether World*). The "netherworld" is the zodiac of the south skies, of course. In the legend she is stripped of her garments (loses her coma and tail), losing one garment at each of seven gates (the rings of the Absu), and her body is hung from a hook (came to a visual standstill), to be rescued later. If Venus moved beyond Earth and further away from the Sun, the coma and plasma tail would certainly reduce. Even moving away from Earth would seem to do this visually. In line with Earth, the tail of Venus would not be seen. The movement through "seven gates" (the Absu) places the story in the southern skies. To be "hung from a hook" implies that a foreshortened plasma tail would have pointed up (or down), away from the location of the Sun 180 degrees removed in the zodiac. But being "hung from a hook" is actually a better simile for the fact that the trajectory of Venus would be slower than that of Earth at this location, and Venus would have been seen in retrograde motion (as Earth passed Venus) and thus seemingly to come to a stop. This happens today with Mars.

Note 6 --

It is suspected by some that Venus might have turned over at this time, so that she started to rotate backwards, as is the case today. I doubt that this happened. As a satellite of Saturn, Venus may never have had much of a spin. The earliest iconography seems to indicate that Venus was already spinning backwards.

Because of Venus's extremely dense atmosphere (almost like an incompressible liquid), it is possible that it did not experience the electric repulsive impulse on one hemisphere, which would have changed its orbit. If the atmospheric shell absorbed the shock, the pressure might have spread entirely around the planet, compressing the more rigid inner sphere of rocky material equally in all directions instead of moving the planet in space. It is also possible that a significant part of the atmosphere was simply blown away from the planet. Venus, in fact, seems to change its orbit very little over the course of 3000 years. See Appendix B, "The Celestial Mechanics" for estimates of the length of the "Venus cycle" from various periods between 2349 BC and today.

Note 7 --

A Pacific Ocean impact might be confused with the Eltanin impact site in the far Southeast Pacific. The Eltanin impact is apparently the only "impact evidence" ever found in an ocean, aside from craters at the continental slopes. The Eltanin impact dates from 2.15 million years ago. This was first detected (in 1955) via ocean bed iridium and displaced diatomic material (ocean bottom sludge). An impact site was determined in 1966 as an 82-mile (132-km) diameter area, in 3-mile-deep (5-km-deep) water. A compressive impact to the ocean, because water is incompressible but very fluid, would leave no evidence aside from tsunami damage to the continents and possible transverse impact to adjacent continental slopes.

The impact of 1492 BC was likely experienced near the equator, since this would have happened "in early spring," as Exodus records. The line extending from the Sun via Venus to the surface impact site would have passed below the center of the Earth, thus moving the southern hemisphere south, that is, away from the Sun. It might be suggested that the very large displacement of the Earth (to a new orbit) was entirely due to the fact that the impact location produced very little of a gyroscopic reaction. Rather than the impact energy being absorbed by a gyroscopic response, it was transmitted directly to the center of the Earth.

Note 8 --

The suggestion that Lake Titicaca was lifted to its present elevation of 12,500 feet through some unspecified catastrophe was made by Velikovsky in *Earth in Upheaval* (1955). The archaeological record would have suggested that this would have happened in historic time, after Tiwanaku (Tiahuanaco) was already built. But the archaeology of this site, the conditions of local agriculture (abandoned terraces at the snow line, sterile conditions, "maize will not ripen"), or geological details (raised beaches, slanted strand lines, marine crustaceans) cannot sustain this. It seems more reasonable to suggest that the Alto Plano and the Andes mountains were raised maybe 3000 or 4000 feet (1000 to 1500 meters) by the intrusion of magma below the established Cordilleras.

What is more convincing is the occupation of the site after 1400 BC and a thorough exploitation of the available agricultural conditions, not the least of which is that the large lake acts as a heat sink -- in a manner also found to be in use on the eastern slopes of the Andes in the same region, resulting in the ability to sustain a population of a half million or more. Tiahuanaco was built after 800 BC. A drought in about AD 1000 ended the preeminence of the site.

It is possible that the Andes moved up in response to the compressive shock in the Pacific. Even though water is an incompressible liquid and the shock would have transferred to the underlying sea bottom, it would also have radiated out from the location of the impact. But I think the occurrence of marine specimens in lakes of the Andes provides the most solid evidence, and that only as evidence of a giant tsunami from the ocean.

Note 9 --

If Venus and Earth were on orbits with radiuses of 0.72 AU and 0.83 AU respectively, which does not allow for the eccentricity of the orbits (see Appendix B, "the Celestial Mechanics" for these values), they would have been traveling at speeds of:

Venus: **2 * pi * 0.72 * AU / 225 = 1.87** million miles per day and
Earth: **2 * pi * 0.83 * AU / 273 = 1.77** million miles per day.

The difference in speed of **100,000 miles per day** would largely determine how long an electric contact would last. If the plasmaspheres of both planets measured about 40 planet diameters, then together they would span about **2 * 40 * 8000 = 640,000 miles**. The total time of the contact would thus be limited to about six days. (On an inner orbit, Venus traveled faster than Earth.)

There was near continuous arcing in 1492 BC, unlike the electric contact in 2349 BC which consisted of discrete plasmoids. But the lifted water vapor which started to cover the skies would have cut short the electric arc. West of the impact location (Asia and North Africa) the arc would have touched down, but after crossing half of the Atlantic, it would have mostly dissipated at the cloud cover which was moving east from the Pacific.

Note 10 --

If Earth and Venus were on circular orbits, they would not have approached closer than 10,000,000 miles, **(0.83 - 0.72) * AU = 10,230,000 miles (16,473,000 km).**

I have used Velikovsky's claim for the "scorched stones" of Arabia. But it might be suggested that this happened in 685 BC, when Assurbanipal notes Venus as "raining fire over Arabia."

Note 11 --

There is a very large secondary literature following up on the hints first supplied by Velikovsky's *Worlds in Collision* (1950). Talbott dismisses Velikovsky's findings, arguing that the "story" of Exodus is largely a formal repetition of elements taken from the events at the end of the "Era of the Gods," but Talbott and his group have never described this ending event. I did.

It is probably true that that older story-constructs were bound to be reused for later events. I have, in fact noted this for the Exodus described in this chapter. It is overwhelmingly obvious.

Velikovsky notes that he had trouble deciding whether to attribute events of 1492 BC to Venus or to Jupiter. He settled on Venus and stated that in the end he was completely convinced. But I am, at times, not completely convinced. Reading *Worlds in Collision* with the development of the Saturnian Theory (as developed in this text) and the plasma information in mind, you will be able to detect when his sources substitute Jupiter for Venus, or when the more likely alternative reading would point to Saturn rather than Jupiter. There are actually sources pointing directly to Jupiter as the agent of destruction, but these are few and probably erroneous, for an electric interaction with Jupiter would have been wildly destructive, as we saw for the event at the start of the Younger Dryas.

More frequently Velikovsky uses sources which are obviously from the 8th and 7th century BC, and applies them to the events surrounding the Exodus of 1492 BC. This includes quotations from the Hebrew prophets, the 7th or 6th century *Zend-Avesta*, quotations from Assurbanipal which are obviously contemporaneous with his reign, and the use of the *Venus Tablets of Ammizaduga*. Unlike the misidentification of Jupiter for Saturn, these are more serious faults.

I also have objections to the frequent application of "modern physical understanding" to ancient texts when these texts are not at all clear. Velikovsky tends to read many phenomena as "meteors" when in fact this is often completely unwarranted from the textual descriptions, and the phenomena would better be left as unexplained. Frequently also texts are taken to be metaphorical (analogical) understandings, which seems totally uncalled for.

Similarly with a number of quotations to the effect that dawn and sunset were interchanged at this time. In fact, if you turn the spinning globe of the Earth upside down, you will find that the sun still rises in the east. Similarly, the period of increased night or day is due only to a change in the location of the Earth's axis. Spin does not stop, for the amount of energy required to bring rotation of the Earth to a stop is a trillion times greater than it would take to turn the Earth upside down.

But the gyroscopic reaction of the Earth to an external torque will cause the spin axis of the Earth to rotate through a circle and the Sun will seem to stand still, depending on where you are located on Earth. The reaction to an external torque is a twist (torque) with the axis of the torque at right angles to both the spin axis and the axis of the applied external torque. The gyroscopic reaction will be smooth in starting and stopping, and cause only minor geological disturbances. Seismic reactions to the initial shock will be violent and longer lasting. Neither Velikovsky, nor any of the later researchers (except one), have considered gyroscopic reactions.

The notion of the Earth turning upside down, or that the pole relocated, is discussed in the Appendix "Polar Relocations."

Note 12 --

John M. Barry, in *The Great Influenza* (2004), writes:

"[T]he relative lack of impact [that the influenza epidemic of 1918] *left on literature may not be unusual at all. It may not be that much unlike what happened centuries ago. One scholar of medieval literature says, 'While there are a few vivid and terrifying accounts, it's actually striking how little was written on the bubonic plague. Outside of these few very well-known accounts, there is almost nothing in literature about it afterwards.'"*

The Black Death (bubonic plague) of the 14th century AD killed half the population of Europe.

Note 13 --

Although repulsive electrostatic forces operate between planets enclosed in a single plasmasphere initially, a difference in charge between the planets will also be seen as a voltage difference (easily amounting to millions of volts), and especially as the charge of the facing hemisphere of the secondary is induced to an opposite polarity from the primary. This will cause an attempted charge equalization, resulting in an arc from one planet to the other. The arc, to avoid increased resistance, will travel between the nearest surfaces, thus impinging at a right angle to the surface. The arc will not remain at one surface location, but will move, as the planet rotates, to an adjacent region as that region comes closer, and will attempt to hang up (slow or stop) at locations of higher elevation. The Earth in rotation moves at a rate of about 500 miles per hour (800 km per hr) past the arc at mid latitudes.

The production of the arc is entirely equivalent to terrestrial lightning. As negatively charged clouds pass over the Earth, electrons are chased away from the surface below the clouds, thus increasing the voltage between the clouds and ground.

Note 14 --

It is actually amazing how accurate the descriptions from various sources are to a view directly up into a Birkeland current. The many heads of Typhon are the tubes of excited electrons. At the thunderbolts.info forum, poster Greycloud mentions that Plutarch in *Isis and Osiris* (AD 200):

"... in a throw-away comment, Plutarch mentions that according to Eudoxus, Typhon (Egyptian Set or Seth) had 56 angles and that Pythagoras assigns the number 56 to Typhon."
-- Apr 20, 2008 12:02 pm; in a thread "dating," which has since been removed.

I would have been sufficiently impressed by mention of the "many heads of Typhon." The 56 separate tubes is the normal count of strands of a massive Peratt plasma column, here seen as if at close quarters.

The battle of Marduk (Jupiter) and the dragon Tiamat -- in which Marduk drives a three-pronged spear into the mouth of the dragon -- as well as Indra and Vrtra, Zeus and Typhon, and any number of other pairs composed of the supreme God and a dragon with the body of a snake, all properly belong to another period -- the fall of the Absu in 2349 BC. The snake-like dragon in 2349 BC is the plasmoid from Venus.

The plasmoid appears again in (astronomical year) 685 BC. This will be discussed in a later chapter.

Velikovsky quotes a number of Roman and later authors and chronographers (at times as secondary sources) to the effect that the apparition was seen as a giant red-globed comet. Pliny in the first century AD writes, "A terrible comet ... twisted like a coil ... [and] a ball of fire." The comet is generally known as Typhon, after the last pharaoh of the Middle

Kingdom, Tau Timaeus, rendered as Typhon in Greek (Velikovsky). Manetho records that, in the time of Tutimaeus [Tau Timaeus], "a blast of God's displeasure" fell upon Egypt and ended the Middle Kingdom (Velikovsky). The end of the kingdom actually came slightly later when the Hyksos invaded the Delta, taking advantage of the widespread destruction in that region.

Since there are many similarities, the Typhon legend is easily confused with the Phaethon legend, where Phaethon, the son of Helios, the Sun, takes his father's chariot for an uncontrolled ride through the sky, burning up parts of the Earth. The ride of Phaethon happens in 685 BC, as I will relate in a later chapter. This is where the trident of Marduk belongs also.

Note 15 --

It should be understood that only the outer layer of the plasmasphere is electrically active in the minor contacts described in the text. The outer layers of a plasmasphere (and the extended tube), called the double layer, are conducting surfaces. The major repulsive electric force interactions happen only when the two planets can "see" each other within the combined plasmasphere.

Note 16 --

Velikovskian investigators have always assumed that the "fallen sky," which, from various sources, lasted 20 or 40 years, was made up of dust from the tail of Venus. Thus there was some disappointment among Velikovskians that no record of "dust" was found in the Greenland ice cores at a location corresponding to about 1500 BC. As I have stated, there was no dust in the edges of the tail of Venus (and certainly very little *within* the tubular form of the tail), and, as others also maintain, dust would, at any rate, have settled out in a few months. But nanometer soot from forest fires would not have settled out very soon. I refer the reader to the chapter "Tunguska and Chicxulub."

This is not to say that the whole of the ice core data is not muddled by many unjustified assumptions about formation of the Greenland glacier. Volcanic dust from the Santorini explosion of circa 1350 BC was at one time held to be detected, but this was later repudiated. The lack of funds has greatly limited study.

On the other hand, both the Grand Canyon of Arizona and the Valles Marineris of Mars show what can happen with massive plasma lightning strikes. The Valles Marineris is 3000 miles (4800 km) long and five miles (8 km) deep. The material which used to be there has disappeared. The same is true for the Grand Canyon. The Grand Canyon is a mile deep in places. But there is no run-off of water-eroded soil to be found anywhere. Valles

Marineris probably dates from 720 BC, due to a strike to Mars from Venus. The Valles Marineris scar has a large left-right symmetry, as would be expected with a massive lightning strike (so says Thornhill).

Note 17 --

The "wanderings in the desert" were most likely a migration into the Arabian peninsula, towards Mecca. The Israelites were herders, and "wanderings" would not be unreasonable.

The years of darkness were real. They are also recounted in the Vedas. The Mesoamerican records specify a darkness happened twice. This would be the events of 2193 BC and 1492 BC. For one of those events, the cloud cover lasted 25 years.

For the Olmecs the period after 1492 BC was the start of history (and the start of the Haab calendar). When the skies lifted again, after a long period, it was celebrated as the creation event (or a re-creation event) with altars which show atlantes (the Gods of the four cardinal points) holding up a platform representing the lifted skies, or show a God in a niche below the table (recalled from 2349 BC). An altar from near San Lorenzo has the edges of the altar marked with the glyph for the word "cloud." The same altar design may be found at Chichen Itza, 2000 years later. The table is still used by the present Maya as part of a "centering" ceremony which celebrates the creation of the world.

Note 18 --

This passage, suggested by Velikovsky, was for me one of the more convincing data points in his exposition. Moses heard the commandments of his God as a cadence of repeating triple syllables -- in the groans of the seismic convulsions of the Earth.

Note 19 --

It is amazing that the results of the literary analysis by Velikovsky, in *Worlds in Collision* (1950), closely matches the results which are expected from physical considerations.

What is almost certain (from later data) is that Venus did not change its orbital period by more than four days as the net result of the interactions, and that the orbit of Venus remained elliptical, although the eccentricity may have changed. The orbit of Venus did not circularize until after 670 BC.

Note 20 --

The length and dates for the rule of the Hyksos are in total confusion. Manetho (AD 200) records 511 years. Scholars of the 19th-century have estimated 200 to 400 years. Traditionally the period extends from 1648 to 1539 BC, which incorporates a dating error of 150 years. Even today this period has not been sorted out. Egypt split into three divisions, the Delta region held by the Hyksos, a central region held by the pharaohs of Memphis, and another independent region south of Aswan, held by Nubians, who modeled their culture on the traditional Egyptian civilization.

Velikovsky suggested 400 years for the intermediate period, from after 1450 to 1040 BC. This has been followed up on, confirmed, and also adjusted, by numerous researchers, but dates are still contested by most archaeologists. See Velikovsky, unpublished documents, "World Fire" and "Hammurabi and the Revised Chronology" at [www.varchive.org]

Note 21 --

Velikovsky makes note of the endless rotation of the names of the Gods, as follows:

"A new catastrophe caused by another member of the planetary family would easily raise it to the position of the supreme deity; on the other hand the fidelity to the protective deity of the previous age would cause one or another tribe to remain faithful to the old cult; religions and gods are tenacious contents of the human soul and peoples do not part easily from them."

"Thus we see how the worship of Jupiter superseded that of Saturn; the worship of Venus (Minerva, Athena, Astarte, Baal) in many regions eclipsed the worship of Jupiter; and the advent of Mars and its participation in celestial wars brought new schisms into religious thinking and caused new religious wars. Thus the Greeks battled under the patronage of the planet Venus (Athena) whereas the Trojans battled under the protection of Mars (Ares); but Ares was also recognized as god by the Greeks and Athena as a goddess by the Trojans. Similarly the Toltecs, faithful to the cult of Quetzalcoatl, the planet Venus, warred and succumbed in the war against the Aztecs, the younger race that proclaimed Mars (Huitzilopochtli) as their god. The Romans regarded Mars as their protective deity but their main sacrarium was dedicated to Jupiter and Minerva (Athena). Egyptians also regarded Amun as their supreme deity and Ra was its other name. In another cult center of Egypt

Osiris and Isis were worshipped as supreme gods; in early times they represented Saturn and Jupiter; at a later time Isis became synonymous with Astarte-Athena, the planet Venus."

"A few peoples through consecutive planetary ages kept fidelity to the ancient Kronos (Saturn), whose age was previous to that of Jupiter. Thus the Scythians were called Umman-Manda by the Chaldeans, and Manda is the name of Saturn. The Phoenicians regarded El-Saturn as their chief deity; Eusebius informs us that El, a name used also in the Bible as a word for God, was the name of Saturn."

-- Velikovsky, unpublished document, "The Birth of Monotheism" at [www.varchive.org]

Enn Kasak and Raul Veede, in "Understanding Planets In Ancient Mesopotamia," in *Folklore*, Vol. 16 (2001), write:

"The functions of different gods tended to vary by city states, but of the Great Seven [of the Sumerians], An was universally the god of heaven, Enlil the god of air and earth, and Enki the god of water and wisdom; less important were Utu the Sun god, Nanna the Moon god, Inanna the goddess of love and war, and Ninhursag, the mother of gods."

"The name and status of the main god depended on who had the power. In Sumerian times, the greatest god was An, whose son was Enki. In the Old Babylonian period, of course, the city god of Babylon, Marduk became the main god and was also to be son of Enki and grandson of An. As An was more like a 'deus otiosus,' Marduk as an acting god started to be identified with the acting main god Enlil, whose son, god of war Ninurta was identified with Marduk's son, multifunctional Nabu."

"Saturn is hard to interpret, as it is connected to Ninurta, but this leads us through Nabu straight to Mercury... . Sumerian Nanna and Akkadian Sin are the Moongod, Utu or Samas is the Sungod without a hint of doubt."

The status of Mercury (Nabu) as a God is curious from our perspective, since we see so little of Mercury. Mercury orbits close to the Sun and today only shows a few degrees above the horizon before sunrise or after sunset and on only a few days out of every three months. It clearly suggests that Mercury was on a radically different orbit and was much more prominent in the skies of antiquity.

Note 22 --

There is a very large voltage difference between the Earth's crust and the ionosphere. The voltage difference can become extremely high even with small changes of elevation, and mountaineers especially have experienced severe shocks under adverse atmospheric conditions -- simply by reaching up to gain a hold on some rock surface.

At ground level the voltage difference amounts to about 600 volts in six feet (2 meters) of elevation. But any tall conducting structure takes the potential at ground level and inserts it into an elevation with a higher potential. Thus the voltage difference at the top of a tall structure is much greater with respect to the surroundings, often enough to ionize the air, especially at the tips of sharp spikes. This will be seen as Saint Elmo's fire.

Note 23 --

I would not make the suggestion that material of one plasmasphere could be transferred to another in "brushing" each other while passing in space, if it were not for the fact that only *this* explains the sweet smells of the 8th and 7th century BC, noted throughout the world. The Olmecs call them "fragrances of flowers." The fragrances were associated with close passages of Mercury.

Note 24 --

It is not at all certain that Yahweh is to be equated with Venus. The planet Mercury is much more likely, with Jupiter even more so. Yahweh was defined in the exile era (563 to 483 BC), or the post-exile era, as a singular spiritual (unsubstantial) entity along the lines of Persian Mazdaism (which actually was an invocation of Saturn or Jupiter).

On the flaming bush, see Joel T. Klein, *Through the Name of God* (2001), which offers "burning bush" as a later mistranslation of an Egyptian word originally equivalent to Shamash.

Note 25 --

Alfred de Grazia is an accomplished academic, and read everything ever written on Moses and the Exodus before writing *God's Fire* in 1983. I am using his text as a source because it reflects on the developing subjective consciousness of this period (which he would probably deny).

Note 26 --

Aris M Hobeth, in *Moses in the Twelfth Dynasty Egyptian Literature* (2002), places Moses, and a dozen others Bible personalities from Exodus through *Numbers*, in the Egyptian 12th dynasty -- some as pharaohs, including Moses as Senusret III (the literary Sesostris), Aaron as the high priest of On, others in secondary roles. The compelling analysis is based on the clear parallels derived from a half dozen narratives extant from the 12th dynasty. The details between the Bible and the literature of the 12th dynasty is amazing and convincing. See Hobeth's site, [ArisMHobeth.com].

Hobeth equates Moses with Senusret III. He suggests dates around 1500 BC. The 12th dynasty is traditionally dated to 1985 to 1795 BC, on the basis of a single Sothic date -- a literary reference to the rising of "Sothis" in the reign of Senusret III and retrocalculated to be in 1870 BC. It is not. The whole system of Sothic dating is bogus, and has today been abandoned, although it still held on to in textbooks.

Relocating the 12th dynasty to around 1500 BC has also been done by a number of other people: Immanuel Velikovsky, *Ages in Chaos* (1952), Bible apologists like Donovan A. Courville, *The Exodus Problem and Its Ramifications* (1971), and academics like Peter James, et alii, *Centuries of Darkness* (1991), and David Rohl, *A Test of Time* (1995).

Damien Mackey makes the same claims as Hobert with *Solomon And Sheba*, in *Chronology & Catastrophism Review* (1997), based on earlier work by Velikovsky, John Bimson, and others.

Note 27 --

It is probably the presence of the Hyksos (or Mitanni) which kept the Israelites from advancing north into Canaan for 40 years. Josephus mentions the Philistines.

Note 28 --

P. Warlow, in "Geomagnetic reversals?" *Journal of Physics* (1978), suggested an inversion of the Earth like the operation of a toy "Tippe Top" which moves the precession reaction torque (the gyroscopic reaction) to the upper portion of the top, making it look as if the initial spin had remained in place. This happens as the globe is inverting. This exchanges the east and west (for the Tippe Top). The Sun will then rise over some western landmark of the horizon. If the rising Sun defines "east" then east and west have interchanged.

The Tippe Top concept is a totally erroneous concept simply invented to satisfy the requirement of seemingly exchanging east and west, something supported with many quotations by Velikovsky, none of which prove the point. See the Appendix "Polar Relocations" for details.

With Warlow's model the Earth would not upright itself again, or if it did, it would happen by means of some other catastrophe (it is claimed). For Warlow this suggests placing one catastrophe in 2300 BC (of which he has no details) and another at the time of the Exodus. Not untypical of catastrophists like Warlow, he then equates one event with Typhon and the other with Phaethon.

Warlow's model also required the Earth to rest on a table top.

Note 29 --

[*Image: An ark carried in a boat by Egyptians. (ND) After de Grazia.*]

There are Egyptian and Mesopotamian images of devices which look very similar to the description we have of the Ark of the Covenant.

In 2 Samuel 6:2 is a description of Yahweh, "... the ark of God, whose name is called by the name of the LORD of hosts that dwelleth between the cherubims." The God of the Israelites dwelt with them, in visible form.

Note 30 --

De Grazia and a number of other people have suggested radiation poisoning as the source for the widespread "leprosy" of biblical times (as well as the barrenness of women and the falling out of hair mentioned by Ipuwer). It has been suggested that the Ark may have contained radioactive materials, and for this reason was returned to the Israelites after being captured by the Philistines, who got sick after approaching the Ark. However, UV and X-ray burns are more likely than radiation poisoning.

On the other hand, the interplanetary lightning strikes at the Great Lakes in circa 10,900 BC, left areas of lower Michigan radioactive. To attribute radioactivity to the *contents* of the Ark seems a little far-fetched.

Others have suggested that the "leprosy" of antiquity was a slow acting viral infection. Today it is known to be a bacterial infection.

Note 31 --

The need for a ground plane which would be responsive to induction of positive charges was known long before the Middle Kingdom of Egypt. Many of the megalithic structures in Northern Europe, dating from 3400 to 3200 BC, are surrounded with ditches and at times with wells backfilled with rock. These would act to collect and hold groundwater, thus providing a larger flat plane which could be "electrified" by induction from an overhead electric field. Even when dry, the ditch acts to increase the potential difference between the tops of the monuments and the ground plane. Certainly many of the locations of ancient sites were chosen for this reason, which is why we often find ancient megalithic monuments grouped together.

Note 32 --

This quote by de Grazia relates to Jaynes's use of the traditionally accepted dating of the event of the battle at Troy to circa 1200 BC (attributable to a hasty comment by Herodotus) and the later reduction to text of the *Iliad* to circa 700 BC. The Asiatic Greeks have disagreed with the early date of the war since 400 BC. (See also the endnotes to the chapter "The Tablets of Ammizaduga" on the dating question.) The late date of the final authorship of the written version of the *Iliad* is unquestionable. It may have been as late as 650 BC. But in that there is no indication of a "development" of Greek literature -- the *Iliad* bursts forth as a fully developed literary masterpiece after 700 BC -- it has always been assumed that it was preceded by a long tradition of oral poetry. It has never been considered that perhaps all previous literary efforts in mainland Greece and Greek Asia Minor were lost during worldwide catastrophes. Even Plato remarked on this.

Jaynes assumed that the *Iliad* represents the compositional efforts of a pre-conscious bard, and used the *Iliad* as a centerpiece in the analysis of a developing subjective consciousness. Jaynes thus had to establish a method of verbal transmission, ending with a last pre-conscious writer, Homer, 500 years later. Jaynes's suggestion is that the songs must have been transmitted by some trance-like mind-state among bards.

But this position is not needed. The theory of verbal transmission is partially based on the studies of Croatian bardic traditions in the late 19th century or early 20th, which in turn was applied to such epics as *Beowulf* and the *Iliad*, especially in terms of the formulaic sentence structure which grates on our sensibilities today but which is explained as a method of line completion within a required meter. But the idea of faithful verbal transmission in the Balkans has not held up on closer scrutiny.

After having read the *Iliad* a half dozen times, I seriously doubt the need for "trancelike states." I think the *Iliad* may have been purposely written in the style of an ancient document. And it certainly captures that flavor and, at the same time, the epic is a masterpiece of political balance by placating the egos of both the Asiatic and the European Greeks. The great care taken with this, as with all aspects of the epic (such as with its internal time structure), would suit Jaynes's research equally well, and perhaps even better than if the *Iliad* were a totally genuine document.

It looks much more like the *Iliad* was written by a fully conscious poet sometime after 747 BC, about a war completed perhaps as much as 300 years earlier, or more likely as fictional. As a fiction there is no need to have a pre-conscious poet who transmits poetry orally. There are just too many "literary devices" in use with the *Iliad* to suggest anything different, including the fact, recognized long ago by the Greek editors of the *Iliad* in 600 and 500 BC, that Homer uses a "poetic diction" which does not match any spoken Greek dialect. He even makes up words as he needs them. There are some notable anachronisms in the poem and far too much heroics among its characters. Even so, I have no problem with the scope of Jaynes's analysis.

When you read how one war chief asks another for a favor with, "Considering the favors you have done me in the past, I thought I could ask for another," you realize that Homer is no rhyming automaton, but a fully subjectively conscious human.

See also the essay by Livio Stecchini, "Gyges and Homer," at [www.metrum.org], which places the writing close to 680 BC, and holds the *Iliad* as a fictional polemic poem written for the benefit of the Asiatic Greeks.

Talbott has suggested that not only is the *Iliad* a fiction, but that it recounts the war of the Gods in 3147 BC. In that there are no references to the solar nova event of 685 BC, it could be suggested that the *Iliad* was reduced to written form before 685 BC (680 BC in Eastern Mediterranean chronology).

Note 33 --

Hosea suggests that Moses was murdered. See Ernst Sellin, *Mose und seine Bedeutung fur die Israelitisch-Judische Religiongeschichte* (1922), and commentary by de Grazia in Chapter 7 of *Gods' Fire*.

Note 34 --

I copied the last line verbatim from de Grazia who transcribed it exactly from Jaynes.

Note 35 --

I have noted the prevalence of Mercury shortly after this time (circa 1200 BC), as if Mercury again passed over the Earth's orbit on a regular basis (which previously had started in 1900 BC). Note the resemblance of the snake wound about a pole and the Caduceus of Mercury. Moses died below Mount Nebo, named after Mercury.

Note 36 --

Earthquakes are often preceded by electric discharges from deep in the Earth. Piezoelectric voltages are generated by the distortion of quartz-bearing rock.

The breeched walls of Jericho have been excavated, and were originally dated to have fallen due to earthquakes circa 1300 BC. The date was later revised to match the "standard" chronology of Egypt, erroneously placing the date about 600 years earlier.

Velikovsky, in an unpublished document, writes:

"The conclusion reached by the excavator of the great-walled Jericho -- a Middle Bronze city, destroyed only a short time after the end of the Middle Kingdom -- is in perfect agreement with the timetable of 'Ages in Chaos': the Israelites arrived at the walls of Jericho only a single generation after the end of the Middle Kingdom in Egypt, still in the Middle Bronze (the beginning of the Hyksos occupation). There is complete agreement between the archaeological finds and the scriptural record."

The city was looted, razed, burnt to the ground, and left unoccupied for 600 years.

Note 37 --

As a demonstration of the physical effect of a lightning strike, it is reported:

"In Fetlar, one of the Shetland Islands, a solid mass of rock 105 feet [35 meters] long, 10 feet [3 meters] broad, and in some places more than 4

*feet [1.3 meters] high, was in an instant torn from its bed by lightning
and broken into three large and several small fragments... . [One
fragment], 28 feet [9 meters] long, 17 feet [6 meters] broad, and 5 feet
[1.5 meter] in thickness, was hurled across a high point of rock to a
distance of 50 yards [50 meters]. Another broken mass, about 40 feet
[13 meters] long, was thrown still farther, but in the same direction, and
quite into the sea."*

    -- A. W. Grabau, *Principles of Stratigraphy*, vol. I (1924)

Note 38 --

    Venus may have made electric contact with Earth repeatedly, as I have
counted six times, but recorded as seven times by various people in antiquity.
Velikovsky and others have presented evidence of additional 104-year cycles
or "ages" in use worldwide. Archaeologists at one time suspected a 50- or
100-year cycle (this would be 52 and 104 "Tun" years) of purposeful
destruction of Olmec ceremonial centers in Mesoamerica, as, for example, at
La Venta (800 -- 400 BC). Although it would be suggested that the "cycles"
would be based on sightings of Venus when it seemed to almost reach Earth
(which it did not), in fact the celebration of the "52-year" interval was a
religious ceremony determined by the calendar, and, since 1442 BC, may
have had little to do with the location of Venus in the skies. See the chapter
"Olmec Alignments" for a discussion of Olmec La Venta and other
ceremonial locations.

    In the *Chilam Balam* books of the Maya, the name for Venus suggests
seven appearances (electric interactions) in prehistory. I can only locate six of
them with certainty, so it is possible that the list of seven may have included
an additional appearance either in 776 BC or in 685 BC.

Note 39 --

    This is also the period of the first appearance of the oracle inscriptions of
the Shang dynasty in China. The *I Ching* is of a later date, since a textual
analysis places it after 700 BC, although the trigrams probably date to before
3200 BC.

---

*   Calculations are in Unix bc notation, where ^ denotes exponentiation; the
functions a(rctangent), s(ine), and c(osine) use radians; angle conversions to
radians or degrees by the divisors rad=.017+ and deg=57.2+; other
functions are shown as f( ); tan( )=s( )/c( )
units: million == 1,000,000; billion == 1,000,000,000;
AU == 93,000,000 miles.*

Recovering the Lost World, A Saturnian Cosmology -- Jno Cook
Chapter 23: Destructions by Mars

Revision: 42.66 (quet.php)
Contents of this chapter: [The Ragings of Mars] [Calendar Reforms] [A Blast From Heaven] [The Death of Quetzalcoatl] [The Ballgame] [The Winged Disk] [Endnotes]

Destructions by Mars

In mainland Greece, of 150 cities noted before the 8th century BC, only 13 survived to 650 BC. The same scale of destruction was experienced in Anatolia, the Middle East, and Italy. The period of 800 BC to 600 BC also saw the largest overseas colonization by the Greeks, as well as the virtual depopulation of the Eastern Mediterranean region and parts of Europe. De Grazia in *The Iron Age of Mars* (2009) estimates that of a population of 200,000,000 before 800 BC, only 5 million survived. The earlier level would not again be reached until AD 1900. [note 1]

This decline in population presents a serious problem to a reconstruction of history, for not only were there few survivors to write history, but they would have been largely illiterate and uninterested, and even adverse to recording history. We only have the braggadocio records of the Assyrians, and the jeremiads of the prophets of Judah. There are some later (a century later) recollections by the Persians which reach back over the previous hundred years. We also have the accumulated clay tablets of the fortune-tellers and astrologers of Babylon, who concerned themselves more with celestial forecasting than actual history (and mostly dated to after 650 BC).

It is thus with difficulty that history between 800 BC and 650 BC is extracted from incomplete and unserviceable records. Even the books of the Biblical prophets were written or rewritten at later dates from older records, to be put in the service of prophecy and monotheism, and are often not at all helpful. Very little of the writing looks to be contemporaneous with the events.

What we do have are archaeological findings for Anatolia, Greece, and Italy, and eventually for a much broader range of territory. The record of destruction is absolutely astounding. Nothing before or after has equalled the catastrophic devastation of the era of the 8th and 7th century BC. I'll fill in some details below.

This chapter will deal with the repeated close calls by Mars between 806 BC and 687 BC at 15-year intervals (closing in to within perhaps 30,000 miles (50,000 km) accompanied by Mercury. It will deal also with the travels in 685 BC of Mercury high through the sky with Venus (which was especially noted by the ancients) and the thunderbolt from Jupiter which stopped the fires at Venus and Mercury.

The Ragings of Mars

Do not let the 15 year intervals presented above detract from the facts of the utter devastation that Mars caused in India, the Middle East, the Mediterranean, Central America, and in the lower United States. Because of the destruction of cities and the dispersal of people, but primarily because Mars appeared at 15-year intervals, we have virtually no written records. Velikovsky never managed to determine the complete scope of the events, except to suggest a 15-year interval. The only suggestion of an actual time span is from the sparse mentions in the Maya *Chilam Balam*, and even here the record has to be reconstructed from inferences. (Although the last event involving Venus, Mercury, and Jupiter is well dated.)

The appearances of Mars was like bad weather, and it took time before astrologers of the Middle East could even determine that the events repeated at regular intervals, and could be predicted. What is generally known for sure today is that, starting in 747 BC with an Earth shock, and for 60 years thereafter, Mars passed close to Earth five times -- very close. But the prophets of Israel had started their warnings long before 747 BC. From the suggestions incorporated in the *Chilam Balam* and less so from the archaeological records of destructions of citadels in the Middle East, it could be suggested that the first strike by Mars was in 806 BC. The complete period of the ragings of Mars thus probably extended over 120 years -- 806 BC to 687 BC. [note 2]

Alfred de Grazia, in *The Iron Age of Mars* (2009), writes:

"Planet-Mars is tightly bound in ancient peoples' minds with gods who are paramount warriors, destructive heroes, crushers of towns and armies, dispatchers of plagues, and depicted as red in color. Many, if not all, nations worshiped the planet-Mars and the god-Mars, under their

national names for both of them. In Babylonia he was Nergal, in Mexico Tezcatlipoca, for example. Hundreds of Mars identities around the world came into prominence at the same time."

Mars was seen on the day side of Earth as many of the descriptions make clear, although the night sky is invoked in some instances. Mars would have crossed Earth's orbit at an acute angle either in front of or behind Earth, moving in the spring from the night side to the day side, and in the opposite direction in the fall -- but 15 years later.

The *Popol Vuh*, in at least one instance where the celestial twins (Mars and Mercury) disappear into the night sky, identifies two stars and a nebula that they pass by (see a later chapter). This allows placing the event both at a seasonal date and at a location in the sky.

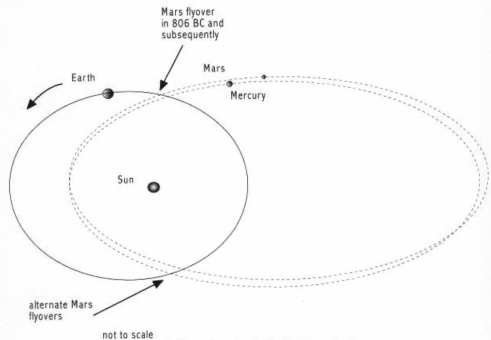

Earth and Mars in the 8th Century BC

Entry of Mars at an angle into Earth's plasmasphere (at an angle and far removed from Earth proper) would have removed the shadow portion of Mars's plasmasphere due to the Sun and replaced it with a shadow due to the Earth's electric field, and thus pointing away from Earth. Mars's plasmasphere would also isolate it from the Earth's field. It seems likely that for this reason there were no repulsive forces between Mars and Earth in all instances except one. We have no records of any instances of a sudden Earth shock except in

747 BC. The difference in charge certainly was exhibited with continuous electric arcing.

Thus it might be suggested that Mars moved to the day side of Earth to cause a sudden massive repulsive shock which changed Earth's orbital period by 5 days in 747 BC.

What about all the damage that is on record? Every year and a half Mars crossed Earth's orbit on its way to perihelion with the Sun, and again on its way to aphelion. At 15 year intervals, Mars crossed Earth's orbit close to earth, either going in one direction or another, and alternating between dates in late winter (March) and early fall (October).

Mars would approach Earth's orbit (the ecliptic) at 1.85 degrees. In coming close to Earth (maybe as close as 40,000 miles) both would come to a near standstill with respect to each other. This might last a few days before Mars would advance beyond Earth and speed up (inbound) or slow down (outbound) with respect to Earth.

When near Earth, Mars would continue to creep up as Earth rotated. In one rotation of Earth (8000 * Pi) Mars would move up about 800 miles. Although this is a rough estimate, it a reasonable indication of the damage done further north than the Mediterranean, like northern Europe and Scotland, and in the Americas in northern Mexico, and the states of Texas, New Mexico, and Arizona, but also in Minnesota and southern Canada.

There are also records of solar eclipses during this period caused by Mars -- a phenomenon completely inexplicable to later researchers looking over Mesopotamian astronomical records. The fact that Mars was at times seen in the day sky, and at times must have blocked the Sun, might explain the obsession of Assyrian kings with eclipses, since it would be obvious that such eclipses were accompanied by wholesale destructions.

Prayers and pleadings to Mars proliferate in Mesopotamia and India during this period. The *Book of Amos* records the first major interaction with Mars as predicted by Amos. The *Book of Joel* also records the threat of Mars. A troop of warriors travels with Mars, called Maruts in Vedic sources, the "Terrible Ones," carrying gleaming spears and throwing fire, lightning bolts, and bolides to Earth. *Joel*, of course, identifies them as the "hosts [that is, the army] of the Lord." Joel also calls them Ariz, "Terrible Ones," the name for Mars adopted by the Greeks, Ares.

The Maruts are the companions of Mars, asteroids which had accompanied Mars since the time of the first dynasty of Egypt, when the Egyptians duly counted them as part of the herds of small and large cattle of Horus. They will also show up in the tales of Hercules as his stolen cattle or as the armies he raised for various exploits. [note 3]

In the Bible the "hordes" which accompany Mars could be equated to the various enormous groups of warriors supposedly slain in battles at that time.

From Ussher:

- 957 BC: "Abijah and his army of 400,000 men, fought with Jeroboam and his army of 800,000 men. Because Abijah trusted in God, he obtained victory against Jeroboam. He killed 500,000 of Jeroboam's soldiers."
- 941 BC: "In the beginning of Asa's reign, Zerah the Ethiopian mobilised an innumerable army to invade the land of Judah. This force had 1,000,000 men... . Asa met this army with 300,000 men from the tribe of Judah and 280,000 from the tribe of Benjamin. He called on the name of the Lord and routed and slew that vast army and took much spoil from them."
- 741 BC: "Pekah killed 120,000 valiant men of Judah in one day. ... The Israelites also carried away captive from Judah and Jerusalem 200,000 women, boys and maids [who they released]."
- 710 BC: "The next morning there were found 185,000 dead men. After this Sennacherib shamefully broke camp and returned into his own land to rest at Nineveh."

All the above dates and the quoted text are from Bishop Ussher, *The Annals of The World*, Chapter 4, "The Fifth Age of the World." The size of these armies, even if half or three quarters were camp followers, is astounding. And they all die. (The World War II invasion of Normandy involved only 176,000 troops, with a naval support of 196,000.)

This recalls the much earlier Egyptian counts of the Followers of Horus, or the contemporary (8th century BC) spear- and rock-throwing Maruts in the company of Indra (Mars) of the Vedas, or even, as pointed out by Isaiah, the attacks by fiery hot sand which entered through windows and under doors.

We might add to these the Myrmidons ("ants" or "ant people"), the troops of Achilles in the Iliad.

Greek legendary history holds the Dorian invasion of Greece to be the "return of the Heraclids," when the banished third-generation offspring of Hercules returned to lay claim to the Peloponnesus. The dates are very uncertain (but 761 or 762 BC could be suggested). Thucydides dates the invasion to 80 years after the Trojan war, where the Trojan war was assumed to have happened as early as 1200 BC. The invaders included the Spartans, who at best can be dated as an organized community to about 750 BC. The two ruling families both trace their descent from Hercules (Mars) but, like all twin kings of antiquity, representing Mars and Mercury.

Except for these, there is no evidence of a "Dorian invasion." The Heraclids are the sons of Hercules which is Mars. They were seen in the sky, not on Earth.

All nations watched Mars during these years with great anxiety. Most notable among the destructive effects of these close passes is the frequency of earthquakes, due to gravitational and electric forces on the crust, but especially a moving electric arc which burned forests and lifted the material along with soil ahead of itself in a tornado the size of a hurricane. In an era of city walls, built as a measure against rampaging tribes, and most frequently built on hilltops, Mars becomes known as the "stormer of walls." The seven- to ten-foot cover of burnt matter and soil, which buried fortified hilltop citadels, far exceeds the amount ever deposited by any forest fires or volcanic eruptions (which is seldom more than a few inches).

Alfred de Grazia, in *The Disastrous Love Affair of Moon and Mars* (1984), notes both the imagined devastations by Mars and the archaeological record. He has reference to the event of 776 BC (the so-called 'ballgame'), but it probably more accurately reflects any of the events from 806 BC through 687 BC. De Grazia describes the destruction of Pylos, one of the destroyed locations, one of hundreds:

> *"Tidal waves wipe out nearly all coastal settlements (where perhaps 80% of the Greek-speaking population was contained in 800 B.C.). Chasms are opened; volcanoes are created and activated. Surface soils are ripped off by winds traveling at hundreds of miles per hour. Communities are obliterated or disrupted by showers of ash and debris, winds, water, fire, and famine."*

At 35 degrees latitude, the Earth's surface would zip by an exterior planet at about 500 miles per hour (800 km per hr). At hilltop citadels the electric arc would pause, and the hurricane winds would drop the burnt soils and the ashes of incinerated forests. This, in fact, is the strange specificity experienced by archaeology. De Grazia continues:

> *"The Palace* [of Nestor at Pylos] *was destroyed in a 'holocaust' which 'consumed everything that was inflammable within it, and even melted gold ornaments into lumps and drops of metal.' The flames melted brick and stone into 'a solid mass ... as hard as rock.' In one room two large pots were fused 'into a molten vitrified layer which ran over the whole floor.' Everything that a human invader might desire was reduced to shapelessness. Stone was burned into lime. No human hands and hand-set fires could have wreaked such ruin."*

He follows this with an exploration of Greek society in mainland Greece and Asia Minor, based partially on the content of the *Iliad* and the *Odyssey*. His analysis of Homer is without a doubt the most cogent I have encountered.

The reader should be aware that, along with many others, I hold that the "dark ages" of Greece do not exist. Mycenaean Greece came to an end in 806 BC, not at the start of the 400-year gap of the Greek "dark ages" following 1200 BC: [note 4]

"The Homeric heroes, Odysseus and Achilles among them, typified the bands of survivors of the extensive Mycenaean civilization that was largely destroyed in the catastrophic interventions of the planets Mars and Venus in the Earth-Moon system in the 8th century. The plots of the Iliad *and* Odyssey, *despite 2700 years of trying to make something else of them, clearly point to the skies as the source of the disruptive and awful events that produced the crazed heroes of the dark times. Western civilization has treasured and imitated the posturings of these mad warriors, hardly ever realizing what they were and how the docile mind of later generations would be affected when this madness was presented to it as normality and for inspiration."*

Greece and Anatolia represented the epicenter of the repeated destructive close passes of Mars after 806 BC. Although Venus was seen near Earth in 776 BC, Venus was not involved in the destructions. De Grazia continues as follows. I have abbreviated the text and added in some of his quoted sources.

- *"The heroes boasted in the names of their parents, some of their grandfathers, and usually stopped at this point; some lapsed into claims of divine forebears in the second generation. ... The absence of 'family trees' among self-assertive 'nobles' raises doubts that they either knew their ancestors or, if they did, could claim any distinction on their behalf. ... This is exceedingly strange. It is not at all like 'primitive peoples' whose lives are bound into communities of blood served by totems. Nor like a bureaucratic society."*
- *"The warriors stayed away from their 'homes' so long that we could question whether they had any. They remind us of Vandals and Vikings who left home never to return. Of all of Ithaca's warriors, only Odysseus ever reached home. Odysseus played the pirate -- looting, killing, raping. Marauding was frequent, if not from one's neighbors then from pirates and foreign warriors."*
- *"It was a society where every man's hand was raised against his neighbor. ... 'The bearing of arms, particularly lance and sword, on all solemn occasions of civil life, was the distinguishing feature which, more than any other, marked the separation of classes in Homer's time.* [Emile Mireaux *Les Poems Homériques et l'Histoire Grecque* (1948)]*"*
- *"In battle one encounters a frenzied behavior whereby fear is whipped*

up in order to gain courage. Eliade's words apply to the heroes: 'The frenzied berserker, ferocious warriors, realized precisely the state of sacred fury ... of the primordial world.' [Mircea Eliade *Cosmos & History: The Myth of The Eternal Return* (1959)]"

- *"A frank, hollow, extreme braggadocio characterized the best and the worst of the fighters. The glorification of destructiveness seems interminable. ... There is a pervading sense of splendors of the past being gone and citations of armies, cities, and wealth appear to be grossly exaggerated. This pretentiousness is not that of nobles, [but] of a people who had lost something they once knew, did not own, but had given them their character."*

- *"They depended upon the seas but were bad sailors. There was no class of specialized sailors. Everyone was a 'sailor.' Maritime ventures were not materially distinguishable from piratical excursions."*

- *"They were meat-eaters: cattle, sheep, and wild game, animals of the uplands. 'For Homer fish is a detestable food, while Hesiod does not even deign to mention it. Never is fish eaten at the Homeric repasts.'* [Mireaux]"

- *"Gift-giving was often a spectacular affair. ... The things given seem often to be for re-giving, to be untouched and unused, even homely objects like linens, and the metal gifts seem all too frequently to have semidivine or divine 'makers' which, as false pedigrees conceal humble origins, may have concealed their origins in loot and theft. Their description, too, conveys an awesomeness, as if they were not familiar objects to the childhoods of the gift exchangers. They are described as pirates would speak of their misunderstood loot of pots and laces."*

- *"Chariots are used, not as battle-wagons, but to convey warriors to places where they would descend and fight. Their use was partly forgotten or had not been familiar to the types who owned them."*

- *"The Greeks of Homer, to conclude, did not come as an invasion from afar. They consisted of all kinds of Greeks. They were survivors, largely from the rural areas and the interior high lands. From personal experience and hearsay, they knew of the centers of their societies that had been destroyed. They often lacked kith and kin; they lacked communal security; they lacked law and order; they lacked education; they trembled upon the trembling earth."*

The analysis by Alfred de Grazia covers only Homer, and the collapse of the Mycenaean Civilization. De Grazia thus places the composition of the *Iliad* and the *Odyssey* after 650 BC.

"For a grandly disciplined, informed, and stylized poet like Homer to

write so sympathetically of his subjects, he had to be of their age, and to be of their age required that their age be the eighth century." [note 5]

But despite the destruction and dislocations, the Olympic Games continued. The attacks of Mars were at 15-year intervals, and not always at the same locations. Attempts at rebuilding destroyed cities (as for example, at Troy) continued, although this was very infrequent.

If Homer was "of their age," as de Grazia suggested, then the poetic response would have been to conditions localized and particular to himself -- the attacks by Mars would have been experienced in his lifetime. De Grazia suggests a composition date of 650 BC.

From the terse information of the Maya *Chilam Balam* we know there were five close passes by Mars between 747 BC and 687 BC (at 15-year intervals). But, from the same source, we know that there were a total of nine contacts, thus there were an additional four passes before 747 BC, starting in about 806 BC, also at approximately 15-year intervals. Some locations likely were only touched once.

The condition of a gigantic arc traveling across the surface of the Earth would have been distinctly localized, although the fall of airborne debris could have covered large areas, and the earthquakes would have spread even further away from the path of destruction. What is peculiar, but not unexpected, is that in some instances the same locations were struck repeatedly.

Only after rereading the essay by Ralph Juergens's "Moon and Mars" did I realize that Mars would most likely have approached to within the plasmasphere of Earth, thus within a distance of 20 Earth diameters -- 160,000 miles (250,000 km). Juergens suggests a relatively close distance between Mars and the Moon for their interaction. Patten and Windsor suggest 27,000 miles for the closest approach to Earth (but based on damage due to gravitational attraction). Maya iconography suggests a lightning tail extending from Mars by 4 or 5 diameters -- thus a distance of 21,000 miles (34,000 km) from Mars to the surface of Earth. [note 6]

At a surface-to-surface distance of 20,000 to 30,000 miles, Mars might have lifted the Earth's crust below its path, creating (as Patten and Windsor claim) ridges of mountains. The Earth crust which was lifted would not have subsided back entirely, since the land area of the Earth is only material floating on a heavier substrate, and this last would have filled the hollow left below the lifted mountain ridges. Mars could have remained in place laterally next to Earth perhaps for some days, since in crossing Earth's orbit it would be traveling at nearly the same speed as the Earth. However, since the Earth rotates, the location below Mars at a 30- to 40-degrees latitude would have moved past at some 500 miles per hour (800 km per hr). [note 7]

Patten and Windsor suggest any number of curved north-south mountain ranges as being due to the lifting forces of Mars, including the Andes and Rockies. I am not in agreement with a north-south path for Mars, since, as a planet orbiting the Sun, it could only approach Earth laterally although this could happen at any latitude, and would be nearly the same latitude each time. Patten and Windsor hold that the orbits of Earth and Mars were coplanar. This is not correct. The only requirement for Mars to show up near Earth is for Mars's orbital path to cross Earth's orbit close to Earth (and, of course, for Mars's perhelion to be within the orbit of Earth).

Under such a condition, with both planets at almost the same location from the Sun, both would be traveling at nearly the same speed. Even though nearly standing still, Mars would seem to fly by as the Earth continued to spin. This might have taken a number of days.

I disagree with the Patten and Windsor notion of "crescent shaped" mountain ridges. Any ridges which were formed in this process of a close approach would have been almost entirely parallel to the Earth's latitudinal lines. That also means that Mars was seen in a side view, that is, with the rotational axis of Mars directed more or less parallel to the Earth's axis, and seen as rotating.

All indications from references in antiquity is that Mars represented a distended and distorted image -- perhaps wildly flailing like a bat, which is how some Mesoamerican sculptures represent Mars. In Europe, Asia, and China, Mars is represented as a dog, a wolf, a sword, a gruesome giant, and a diseased person. The shapes of the imagery are likely the Martian dust extending into the Earth's magnetosphere. The diseased look probably derives from the pockmarked lower hemisphere. Mars is frequently noted also for its bloodstains and fire. The fire is sand and dust brought to flaming incandescence at Mars or the Earth by the arc between the planets.

The center of the Aztec "Calendar Stone" shows a face with a tongue lolling out. This is Mars. The same tongue appears on images of the Gorgon of Greece, the dreadful snake-haired woman whose gaze would turn to stone anyone who looked (although this image date from10,000 years earlier). Add together the snakes, the tongue, the Mesoamerican mention of Mars smoking a cigar (only seen as such by cigar-smoking Olmecs), or with a smoking celt lodged in his forehead, and you end up with a varied and frightening apparition flying by in the skies overhead. In Mesoamerica Mars is also described as carrying a smoking mirror on its forehead, which clearly is the northern ocean (or the remnant of the included deeper ocean, Deuteronilus) steaming water into space. The 13th century AD Icelandic *Younger Edda* also recounts Thor (who is Mars) with an axe lodged in his head after an encounter:

"Thor went home to Thrudvang, but the flint-stone still stuck fast in his head."

In passing over Earth' surface Mars would have induced an opposite charge below it. The result would have been a continuous lightning strike in an attempt at charge equalization. From the evidence of fire, the melting of metals, and the calcification of building stone, as at Troy (Hisarlik), Pylos, and numerous other places, it would seem that Earth was the anode for the lightning strikes.

This is exactly how lightning occurs under "normal" conditions today: negatively charged clouds chase away electrons at the ground below the clouds, resulting in a higher potential difference, which leads to lightning strikes. And like a "normal" lightning strike, the Earth's surface would have been the anode in the strike.

But the passage of Mars is also (or especially) noted for fire, and flames of extreme temperature. An electric arc would certainly qualify, but more likely, it was the dust ionized and ejected from the arc contact point -- burning sands, as Isaiah at one point suggests. Disassociated silicate dust, generated at Earth's surface and ionized as cations.

At Mars the plasma stream was possibly as wide as the planet -- 4000 miles (6400 km) diameter. This is the dimension of the limited plasmasphere of Mars, the small size resulting from lacking a magnetic field and an atmosphere. Within the plasmasphere of Earth, Mars would only have sported a limited plasmasphere, with a double layer perhaps a hundred miles above the surface, and constituted entirely of ferrous and ferric cations (Fe^{2+}, Fe^{3+}) plus the requisite electrons as the negative charges. At the Earth's surface the stream of plasma would concentrate to a much smaller dimension, possibly only tens of miles wide -- and in arc mode. [note 8]

The lightning strikes of the 8th and 7th centuries BC traveled west across the surface of the Earth (because Earth rotates to the east). The lightning strikes may have ignited, extinguished, and restarted numerous times, preferring high ground to land on. The lightning bolts must have been enormous and mostly continuous. The bolt would probably be seen coming from over the far horizon, for in a number of instances we have evidence of people evacuating hilltop locations only minutes before being struck. At Pylos we have written records (clay tablet) of "watchers" posted at the shoreline. To no effect: Pylos was utterly destroyed.

The arc would have resulted in hurricane level forces which tore apart city walls and buildings. As a continuous arc, the bolts would have left behind a path of incinerated trees and grasses and upturned soil. And the arc would have been surrounded by a circular magnetic field which would lift up most of the debris and ashes and send it swirling up. This is how a tornado operates. Tons of loose soil and ashes would have been lifted into the air. The lightning bolt would linger or slow at a hilltop citadel rather than increase its resistive conduction path in leaving a hill. If the bolt stopped or extinguished on a hilltop, the suspended material would have been dropped. That is how Hisarlik got covered in a four- to six-foot layer of burned material.

If the lightning bolt was tens of miles across, the flaming sand would have spread horizontally from its base to a width of perhaps a hundred miles (160 km). Michael Steinbacher has reported that in the southwestern United States, at about 30 degrees latitude, there are gullies running up mountain slopes where the tops have been metamorphized -- altered physically and chemically by heat. It is clear that if flames of ionized sand were forced up these gullies they would concentrate to a greater temperature where the width of the gully decreased. Dennis Cox has made note of top ridges of mountains in northern Mexico which have been melted, and similar metamorphic damage in Texas and Colorado. Let me quote Cox from [sites.google.com/site/dragonstormproject]):

> "There are tens of thousands of square miles of assorted ejecta, and breccias, and of rivers of melt, and pyroclastic materials in Northern Mexico. All in pristine, unweathered condition like they only happened yesterday. And if you follow those materials upstream back to their respective sources you find no volcanoes, and no craters, only bare patches of smoothly melted stone. Or miles-wide, irregularly shaped melt basins, or strangely shaped denuded mountains with all traces of alluvium blown away. And which, sometimes, in their undulating lines, and angular scale-shaped ridges, look for all the world like the spine of a dragon sleeping in the earth."

Cox assigns the causes to meteors, and thus talks of objects cast down from the skies. Close enough for identical effects. He continues:

> "... almost all of the object's kinetic energy gets translated to heat. The heat hits the ground in a supersonic, hyperthermal downdraft of perhaps millions of degrees. Most of the time even the detonation shock wave itself gets transformed into the heat. But here is no missing energy. And it doesn't 'dissipate harmlessly' in the atmosphere. The mountain is still history; it just very quickly, and violently, melts and goes away. Think about a gust of wind so hot that it instantly makes granite flow like water, and is just another gust in a turbulent storm. Then realize it's not imaginary. Such things have happened in the recent past. There are mountaintops at 13,000 feet (4300 meters) elevation in the Rocky Mountains of Colorado, their glacial ridges melted, blasted, and blown

over the ridge top in runnels of melt, like wax on the sides of a candle. And recent enough that the blast melt materials have never been subjected to the grinding action of a glacier. Or mountains in Eastern Texas softened and tossed around like waves in an angry sea."

Mars came close enough to Earth to have its two close satellites observed and described. Both are very small and they circle Mars on extremely tight orbits. To Homer they are Ares's dogs of war, Deimos and Phobos -- Fear and Panic -- rushing madly about his chariot. Hesiod says they are the horses of his chariot. Dean Swift describes the satellites of Mars quite accurately in *Gulliver's Travels* (1726), apparently on the basis of sources from antiquity, for they are only discovered by telescope one hundred and fifty years after its publication. [note 9]

In the *Iliad*, Ares, "the bloodied stormer of walls," always loses. Yet a number of belligerent nations take Mars as their primary God. Mars is the chief God of Rome. Their calendar year starts with the month of March in his honor and the founding of Rome is dated to the middle years of the eighth century BC -- coincident with a major disturbance of Earth by Mars in 747 BC which altered the length of the year. The Cimmerians and Scythians, Eastern European steppe peoples, also take Mars as their chief god and start destructive raiding expeditions into Anatolia in the 8th century BC. In the middle of the 8th century BC, coinciding with the return of Mars, Assyria, a small nation in Northern Mesopotamia, models its army after Mars's "horse mounted" hordes, and with similar tactics of speed and utter destruction, expands its conquests over a region from the Persian Gulf to the Mediterranean and to Aswan in Egypt.

The Aztec's chief god is Huitzilopochtli, "destroyer of cities and killer of people," and the Aztecs proceed (at a much later date) to terrorize the other nations of Mexico. Huitzilopochtli is Mars. (There are other Mesoamerican gods associated with Mars, such as the "flayed god" and the "scarfaced god.") [note 10]

Mars caused a disturbance of the Earth's orbit on February 26th, 747 BC. A second significant disturbance happened in 686 BC, on March 23 (some catastrophists suggest 702 or 701 BC). But this second shock was due to Mercury, not Mars. Subsequent events verify this notion. [note 11]

The events of 747 BC and 686 BC stand out, for the Earth experienced a seismic shock and the axis of the Earth was disturbed. During the gyroscopic reaction which swung the axis through a loop, the day was temporarily lengthened or shortened. In the *Iliad*, Hera sends the Sun unwillingly into the ocean, that is, she is shortening the day. In the *Odyssey*, Athena holds back the dawn at the edge of the ocean, thus lengthening the night. [note 12]

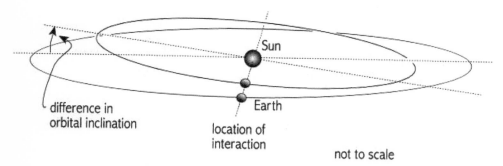

difference in
orbital inclination

location of
interaction

Sun

Earth

not to scale

Two Planets in line with the Sun

[*Image: Two planets in line with the Sun. When the inner planet's plasmasphere tail, directed away from the Sun, intersects the leading edge of the other planet's plasmasphere there will be an electric interaction. Illustration by J. Cook.*]

The reaction to having the plasmaspheres of two planets touch would be the sudden experience of each other's electric fields. This would result in an instantaneous repulsive force -- an Earth shock. As the planets would both move away from each other (in the direction radial to the Sun), the force would decrease, and stop as the planet with the larger negative charge would induce an opposing charge in the facing hemisphere of the second planet. Since this involves the movement of electrons through the crust or atmosphere, it would take some time, perhaps minutes, or even only seconds. The reversal of electric field would result in an attractive force between them, enough certainly to halt the movement away from rhe Sun. The increased difference in charge between the planets also would result in arcing from one to the other in an attempt to achieve charge equalization. [note 13]

Because of the initial repulsive electric force, the crust would be depressed over a large area, resulting in an uplift at the margins. As the Earth rotated, the center of the compressive forces would rotate toward the west or southwest but would diminish very rapidly with the change of the induced charge to an opposite value.

The shock would be transmitted to all of the globe of the Earth, and would both move the Earth in space, and, if the center of the impact was off-center to the Earth's equator, it would tilt the rotational axis. A gyroscopic reaction torque would result if the Earth's axis tilted -- a second twist which would attempt to bring the Earth's axis back to its original position. The Earth's crust might react to the initial shock for a long time. Mesopotamian records indicate earthquakes on an almost daily basis during these two centuries and, even four hundred years later, Rome still records over 50 earthquakes per year. (See Appendix B, "Celestial Mechanics" for the mechanics of the interactions.)

Calendar Reforms

After the Earth shock of 747 BC, the year lengthened by five days, six hours, and 20 minutes to become 365.24 days -- nominally a change of 5 and 1/4 days. Calendar reforms were instituted worldwide, some in 747 BC but a few much later. Egypt attempts an additional correction to the calendar in 239 BC when the priests issue a decree which added one day to the civil calendar every four years. [note 14]

> "... that the case shall not occur, that all the Egyptian festivals, now celebrated in winter, shall not be celebrated some time or other in summer, on account of the precession of the rising of the Divine Sothis by one day in the course of 4 years."
> -- *Canopus Decree*, 239 BC, found at Tanis.

However, the previous Egyptian Venus calendar, based on the heliacal rising of Venus (Sothis in this case) every 8 years, remained in use until Julius Caesar's calendar was introduced 200 years later under Roman occupation. [note 15]

Between 2193 and 1492 BC there probably were ten lunar months of about 28 days in the year. Shang dynasty oracle records indicate months of 27 and 28 days. I have used a year of 270 or 280 days for this earlier period, which I think it was probably 273 days. This is reason enough why Shang records use both 27-day months and 28-day months.

In the following era, from 1492 BC to 747 BC, the year was 360 days, and the Moon on an orbit of 30 days. Both of these periods are well established. Many people, however, kept to the ten month year of the previous era, and made correction in a number of ways.

When, after 747 BC, the period of the Moon (the month) was no longer a whole-number interval of the year, the religious feast days started to wander around the year, and efforts were made throughout the world to rectify this. Here is a list of how the ancients took notice of the new celestial order of 365 and one-quarter days:

- On February 26, 747 BC, Nabonassar, king of Babylon, introduces a new calendar and an era called "the Era of Nabonassar." This dating schema is used to start compiling a yearly account of activities called the *Babylonian Chronicle*. Ptolemy (circa AD 150) and later astronomers would continue to use this astronomical record into the 15th century AD. Ptolemy also published a 900-year list of Babylonian kings up to his time using the *Babylonian Chronicle*. [note 16]

- Ptolemy uses the dates derived from the *Babylonian Chronicle* for a compilation of lunar eclipses (based on records obtained by Alexander in 331 BC from the Chaldeans), and marks 747 BC as the starting year of the collection, with the first eclipse in 721 BC. It is not certain if earlier records existed, but before 747 the skies were different, and earlier records would be invalid. China starts a record of eclipses at about the same time. [note 17]

- In the previous period, 1492 BC to 747 BC, the Earth year was 360 days and there were 12 lunar months of 30 days. When the number of lunar months changed to slightly more than 12 after 747 BC, a considerable number of people in the world retained the 12-month lunar calendar of the previous era, which ran about 11 days short of a full year, and made adjustments by periodically repeating one of the months. Some of these calendars have lasted into the 20th century AD. [note 18]

- The founding of Rome is dated to 747 BC, the year of the major disturbance of Earth by Mars. Probably long before 747 BC Rome had added two months (January and February) to their original ten-month lunar calendar (dating from before 1492 BC) and set all the months to 30 days, corresponding to the 30-day lunar month of the then-current era. (King Numa, who supposedly arranged this, is a fiction, and all the early records of Rome were destroyed by the Celts.) With the changes of 747 BC, the solution for the Romans was to end the year on February 28th (starting the year on March 1, the month of Mars), abandon lunar months in favor of calendar months, and distribute the extra days of the year equally among the remaining 30-day months. The change to starting the year on January 1 happened 700 years later after Julius Caesar's calendar reform of 40 BC. Appointments to the office of Consul already started on January first a hundred years earlier. [note 19]

- An interval of 4 years, called an "Olympiad" had become the standard of chronology among the Greeks. The Olympiads were counted from the first Olympic Games in 772 BC (four years after the so-called 'ballgame' of 776 BC; see below). The four-year cycle used for the Olympiads is actually based on the coincidence of the synodic periods of Venus and Earth. Five complete orbits of Venus (as seen from Earth) are equal to eight complete orbits of Earth (at that time). At the end of eight Earth years Venus would rise again in the east against the same background stars, and of course on exactly the same calendar day as eight Earth years earlier. Both the convenient halfway point of four-years and the full eight-year cycle of the "Venus calendar" were observed in Greece, Egypt, Mesoamerica, and South America. With the change of 747 BC, the four-year interval fell one day behind each Olympiad. [note 20]

- Five days were added to the Mesoamerican calendar of 360 days, before the end of 747 BC, and were known as the "Sleep of the Year". The same addition to calendars happened in almost every nation around the world, from Peru to Rome, and also to the Egyptian "civil" calendar. The Peruvian calendar included a leap day every four years to account for the quarter day left over at the end of the year. The Egyptian and Mesoamerican calendars did not account for the extra 1/4 day. [note 21]

- The "Long Count" was initiated by the Olmecs on February 28, 747 BC, with the count of double-decades, years, months, and days all set to zero. The "years" are 360-day years (18 "months") where the "month" is 20 days long. A larger measure, the Baktun, consisting of "400-year intervals," was set initially at 6. This is "6.0.0.0.0" in Long Count notation; see "The Maya Calendar" for details. The Long Count continued to be used by the Maya until AD 900. [note 22]

- The Maya considered that all pre-history happened in a Katun named "11-Ahau," which is named after the name of its last day. In the *Chilam Balam* there are a number of lists of events which always start with Katun 11-Ahau. Significantly, a Katun 11-Ahau ended on February 28th, 747 BC (Gregorian), when the Long Count calendar was started. The concept of assigning all prior history to Katun 11-Ahau may have its origin with this start of the Long Count. Katuns were named and likely were counted prior to this date. [note 23]

- The contemporary Maya of Chiapas, Mexico, still retain the use of the Haab calendar of remote antiquity, and start the 5 intercalated days (the five extra days added to the 360-day year) on February 26 of our calendar. The year thus ends after February 26.

- The Romans in effect did the same thing with the pre-Julian calendar, ending the year in mid-February, but used a 365-day year: *"February was split into two parts, each with an odd number of days. The first part ended with the 'Terminalia' on the 23rd, which was considered the end of the religious year; the five remaining days formed the second part."* -- Wikipedia

- Tedlock reports that among the Quiche Maya of Guatemala the arrival of a new solar year is celebrated on February 25th, two days early from the Chiapas calendar.

- February 26th, the day of the disturbance of 747 BC, was celebrated as the start of the year (New Year's day) among the Aztecs at the time of Cortez. [note 24]

- At about this time, China declares that there are now 365.25 "degrees" in a circle. We do not know for certain when this practice started, since all books were burned in 213 BC. But it was certainly in use by the first or second century BC. It did not turn out to be convenient in geometry, but worked fine for celestial navigation on the seas. It was still in use in the 15th century AD.

Before 747 BC there had been 12 lunar months of 30 days during a year of 360 days. Since, during this period, an exact multiple of lunar months coincided with the solar year, lunar calendars were in use universally to govern the dates when religious observations were to be held, but many of these counted ten months to the year as their calendars had before 1492 BC. The phases of the Moon would represent a very visible public calendar, which everyone could understand.

The change to a new year of an odd number of days and a fractional day left over, and with a month no longer composed of an even fraction of the year, brought religious observances into total confusion. Attempts at corrections were made worldwide, resulting in many very complex calendars. All of these reforms we are aware of are obvious attempts to bring a lunar religious calendar into conformity with a new solar year, because following a strict lunar calendar during the new era would continuously displace all celebrations by many days over the year.

It should be noted that there is worldwide disagreement on which day constituted the start of the new era. As Hera sent the Sun into the ocean, shortening the day in the Mediterranean region, the Indians of Mesoamerica experience a night which lasted four nights -- thus equal to two full days. Just as in the Mediterranean region we have the Era of Nabonassar starting on February 26th (after nightfall) and the Roman calendar starting after February 28th (the changes to new calendars were independently arrived at), so in Mesoamerica we have a similar disagreement over when the new era started.

In the case of Mesoamerica, the question of dates has become an issue among scholars, and deals with the retrocalculated initial date of the Maya (Olmec) Long Count. John E. Thompson first suggested in 1927 that the Maya Long Count of days starts on August 13, 3114 BC. In 1935 Thompson revised his calculation to August 11, validating the opinion of other scholars who had arrived at a date of August 11, 3114 BC.

This last date (the "August 11" starting date correlation) has become the accepted archaeological standard and is generally used today, although any number of researchers think that the date of August 13, 3114 BC, is more likely to be correct, because a calendar based on August 13 correctly dates many known recorded eclipses. A calendar based on August 11, however, is still used by some people in Mexico and Guatemala. [note 25]

There have been suggestions that the Maya made a two-day correction at some time in the past, but this assumes an absolute and uniform use of the calendar since remote antiquity. Considering the widespread adoption of the Olmec religious practices among the diverse tribes of Southern Mexico, the Yucatan, and Guatemala, as well as the universal use of the (now) 4300-year old Tzolkin calendar, it can be assumed that in 747 BC, when the Long Count was devised, there were some diverse regional opinions on the concept of where one era ended and another started, as well as questions about the existence ("completion") of two days which had not been seen in progress.

A Blast From Heaven

Another strange incident at the time of the last disturbance (the second Earth shock in this era) was widely known in the Middle East. In 687 (or 686) BC the Assyrian army of Sennacherib, on its way to quell a revolt in Egypt, camps some distance from Jerusalem and demands its capitulation on threat of a siege. The prophet Isaiah urges Hezekiah, the king of Jerusalem, to resist, telling him that Sennacherib's army would never arrive. Apparently Sennacherib had been similarly warned by his advisors. [note 26]

> *"The very same night God sent his angel to their camp. He destroyed every man of valour, every commander, and chief man in the Assyrian army. The next morning there were found 185,000 dead men. After this Sennacherib shamefully broke camp and returned into his own land to rest at Nineveh."*
> -- paraphrased by Bishop Ussher

Since antiquity there has been endless speculation as to what really happened, starting with Herodotus (fifth century BC), who attributes it to mice. Josephus (first century AD), along with modern historians, suggested a plague. But Biblical and Egyptian sources plainly state that it was *Ignis Coelis* -- "a blast of fire from the heavens." Such would be one of the effects of an electric interaction with another planet. [note 27]

There are two independent records of this event from China. The following is quoted from the *Bamboo Books*:

> In the tenth year of the Emperor Kwei, *"... the five planets went out of their course. In the night, stars fell like rain. The earth shook."*
> -- *Annals of the Bamboo Books*

The *Bamboo Books* were found in China in a grave in AD 279. The *Spring and Autumn Annals,* compiled for the state of Lu by Confucius and completed about 480 BC, reads almost identically, but does not recognize the Earth shock.

"In the seventh year of the Duke [Chwang] *... In summer, in the fourth month, on Sin-maou, at night, the regular stars were not visible. At midnight, there was a fall of stars like rain.*

-- James Legge, translator, *The Ch'un Ts'ew and The Tso Chuen* (1872)

The seventh year of the Duke Chwang of Lu is identified as 686 BC by Legge. The quote from the *Bamboo Books* lists the date (-687) in astronomical notation, which is equivalent to 686 BC, Julian. [note 28]

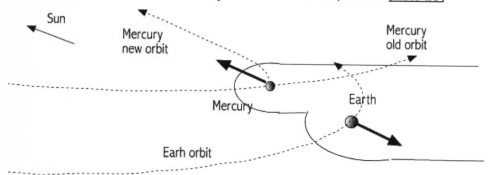

Oblique view of 686 BC contact
Gravitational forces are not shown   not to scale

[Image: Mercury in 686 BC. The separation was 50,000,000 miles (80,000,000 km). Illustration by J. Cook.]

These terse Chinese historical notes, which have been dated to March 23, 686 BC, can be interpreted as a swing of the spin axis of the Earth as it underwent a gyroscopic reaction to an external torque induced by the Earth's plasmasphere contact with the plasmasphere of another planet. The other planet, in this case, was Mercury -- not Mars, as every researcher expected.

The first effect of the sudden electric repulsive force experienced from Mercury, as the plasmaspheres connected, was a shock felt worldwide. The stars would seem to fall, or, on the day side of Earth, the Sun would move away from its normal path.

Sennacherib returned to Assyria, did not record this nighttime disaster (or the campaign) among his records, and spent the next 8 years in seclusion.

Two of his sons kill him while he is at prayers in the temple of Nergal (Mars).

There was an Egyptian monument in the eastern delta (at Letopolis, "Mouse City," also known as the "City of the Thunderbolt") to a "mouse god" (per Herodotus), erected in commemoration (apparently) of the defeat of Sennacherib's army which had left Egypt in 686 BC (or never reached Egypt). There are also extant temple inscriptions bearing on this.

I would suggest that it was Mercury which was involved in the incident of 686 BC. Mercury is Hermes among the Greeks, but known as Smintheus or Apollo Smintheus ("Apollo of the mouse") in Asia Minor at the time when Mercury was still known as Apollo, the Archer God, among the Greeks, as in the *Iliad*. The name Apollo was transferred to the Sun at a later date.

Mercury, although today only a little larger than our Moon, possesed an atmosphere in antiquity, and would have looked maybe four times larger than the Moon. Always in the company of Mars, and traveling only some 180,000 miles above Mars (the Moon is at a distance of 250,000 miles), Mercury would have loomed large in the sky.

It certainly might have looked like a mouse with its plasma coma and plasmasphere tail, just as it might have looked like a bow and arrow with its bow shock and tail. Although the date, supposedly March 23, 687 BC (Julian), would seem to argue for Mars as the agent, a second Earth shock by Mars is not at all well supported. I would opt for Mercury as the agent, and I would place the event in 686 BC rather than 687 BC. For more information bearing on this see Appendix B, "The Celestial Mechanics."

The Earth shock was experienced at night in Peking and Jerusalem. Chinese sources read "at night" as does the Bible. Although Mercury was not seen during the daytime in Asia or the Middle East, it was seen by North American Indians in the daytime. The impact can be located in Northern Alabama and shows as a circle of mountains.

To paraphrase from various legendary North American Indian sources, this is what transpired:

The Sun was in the day sky at about noon when it turned black and started to move down, that is, moving directly toward the horizon and additionally toward the southeast. The Sun was choking, and as it dipped down in the sky, the sky darkened and Coyote (Mars) was noticed in the east. Coyote had just crossed over the Earth's orbit in the last few days. Obviously Coyote had snared the Sun, and was dragging it backwards. Only after an hour did the Sun brighten again and return to its path across the sky. Then it was seen what had happened. A mouse had chewed through the lasso. It could still be seen just west of the Sun, with its tail pointing away. [note 29]

The tale of a mouse in the sky is known throughout the world in various forms, as De Santillana and Von Dechend point out in an appendix to *Hamlet's Mill*. Some of these are not accurate for an involvement with the Sun, however. Most of the daylight during this incident spread only from far Western Europe to the middle of the Pacific. Thus tales of winged mouse Gods from India are suspect. The Polynesians have myths dealing with a rat God that gnawed through the nets of the Pleiades. Mercury was within a few degrees of the Pleiades on March 23, 686 BC. This is correct if it is considered that at this time the dome of the stars had not yet shifted (that would happen in 685 BC) so that the Sun stood directly below the Pleiades at the spring equinox.

As I have previously noted, this event also represents the Tower of Babel incident: a plasma cone in glow mode extended from Earth to Mercury and ignited Mercury's atmosphere. The plasma connection may have lasted a day or more. In that case, everyone saw it, and certainly everyone saw the flaming planet. The reason this story is known worldwide is because it came so late in the history of antiquity. The loss of memory and speech may have been associated with this specific incident, or may reflect the changed condition of the Sun's electric field the following year. More on this last later. [note 30]

The Death of Quetzalcoatl

The shock which cast Mercury into an orbit close to the Sun may have changed the eccentricity of Earth's orbit (which would not change the length of the year but would allow for a required change in Kinetic Energy), because soon after the encounter with Mercury, Earth seemed to have moved its orbit away from intersecting the orbit of Mars and was thereby removed from the threat of Mars. Shortly after Earth was removed from the vicinity of Mars, Venus, too, fell from the sky. [note 31]

"How art thou fallen from heaven, O Lucifer, son of the Morning?"
-- Isaiah.

What happened to Venus? From what little we know, it looks like Venus was suddenly involved in a massive plasma discharge. The discharge also involved Mercury. But less notice was taken of Mercury, for at the start of the nova event Mercury was very close to Venus in the sky. Most peoples recognized Venus, but not Mercury. The starting and ending dates of this event are developed in the chapters "Modern History" and "Olmec Alignments." [note 32]

In Mesoamerica, Quetzalcoatl, who is Venus, is represented as the bearded man or God, who had come from the east to deliver all the benefits of civilization. In their recycling of all history, the Mesoamericans make Quetzalcoatl into the last king of the abandoned and famed city of Tula, already an ancient ruin at the time of the Mesoamerican authors of the 15th century AD. To paraphrase, "Quetzalcoatl, the last King of Tula, traveled east, and set himself on fire. Eight days later he arose in the sky as the Morning Star (Venus)." Both the *Popol Vuh* and the *Annals of Cuauhitlan*, two documents independently written a thousand miles apart, agree on this. In the *Codex Borgia* the mythical hero Quetzalcoatl is burned while his heart ascends to heaven as the Morning Star. [note 33]

The "burning of Quetzalcoatl" happened far from Earth, since it did not involve any noticeable geological disturbance on Earth, although we have many notices of the "Ignis Coelis" during this period. It may very well be that the condition of electric charge for Venus had mounted to the point where only a plasma discharge or a mass ejection could balance forces. At any rate, after its last passage behind the Sun in 680 BC (in eastern Mediterranean chronology), Venus seems to have undergone a massive plasma discharge, and, at some later time, assumed a circular orbit. It must have been an enormous energy outpouring, for Venus lost its coma, its talons, its feathers, and its flowing hair. It assumed the looks of a star. But it took months.

If, as I have suggested, Mercury was involved in the March 23, 686 BC, plasma contact with Earth, then it might also be suggested that we are not seeing Venus involved in a nova event, but that this was a nova-like event of the Sun, involving Mercury and Venus. When Mercury changed its orbit to fall well within the orbit of Venus, it disturbed electric conditions close to the Sun. Today the Sun still reacts to comets which come close by hurling coronal mass ejections toward them into space. That would make more sense of the description, from China, that two suns were seen battling in the sky at this time. The two Suns do not imply that one of them was the actual Sun. But since Mercury remains close to Venus at first, and within a month was close to the Sun, it is certain that for many observers the display involved only Venus and the Sun. The sudden brightening of Venus was recorded in extensive references to "a prodigy in the sky" and of Venus "blazing through the day sky brighter than the Sun," as well as references relating to the changes in the sky. [note 34]

We do not know exactly when this happened, but my suspicion is that it occurred during the year 680 BC in Eastern Mediterranean chronology, which is 685 BC in absolute astronomical chronology (to be discussed below). There are a number of reasons why we have no certain date for this event. First, because the blazing of Venus spanned a considerable amount of time. It was not an event lasting only a day. In fact, it lasted a month and a half, 40 days. Second, the event was not associated with any cataclysmic changes on Earth. And third, the effects were not noticed until the following year, or later.

Only later were the lasting changes recognized: Spring started two weeks later, the constellations had moved in the sky, and the polar axis no longer pointed to a location in Ursa Major. When later attempts were made to understand the changes, it came as a massive shock to ideas about the Gods, about knowledge, and about the workings of the Universe -- which will be the subject of the following chapter.

The blazing planets must have represented a cataclysm equivalent to a supernova. The event should have been noted in Chinese records as a nova. It was not. The earliest Chinese record of a supernova (a "guest star") is for AD 185. The eruption of Venus was not considered a "guest star" because although the display was immense it happened during daytime. It was not a star, it was obviously the planet Venus, which, because of its coma and tail, would have readily been seen in the daytime in antiquity, and the planet Mercury.

For both the Mediterranean region and Mesoamerica, the blazing of Venus became the end of mythical and divine history. No new Gods enter the pantheon after this -- with the exception of the personification of Venus as the savior of mankind as Quetzalcoatl, Mazda, Mithra, and Christ.

When Venus and Mercury started to blaze in the skies, it must have seemed as if the end of the creation was at hand. But it ceased, on July 25th, 680 BC (685 BC), suddenly, when a massive plasmoid lightning bolt by Jupiter stopped the blazing planets. I'll discuss this in the next chapter.

The Ballgame

In the 8th century, not only did Mars come close to Earth, but on at least one occasion this happened at the same time that Venus was "near Earth" -- but only visually so. This was 700 years after the post-Exodus date of 1440 BC. Venus was seen streaking across the daytime skies and this event was recorded, apparently in 776 BC, but only because Mars also appeared near Earth at the same time, making it look like the planets were in a race.

Venus could not have come close to the Earth without causing the complete destruction of the Earth. Venus, a much larger planet than Mars, with a very large coma, might have looked perhaps half the size of the Moon if it was seen from 10 million miles (16 million km) away. (The Moon is only a quarter million miles away.)

Thus both Venus and Mars were seen on the day side of Earth, and the two planets seemed to chase each other across the sky towards the west (due to the Earth's rotation). If Mars passed Earth at a distance of one-quarter to one-half million miles, Mars would have looked the size of the Moon. Because Mars was much closer to Earth, it might indeed have looked as if

Mars was gaining on or overtaking Venus. This may have played out over a number of days.

It has been suggested by Velikovsky that the Earth's Moon seemed to cross the path of the two planets (as if they were near) in its normal rotation around the Earth, but in the opposite direction. Velikovsky proposed that the Moon may have started to change its orbit in response to gravitational forces from three directions. That is totally unrealistic. Almost all imaginings of gravitational forces between planets, even if supposedly close together, completely neglect the absolutely overwhelming effect of the Sun in determining the orbits, and the role of forward momentum which simply does not allow a planet moving through space at 67,000 miles per hour (100,000 km per hr), as the Earth does, to diverge by even a fraction of an inch from its path.

Followers of Velikovsky identified the globes seen in the sky as a "ballgame" between Venus and Mars, with the Moon playing the part of the ball. The Moon was selected as the ball for want of any other likely planet, and the notion that the Moon is small. Problems with this identification are two-fold. First, the idea of a "ballgame" is a Mesoamerican notion, which is here being transferred to the Eastern Mediterranean, where there was no such thing as a "ballgame." In Greece it was a foot race instead.

Second, it is much more likely that Mercury played the part of the ball, although from Greek sources (the *Odyssey*) the Moon certainly was involved in an electric contact with Mars (but this was not the ballgame). Traveling faster than the Earth, Mars and Venus, or Mars and Mercury, eventually disappeared into the celestial east. This race, of course, was seen from the day side of the rotating Earth, so the planets would seem to be moving to the west. [note 35]

The *Popol Vuh* records the interactions between One-Hunahpu and Seven-Hunahpu, the father and uncle of the celestial twins, Hunahpu and Xbalanque, as the "ballgame." The father and uncle here were Venus and Mars, most likely using Mercury as their ball. Mesoamerican balls were very large. Here there is a ball in play, since we are here among the ball-playing Olmecs who invented rubber balls. In the *Popol Vuh* the father and uncle (as later with Hunahpu and Xbalanque) are said to travel west to reach the ballcourt of the Gods of the Underworld.

The exact year in the eighth century BC of this race between Venus and Mars (or the ballgame involving Mercury) has never been certain, although a date (780 or 776 BC) can be inferred from the date of the first Olympic Games in Greece which was in 772 BC. [note 36]

Venus and Mars may have met "near Earth" (visually) at other times in addition to 776 BC, for in 742 BC, Isaiah declared a prophetic sign "in the height above," to King Ahaz of Judah, saying:

"Behold, the Virgin shall conceive and bear a son, and shall call his name Immanuel ["God is with us"]. *Butter and honey shall he eat...."*
-- Isaiah 7:12-14

"The Virgin" is Venus. "Virgin" is a Greek translation of the Hebrew word "the maid" (Ha'almah, per Fritzius, below), that is, "young woman," as Isis/Astarte (Venus) had been known for 2500 years. The date of 742 was derived by Ussher.

Bob Fritzius contends that the "child" is Mars appearing from behind the coma of Venus, and moving though the tail. (He later disclaimed Mars, but offered no substitute.) It is actually Mercury, not in the tail of Venus, but visually behind Venus. See the website at [www.datasync.com/~rsf1/vel/ha-almah.htm].

A later addition to his webpage suggests that what may have been seen was an aborted fissioning of Venus (but I think this is suggested because the phenomenon cannot be tracked to any particular dated event from antiquity). Fritzius believes there is support for this from Greek mythology. Fritzius is a published astronomer and an electrical engineer, but has yet to find mythological support for this event.

There are some problems with the "Immanuel" prophecy. I cannot find anything in Greek mythology that refers to this except a very brief mention of the parentage of Phaethon (who is Mercury) by Hesiod, which Marinus van der Sluijs has pointed out in an article, and which I will address later.

I think the prophecy by Isaiah refers to 685 BC, not 742 or 747 BC. The "fissioning event" recalled in mythology is more likely a recollection of the blazing of Venus and Mercury after June 15 (Gregorian) of 685 BC (the astronomical year), when Venus and Mercury were visually within a degree of each other, but so bright that their comas seemed to merge. Over the following weeks Mercury would be seen moving away from Venus, as if Mercury had just been born. And this planet, smaller than Venus, and only recently relocated to an orbit close to the Sun, had not been seen in the daytime sky in the previous two years, and never again after 685 BC. Mercury had lost its atmosphere the previous year when an Earth shock relocated it to within the orbit of Venus. Without an atmosphere Mercury, at one time looking nearly as large as Venus, had become much smaller. I think that this later element of 685 BC was written into the much earlier warning issued by Isaiah.

In Egypt Mars appeared as "Horus the Child" in sculpture at about this time (after about 750 BC), an inexplicable third Horus. This is possibly Mercury, although it is unlikely that the Egyptians misidentified Mars. The child Horus is originally shown trampling snakes and scorpions, and his image is a charm against snakebites and scorpion stings from the application of water run over the limestone image (as is used today also). He is soon depicted at the breast of Isis. (What a change in imagery!) This "Mother and Child" image spreads to the Middle East and the Roman empire, and eventually to Buddhist India through Greek influences, and is introduced to China. For the Egyptians of the New Kingdom, the second Horus had been assumed dead since circa 2700 BC (or after 1936 BC) when he last passed close to Earth, but at this time, in 747 BC, Mars is recognized again as Horus.

As noted above, Mars, when seen (at one instance) in the proximity to Venus, would look very small and the "Horus the Child" image may have derived from this comparison. The snakes being trampled are described in Vedic literature in the 7th and 8th century BC as contemporaneous companions of Mars. The Vedic hymns, as well as Bible passages and Mesopotamian documents, describe the furious rotation of Mars's satellites accompanied by moving plasma streams, looking like scorpions with waving tails. Vedic literature equates the satellites also with chariot wheels. This last places the description well after 1500 BC, in the age of chariots. The furious rotation of the satellites of Mars were in a direction transverse to the visual travels of Mars past the Earth. Once inside Earth's plasmasphere, the satellites would have trailed sweeping tails of plasma in glow mode, likely composed of the extensive dust of Mars.

Olmec sculptures of this era are of a full-sized adult jaguar or were-jaguar (a half human, half jaguar form), which probably represented Venus (although it may have been Mars), carrying a baby jaguar (depicted as a small adult) who also probably is Mercury.

In the Quiche Maya *Popol Vuh* of the 16th century AD we again meet these characters. The *Popol Vuh* takes liberties with history in order to come up with a smooth narrative, although the core of the narrative was well established nearly two thousand years earlier as can be seen from murals and inscribed scenes.

The hero twins, Hunahpu and Xbalanque, are clearly meant to represent Mars and Mercury, although by the story of their birth they would be Venus and Mars. But they are twins, and as twins most likely they are Mars and Mercury. The "twins" are a celestial phenomenon; a feature which occurs throughout the world at this time -- Italy, Greece, the Middle East, India, China, Australia, and Mesoamerica. Worldwide the twins are identified as black and white, with Mercury (yet with an atmosphere) as the white twin.

In the *Popol Vuh* one twin, Hunahpu, is identified by the Tzolkin day-name of the first day of the Venus cycle. (The *Popol Vuh* is a symphony orchestrated to the day-names of the Tzolkin.) The second twin's name, Xbalanque, could be translated from Quiche as "Little Jaguar of the Night." This is a transliteration from the notes of the book by Dennis Tedlock, *Popol Vuh* (revised edition 1996). Xbalanque is thus most likely Mercury.

In the *Popol Vuh* the appearance of Venus and Mars (although probably Mars and Mercury) a hundred years earlier (or at some earlier time) was understood to represent their father and uncle, who were put to death by the Lords of Xibalba, the Underworld. Both planets had simply disappeared into the night sky after some incident of the 8th century BC and not returned.

The activities of Hunahpu and Xbalanque are modeled both on the simultaneous appearance of Mars and Mercury in the 8th century BC and on the blazing of Venus and Mercury in the day sky in 685 BC (see later text).

During the various encounters of the 8th and 7th centuries BC, plasma interactions occurred between Venus and Mars, and between Mars and the Earth's Moon. These are described in the *Iliad* and the *Odyssey*. The *Homeric Poems*, which follow closely in time to Homer's epics, have similar descriptions. The *Iliad* retells the events of the 8th and 7th century BC as the interaction between the Olympian gods in the skies above Troy.

One event was an interaction between the warrior goddess Athena (Venus), and the bloodstained god of war Ares (Mars), with Aphrodite (the Moon) as a bystander. To keep Ares from aiding the Trojans in the battle of Troy, Athena drives a spear into Ares's "lower belly, below his belt." The scar still shows as a 3000-mile-long (4800-km-long) gash below the Martian equator. As Aphrodite approaches to help Ares, Athena bashes her in the breast. "And her heart bled [or melted]," reads the *Iliad*. [note 37]

Velikovsky notes that Roman historians for the 8th century BC record wildly erratic "months" which remain unresolved for a century. Despite the descriptions from the *Iliad* and the *Odyssey*, it is unlikely that the orbit of the Moon changed because of plasma strikes. Plasma strikes will wear away the crust of a planet before "moving" it in space. [note 38]

In the *Odyssey*, Demodocus, one of the fictional characters (and a poet), recites a poem dealing with a tryst of Ares (Mars) and Aphrodite (the Moon in this case). In this poetic interpretation, Ares's repeated arc mode plasma discharges to the smaller Moon are his ejaculations. Ralph Juergens mentions that, as Mars closed in, the display would have changed from long-range single arcs to much smaller arcs encompassing the whole sphere of the Moon. This last is the net devised by the smith Hephaestus (played by Venus) which falls on the lovers and holds them captive. [note 39]

Seen traveling across the daytime skies, and visually at close range, Venus is here known as the smith Hephaestus, a name which otherwise cannot be related to a planet. Alfred de Grazia, in *The Burning of Troy* (1984), wrote about Hephaestus: "whose name Robert Graves says means hemerophaistos (he who shines by day)."

De Grazia also discusses at length what is thought to be the event, in *The Disastrous Love Affair of Moon and Mars* (1984), under the assumption that the love affair, which is presented in comic form, is a disguise for the actual terror it produced in the watching humans.

To put all of this together: Venus and Mars appear in the sky, Venus drives a spear into Mars, and bashes the Moon, a hundred years later Mars makes love to the Moon and is caught in a net. Suddenly in 772 BC the Greeks start up the Olympic games at a location as far removed from almost all of the warring Greek nations as can be imagined: the northwest corner of Peloponnesus. Although I have no idea what this really meant politically, it could be suggested that it was selected to be in the direction of the earlier contact point of a Saturnian plasma stream with Earth.

The Olympic Games in Greece were instituted in 772 BC (Wikipedia says 776 BC) to commemorate interactions between the planets Venus, Mars, and the Moon four or eight years earlier. Originally the games consisted of just one foot race. With each of the following Olympics at 4-year intervals, the activities were expanded to include additional races. Other types of athletic contests did not enter the Olympics until many decades later. [note 40]

We would need to ask, Why the celebration of the Olympic Games? It would follow directly from the logic of the ancients: that Mars showed the people what had to be done in his honor to avoid his wrath in the future. At least in the short run that was an efficacious solution, good for 15 years. Like recasting of the terrifying Mars and Aphrodite event as a comedy in the Odyssey, the "celebration" of the Olympic Games might be another anti-celebration of the experience of terror. The dating of the event to four-year intervals would bring Venus back into the same region of the sky as 4 years earlier, but not Mars. Venus was definitely a part of the celebrations. I should point out that the sequences of Olympic Games became the chronological base for all of Greek history.

In Mesoamerica the "ballgame" event receives an entirely different interpretation from the "foot race" in Greece. The Olmecs engaged in a game involving a large rubber ball. In Mexico the ballcourt comes into use, although possibly not until some 800 years later. The shape of the ballcourt seems to be based on the look of the equatorial rings in the south night sky at the time of the equinoxes before 2349 BC when the shadow of the Earth opened up the center of the rings as an inverted equilateral trapezoid. The ballcourts, which were ubiquitous in Mesoamerica and in use for 2000 years, consisted of two sloped surfaces between which a giant rubber ball was in play between contestants. In later versions there were enclosed end zones at each end of the alley, giving the overall plan view the shape of a capital letter "I."

We know nothing of how the game was played. I'll propose for this narrative that, when played ceremonially, the ballgame was the religious re-enactment of ball-playing twins mentioned in the *Popol Vuh*; or perhaps the planet Venus and the Sun playing ball in 685 BC, perhaps with Mercury.

The ballcourt is a feature which came to be in near-universal use throughout Mexico and the game, in typical Mesoamerican style, was (apparently) a deadly affair. It is today suspected that the loser (or the winner, some say) was decapitated. It is also, as ever and everywhere in antiquity, in imitation of what was seen in the sky. [note 41]

The concept of a celestial ballcourt becomes an architectural feature of many (but not all) Mesoamerican ceremonial centers, at a minimum so that the ceremonial center and the setting location of the Sun along the horizon, become the two bouncing walls of the ballcourt. The ceremonial centers thus controlled the travels of the Sun. This is the case at Teotihuacan where there are no ballcourts.

Early excavators at the Olmec site of La Venta (900 BC to 400 BC) thought they had discovered a ballcourt (the area between two berms, directly north of the pyramid), but it turned out not to be so. One of the discovered sculptures, however, is still known today as "the football player." They did find rubber balls, to be expected, since the Olmecs cultivated the rubber tree. Apparently ballgames were played at La Venta and the earlier San Lorenzo (1450 BC to 900 BC), for sculptures of the gear and accessories have been identified. Additionally, the colossal heads found in the surrounding jungles all have "helmet" head wrappings, also suggestive of later ballcourt players elsewhere in Mesoamerica (but the original suggestion for this is based on American leather football helmets of the 1920s).

The head wrap may represent a means by which the Olmec people identified themselves with Mars, whose smooth upper half was seen on the close approaches in the 8th and 7th century BC, but this does not explain its use with the 10 heads found at San Lorenzo, which, as I will suggest later, most likely represent Venus rather than Mars. Of course in both cases (Mars and Venus) the planets jolted the Earth like a ball in play between contestants.

See also Linda Schele and David Freidel *Maya Cosmos* (1993), which discusses three ballcourts at the Maya site of Yaxchilan. The ballcourts were named "First Creation," "Second Creation," and "Third Creation," and have, in addition to the dedication date, appended time intervals pointing to earlier (or first) manifestation of these events (to which these ballcourts were dedicated), all of which can be placed, as suggested by Schele and Freidel, in the 7th century BC. And all of which are the wrong dates by thousands of years -- as a complete misreading of the information of the Day Books which were inherited by Yaxchilan. As I will point out in a later chapter, the historical references are to "creation" celebrations involving the large "altars" found at La Venta, not to celestial ballgames.

The Winged Disk

During this period especially, from 806 BC and continuing a thousand years, we run into a curious iconography in Egypt and the rest of the Eastern Mediterranean: the winged disk. Actually, the symbol of a disk with wings left and right can be found on all continents. In Egypt we can date its first appearance as early as the Old Kingdom, and elsewhere in the Eastern Mediterranean from about 2000 BC. I had initially thought that this might have been a representation of Saturn at the north pole, but more likely it represented the planet Mercury.

Velikovsky and others have pointed out that Mercury has a very long history of providing the names of kings. The veneration of Mercury became prominent, for example, around 2000 BC, and again in the 8th and 7th century BC. The Turin papyrus claims a longer life for Mercury than any other planet, dating it to the nova event of Saturn in 4077 BC.

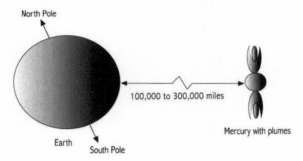

[Image: Winged Disk, view of Mercury from an equatorial perspective; tail and bow shock not shown. Illustration by J. Cook.]

Mercury, I have noted, would have accompanied Mars on its excursions near Earth. Thus Mercury first showed up for 300 years starting in 3067 BC, then for an equal period starting in 1936 BC, and last for a 120 year period starting in 806 BC. In between these times Mars and Mercury did not cross Earth's orbit anywhere near Earth for a span of more than 800 years. The start of the cycles of close calls are separated by 1100 years. The orbits of Mars and Mercury would have precessed away from Earth's orbit between these times.

Mercury had a magnetic field and an atmosphere, and therefore had plasma plumes at its poles. These would have pointed north and south as Earth passed Mercury, and likely would have been in constant motion. As the Earth turned toward the east, Mercury would have been seen traveling west like a flapping bird.

Special thanks S Borruso for the note on Josephus.

Endnotes

Note 1 --

The destruction was in fact much worse than presented here. Whole islands disappeared, others rose out of the sea. The destruction extended into Northern Europe. See in particular Velikovsky's unpublished documents at varchive.org, "The Dark Ages of Greece," the particular chapters ["Changes in Land and Sea"] for Roman recollections, and ["Closing the Gap"] for Greek, Egyptian, European, and Mesoamerican notes.

Note 2 --

During the 8th and 7th century over 300 cities in the Middle East were destroyed by earthquakes and fire. The Mycenaean Greek culture came to an end at this time (although conventionally dated 1200 BC). Mesoamerican farming villages, originally established after 1500 or 1200 BC, also suddenly disappear after about 800 BC.

In *Chaos and Creation* (1983), Alfred de Grazia writes about the book by Claude Schaeffer, *Stratigraphie Comparée et Chronologie de L'Asie Occidentale, IIIe-IIe millénaires* (1948):

"Certain outstanding events ... struck simultaneously a definite number or even the totality of urban centers of Western Asia. ... Not only is this conclusion persuasive as originally inscribed, but many locations can now be added to the doomsday list."

De Grazia notes the dates of about 2350, 2100, 1700, 1450, 1365, and 1235 BC, and adds:

"all that Schaeffer "automaticaly" consigns to the end of the Middle Bronze Age, at around 1750 BC I assign to the same time, but dated at about 1450 BC. The many destructions that he consigns to 1200-1300 BC, I assign to 800-700 BC."

"The results are remarkable. Suddenly, the vast 'hiatus' between '13th century' destruction and 6th century proto-classical times becomes only a brief hiatus. It is clear that the vast movements of 'the peoples of the seas' were a fiction employed by scholars to explain the widespread

natural disasters of the 8th and 7th centuries, the Mars disasters of our calendar."

In 1961 de Grazia contacted Schaeffer about updating the 1948 information. The project was cut short by Schaeffer's death.

The "people of the sea" are today held to be real by archaeologists, despite their admission that absolutely nothing is known about them, and there is virtually no mention of them in Egyptian records. I would suspect that the "people of the sea" are asteroids, comets, and bolides in the company of Mars. The sea, in that case, is the sky, even though the Absu had long ago disappeared.

But these could also be refugees from the northern regions devastated by Mars. Revisions of Egyptian chronology have moved the 19th dynasty 500 years into the future, resulting in a coincidence of some of the "sea people" incidents (there are plenty of casual although unspecific Egyptian mentions) with the suspected overpasses of Mars. See, for example, to begin with, Immanuel Velikovsky, *Ages in Chaos* (1952), and following texts. Also see Jim Reilly, *Displaced Dynasties* (displaceddynasties.com, circa 2000).

De Grazia's suggested changes of Schaeffer's dates are only "more or less" correct for the lapses in chronology of the Eastern Mediterranean region. First, 2350 BC and 2100 BC can be left to stand for my dates for changes in the Earth's orbit in 2349 BC and 2193 BC.

Schaeffer's date of 1750 BC is 300 years earlier than de Grazia's date of 1450 BC (as representing the Exodus). I should note, however, that except for Schaeffer's collected data, there is little other indication of destruction anywhere else in the world. A considerable portion of the lack of backup studies of the archaeology of this era is designed to avoid confirming the theories brought forward by Velikovsky.

The dating hiatus of the Greek "Dark Ages" starts in about 1200 BC, when the last of the Mycenaean structures are today dated. Thus Schaeffer's dates of 1365 and 1235 BC are probably correctly moved by de Grazia to the period of 806 BC to 687 BC.

Patten and Windsor, in *The Mars-Earth Wars* (1996), maintain that Mars alternately showed up at the spring equinox and in October. I have included the alternations between spring and fall suggested by Patten and Windsor (but not specific to the spring equinox), but at an interval of 15 years, as initially suggested by Velikovsky, and as can be verified from the Maya *Chilam Balam*. This series makes much more sense in terms of Bible chronology, and especially the series of prophets who warned of these events. Patten and Windsor suggest that the length of the year changed in -701, but it is fairly certain that this actually happened in 747 BC.

The *Chilam Balam* is a collection of post-colonial (16th century AD) native manuscripts in the Mayan languages, using European script, which recorded histories and prophesies, many dating back with certainty for hundreds of years, while others recollect events dating back thousands of years before we have any archaeological inkling of the Maya.

Extending the close passes of Mars backwards from 747 BC (-747), give the following set of dates extending to 806 BC, based on the simple supposition of an interval of 15 or 14.5 years. At any rate, the change in the length of the year in 747 BC would not significantly alter these dates. This combines the suggestion of Patten and Windsor with what I have from other sources. (I have added the 686 Mercury event, and the 685 Venus and Mercury nova -- to be discussed later.)

If the last (and only) Earth shock involving Mars happened in 747 BC, then the current synodic period of Mars can be used with an ephemeris for the dates after 747 BC, since there would have been no further changes in the orbit of Mars, except for a change in ellipticity (which does not change the orbital period). That means that the "contacts" of Mars with Earth before 747 BC might have involved only a slightly different synodic period for Mars. The last few calendar dates are accurate, and can be verified from Chinese and Mesoamerican sources. The "Sennacherib event" likely happened on March 23, 687 BC (Julian) and did not involve Mars, as an ephemeris will show. See endnotes of the following chapter for additional details plus Appendix B, "The Celestial Mechanics."

```
     year      date
    Julian   astronomical                    notes
    -------  --------------         --------------------

    806 BC   Spring -805
    791+     Oct
    777      Feb -776               the 'ballgame'
    762+     Oct                    lesser violence
    748      Feb 28 -747            Earth shock, year changes
    733      Oct                    lesser violence
    718      Mar
    703      Oct -702               lesser violence
    688      Mar -687               last sighting of Mars
    additional data:
    687      Mar 23 686             Sennacherib; shock by Mercury
    686      Jun-Jul 685            Venus and Mercury in nova
```

The archaeological record at Olmec La Venta only records the last five events, including 687 BC, although this might be the Earth shock by Mercury in 686 BC. The Guatemalan *Popol Vuh* also records a mythology of five close contacts. It is possible that Mesoamerica was differently affected by the first four contacts by Mars before 747 BC, since the Earth's orbit changed in 747 BC, although the archaeology of Central America records the disappearance of many villages in the 8th century BC.

I think it is the lack of Day Books based on the Long Count (which was instituted in 747 BC) that kept the previous four contacts with Mars from showing up in later transmitted records. The *Popol Vuh* thus only recounts details of the last five contacts recorded in the Day Books.

Note 3 --

Mercury, which apparently accompanied Mars, and was known at that time as Apollo, also steals cattle. It is amazing that there are so many stories about the doings of Apollo, if indeed this planet was only seen on occasion and for very short periods at sunrise or sunset.

Velikovsky quotes from Vedic hymns and from Joel. Inadvertently many of the descriptions match plasma effects and interactions within Earth's plasmasphere of the asteroids closely following Mars.

The Maruts number seven, writes Cardona, from information gathered from Indian sources. Away from the mass of Earth the gravitational sphere of influence for Mars would have been about 400,000 miles (650,000 km) (100 times the diameter of Mars, per Van Flandern). This is twice as far as the Moon is from Earth, and well within the gravitational sphere of influence of Earth. We can only assume that the Maruts remained with Mars because their velocity never matched the required speed needed to become Earth or Mars satellites or escape.

Note 4 --

Plato, in *Timaeus*, recalls what Egyptian priests told Solon:

"... you and your whole city are descended from a small seed or remnant of them which survived. And this was unknown to you, because, for many generations, the survivors of that destruction died, leaving no written word."

"For when there were any survivors ... they were men who dwelt in the mountains; and they were ignorant of the art of writing, and had heard only the names of the chiefs of the land, but very little about their actions."

The phrase, "men who dwelt in mountains," supports de Grazia's characterization of the survivors.

Note 5 --

The linguistic analysis by de Grazia and others exemplifies the impact that Homer's writings and language had in subsequently unifying the geographically widely separated Greeks. Alfred de Grazia writes:

"Homer used metaphors of the clearest and most ordinary kind, to the exclusion of far-flown and fancy comparisons. His poetry seems to be addressing audiences of low verbal ability; or they might have understood a melange of dialects and phrases, a lingua greca like a lingua franca or both. On the other hand, his similes are prolonged and complicated, dealing with rural and pastoral comparisons."

"More significant is the non-use of a sacred, liturgical language. If there had been a Mycenaean dead language, like classical Greek is to modern Greek, or Latin to Italian, then would not that have been the basis for portions of the epic poems? But it was not, not even for prayers. Therefore it did not exist. Mycenaean Greek was probably a living and related set of dialects whose standard expression had disappeared with its ruling class and scribes."

"The linguistic melange (with its numerous catch-phrases of all Greek sub-cultures), which was Homeric Greek, was 'instant prosody.' There had been no time, no more than a couple of generations, to build an epic language. Yet such an epic language would surely have evolved smoothly and uniformly over the several centuries of any 'Dark Ages.' What emerges therefore is a people and culture exploding in space and time, whose language, that of Homer, had not yet caught up with its expanding front."

By 600 BC the Greeks of Asia Minor make a concordance of Homer's vocabulary and are unable to place or define many of his words. It should be noted that Homer probably reintroduced the alphabet to the Greeks, since it seems clear that his works were not recited for 400 years, as conventionally understood, but written down.

Note 6 --

The iconography of the Maya, as well as the Quiche *Popol Vuh*, describe a direct connection between Mars and Earth by having Mars (K'awil, in Mayan; Tohil in Quiche) stand on a single leg, often a snake, which is a representation of lightning, reaching down four or five diameters from the bulbous body (or head) of Mars.

Mars, lacking a magnetic field and atmosphere, would have shown with a surrounding dust-laden plasma coma which would have been very little larger than the actual planet.

Note 7 --

Only where Mars came closest to Earth could mountain ridges be generated (claimed by Patten and Windsor). The mountain ridges (if any) would be formed in strips parallel to latitudinal lines. There are, however, only a few. Similarly, as the Earth rotated, the electric arc of Mars would travel at nearly the same latitude around all of the Earth. The seasonal tilt of the Earth has no influence on this, despite the claims to arc-shaped mountain ridges made by Patten and Windsor. There would be widening of the area devastated by lightning, and lessening, for Mars would shift north or south on its orbit in moving past Earth.

Without needing to find the length of Mars's orbit, or the lateral separation distance to Earth, the rise of Mars can be found as,

pi * 8000 * tan(1.85/deg) = 811 mi.

Where **pi * 8000** is the circumference of the Earth, and thus approximately equal to the horizontal distance traveled by Mars in one day with respect to the surface of Earth. The orbit of Mars is inclined at 1.85 degrees to the ecliptic (which is the orbit of Earth). Thus in one day (one rotation of Earth) Mars will move "up" by the circumference multiplied by the tangent of 1.85 degrees, while advancing along its own orbit next to Earth.

The value of 811 miles can be compared to the separation of locations of recognized damage by Mars. The distance from Athens to Scottland (at latitudes of 38 degrees and 56 degrees north) is 1242 miles. The distance from Mexico City to Arizona (at latitudes of 19.4 degrees and 34 degrees north) is 1007 miles. Both of these are close to the value of the expected creep northward of Mars, after allowing for another 1000 miles lateral movement.

We could calculate backward on the same basis of the latitudinal distances (1442 and 1007 miles), to calculate how long it would take Mars to travel this far north. That turns out to be 1.23 and 1.52 rotations of the Earth (not counting longitudinal differences), and thus provides a measure of how long it would take Mars to pass Earth.

Note 8 --

De Grazia suggests the deposition of iron ores (iron oxides) at the time of these close approaches of Mars. But disassociated ferrous and ferric iron ionize positively, and would have remained at Mars, under the assumption that Mars represented the cathode during lightning strikes. De Grazia bases much of this on the association of the start of iron smelting and forging -- the start of the "Iron Age" -- with the two centuries when these events happened. Iron ore is not confined to horizontal bands in the northern hemisphere, as it should be if it was deposited by Mars.

Note 9 --

There is a third companion or satellite of Mars mentioned by Homer ("Discord" or "Strife"), which is missing today. However, the description is closer to a rising stream of plasma, reading, "Strife, whose fury never tires, sister and friend of murderous Mars, who, from being at first but low in stature, grows till she uprears her head to heaven, though her feet are still on earth."

Jonathan Swift wrote the following in *Gulliver's Travels* (AD 1726):

"They [the Laputans] *have likewise discovered two lesser Stars or Satellites, which revolve about Mars, whereof the innermost is distant from the Centre of the Primary Planet exactly three of his Diameters, and the outermost five* [Diameters]; *the former revolves in the Space of ten hours, and the latter in twenty-one and a half."*

He follows this with some mathematical information. The information is nearly correct, and involves Keplerian and Newtonian mechanics. Swift knew both Isaac Newton and Edmund Halley, although neither knew of the satellites of Mars. No telescope could resolve the satellites until 1877, 150 years after Swift. The actual distances are 0.4 and 3.5 diameters and the periods of rotation are 7.5 hours and 30 hours. Patten and Windsor make the following observation in *The Mars-Earth Wars* (1996):

"At that time, in 1725 and 1726, astronomers did not know the diameter of Mars. Laputans disclosed the distance of Phobos and Deimos from Mars not in English miles but rather in Mars diameters. Astronomers in the early 1700's did not know the accurate value for the length of the astronomical unit. And they didn't know how far Mars was from the Sun. This unit of measurement in the satire suggests a very ancient sketch was involved, or a copy thereof from the Catastrophic Era."

Isaac Asimov, in *The Kingdom of the Sun* (1960), dismisses Swift's claims as a lucky guess, but then writes:

"However, his guess that Phobos would rise in the west and set in the east because of its speed of revolution is uncanny, it is undoubtedly the luckiest guess in literature."

Others have suggested that the information came from China or Japan during the 18th century. Swift places Laputa as a small island off the coast of China.

Note 10--

Although the Aztecs arrive very late to Central Mexico (AD 1100) they derive the qualities of their war God (Huitzilopochtli) from the Toltecs (since circa AD 800) whose war-like God (initially Xipe Totec) had been imported into the region. The people of the earlier classical phase, as at the ceremonial city of Teotihuacan, lasting from circa 200 BC to circa AD 700, had worshipped more benign deities (as far as we know).

It was visitors from Teotihuacan, however, who introduced a magic shield consisting of a flayed human face to the Maya, along with a considerably less effective dart thrower. The genesis of the flayed face, as a mask or shield is clearly seen in earlier Olmec sculptures.

Note 11 --

The year 687 BC is four 15-year periods after 747 BC, thus suggesting 5 close passes of Mars if 747 BC is included. The year 702 BC is three 15-year periods after 747 BC, equivalent to four close passes.

Note 12 --

From the timing of the effects on dawn and dusk, it seems clear that the episode of the *Iliad* recounts a shock by Mars in Northern Asia in 747 BC. The episode of the *Odyssey* recounts a shock by Mercury in North America in 686 BC, and thus experienced at nightfall in Greece. Electric contacts always happen at about noon local time, and thus at a location of Earth facing the Sun. The *Iliad* and *Odyssey* recount what happened at dawn and dusk, a quarter turn away from the location of the noon sun. With these details in place the respective compositional dates of the *Iliad* and the *Odyssey* can be determined as after 747 BC and alternately after 686 BC.

Note 13 --

See the article by Ralph Juergens, at [saturniancosmology.org/juergensa.htm]. From this, by the look of the rilles of craters of the Moon, it might only take seconds for electrons to course through crustal material.

Note 14 --

With the second Earth shock in 686 BC the length of the year did not change at all, since we have no record anywhere of additional calendar reforms. I would suspect that the ellipticity of Earth's orbit might have changed. That allows a change in Kinetic Energy without changing the orbital period.

Note 15 --

More details and ephemeris data may be found in the Appendix "The Canopus Decree."

Note 16 --

The "Era of Nabonassar" actually starts on February 27th of the Julian calendar. Ussher relates:

"From twelve o'clock [noon], *on the first day of the Egyptian month Thoth, from Wednesday, February 26th, in the evening, in the year 747 BC, all astronomers unanimously start the calendar of Nabonassar."*

Ussher is here supposedly using the Julian calendar. The date matches the starting date of the Roman calendar (which we use today) as starting on March 1, the day after February 28th. The Olmec Long Count starts on February 28, 748 BC (-747), but on the Gregorian calendar. I suspect that in all these cases the actual dates are on a seasonal calendar, a Gregorian equivalent calendar.

"Starting at noon" has been the bane of Julian day chronology ever since Ptolemy. "In the evening" is the traditional Egyptian (and Hebrew) start of the day.

Note 17 --

Before 747 BC, when the Moon's orbit was 30 days, the Moon would have been on an orbit around the Earth which was considerably larger than today. There would not have been any eclipses (lunar or solar) seen on Earth, for the hard shadow of the Moon, the umbra, decreases in size with distance, and at some distance completely disappears. This happens on occasion today because the distance between Earth and the Moon varies somewhat over time.

Ptolemy does not list all the eclipses which might have been available to him, even though certainly by AD 200 these could have been retrocalculated. Ptolemy lists ten lunar eclipses between 721 BC and 381 BC, from Babylonian sources, 5 eclipses from 201 BC to 141 BC, from Greek sources, and four between AD 125 and AD 136, from his own observations (at

Alexandria). The number is certainly much less that the 400 or more eclipses which might have been visible in Mesopotamia (although, eclipses are visible only in limited and variable portions of the world).

Robert R. Newton, in *The Origin of Ptolemy's Astronomical Tables* (John Hopkins, 1985) (also, *The Crime of Claudius Ptolemy* 1977), questions the validity of many of these eclipses. Others are of a different opinion, although John M. Steele, in "A Re-analysis of the Eclipse Observations in Ptolemy's *Almagest*" in *Centaurus 42* (2000), also questions the validity of some dates.

The point, however, is that both in Alexandria and China, records of eclipses start to appear only after 747 BC, although the earliest in both instances are in 721 and 720 BC. Some of the first eclipses of the Sun experienced in the 8th century BC were at times produced by Mars, and would have been associated with the destructive contacts by Mars. These solar eclipses would have struck terror in the people of the Mesopotamian region.

Alfred de Grazia has noted:

"When Velikovsky's Worlds in Collision *appeared in 1950, many a critic leaped at it claiming that eclipses of the times before 700 B.C. were known and hence the skies had been orderly for long before then. Over the years he and his supporters put to rest this claim. No such historical record exists; there is no anomaly present."*
-- De Grazia, *The Burning of Troy* (1984)

Note 18 --

In the previous era, 1492 to 747 BC, the year had been 360 days and the period of Venus was 225 days. The synodic period of Venus (the time of an apparent revolution around the Sun as seen from Earth) would be
$(360*225)/(360-225) = 600$ days.

The continued use of a 10-lunar-month calendar (from the previous era of 2193 BC to 1492 BC), after the year had changed to 360 days (and 12 lunar months of 30 days), would match the 600-day synodic period of Venus. Two rotations through 10 months would bring the year around to another heliacal rising of Venus. After six rotations through 10 months the heliacal rising of Venus (which, I should point out, was absolutely spectacular in antiquity) would again fall on the same solar year day as 5 years earlier, **$5*360 - 3*600 = 0$**. Five 360-day years is 1800 days; six rotations of 10 months of 30 days is also 1800 days.

This explains why after 747 BC, when the period of the Moon no longer divided the Earth's year into equal and repeating segments, the "Venus calendar" was kept in use. Even though it fell behind a day every four solar years it was much more useful than a calendar based on the Moon.

Note 19 --

Ussher states:

"748 BC -- Rome was founded by Romulus according to the reckoning of Fabius Pictor, the most ancient of all Roman writers. This date is confirmed according to the account of the secular games held by the ancient Romans most religiously. This happened shortly before the beginning of the 8th Olympiad, on the feast of their goddess Pales, on the 10th day of April."

The 8th Olympiad is **776 - 8*4 = 744 BC**, shortly after 747 BC.

Velikovsky suggests that the changes in the Roman months were made following 747 BC, but this is not likely to be correct. Because it is certain that before 747 BC there were 12 months of 30 days in the year, the only reason to add two months to the year would be to correct the 10-month calendar held over from the previous era, when there were 10 months in the year.

Before 747 BC, all the months were 30 days, adding up to a 360-day year. In 747 BC the decision was made to start the year (March first) after the 28th day of February, since that day coincided with the disturbance (or the end of the disturbance) by Mars. But with the month of February now short by two days, and the new year five days longer, seven extra days had to be distributed over the 12 months of 30 days.

The extra days of the year were distributed to the first, third, and fifth months of the first five months of the old 10-month calendar (March, May, July) and in the same manner to the second five months (August, October, December), with the last additional day going to January.

Later Roman historians, noting the nearly symmetrical distribution of extra days to alternate months of the 12-month calendar, suggested that the emperor Augustus stole a day from February to be added to the month named after himself, August, just as Julius Caesar had done for his month, July.

The Julian calendar instituted by Julius Caesar included a provision for a leap day. February 24th was doubled, that is, used twice, to accomplish the leap day. Note that this is 5 days from the end of the month. It is five days before the day of the Earth shock by Mars.

But things are not as simple as all this. See, for example, the topic of "Roman_calendar" at Wikipedia, some of which is made up on the basis of uniformitarian principles.

Note 20 --

Assuming a 584-day synodic period for Venus based on the canonical values of the Venus calendar of the Maya *Dresden Codex* (dating at the earliest to AD 700), when the Earth's year changed to 365.25 days after 747 BC, the coincidence of an Earth/Venus calendar would have been **(5*584) - (8*365.25) = 2 days** -- representing a slippage of two days over 8 Earth years. A half period (4 years) would only displace the calendar by one day. This Venus calendar was in use throughout the world -- as for example, among the Egyptians and the Inca. It was used nominally also by the Greeks, who base their "Olympiads" on 4- or 8-year intervals, starting in 772 BC. Actual local calendars of the Greek city-states varied enormously, being based on local religious feasts and later on civil tax collection needs.

The Romans, by the first century BC, had done something similar, repeatedly shifting the start of the year by edict of the Senate so as to increase tax collection. Julius Caesar's reform in 40 BC was welcomed universally as a return to sanity. This is also why he was allowed to move the start of the year from March 1 to January 1, breaking a 700-year-old religious tradition.

Note 21--

In Mesoamerica only the Zapotecs of Monte Alban in West Central Mexico added a leap day. Apparently this was done in 607 BC, when a switch could be made to the Zapotec annual calendar without missing a day of the traditional Tzolkin calendar. See the chapter "The Day of Kan" for details.

Note 22--

The Mesoamerican Long Count calendar "completed a Baktun" on February 28, -747 (Gregorian), going to a count of six Baktuns, zero Katuns, zero Tuns, zero Uinals, and zero days (6.0.0.0.0 in Long Count notation), on day 11-Ahau, 8-Uo.

The year is the astronomical year of -747, which is actually 748 BC on the Gregorian calendar. (Astronomical dates include a "year zero," which is not used in BC/AD calendar notation.) I have quoted (as elsewhere) an astronomical date (like -747) as a historical date (747 BC, instead of 748 BC).

Additionally, because of the Mesoamerican concepts that a day does not exist until it is completed, the Long Count use of "day zero" actually signifies the first day of the new era, so that the actual era-ending date is February 27th. I should also note that I am using the Thompson "August 11" correlation for conversion to the Gregorian calendar in this instance. See the chapter "The Maya Calendar" for additional details. The "August 13" correlation was, I suspect, instituted in the Valley of Mexico sometime around 600 BC or later. It spread to the coastal Olmec region, and most of the Maya in the Peten and the Yucatan, but not to coastal Guatemala where the "August 11" Long Count was retained to today.

Note 23--

The "Post Classical" Maya, after about AD 900, reduced their dating to a repeating cycle of 13 Katuns. This is the Maya "Short Count" calendar, where years rotate through a series of 13 Katuns (20-year periods of 360-day years), before repeating again (thus representing about 256 years). The 13 Katun periods are named after the name of the last day of the Katun on the Tzolkin day calendar. The series rotates, in turn, through the Katun names of 11-Ahau, 9-Ahau, 7-Ahau, 5-Ahau, etc., followed by a decreasing series of even-numbered Ahau days, and ending in 13-Ahau.

The texts of *The Book Of Chilam Balam of Chumayel*, translated by Ralph Roys (1932) insistently claims that Maya history starts with Katun 11-Ahau.

A Katun 11-Ahau ended on February 28, -747, Gregorian, thus starting a new era. Although we would hold that Katun 9-Ahau would be the start of the new era, in the languages of Mesoamerica it is the completion of a previous time period which marks a beginning. (See the chapters "The Maya Calendar" and "The Chilam Balam" for more details.)

Note 24--

As a comment on the validity of the date of February 26, 747 BC, for the Earth shock by Mars, Velikovsky wrote, "It is worth noting ... that the ancient inhabitants of Mexico celebrated their New Year on the day which corresponds, in the Julian calendar, to the same date [of February 26]." He quotes from J. de Acosta *The Natural and Moral History of the Indies*, which was translated in AD 1604 and re-edited in AD 1880. "The Mexicans" are the Aztecs, since the Maya celebrated New Year on July 26th when the Sun passed directly overhead in Central Yucatan. However, the quoted date is on the Gregorian calendar, not on the Julian calendar. In about AD 1550 there was a ten-day difference between the Julian and the Gregorian calendars. The date may have been converted from Julian calendar notation to Gregorian calendar notation by the translator or editor.

The information attributed to J. de Acosta does not match other sources for the start of the Aztec new year. Vincent Malmstrom writes, "the Spanish clerics Sahagún and Durán, disagreed: The first cited a beginning Julian calendar date of February 2; the second, March 1."

Note 25--

Linda Schele and David Freidel used the August 11 correlation in their 1990 book *A Forest of Kings,* but switch to the August 13 correlation with the publication in 1993 of *Maya Cosmos.*

Note 26--

Patten and Windsor quote from Louis Ginzberg, *The Legends of the Jews* (1928):

"When Rabshakah [the Assyrian commander in chief] heard the singing of the Hallel he counseled Sennacherib to withdraw from Jerusalem, as on this night -- the first night of Passover -- many miracles were wrought for Israel. Sennacherib however did not accept the wise counsel given him."

Egypt had been under Assyrian control for a number of years, an event not much recorded by Egyptians, when a revolt aided by the Sudanese king Tirhaka ousted the Assyrians shortly before 686 BC. Sennacherib's campaign was meant to retake Egypt.

Note 27 --

More than a "blast from heaven," the incident of this year (held to be either 686 BC or 687 BC) also has to be recognized for simultaneous worldwide earthquakes. But in those days no one paid attention to earthquakes.

Dwardu Cardona, in "Velikovsky's Martian Catastrophes" (Aeon 1990) wrote about this incident:

"If the sources are to be believed, the suddenness of the slaughter as the army lay resting during the night plus the 'burned' nature of the victims, with their garments remaining intact, do not imply the effects of a hurricane. But with so many contradicting reports, including that given by Herodotus, all of which invoke 'miraculous' phenomena, should any of these bizarre details be given credence? And if so, which?"

"Thus the aura of mystery remains attached to Sennacherib's last campaign but, as matters stand at present, the issue cannot be resolved by attributing any of this to a close Martian flyby which was apparently noted by no one."

The blast of wind happened almost directly opposite the location of the

North American contact site of Mercury, not antipodal, but certainly in the northern hemisphere and at almost exactly the same latitude.

Note 28 --

Eric Miller, at the Saturnian Conference "Velikovsky -- Ancient Myth and Modern Science" (1994, Portland, OR), introduced his talk with the following:

"I was going to go through Velikovsky, show that his dating of 687 B.C. for the second catastrophic event is probably an error, that Velikovsky's sources are incorrect as to his Chinese sources."

The "sources," however, are competent 19th century European astronomers.

Note 29 --

[*Image: Semi-circle of compressed mountains centered on Northern Alabama. Courtesy of Dennis Cox, http://sites.google.com/site/dragonstormproject/*]

The source is from Velikovsky and attributed to the Menominee Indians of North America. The Menominee are indigenous to Wisconsin, and thus located well away from the area of destruction. Velikovsky has, as an added detail from an original Ute source (S. Thompson *Tales of the North American*

Indians, 1929), "... a huge conflagration enveloped the American prairies and forests as soon as the sun, frightened off by the snarer, returned a little on its way." The timing is absolutely correct. The event was also noted by Hawaiians and Polynesians, who recall (from their perspective) that at the onset the Sun rose and reversed itself before appearing again.

The North American site of the impact is clearly in Northern Alabama in the USA, centered on Huntsville. The particular shape of the compressed mountains follows the form predicted by consideration of the application of an initial compressive force. The "burning prairies and forests" were due to a path of electric arcing which traveled west from the "impact" location, and were noted by Plains Indian tribes.

It is quite possible that Venus played the role of Coyote in this tale. Venus was in the day sky west of the Sun. As the skies darkened, Venus would have been seen with the cord of a snare (its plasma tail) in hand, extending away from the Sun.

Consideration of the applied torque (due to the electric contact with Mercury) in the northern hemisphere in North America, and the gyroscopic reaction torque, will support the movements of the Sun and Mars described in the text. (See Appendix B, "The Celestial Mechanics" for additional details.)

Note 30--

Velikovsky was initially uncertain about the date of the second close approach, but in the chapter "The Later Campaigns of Sennacherib," of the later unpublished text "The Assyrian Conquest," Velikovsky notes:

"In the last century scholars became aware that there were two invasions of Palestine by Sennacherib and that it is possible to discern in the scriptural record an early and a late campaign against Hezekiah. The first campaign to Palestine took place about -701. The second campaign is dated by modern historians to -687 or -686."

He sources Henry Rawlinson and, more recently, John Bright (1962), William Albright (1956 ?), and Edwin R. Thiele (1951).

Likewise Donald W. Patten and Samuel R. Windsor, in *The Mars-Earth Wars* (1996), use 701 BC as the year of Sennacherib's disaster, based on the chronology developed by Edwin R. Thiele in *The Mysterious Numbers of the Hebrew Kings* (1965, and 1951 above).

I am not at all convinced that either 687 BC or 701 BC should be used for a second Earth shock. The selection of dates hinges on the supposition that the catastrophe which befell Sennacherib at the gates of Jerusalem needs to be identified directly with an Earth shock by Mars. This is simply not so, since

Sennacherib's army obviously was afflicted with a localized Ignis Coelis. Earth shocks are not required for that to happen, as subsequent history -- into the 20th century AD -- testifies. See Appendix B, "The Celestial Mechanics."

The *Chilam Balam* only has reference to the first and the last appearance of Mars. The first recorded appearance of 747 BC produced the Earth shock, and changed the orbit of the Earth. Earlier close passes of Mars (before 747 BC) were not recorded as significant, or were missing from the Day Books of the Long Count which was started in 747 BC.

Additional text of the Maya *Chilam Balam* states that some other planet showed up 9 times ("Bolon Mayel" -- Nine Fragrances), bringing flowers and perfumes. To show "flowers" the planet had to have a magnetic field. As I point out in Appendix B, "Celestial Mechanics," this was Mercury. Mars has no magnetic field. I will insist on the date of 686 BC, not 687 BC, and suggest that Mercury, not Mars, was the agent for the second Earth shock. Two independent Chinese sources confirm the date.

Note 31 --

I will later suggest that the interactions with Mars stopped in 670 BC, when Earth's orbit became nearly circular (as noted by Rose and Vaughan), and thus Earth no longer came near the orbit of Mars -- which even today is still quite elliptical. See following text for details.

Note 32 --

It is likely that Isaiah addresses Mercury, that is, Phaethon, not Venus. Phaethon can be placed in 685 BC as Mercury. "Helel ben-Shahar," which is how Isaiah addresses Mercury, reads then as "Shining son of Dawn" (Eos), which is exactly how the Greeks addressed Phaethon.

Note 33 --

The *Popol Vuh* actually shrouds this in a narrative of the ball-playing twins Xbalanque and Hunahpu, and reads, *"And then the boys ascended this way, here* [that is, toward Earth], *into the middle of the light, and they ascended straight on into the sky. ..."*

The "eight days" of the inferior conjunction mentioned in the text -- the time after which Quetzalcoatl rose as the Morning Star -- are from the canonical Venus calendar. The Maya values are from the *Dresden Codex*, and were last recopied in circa AD 1200, from manuscripts dating to AD 700. The Maya values and today's values (from first eastern visibility through the following inferior conjunction) are as follows:

236 90 250 8 (Maya canonical values)
263 50 263 8 (Current Values)
     ...both add up to a total of 584 days. The values above represent, in order:
-- the visibility of Venus after first rising in the east
-- the days Venus disappears after setting in the east
-- the visibility of Venus after first rising in the west
-- the days Venus disappears after setting in the west
     After setting in the west, Venus would reappear in the east. Neither the 8 days nor the 50 days are hard and fast, since they vary somewhat with the elevation of Venus above or below the Sun, and the relative elevation of Earth. The total, which represents the synodic orbit of Venus, remains the same. The only differences in the values are due to the ellipticity of the orbit -- which will not change the orbital period. The critics of Velikovsky should have understood that, but remained ignorant of basic astronomy.
     The canonical Venus calendar of Mesoamerica is only marginally different from current observations. Of note is the longer time of the superior conjunction. The finely tuned tables of Venus predictions of the *Dresden Codex*, for which the Maya have gained some fame as astronomers, consist entirely of observational corrections to this chart. From this we could guess that the canonical values were derived at an earlier time -- long before AD 700.
     William Douglas, in *Kronos* (1982), supplied the visibility and disappearance of Venus in the seventh century BC from the *Tablets of Ammizaduga*, as follows:

```
240.2 90 249.4 7 (total 586.6) (Section I)
245 90 245 7    (total 587)   (Section II)
```

     As the data shows, the synodic period of the orbit of Venus has decreased by 3 days since the 7th century BC. Since at that time the Earth's period was 365.25 days, the orbital period of Venus was only slightly longer than today, 225.1 days, as can be found from the formula for the synodic period, **(365.25 * 225.1)/(365.25 - 225.1) = 586.6**.
     Also note that the Maya canonical values are close to the 7th century BC values. It would suggest that Venus was still on an elliptical orbit at the time when the Maya (or their Olmec predecessors) first collected this observational data.

Note 34 --

     See for instance the collection of references to "a prodigy in the sky," and other notable displays of Venus, by Velikovsky in *Worlds in Collision*.

Velikovsky, however, often places events in the wrong era and at times he also identifies celestial bodies as Venus and Mars, when it is obvious from the quoted texts that the references are to Venus and Mercury or Venus and the Sun.

If the flaming up of Venus and Mercury was due to a massive plasma expulsion by the Sun (as seems very likely from the follow-up reaction by Jupiter), then the Earth also would have ended up doing the same thing, but because of the Earth's magnetosphere and enclosing atmosphere, the Earth might have been spared the creation of thousands of electric burn craters. There is the contemporaneous statement by Assurbanipal, king of Assyria, about Ishtar (Venus) "raining fire over Arabia" (quoted in the text). Later Roman writers make the same claim of the Earth burning up because of the close approach of Phaethon, as did Plato.

Note 35 --

It had been assumed that the "ball" in the celestial ballgame of 776 BC was the Moon. This was partially based on reports by Velikovsky from Roman sources that the "month" varied greatly around the time of the founding of Rome, circa 747 BC. However, the Roman "month" was a calendar measure, not the orbital period of the Moon. It was an attempt by the Romans to adjust the calendar to the new length of the year after 747 BC. It is just doubtful that the orbit of the Moon would be affected, especially repeatedly. There is also no information on this from any other sources.

Considering that Mercury shows up repeatedly during the period of 806 BC to 686 BC (as it had for periods after 3067 BC and after 1936 BC), it is more likely that it was Mercury which is to be understood as a participant in the foot race.

Note 36 --

The Olympic Games were said to have been founded by Hercules (Mars) at Pelop's tomb at Olympia in the northwest Peloponneses. An ephemeris shows a near conjunction of Earth with Mars and Venus in 776 BC (assuming Mars to be within the orbit of Earth, rather than without). Notes on this may be found in Appendix B, "Celestial Mechanics."

The Chinese Book of Shih King, the *Book of Odes*, lists a "celestial event" for 776 BC. In the 19th century it was reputed to only be an eclipse of the Sun. As a book of collected poetry, the Shih King is not concerned with celestial events. It is the only "celestial event" which entered the book. Since the Moon was on a slightly larger orbit at that time, it is unlikely that the eclipse was caused by the Moon. (No hard shadow would be cast on Earth.)

Thus it might have been a planet on an inner orbit.

Another source for celestial phenomena during this period of time, the *Spring and Autumn Annals*, compiled by Confucius and completed about 480 BC, lists some 35 eclipses, almost all of which were verified in the 19th century, but includes no dates significant to conjunctions with Venus or Mars.

The games have to be understood as religious. Mars set the example in the skies of what activity among humans would keep punishments away.

Note 37 --

In the 5th century BC Herodotus placed the Trojan war in 1200 BC, a date later taken up by Eratosthenes. However, the date has been in controversy since the time of Herodotus. The Trojan War should be placed in the 8th or 7th century BC -- not in the 11th century BC. The testimony of the Asiatic Greeks, who traced their ancestry to the heroes of the *Iliad*, agrees on this. Velikovsky also makes a good case for placing the war in the middle of the 8th century BC, after 747 BC.

Following is a footnote from an unpublished document by Velikovsky on the later dating of the Trojan war. The footnote was added by Jan Sammer. The actual document expands on this considerably:

A. R. Burn, *Minoans, Philistines, and Greeks: B.C. 1400-900* (London, 1930) pp. 52-54: *"It cannot be too strongly emphasized that the traditional date of the Trojan War, 1194-84, adopted by Eratosthenes and more or less tentatively accepted in so many modern books, is absolutely worthless"* being based on Eratosthenes's *"wild overestimate of the average length of a generation."* Cf. idem, "Dates in Early Greek History," *Journal of Hellenic Studies* 55 (1935) pp. 130-146. Cf. also D. Page, *History and the Homeric Iliad* (University of California Press, 1959) p. 96, n. 159: *"(the date) given by Eratosthenes is nothing but a guess proceeding from flimsy premises which could not possibly have led to a scientific calculation."* Another writer adds: *"sober historical judgment must discard the ancient chronological schemes in toto; they are nothing more than elaborate harmonizations of myths and legends which were known in later times and have no independent value whatever for historical purposes."* (G. Starr, *The Origins of Greek civilization: 1100-650 B.C.* (New York, 1961) p. 67.
    -- Velikovsky (Sammer) unpublished document at [www.varchive.org]

The actual dates of the war do not matter. The war was probably a fiction. It is the retelling by Homer and others which weave into the tale the doings of the planets in the 8th century BC that is of interest.

Alfred de Grazia suggests that the characterization of the heroes as berserkers, pirates, and incompetent warriors and sailors corresponds to the expected reaction of survivors of calamities of enormous scope, which removed all prior institutions of government, religion, history, and literacy.

Note 38 --

The new period of the Moon after 747 BC did not fit evenly into a solar year of 365.25 days. In the previous period, 12 months of 30 days had equaled a year of 360 days. Actually, it is my suspicion that the Roman people of Italy were still using a 10-month calendar cycle, left over from the calendar of an earlier epoch (when two 10-month periods exactly matched the synodic period of Venus). Romulus, mythological founder of Rome, instituted a 10-month calendar, says Ovid (de Grazia). There is also a claim by Roman historians, however, that the second king of Rome, Numa, added two months, January and February, at the end of the ten-month civil year, whose original names ended in October, November, and December, which translate as eighth, ninth, and tenth.

Note 39 --

See "Of The Moon And Mars, The Origins Of The Lunar Sinuous Rilles" Ralph E. Juergens, Published in *Pensee Journal*, 1974, in two parts and available locally as [saturniancosmology.org/juergensa.htm] and [saturniancosmology.org/juergensb.htm]

Note 40 --

There is a clear reference to the Olympic Games in the *Iliad*, about a chariot race, recounted by Nestor, which was recognized as an anachronism by the Greek editors in the sixth century BC. This anachronism, one of a number of instances, would date the authorship to well after 680 BC, when chariot racing was added to the foot races.

Note 41 --

Despite the universal use of the ballgame by many diverse societies in Mesoamerica over a 2200-year time span, we do not have a single description of how it was played. It was banned by the invading Spanish. All the information which has been gathered is inferential.

Calculations are in Unix bc notation, where ∧ denotes exponentiation; the

functions a(rctangent), s(ine), and c(osine) use radians; angle conversions to radians or degrees by the divisors rad=.017+ and deg=57.2+; other functions are shown as f( ); tan( )=s( )/c( )
units: million == 1,000,000; billion == 1,000,000,000;
AU == 93,000,000 miles.

Recovering the Lost World,
A Saturnian Cosmology -- Jno Cook
Chapter 24: The Tablets of Ammizaduga

Revision: 42.42 (bolt.php)
Contents of this chapter: [The Tablets of Ammizaduga] [The Golden Throne] [The Blazing Star] [The Bolt from Jupiter] [The Planets in the Sky] [The Twins] [The Last Changes] [Endnotes]

The *Tablets of Ammizaduga*

For such significant events as described in the previous chapter, we have surprisingly few accurate written records. From Mesoamerica we have the story that Quetzalcoatl set himself on fire. We do have dates from late Maya sources (the *Books of the Chilam Balam*), which can be verified against the alignments of Mesoamerican ceremonial centers (detailed in the chapter "Olmec Alignments"). Other than that we have the Phaethon legend from the Mediterranean and a few other curious documents. I'll discuss calendar dates in the year of this event later in this chapter. First I need to establish the year.

Among Mesopotamian sources we have, almost as a coincidence, the most curious and frequently misread, *Venus Tablets of Ammizaduga* -- a 21-year Babylonian record of the appearances and disappearances of Venus. Velikovsky had used the information from the *Venus Tablets of Ammizaduga* to demonstrate the erratic behavior of Venus in the era of the Exodus of Moses in 1492 BC. The *Venus Tablets of Ammizaduga* have traditionally been assigned to 1900 to 1000 BC. But an investigation by Lynn Rose and Raymond Vaughan in 1974 (and through 1980) determined that the *Venus Tablets of Ammizaduga* belonged to the 7th century BC, as others have also suggested earlier. Additionally, despite claims that the tablets represent completely confusing and erroneous data, Rose and Vaughan revealed the data for Venus to be inherently consistent.

The *Venus Tablets of Ammizaduga* are clay tablets found in the library of Assurbanipal of Nineveh, which burned down in 612 BC. Some 20 copies have been found (including some at other locations). Assurbanipal was a king of Assyria, the grandson of Sennacherib, and a collector of ancient literature. The tablets record the first and last visibility of Venus in the east and in the west, what we today call the disappearance before showing up as the Morning Star or the Evening Star. It is important to realize that the tablets record when Venus disappeared and when it reappeared -- nothing else. They read (for example), "Venus disappeared in the east on ... remained absent ... months and ... days and reappeared in the west on... ." [note 1]

Dating these tablets has been a problem. The only clue has been an insertion on a line of the tablet which should show the record of the second half of the cycle of year 8 (year 9 of my tabulation). "Venus was not observed for a period of nine months and four days." The data is missing and instead we find the words "The Golden Throne." [note 2]

"... this phrase meant 'year of the golden throne' ... a year-formula that had been used to refer to the eighth year of the reign of Ammizaduga [what an amazing coincidence], *the next-to-last king during the first Babylonian dynasty* [circa 1500 or 1900 BC]. *... it is located in the space that would originally have contained the rest of the observational material for the eighth year* [the 9th year as shown on my tabulations]. *As it is now, we have only the date of Venus's disappearance* [in the east], *not the interval of invisibility and not the data of reappearance* [in the west]."

-- Lynn Rose and Raymond Vaughan, Kronia Conference, Portland, (1994)

The tablets are at times dismissed as "omen tablets" because the data for each year are annotated with what is thought to be omen information, like "... and there is war in the east" or, "the harvest is good." But omens traditionally read as "if-then phrases," like, "if earthquakes last all day, then there will be destruction in the land." The *Venus Tablets* do not read like this. Of course there are also problems distinguishing tenses, but the few I have seen read like contemporaneous observations.

Separate tablets have small errors of a day or so between them, as if we are looking at a collation of separate observations. But the tablets had to be important. They may have been used in a scribal school, which generally copied only important documents. And they are unique. No other planets were observed closely at that time. The movements of Venus must have been regarded as very significant.

But the biggest problem with the tablets has been the fact that the data -- the times of visibility and invisibility -- do not match the observations of today. That has been very disconcerting to astronomers who expect that the orbits of the Earth and all the planets have remained the same since the beginnings of the Solar System, 4 billion years ago. If the orbits had always remained the same, the risings and settings of Venus could be calculated back to the eighth century BC or even earlier, but backwards calculations do not match the Babylonian data for Venus. This is disconcerting because the same Babylonians plotted the stars accurately to within a few seconds of a degree, measured the length of each day of movement of the Sun against the stars during the year, kept detailed records of the travels of other planets, knew the length of the year to within 20 minutes, and could measure the latitude of cities to within a fraction of a degree. Something was wrong. [note 3]

The *Tablets of Ammizaduga* have been investigated and discussed in archaeological and astronomical literature repeatedly since AD 1865. A number of these studies held that the data was in error, or suggested that it was made up. The studies all assumed that the orbits of Venus and Earth were nearly perfect circles in the past, as they are today.

From 1974 through 1980 the tablets were investigated again by Lynn Rose and Raymond Vaughan, but without the bias of academic astronomy which, over a century of investigations, had simply removed data which did not fit (variously reported on in *Kronos* in 1980).

Rose and Vaughan hold the data to be from the eighth century BC, not from the reign of Ammizaduga nearly a thousand years earlier as had previously been assumed, although exact dates were not determined. (However, *I did* determine the exact dates, for which see further below.) Rose and Vaughan used the fact that the orbits of Venus and Earth did not intersect. This was an unneeded assumption based on the "collision" of planets proposed by Velikovsky in *Worlds in Collision* which could be dropped.

Schiaparelli in 1906 also dated the tablets to the 8th century BC, but based on mention of an invading Asiatic tribe which could be dated to the eighth century BC.

What Rose and Vaughan did was to normalize the data with respect to planetary orbital eccentricities. (Eccentricity is a measure of how much an orbit deviates from the circular.) That process removed the variations in actual day counts, yielding dimensionless units related to planetary eccentricities. In "normalized" form, the data tells very little about actual orbits, but it does tell of changes in eccentricities, and changes in perihelion. There is a change in the perihelion of the Earth's orbit after year 9 (year 10 and later), and a rather radical change in the eccentricity of Earth (from 0.10 to 0.0) after year 19.

Normalized, the data looks little different from today's observations. The large remaining discrepancy is the missing second part of the data of year 8, and the insertion of the phrase "The Golden Throne." [note 4]

The Golden Throne

I think the tablets record planetary events following the destruction of the temple of Marduk at Babylon in 689 BC, and its subsequent restoration in 680 BC. To point up the disruptions of the seventh century, Velikovsky had written that Babylon "did not celebrate New Year's day for a twenty year period" from 687 BC to 669 or 667 BC. "Eight years under Sennacherib, twelve years under Esarhaddon," Velikovsky quoted from the records from Nineveh, a sum of twenty years. He fit this period to what he thought to be the Earth shock of 687 BC as the starting date and the death of Esarhaddon in 668 BC as the end date -- also a difference of twenty years. However, it adds up to 21 years if different end points are counted -- 689 BC, the destruction of the temple at Babylon, instead of 687 BC (the second shock to Earth), through 668 BC, the crowning of a new king of Babylon. Velikovsky never connected the 20-year hiatus of New Year celebrations with the 21-year record of the Venus tablets which he had quoted earlier in his book.

Additionally, Velikovsky does not mention that Babylon, occupied by Elam, was destroyed under an Assyrian siege in 689 BC, the temple compounds at the center were razed and left unoccupied for eight years, and not rebuilt until 680 BC. No wonder there were no New Year celebrations.

In about 695 BC, Sennacherib, king of Assyria, who later lost an army in the siege of Jerusalem (686 BC), had attacked the kingdom of Elam on the Persian Gulf, by sending ships and troops down the Tigris river from Syria. Elam, although an Iranian nation, at that time held most of Babylonia (Mesopotamia) from south of the city of Babylon to the Persian Gulf. Elam struck back with an overland expedition which took the city of Babylon from Assyrian control.

By 693 BC the Assyrian army had made its way back north to Assyria, having defeated the Elamites (in six campaigns) throughout Babylonia, except for the city of Babylon. Sennacherib spent the next 4 years on other punitive expeditions throughout the Assyrian empire, and finally in 689 attacked Babylon, then still held by the Elamites.

Babylon was taken and sacked. Some 60,000 lives were lost in the siege, according to the records of Sennacherib. The city fortifications were destroyed and the temple compounds leveled. The God Marduk was removed to Ashur in Assyria. A canal off the Euphrates was rerouted to flood the central area of the city. The center of Babylon, where the temple had been, stood empty for eight years.

Babylon had become important a thousand years earlier, in the time of Hammurabi (circa 1700 BC, in revised chronology), and, although at different times it was under the rule of different tribes, Babylon represented all of Mesopotamia. The whole region, once known as Akkad and Sumer, had become known as "Babylonia." The city God of Babylon, Marduk, had become the "King of the Gods," replacing the much older Mesopotamian God Enlil of Nippur as the region-wide God who would approve kingships and settle border disputes. Marduk had originally been a god of thunder and lightning, and can be identified with Jupiter.

Kingship in Mesopotamia had been secular since the very beginning and the concept of a "King of the Gods" was an attempt by the priesthood to impose some control over the city-states of Mesopotamia and their individual kings. The priests of Enlil at Nippur had attempted to gain control over the kings of the individual cities at an earlier time. When Hammurabi unified the country after circa 1700 BC and made Babylon the most important city, the priests again saw an opening. They elevated Marduk to the status of a region-wide God and wrote a new creation epic, the *Enuma Elish*, around the exploits of Marduk -- based on the celestial events of 2349 BC (the fall of the Absu).

At the time of Sennacherib, Marduk had been the primary God of Mesopotamia for a thousand years. He was recognized throughout Babylonian Mesopotamia, in Elam in the south, and even in Assyria in the north. Even later, Cyrus, the Persian, paid homage to Marduk when he took Babylon in 539 BC. All the Gods of Mesopotamia came to Babylon ("The Gate of the Gods") to honor Marduk, reminiscent of the state councils often employed by the earlier earthly kings of Sumer and Akkad. The *Enuma Elish* related this new theogony, with Marduk even elevated as Creator God. On New Year's day (Spring Equinox) the *Enuma Elish* was recited at the temple of Marduk. The celebration of New Year was the most important festival of Babylon, in which the king himself participated, playing the role of Marduk.

Sennacherib's very long struggle against the Elamites, and his failures at Jerusalem three years later, added to his growing unpopularity among the Assyrians. His kingdom apparently suffered from crop failures also. His removal of Marduk from Babylon was seen as the cause of his misfortunes.

"Even many Assyrians were indignant at this, believing that the Babylonian God Marduk must be grievously offended at the destruction of the temple and the carrying off of his image."
-- *Encyclopaedia Britannica*, 15th edition

Attempts were made by the Assyrian court to rewrite the *Enuma Elish* to show Marduk at fault. The politics came to a head in 681 BC. There was a revolt and Sennacherib was killed by two of his sons. The two sons had to flee the country and were pursued by Esarhaddon, the son of Sennacherib's surviving wife. He was subsequently crowned as King.

Esarhaddon immediately made amends for his father's behavior and in 680 BC rebuilt Babylon and the temple compounds, although the statue of Marduk remained in Ashur. He continued to maintain good relations with Babylon, spending part of the year there, but calling himself only the "Governor of Babylon." In 677 BC he installed one of his own sons, Shamash-shum-ukin, as Crown Prince of Babylon, but the prince did not assume kingship of Babylon during Esarhaddon's lifetime. [note 5]

Esarhaddon spends the remainder of his reign maintaining his father's kingdom. He worried much about his failing health and, at times of impending lunar eclipses, installed temporary substitute kings of Assyria so the Gods could not find him. Esarhaddon died in 669 BC while on a punitive expedition to Egypt, which was then again in revolt.

In 668 BC his third son, Assurbanipal, took the crown of Assyria and Shamash-shum-ukin was crowned king of Babylon. In the following year the Babylonian New Year festival was again celebrated. The statue of Marduk had been returned. It had been twenty-one years since the destruction of the temple. It is in Assurbanipal's archives at Nineveh that the *Venus Tablets of Ammizaduga* were found 2500 years later. [note 6]

There is a remarkable coincidence between the 21 years of observations recorded by the *Venus Tablets of Ammizaduga* and the 21 years without a New Year celebration in Babylon. If we place the end points of the 21 year record at the beginning and end of the period when no New Year celebrations happen in Babylon, then the year of "The Golden Throne" falls in 680 BC, the year the temple of Marduk was rebuilt.

It was the phrase, "The Year of the Golden Throne," which caused the initial researchers of the 19th century to date the tablets to 1900 or 1500 BC. However, what the insertion "The Golden Throne" strongly reminds me of is not Ammizaduga, a minor king in the declining days of the First Babylonian empire in 1500 BC, but the "Lowering of Kingship" at the start of time before the flood and again with the first king after the flood. As always, the Mesopotamians look backwards to the beginnings. [note 7]

> *"After the ... [missing text] ... of kingship had descended from heaven, after the exalted crown and throne of kingship had descended from heaven, the divine rites and the exalted powers were perfected, the bricks of the cities were laid in holy places ... "etc.*
> -- Ziudsura tablets, segment B, (some parts missing) circa 2700 BC.

To the Babylonians the rebuilding of the temple of Marduk must have seemed like the "Kingship of God" had again descended to Earth, and in the same manner as at the beginning of time. Most likely the Venus data was compiled to these tablets for the sole purpose of declaring how the "Kingship of God" had returned to Babylon by the will of the Gods. The data for Venus was used because the sudden blazing of Venus in 680 BC (astronomical year -685) clearly declared the event.

The beginning point of the Venus Tablets follows the destruction of the temple precincts by Sennacherib in 689 BC. A central panel which recorded the phrase "The Golden Throne" corresponds to the rebuilding of the temple in 680 BC. The end point of the data follows the coronation of Shamash-shum-ukin as king of Babylon in 668 BC following the return of Marduk.

The long delay in celebrating the New Year was due to the fact that there was no acknowledged king of Babylon until Shamash-shum-ukin was crowned and because Marduk was missing. Esarhaddon, son of Sennacherib, had taken the title of "Governor of Babylon," for political reasons, and his son had remained the "Crown Prince of Babylon." Only after 668 BC was there again a "King of Babylon." [note 8]

The Blazing Star

What was the year of the Golden Throne like? The account from Mesoamerica, that Quetzalcoatl "set himself on fire," suggests an absolutely astounding sight. After having set in the east early in the year and a month late (I'm not certain what calendar month), as noted by Rose and Vaughan, Venus became visible after having passed from behind the Sun and started to appear in the day sky, following the Sun across the sky for some 60 days, blazing for 40 days, together with Mercury which suddenly became visible in the daytime sky. It was as if Venus was on fire, an apparition as bright as the Sun, climbing up with the Sun on rising in the east, blazing through the day skies, initially trailing the Sun and progressively moving away from the Sun, until it "lit up the western night sky" at dusk after the Sun had set.

Normally after disappearing in front of the Sun in the west, Venus remains out of view, caught in the glare of the Sun, for about 8 days. After disappearing behind the Sun in the east, however, Venus remains invisible for an extended period of time. This is both because of a longer path it has to travel behind the Sun, and because the Earth keeps moving, making the disappearance even longer. Today Venus remains hidden for about 50 days (it varies somewhat with the inclination of its orbit). At the time of the *Venus Tablets of Ammizaduga* it varied wildly and inexplicably. Velikovsky quotes some figures from the *Venus Tablets* which range from 2 months to 9 months. Even the passage in front of the Sun is at times far too long. But, with both the Earth and Venus on elliptical orbits, this is to be expected. Under the concept that the orbits of Earth and Venus were the same in the 7th century BC as today, this becomes inexplicable. Records from Hindu sources apparently concerning the same dates show the same inexplicable variation -- the *Panchasiddhantika* tables, transcribed 200 years later and published in AD 600. There are Egyptian data also concerning the changes in the sky (the *Ramesside Star Tables*).

Today Venus is on a nearly circular orbit. We do not know when the orbit changed, for over the next 1000 years, the Babylonians had stopped looking, the Europeans had no interest, and the Arabs had not started observations yet. Only in Mesoamerica were observations made. These show up in the Maya *Dresden Codex*, a 13th-century AD document which uses observational values dating to AD 700. The *Dresden Codex* lists the disappearance of Venus behind the Sun as lasting 90 days, not the 50 days of today.

Venus extinguished, I suspect, by July 26th of 685 BC. Its coma and tail may have disappeared somewhat later. No record was made of its disappearance in front of the Sun because Venus indeed did not disappear in the west (expected in December), but rode through the skies above the Sun by a large amount, about 8 degrees. This is not an unusual condition, but it is a very large amount. Venus in this instance went almost directly from being visible in the west as the Sun was setting to being seen in the east as the Sun was rising -- without the 8 days of hiding in the glare of the Sun. For a few days it was seen both in the west after sunset, and in the east before sunset. Rose and Vaughan did not take the altitude of Venus into account, as a matter of keeping their model reasonably simple. [note 9]

Sources describing the blazing of Venus abound, although most cannot be dated. In a Greek "legend" Phaethon (Phaëthon), the planet Mercury, borrows the chariot of his father the Sun and goes on an uncontrollable ride through the sky. His ride ends when he is struck by a thunderbolt from Jupiter (Zeus) and placed in the sky as the Morning Star. Augustine notes the same as a secondary recollection from other sources, relative to Venus. Being changed to the "Morning Star" is a confusing concept, for this is usually understood to be a condition of the planet Venus, although even today Venus can be seen traversing all of the sky during daylight hours. But with Mercury placed on an orbit much closer to the Sun, so that it would show as the Morning Star for about a half hour before sunrise (and also seen as the "Evening Star"), it would make more sense for Mercury to be called the "Morning Star." [note 10]

Once we understand the stupendous eruption of 680 BC (685 BC), we should be able to recognize other mentions of this event. As a matter of fact, Isaiah, who had asked, "How art thou fallen from heaven, O Lucifer, son of the morning!" continues on with:

"For thou hast said in thy heart, I will ascend into heaven, I will exalt my throne above the stars of God" -- Isaiah 14:12-13

It is thought that Isaiah is addressing Venus (Lucifer) as a self-willed animate phenomenon. But it seems much more likely that he is addressing Mercury, "son of the morning," as Hesiod also called Mercury, even though this condition was only a year old in 685 BC. His text recognizes that the apparition rose high in the sky (as also noted by other sources) and expresses his contempt for a spirit who would rival God by setting up a throne above the stars. These lines would have been written after 680 BC (in Eastern Mediterranean chronology).

I should add a note about the "Golden Throne." A "throne" in antiquity is not the high-backed armchair we think of. It is, after all, a coma and plasma tail we are looking at. It would perhaps look like the presentation of the mountain of Horus between 3100 BC and 2700 BC -- a vertical section of a truncated cone in profile and perhaps with distinct legs, depending on how the Sun illuminated the coma and the plasma outpouring.

Because Venus or Mercury orbits between the Earth and the Sun, for part of the time when either appeared close to the Sun, the plasma tail would be directed toward Earth and foreshortened, and the planet with its plasma would have looked more like an inverted bucket than a blazing ball with a tail stretching halfway across the sky. The rationalization of the image, of course, depends entirely on expectations. Once you see a throne in the celestial display, it will remain a throne through any amount of distortion.

The Persian Zend-Avesta (written contemporaneously, or within a generation) is filled with offers of supplication and sacrifices to Tristrya (Venus), and also evokes an image of light similar to Isaiah's text: [note 11]

"For ten nights ... Tishtrya, the bright and glorious star, mingles his shape with light, moving in the shape of ... [a boy, a bull, a horse]". [this phrasing is repeated three times]

"We sacrifice unto Tishtrya, the bright and glorious star who from the shining east moves along his long winding path, along the path made by the Gods."

-- Zend-Avesta II, "Khorda Avesta" Section 8, "Tishtar Yasht" James Darmesteter, translator (1880)

The description matches what we would expect. At this time, when Venus was still regularly seen in the daytime skies, the "long winding path" describes the loop traveled by Venus around the Sun in the daytime. This would loop and advance to the west over the course of some months. It is "long" because Venus extends some 40 degrees from the Sun as seen from Earth. The "path made by the Gods" is of course the ecliptic. Despite the "winding path" Venus stayed mostly near the ecliptic.

The ten nights (actually, days) are repeated for three different shapes. This is a total of thirty days. In the "Khorda Avesta," after a lapse of 30 days, Tishtrya engages a demon in battle, but loses during the first three days. An appeal is made to Ahura Mazda [Jupiter] for intervention -- a sacrifice to give Tishtrya strength. This happens, and on the last day, Tishtrya proves stronger. Thirty-four days have passed (there may be additional days at the end of the hymn). The time span is close to being correct. I will get back to this. [note 12]

There are similar descriptions of a blazing apparition among Hindu sources, describing it as a "horse without hips." Assurbanipal, the king of Assyria who reinstalled Marduk to the temple at Babylon, also witnessed the event, and wrote about Ishtar (Venus):

"... who is clothed with fire and bears aloft a crown of awful splendor, raining fire over Arabia."

The "raining fire" is noted in a number of other contemporaneous and later sources. It is the "Ignis Coelis" which will continue to fall sporadically on regions of Earth far into the future.

With this display in the sky in 685 BC, we should find similar activities among humans -- as ever in imitation of the spectacle in the skies. And we do. There are two recorded instances, dated to the seventh century, of kings in Western Anatolia committing suicide in their burning palaces -- Rusas I of Urarta, and Midas of the Phrygians, both after attacks by the Cimmerians. In Mesopotamia we have two Assyrian kings who are reported to have gone up in the smoke of their besieged palaces -- Shamash-shum-ukin in 648 BC, after a three-year siege of Babylon by his brother Assurbanipal, and Sin-shar-ishkun in 611 BC, after a siege by the Medes under Cyaxares. Ussher writes about Shamash-shum-ukin (under the identity of Sardanapalus):

"... he made a huge pile of wood in his palace court and set it on fire, which burned himself, his concubines, his eunuchs and all his riches. The palace itself was also burned to ashes."
-- James Ussher *The Annals of The World* (1650)

Croesus is reputed to also have been burned to death when Sardis was taken by Cyrus in 546 BC, although Herodotus has it that he was taken prisoner by the Persians.

As always, a touch of the supernatural is added to history. I have not found earlier instances of this, except as detailed below.

In China the last emperor of the Shang dynasty is said to have similarly set himself on fire. The Shang ends in 1125 BC, but the report is from the Chou dynasty, and may be apocryphal, in which case I would presume it was created by the Chi or Eastern Chou, and dated after the eighth century BC, when extensive historical records first appear.

Lastly, Hercules of Greek and Roman mythology, who represents Mars, but especially the destructive visits by Mars in the 7th and 8th century BC, similarly sought deification through self-immolation. [note 13]

The Bolt from Jupiter

Having established the year of these events (-685 astronomical), I should at this point indicate the likely dates, the sources for which I will discuss in the next chapter in more detail. The following seems the most likely sequence of events for the year 685 BC. I'll embellish the chronology with some quotations from various sources, which I will cover in more detail later.

- In spring of the previous year Mercury made electric contact with Earth (a shock), which may have changed the shape of Earth's orbit, and radically altered Mercury's orbit. (But Rose and Vaughan did not detect a change for Earth until the following year.)
- Mercury may have altered Venus's orbit, for it would have passed Venus much closer at least twice. At the end of the year Venus disappears behind the Sun some 30 days early from what was expected, as Rose and Vaughan have noted. This has to be seen as a change in ellipticity, for the orbital period apparently remained the same. (Rose and Vaughan, however, did not detect a change.)
- On June 15 (Gregorian equivalent) the Sun went into high activity, for a one-and-a-half-month-long series of continual Coronal Mass Ejections (CMEs), hurling billions of tons of material, mostly as protons, into the surrounding space. It caused unusual auroras on Earth, would reinstate the polar plasma columns, but would not change its orbit, except that the polar axis would start to incline to a different value.
- On June 15 the Olmecs note that the Sun was not setting in the proper location. "It changed its path," states the *Chilam Balam*. This condition would last for some 40 days, through July 25th.
- On June 15, a day of the new Moon, Venus and Mercury, located close together in the sky and east of the Sun and Moon, started to blaze like suns. "Two suns were seen battling in the sky," China records. Franz Xavier Kugler, interpreting the *Sibylline Oracle Books* of AD 115, which retells the same display seen in the skies (but written about 800 years later), assumes the Earth was met with two large blazing comets.
- Since Mercury was likely invisible in the daylight sky until it also

started to blaze like Venus, it looked as if Venus gave birth to Mercury, who is called Phaethon in the Eastern Mediterranean. Because of the spikes of flames reaching across the sky, and with a later knowledge that Phaethon was the planet Mercury, Roman philosophers later developed a theory that comets are produced when two planets clash in the sky.

- Because Mercury in the role of Phaethon was obviously new, and probably smaller than the blazing Venus, another theory (or myth) developed that Venus (here as Aphrodite) had taken a young boy as a lover, but soon destroyed him with a blast of fire, a thunderbolt. Hesiod mentions the first, but not the second. [note 14]

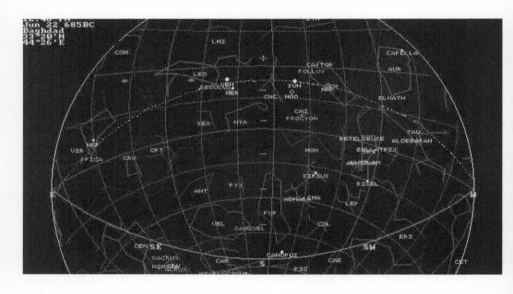

[*Image: Daytime sky at noon, June 22, 685 BC. Image from SkyGlobe 3.6.*]

In the Guatemalan *Popol Vuh*, Hunahpu and Xbalanque, Venus and Mercury, sacrifice themselves in order to defeat the lords of the Underworld, and start creation.

"Watch! they said, then they faced each other. They grabbed each other by the hands and went head first into the oven."
   -- Popol Vuh

It is this phrasing from the *Popol Vuh* which allowed me to pinpoint the starting date of this event. Dennis Tedlock, translator of the *Popol Vuh*, inadvertently pointed this out when he proposed that there should be a relationship between Hunahpu and Xbalanque and the Sun and Moon.

- Immediately after June 15, Mercury, on a much smaller orbit than Venus, starts to reapproach the Sun, and passes above the Sun and on toward its west side on about July 9th. The *Sibylline Oracle Books* recall the movements of the Sun and the two planets during the 40-day period. I'll discuss this in the chapter "The Sibylline Star Wars."
- Jupiter also received the plasma outpouring of the Sun, but because of it is much larger and much further away, did not flash into a visible coma immediately. Jupiter switched to a glow mode on July 9th, producing a large coma, a three-pronged plume at its north (upper) pole and a gigantic split outpouring at it south pole (which is its magnetic north pole) -- recalled in the *Chilam Balam* and graphically recorded by the Olmecs at La Venta. In fact, on this date, the Sun, Mercury, Earth, and Jupiter were all in line. (At this time Mars was almost directly behind the Sun, and Venus was at a right angle to the lineup.)

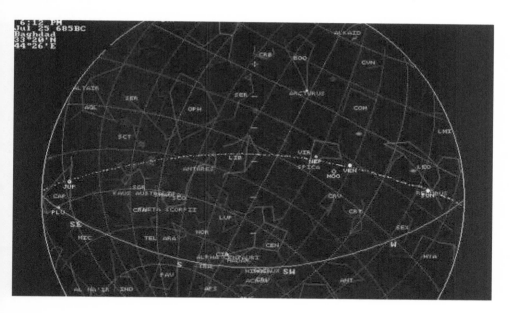

[Image: Late afternoon sky July 25, 685 BC. A south by southwest view to show Jupiter and the Sun. The travel path of the plasmoid followed the ecliptic, and it may have looked as if Venus was hit. Image from SkyGlobe 3.6.]

- On July 14th Jupiter responded with a return lightning stroke, directed at the Sun. A massive plasmoid was released, seen and recorded worldwide. Its travel was followed for 11 days. Asia and Europe saw the plasmoid as it was approaching. The people of the Americas got a full broadside view of the plasmoid as it passed by Earth at a distance of some 30 million miles (48 million km).

On July 25th the plasmoid hit the Sun. The people of the Eastern Mediterranean saw the plasmoid again after it had passed by Earth but only saw it in the early morning (two days later), saw the east horizon light up as it landed at the Sun, and assumed that Mercury (Phaethon), which preceded the Sun in rising, had been hit -- or that Venus was the target. Mesoamerica saw nothing of the final splashdown, and assumed that the lightning bolt was meant for Mars, the nemesis during this period, located just west of the Sun in the sky. But here, too, some opinions held that Venus had been hit.

The lightning bolt from Jupiter was, as I will show below, 1.5 million miles (2.4 million km) in diameter -- twice the width of the Sun -- and 15 million miles (24 million km) long. It would have taken some 9 hours to complete the landing at the Sun. It would have lit up both the day and night sky. The *Popol Vuh* suggests that the planets near the Sun, Venus and Mercury, were not seen for the next four days.

With that the blazing of Venus and Mercury apparently came to an end. At least, in Mesoamerica July 25 was held as the end of the event. It is possible that the arc mode plasma displays of Venus and Mercury simply diminished, switched to glow mode, and then to dark mode. Jupiter may have continued with its glow mode display longer, since a single spark will not likely "discharge" a massive planet. Apparently there were additional, lesser, plasmoids released by Jupiter. [note 15]

The *Popol Vuh* relates that Hunahpu and Xbalanque, after they jump in the oven of the Xibalbans, are seen by people as catfish in the river where their ashes were deposited. The river is the ecliptic, which was still aglow certainly at this time (it lasted to AD 1840). They *"looked like catfish."* These are likely the lesser bolts from Jupiter. As will be recalled from the narrative of Egyptian predynastic history, catfish is an apt description for a plasmoid.

When I first came to a realization of the above events, I simply could not believe it, and was reluctant to put together this narrative. It is absolutely unimaginable that a planet could have bolted its star with an electric arc which had to travel 480,000,000 miles (773,000,000 km) to reach its destination. I was familiar with the plasmoid imagery of Rome and Babylon, as well as the numerous "model plasmoids" in Asia, shown in *Thunderbolts of the Gods* (2005) by David Talbott and Wallace Thornhill. The plasmoids are depicted on coins also. These images were all from late antiquity, none from before 650 BC. That was a troubling fact, for the previous depiction of a plasmoid was nearly 3000 years earlier, the predynastic Egyptian king "Catfish-drill."

I was also familiar with the "rigid bar" insignia of Maya rulers in the Classical Era (AD 400 to AD 900), but it was only when I started to look at the iconography of the Olmec site of La Venta, which can clearly be dated to before 650 BC, that I was forced to accept the fact that I was obviously looking at a depiction of Jupiter in glow mode plasma discharge (easily recognizable because of Jupiter's reversed magnetic field), and a massive plasmoid lightning bolt shaped exactly like the classical laboratory forms. The sculpted or engraved god-figure is holding the plasmoid in his arms, as all later chiefs among the Maya will also. At La Venta the first pyramid of Mesoamerica was constructed, called a "red mountain." It is an image which reflects the contemporaneous form seen in the sky at its period of creation and which recalls the much earlier celestial mountain form from thousands of years earlier.

The diverse imagery suddenly came together to explain the connection between what the Greeks considered the "mythological past" and what they and we consider the "modern world."

The plasma bolt launched from Jupiter is the "lightning bolt of Zeus" which toppled Phaethon from his father's chariot. The myth of Phaethon is thus the last "mythology" from antiquity. In 685 BC, before releasing the plasmoid, Jupiter must have expanded and again assumed the size of a mountain. The bolt traveled over 480 million miles to the Sun. It is little wonder that Jupiter, despite its diminished visual display since 2150 BC, continued to be held as the chief God everywhere in the world.

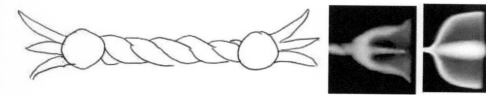

[*Images: Left: Plasmoid lightning bolt shown in its full extent. Illustration by J. Cook. Right: The end form is based on viewing the denser edge of the cup-like form and a dense central core. After David Talbott and Wallace Thornhill, "Thunderbolts of the Gods" (2005).*]

We have to ask how this could have happened. What would normally happen to cause lightning between planets, is that a conductive path has to pre-exist and that the voltage difference has to be sensed. That would happen if the plasmaspheres of two planets touched.

[*Image: The Plasmoid lightning bolt depicted as the "Rigid Serpent Bar" in Maya illustrations, meant as a token of office. Two Gods are coming out of the distended mouths of the serpent. The two Saint Andrew's crosses on the body denote the "vernal equinox" and "autumnal equinox" of the ecliptic. After Linda Schele and David Freidel "A Forest of Kings" (1990).*]

Although the existence of a long tail would have furnished the electric path for a return lightning strike, it is just not likely that the plasmasphere tail of Venus (or Earth) would have reached 500 million miles (800 million km) into space, through the Asteroid Belt, to Jupiter. But there is an entirely different condition which fulfills the need for a conductive media between Jupiter and the Sun, and for sensing the voltage difference.

It already was my suspicion that the "Venus nova event" was in actuality a month-long coronal mass ejection of the Sun. It lit up Venus and Mercury like suns. It was at this time that both planets ended up becoming pockmarked with craters and electric scars. It altered the spin axis of the Earth.

And it provided a highly conductive path between the Sun and the far reaches of space, certainly to the location of Jupiter -- a distance of 5.2 AU. A continuous plasma expulsion of the Sun would extend the high-voltage inversion layer which is normally relatively close to the Sun, far out into space. Rather than having to breach 500 million miles (800 million km) of a very large voltage difference, Jupiter was suddenly in almost direct electric contact with the Sun. The voltage difference between Jupiter and the Sun would be sensed by the plasmasphere of Jupiter which, like those of the other planets, actually travels within the plasmasphere of the Sun.

Earth, Venus, and Mercury were not involved in the bolt from Jupiter. Earth and Venus remained invisible to Jupiter, protected by their own plasmaspheres. Earth and Venus were also well away from the line of fire.

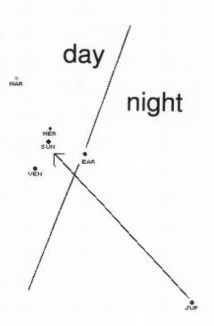

5:00 PM
Aug 02 685BC
Cairo
30°03'N
31°15'E

day

night

MAR

MER
SUN
VEN
EAR

JUP

[*Image: Planets about the Sun, July 26, 685 BC, seen from "above."
Orbital rotation is counterclockwise. Illustration by J. Cook.*]

Scaled from the diagram above, it would appear that Earth was some 30 or 40 million miles (48 or 64 million km) from the path of the lightning bolt (at a right angle). The plasmoid from Jupiter aimed directly at the Sun. The people of Earth witnessed the travel of the plasmoid through the night and daytime skies. Even if the bolt was only 1/10th of the diameter of Jupiter, it would have been the diameter of the Earth.

In November of AD 2003 the Sun sent a number of Coronal Mass Ejections (CMEs) into space. These usually travel at a speed of about 2 million miles per hour (3 million km per hr) by the time they reach the Earth's orbit (as does the Solar Wind). The CMEs of 2003 traveled across the 93 million miles (150 million km) between the Sun and Earth in 30 minutes, averaging 200 million miles per hour (320 million km per hr) -- a quarter of the speed of light. There is no reason to believe that the lightning bolt from Jupiter in 685 BC could not have traveled at a wide range of possible speeds. I'll make a speed and time estimate further below.

[Image: Chinese depiction of the dragon. After Ramona Jablonski.]

From a comparison of the depictions of plasmoids in Europe and Asia with Mesoamerica, it is clear that Europe and Asia saw the bolt when it was released from Jupiter, saw it travel for 10 or 12 days and entirely missed the plasmoid as it passed closest to Earth. The bolt was traveling 40,000,000 miles per day (64,000,000 km per day), so it would relocate that far between sightings. Mesoamerica had the privilege of seeing the plasmoid pass by Earth during the daytime, visually extended to its full size. [note 16]

The plasmoids depicted in Mesoamerica are therefore much longer than the short hand-held objects depicted in Asia, or the medium sized "thunderbolts" shown in graphics and statuary in the Mediterranean region. The Mesoamerican plasmoid is depicted as carried in the arms of persons and looks to be a five- or six-foot long object.

China earlier, in 2349 BC, had understood plasmoids as dragons approaching from the east, and records dragons in exactly the manner in which the plasmoid was seen in the sky, head first, with an open mouth, long feelers attached to the mouthparts, and what looked like legs attached further away along the body.

Mesoamerica also recorded a dragon, but it had no legs. Instead it had heads at both ends of the body, but also with the wide-open mouth and the tendrils attached to the mouth parts as in China. What was understood as rear legs in China, was properly attached parts of the rear mouth of the dragons of the Maya.

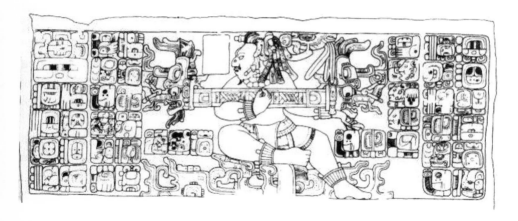

[Image: The Plasmoid lightning bolt depicted as the "Rigid Serpent Bar" in Maya illustrations. Two planetary Gods are coming out of the distended mouths of the serpent. After Linda Schele and David Freidel "A Forest of Kings" (1990).]

Mesoamerican chiefs carry a rigid bar in their arms as an emblem of office, with triple tines at both ends. A bar like this is first shown held by a person (actually the God Jupiter) on stela 2 of La Venta and on a number of engraved dedicatory celts at the same location and period. By the time of the Classical Maya (AD 400 to AD 900), the bar is four times as thick as in Olmec times of 650 BC, and it is conceived of as a tube, a rigid snake, or a dragon with a head at each end. The tines have become mouth and jaw parts of the dragon, and Venus and the Sun are shown emerging from the two mouths.

[Images: Plasmoid models from Tibet, India, Japan. After David Talbott and Wallace Thornhill, "Thunderbolts of the Gods" (2005). Named Vajra in Sanskrit, or Dorji in Tibetan, meaning thunderbolt.]

Short hand-held "model" plasmoids, dating from this era, are found today in Tibet, India, and Japan, nearly identical to European sculptural and mural depictions, but shorter. All of them mostly follow the shape of laboratory plasma discharges: a twisted body with balls at both ends, from which emerge three tines like flower petals.

The same triple-tined objects with a twisted center are shown as being held in the hand of Zeus in Roman statues. The trident arrow appears (as the weapon of Marduk) in wall sculptures in Mesopotamia after 600 BC.

The Roman naturalist Pliny, in the first century AD, still discusses lightning bolts from planets, and distinguishes between various types. If the plasmoids had last been seen shortly after the end of the "Era of the Gods" in circa 3100 BC, it would have been unlikely to suddenly reappear in philosophical discussions during the last few centuries of the previous era to become the object of speculation.

[*Images: Short Plasmoid lightning bolt depicted as vase paintings, statues, and murals (left to right: Greek, Roman, Babylonian). All dated after circa 600 BC.*]

It seems clear that the difference in the images between Asia, Europe, and the Americas is entirely due to seeing this object in different stages of its travel. If Mesoamerica saw the plasmoid bolt in the day sky (with Asia and Europe turned away to the night side of Earth) just as it passed Earth, then the bolt would have been seen in full profile. From this the size can be estimated.

I would suggest that, as seen from Mesoamerica, it probably subtended an angle of about 30 degrees in the sky -- understood as a five- or six-foot long object held by a God. With the Earth 30 million miles (48 million km) from the path of travel of the plasmoid, it must have been about 15 million miles long (24 million km) (**30,000,000 * sin(30) = 15,000,000 miles**).

In early depictions in Mesoamerica the object looks to have a diameter of about 1/10th of its length. That would make the lightning bolt 1.5 to 2 million miles (2.5 to 3 million km) in diameter. This is certainly larger by far than the diameter of the planet Jupiter (80,000 miles; 129,000 km), but the plasmasphere of Jupiter, under normal conditions, is on the order of 40 planet diameters, thus 3.2 million miles (5 million km) wide. Plasmoids also tend to shorten on cutting loose from their cathode, and thus thicken.

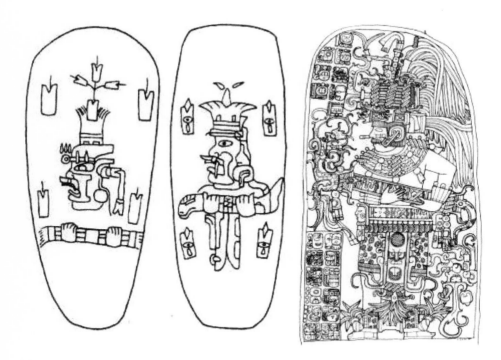

[*Images: Left two: Long Plasmoid lightning bolt depicted on two celts from La Venta, circa 650 BC. The second figure, with the crocodile legs, is carrying a bar in the shape of snake or cayman. Right: Stela 11 at Seibal, dated 10.1.0.0.0, AD 849. After Linda Schele and David Freidel "Maya Cosmos" (1993), and "A Forest of Kings" (1990).*]

Mesopotamia and the Eastern Mediterranean saw the plasmoid again as Earth turned back to the day side, but the plasmoid had passed by. Mesopotamia possibly saw the plasmoid contact the Sun (it would have caused a stupendous brightening in the eastern sky). Mesoamerica probably never saw the plasmoid reach the Sun, which would have required another 30 million miles (48 million km) of travel (about a day of travel), but assumed it was destined for Mars, which stood in the sky just past the Sun in the west (and would rise before the Sun the next day, obscured by the light of the impact).

From these rough estimates it could be suggested that the plasmoid was traveling at a rate of about 20 to 30 million miles per half day -- or 1.5 to 2.5 million miles per hour (2.5 to 4 million km per hr). These estimates are in line with what we know of the solar wind and normal CMEs traveling from the Sun.

How long did it take to travel from Jupiter to the Sun? Assuming that the gradient of the electric field between Jupiter and the Sun was low enough that acceleration during travel could be neglected, and at an average rate of 1.5 to 2.5 million miles per hour, it would take 8 to 13 days.

This is based on **(5.2 * AU) / (2500000 * 24) = 8.06 days** and **(5.2 * AU) / (1500000 * 24) = 13.4 days**.

The people of Mesoamerica seem to claim it took 12 days. It would thus have been traveling at a rate of **5.2 * AU /12 = 40,000,000 miles per day --** 1.66 million miles per hour.

The Planets in the Sky

During much of the ninth century and a portion of the eighth and seventh century BC (806 BC to 685 BC) the skies of Earth were crowded with unwanted planets. Then, after 685 BC (680 BC in Eastern Mediterranean chronology), they all disappeared.

... Venus

Venus, without a magnetic field, would not likely have produced the tri-lobed plumed headdress shape, but only the tail of its surrounding coma, directed away from the Sun, plus a tail of sputtered particles which would split into two parts. This is seen in comets today (which also do not have a magnetic field). Additionally there might have been long wisps of plasma from its polar regions. These would seem to be coherent plasma streams, bent to the direction of the Sun, but not organized into tri-lobed plumes.

In 685 BC Venus brightened enormously, and all of these features, which had been seen for ages, suddenly increased in intensity. Assurbanipal described Ishtar (Venus) as *"... who is clothed with fire and bears aloft a crown of awful splendor."*

I suspect that Venus lost its tail and perhaps much of its coma, because some time after 685 BC Venus was admitted as a planet in the astronomy of Babylon -- it had started to behave like a planet. A hundred years later much had been forgotten. No one remembered, or wanted to remember. History was turned into mythology.

... Jupiter

The tri-lobed plasma formation, described above, would appear at the poles of a planet with a magnetic field when in glow mode plasma discharge. Jupiter did this in 685 BC. Jupiter has a very strong, but reversed, magnetic field (ten times that of any other planet), and it produced a three-lobed flower form extending from its north pole above the coma surrounding the planet. The surrounding coma probably looked the size of the Moon.

[Images: Left: An Olmec celt, circa 685 BC, Jupiter with the body of a crocodile, holding a cayman. Shown amid the four trees (or flames) of the cardinal directions. Middle: Maya crocodile maize plant with a bird at the top, Izapa stela 25. Right: Maya crocodile tree on a blood offering plate. After Linda Schele and David Freidel "A Forest of Kings" (1990), and "Maya Cosmos" (1993).]

The same strong magnetic field produced another tri-lobed form, but much larger than the top, at its south geographical pole (the north magnetic pole), making it look as the "body" of the planet, or as a mountain, although, and as noted by the Olmecs, the body looked like the open jaws of a crocodile, the central tongue of which might have been missing or not observed. Crocodiles have only a short tongue.

These features were recorded after 685 BC by the Olmecs on stelae and engraved ceremonial celts. Archaeologists hold that the headdress is to be identified as a corn plant, with two leaves pulled away from an ear of corn. (Even though the ear of maise plants was turned down in cultivation.) But the figure universally recognized as the "Corn God" in the Classical Maya era does not wear such a hat. The tri-lobed headdress shows up, instead, and from very early times, among the Maya as the "jester hat" of a scepter or headband representing Venus, known among archaeologists as the Jester God. [note 17]

Jupiter in this condition was also identified as the central (or southern) tree of creation, the World Tree of the Maya. The same World Tree is often shown by the Maya with branches and leaves at the top, but with the head of a crocodile as its base at the bottom.

The tri-lobed crown of Jupiter waved back and forth, since the magnetic poles of planets do not coincide with the rotational axis. At a rotational rate of 9 hours, the rotation of Jupiter's tri-lobed plasma outpouring would have been seen as a plant waving in the wind. Jupiter was probably also seen during the day. At Teotihuacan the favored headdress of dignitaries and Gods becomes a hat of feathers and plumes. This fashion carried through for a thousand years to the Maya and the Aztecs.

In the Eastern Mediterranean region the Gods had already taken human form, and the only strange animals depicted as supernatural beings are the demons they battle.

... Mars

In Mesoamerica Mars is often depicted as "smoking" (a cigar) or with a smoking mirror on his forehead. As I have mentioned earlier, the smoking mirror is likely the sublimation of water from the remnant upper ocean. This suggests that at some point in time Mars had lost its atmosphere, but had retained one of its oceans (the smaller ocean is within the confines of the larger polar ocean).

The smoking cigar might be an unshaped plasma discharge, or a plume of impinging electrons brought to arc mode near Mars's surface. But one wonders if the "smoking" represents the lightning bolt suspected to have been delivered by Venus in 776 BC. When Mars is depicted with an axe piercing his forehead, recognition has to be given to some gigantic impact of the past - - probably the thunderbolt excavation of Valles Marineris. Olmec sculptures depict Mars with the features of a bat and the snarl of a Jaguar, which might be additional aspects of dust lifted from the surface and shaped by the Earth's magnetic field (when Mars closed in on Earth).

At later times among the Maya, Mars (God K), is depicted with the leg of a snake, which archaeologists have determined is a symbol for lightning. That describes the effect of electric contacts after 806 BC.

An estimate of the number of visits by Mars after 747 BC might be deduced from the religious monuments at Olmec La Venta between 747 BC to about 400 BC. There are, within the confines of the pyramid and adjacent plazas, five elaborate graves (one of the graves is a coffin shaped as a gigantic cayman), five massive offering caches of serpentine blocks, and four colossal stone heads. The first passage of Mars perhaps did not require a stone head. Or it has not yet been found. The three mosaic tiled floors (two were buried) read "9 Jaguar" -- a bar and 4 dots, shaped like a jaguar face with the characteristic forehead cleft -- which in effect equates to the name used in the *Chilam Balam* for Mars, Bolon Dzacab, "Nine Lives."

Except for this repetition of five, along with the four giant heads, there is no clear record of the number of visits. The only additional suggestion comes from the *Chilam Balam*, which records, after the first mention of the appearance of Bolon Dzacab, Mars, in 747 BC, the descent of four "mighty demon bats."

The best reconstruction by Velikovsky from Biblical sources was to suggest appearances of Mars at 15-year intervals. The 60-year time span of 747 BC to 687 BC represents five visits if they were 15 years apart. This is also the sequence of events in the Quiche Maya *Popol Vuh* -- five ballgames are played in the underworld. However, the number of visits at 15-year intervals between 806 BC and 687 BC is nine.

Despite the coincidence of "nine" in "Nine Lives" and the suggested number of close contacts by Mars, the certainty for the number nine comes from the name of the flower vendor, Bolon Mayel [Nine Fragrances], who is Mercury, and who is said to have accompanied Mars in each instance.

... Mercury

The *Chilam Balam* lists nine close calls by a planet named Nine Fragrances in the eighth and seventh century BC (probably from 806 BC to 687 BC), described as delivering flowers and fragrances. If these were being delivered by Mars, then the "flowers" are curious, because a flower-form (the tri-lobe form) would not be expected for Mars. Nor would the fragrances, for Mars has no atmosphere. This would suggest that the planet called "Nine Fragrances" was Mercury, instead. Mercury has a minor magnetic field, and still has a strange mix of gases as a thin atmosphere.

When the *Popol Vuh* describes the northern Gods after 10,900 BC, Mercury was confused with the later appearance of Venus, and called "Sovereign Plumed Serpent." But very little atmosphere would be needed to create a coma in glow mode.

The fragrances are recorded in Vedic sources also. Velikovsky mentions them, although he assigns them to the era of 1500 BC. The exterior of the plasmasphere of Mercury (the "double layer") would have included gases in ionized forms from its atmosphere. Close passes to Earth would have transferred many of these to Earth's plasmasphere, and eventually to the Earth's atmosphere.

The repeated destructions of sites in Persia, the Middle East, Greece,

Italy, and apparently Mesoamerica, together with the identification of Mars, and lamentations about the followers of Mars, would suggest Mars as the main agent of the destructions of the 8th century BC. But the flower forms and the associated fragrances point to Mercury. These are not even mentioned (except for the fragrances) in the Middle East.

What I will suggest is that Mercury had been a companion of Mars since remote antiquity, so that the two would always appear together. I had already considered that Mercury was likely the "other planet" which showed up along with Horus/Mars in the period of 3067 to circa 2700 BC to constitute the twenty-some pharaohs of the first and second dynasty of Egypt and similarly the 20 early kings of Kish in Mesopotamia. The two planets show up along with the "Followers of Horus" and the large quantities of cattle and dead people in the skies which were recorded by the Egyptians in the first and second dynasty. I have also suggested that the "sandal bearer" shown following the pharaoh on the "Palette of Narmer" is not his son, but Mercury.

The "Palette of Narmer" shows the "Followers of Horus" as six papyrus buds led out of the Duat by a nose rope held by Horus the falcon. On the obverse side are the standards of the cardinal directions, followed by a woman with a bola, Narmer as Mars, and Mercury bringing up the rear. Of course it is not certain if Mercury always followed the travel of Mars. But at any rate in the 8th and 7th century Mercury would show up near Mars at each of the 9 instances when Mars cruised close to Earth on 15-year intervals.

The 16th century AD *Chilam Balam* lists "Nine Fragrances" as he who descended when "it was that the word of Bolon Dzacab [Mars] descended to the tip of his tongue."

> *"With it descended Bolon Mayel* [Nine Fragrances]; *sweet was his mouth and the tip of his tongue. Sweet were his brains."*

The "nine" of the "Nine Fragrances" represents, as these numeric prefixes do throughout the *Chilam Balam*, nine appearances of Mercury. This matches the nine appearances of Mars between 806 BC and 687 BC. By coincidence the nine appearances of Mars is the same number assigned to him before 3147 BC ("this first Bolon Dzacab"). Curiously, the giant jade or greenstone mask-shaped floors at Olmec La Venta, apparently buried as a means of warding off or appeasing Mars, represent the face of a Jaguar in the form of the glyph for "nine," were installed long before the nine close passes of Mars had been completed.

The mouth, tongue, and brains (top of the head?) of Bolon Mayel probably describe the plasma plumes above and below Mercury, and are, as a matter of fact, described in the *Chilam Balam* as flowers.

Today Mercury still has an externally induced magnetic field (it is thought), due to the fact that on its (current) orbit it travels to a distance twice as far from the Sun between perihelion and aphelion. Previous to the 7th century BC, traveling on an orbit which took it well beyond the orbit of Earth, it might have had a much greater magnetic field. Mercury also, gauging from the remaining thin atmosphere, might have held a considerable gaseous envelope, able to support a shaped plasma.

... Earth

The Earth, another planet with a magnetic field, would, at various times of excess electric activity, also have had the same tri-lobed vortexes standing above the Earth's north and south magnetic poles, and extending perhaps 10 or 20 Earth diameters into space. The plasma above the north magnetic pole would have been larger than the plasma of the south magnetic pole. But the southern plasma was most likely visible also in the northern hemisphere, for the plumes would have bent away from Earth into the tail of the magnetosphere.

It is quite likely that the outer shell would be mostly transparent, and only the central spikes were seen. Alternately, as I have detailed in previous chapters, the plumes rose up as a coherent structure with ball plasmoids at the end and the plant-like wisps (the terminating cup and spike) beyond that. (See also an endnote to the chapter "The Gods Leave," detailing the recent discovery by NASA, in early 2009, of these plumes, in dark mode, and separated as two counter-rotating streams at the northern aurora). A plasma stream above the north and south magnetic poles would answer to the claims of the four trees of the cardinal directions of the Maya, which appeared four times since 3147 BC, according to the *Chilam Balam*. Other Mesoamerican sources claim 8 and 9 appearances for the northern plume. [note 18]

The Twins

The combined appearances of Mercury and Mars came to an end in 686 BC, when a line-up with Mercury caused an Earth shock and Nercury was, as I have described, jolted into an orbit much closer to the Sun. The Earth changed the location of its aphelion, as Rose and Vaughan have pointed out (detailed below), inadvertently moving it away from the orbit of Mars.

In fact, the mythological and quasi-historical tales from this era are obsessed with twin celestial Gods. With the Greeks they are the Dioscuri, Castor and Polydeuces (Pollux). Castor is a tamer of horses and mortal, Pollux is a boxer (no kidding!) and immortal. Homer places them in Sparta.

The Spartans, in fact, hold them to be the younger twin brothers of Helen.

(Homer's Helen in this may be equated with Venus.) Both travel with the Argonauts at one time. They steal cattle in Arcadia and drive them east to Sparta. At the conclusion of some fights and pursuits, Zeus kills one of the pursuers with a thunderbolt. This last represents the eruption of Venus and Mercury in 685 BC.

In Italy the twins are the founding patrons of the city of Rome, Romulus and Remus, sons of Mars. This is strange, but then, Rome's historical records were destroyed in antiquity. Remus was killed by Romulus in a dispute. Romulus founded and ruled the city of Rome, and is then taken up into heaven. After 686 BC Mercury had, for all practical purposes, disappeared from the skies.

The constellation Gemini is generally held to be the Dioscuri twins, but Hyginus (in *Astronomica*, attributed to Hyginus, but dated circa AD 200) says the twins are Apollo and Heracles (Mercury and Mars). Santillana and von Dechend mention twin deities of China, and there are without doubt others.

In the *Popol Vuh* two sets of twins are identified, first as One-Hunahpu and Seven-Hunahpu (probably an appearance of 776 BC), and then as Hunahpu and Xbalanque (the five appearances documented in the Long Count for 747 BC and after).

Talbott, in *The Saturn Myth*, notes that almost always one of the twins is white and the other is black. He references not only Greek sources, but also Mesoamerican, Indian, Chinese, and many others. Australia could be added, as well as the *New Testament* apostles James and John -- the Sons of Thunder (Mark 3:17). We could add Cain and Able as an earlier manifestation. Talbott, of course, relates the black and white aspects of the celestial twins back to the polar configuration in the north. But it should be obvious that the white twin is Mercury with a cloud cover of an extensive atmosphere, and the black twin is the dark Mars, with neither an atmosphere nor a coma except as wings of dust.

The two planets only became prominent in the skies of Earth when their orbits intersected the orbit of Earth periodically. This happened in the 8th and 7th century BC, as had happened for a period, 2200 and 1100 years earlier, after 3067 BC and again after 1935 BC. Before that, during the "Era of the Gods," only Mars interacted with Earth. Mercury hung below Saturn, initially very visible when Saturn was blazing, and probably mostly obscured after Saturn quieted down. Despite the fact that Mercury is the smallest planet of the Solar System today (our Moon is smaller), it supported an atmosphere and a coma, which would have made its apparent size much larger than Mars. Together these two would have constituted the iris and pupil of a huge celestial eye.

The Last Changes

There is another very interesting and related consideration arising from the analysis by Rose and Vaughan. They note a change in the aphelion of Earth's orbit in the year immediately following the year of the "Golden Throne" of 685 BC, thus 684 BC. The orbit of the Earth changed its shape, or as Rose and Vaughan note, the Earth's aphelion moved elsewhere in its orbit by 10 or 15 degrees. Probably the most important aspect of the change in aphelion is the fact that it immediately removed the Earth's orbit from further intersections with Mars's orbit, by rotating away from the location where it crossed Mars's orbit.

Moving aphelion by 10 or 15 degrees within the time of a single rotation around the Sun is not a small amount. This clearly is in conflict with any current theories of how orbits might change, which could only happen under the gravitational effects of other planets. Such gravitational tugging is a very small percentage of the effect of the gravity due to the Sun, and would take millions of years to have any effect.

What also happened simultaneously, as a result, was a change in the place in the heavens to which the axis of the Earth pointed. The result would amount to a 15-degree shift of the vernal equinox (the first day of spring, and the start of the year for most nations), and thus a 15-day delay in the start of spring. Instead of the Sun rising in the constellation of the Bull, Taurus, as it had for thousands of years, it suddenly started to rise in the constellation of the Ram, Aries. I'll detail this in the next chapter.

Chaldean priests had kept records of the movements of the planets since 747 BC and certainly by 652 BC (we have records from that date), but often on differing coordinate systems. These make no sense to astronomers today. The Vedas mention a sinking of the Earth. Numerous Greek, Roman, Egyptian, Chinese, and Indian sources mention the change in the Earth axis, and even a later Roman playwright incorporates the well-known "change in the heavens" into a play -- specifically in reference to the zodiac. [note 19]

It was as if a power outside the dome of the stars had suddenly shifted the heavens by rotating them away from the horned bull -- the age-old symbol of the celestial Gods. This was a power greater than that of any of the Gods worshipped up to that time. It closed an era.

Although the changes in the night sky were seen immediately, the significance of the change was not initially appreciated. But within a few hundred years this entered religious and philosophical thinking in the Middle East, India, and China. It is almost certain that Buddhism can trace its inspiration to this event of 685 BC. The Persian Zoroastrianism similarly dates from this period, and strongly influenced Judaism. In China the concepts are expressed in the philosophy of Taoism. The Tao proposes to explain "the change of the path." The "mystery religions" of the Middle East and Greece date from this period. I will get back to this topic in a following chapter.

Additionally Rose and Vaughan report that 9 years later, in 670 BC, for some unknown cause, the eccentricity of the Earth's orbit changed significantly (from 0.10 to 0.0+). This means the orbit of Earth became nearly circular, and no longer overran the orbit of Mars. With that the drama in the skies was over. [note 20]

Endnotes

Note 1 --

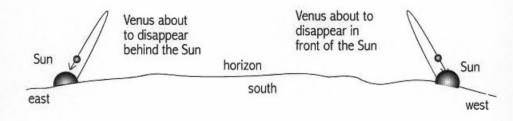

Path of Venus as Morning Star and Evening Star

To explain the strange behavior of the planet Venus: Today Venus is mostly seen only at night, and never more than about 40 degrees alternately above the east or west horizon. Once the Sun rises, Venus is (generally) no longer seen.

Venus is an inner planet. It revolves around the Sun between Earth and the Sun. Its path in the sky describes its orbit around the Sun.

In antiquity Venus was seen also in the day skies (today also, but infrequently). During night hours it was seen preceding the Sun before rising (in the east), or appearing after the Sun set (in the west). In the west, in showing directly after sunset, it would distance from the Sun over the following days, that is, be seen higher in the west sky every day, and then start to come closer again, to suddenly disappear for 8 days, to then rise before the Sun in the east. In rising before the Sun, it would also slowly distance from the Sun and then return, to then disappear for some 60 days or more, after which it would again rise in the west.

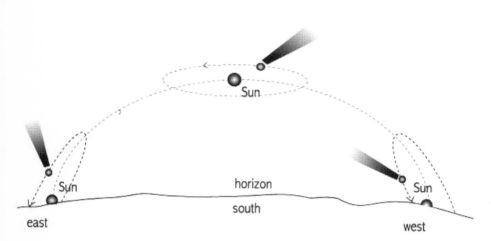

Path of Venus through the day Skies, before 685 BC

In antiquity, Venus was seen as a brilliant object near the Sun. It would seem to circle around the Sun, always with a tail pointing away from the location of the Sun. But it would disappear completely from the skies twice during its 584-day synodical period, once for 8 days, and once for 50 days as it passed in front of the Sun or behind it. These are the current values. In AD 700 the Maya recorded 90 days for the second value.

The Venus tablets stand out as a singular early record not involving any other planets, included with a cache of omen tablets known as the *Enuma Anu Enlil*. Hope Anthony, in "A Guide to Ancient Near Eastern Astronomy" (University of Texas), writes:

Enuma Anu Enlil: *An astrological omen series comprising some 68 tablets. The tablets themselves were found in the Assyrian king Assurbanipal's library in the ancient city of Nineveh, and were written in the 7th century BC. However, evidence suggests the collection of omens is much older than the tablets found in the library, and the original series probably dates back to the Old Babylonian period at the beginning of the 2nd millennium BC."*

"The Enuma Anu Enlil *deals mostly with the constellations, or 'fixed' stars, and, to a lesser degree, with the planets. The exception to this is tablet 63, known as the 'Venus Tablet of Ammizaduga'.... Several copies of tablet 63 have been recovered in varying degrees of preservation, but a composite of these reveal the tablet to be a record of rising and setting dates for the planet Venus over a period of 21 years. As with* Enuma Anu Enlil *as a whole, the 'Venus Tablets' also contain omens."*

Anthony gives an example of an omen text as:

"If in month I the Demon with the Gaping Mouth (Cygnus) rises heliacally: for 5 years in Akkad at the command of Irra [Mars] *there will be plague, but it will not affect cattle."*

The reference to Akkad places the above text to an era well before the era of Babylon or the third Assyrian empire. But by similar references to contemporary events, the Venus tablets themselves can be placed after the start of the 7th century BC.

Note 2 --

The data is not missing. Venus was not "observed to disappear" for nine months, which would have been from March through December.

```
Year      Invisibility During      Invisibility During
          Inferior Conjunction     Superior Conjunction
1         3 days
2                                  2 months, 8 days
3         20 days
4                                  2 months, 1 day
5         15 days                  2 months, 4 days
6         3 days
7                                  2 months, 11 days
8         7 days                   2 months, 7 days
9         9 months, 4 days  <-----
10                                 2 months, 6 days
11        11 days
12                                 5 months, 16 days
13        7 days                   2 months
14        1 month, 16 days
15                                 2 months, 15 days
16        15 days                  3 months, 9 days
17        4 days
18        ---                      ---
19        15 days
20                                 2 months, 6 days
21        7 days                   2 months

-- after Livio C. Stecchini, "The Twenty-One Years of Venus"
Kronos Volume 7 number 3, 1982
```

An ephemeris shows that rather than disappearing in front of the Sun in the west in 684 BC, Venus rode some 8 degrees above the Sun. Thus it moved from being seen in the west above the Sun, rather than in front of the Sun, to next being seen in the east, also above the Sun, without the disappearance period. This is a rare condition, and could be held as proof that the data does not belong in 1500 BC, but properly describes conditions in 684 BC as I have determined.

An ephemeris can be used because the later changes in eccentricity do not change the location of Venus or Earth by more than a few days. Both Earth and Venus were on orbits very little different from today. Also, eccentricity does not change the orbital period.

It was during the course of the previous year (685 BC, astronomical) that the planets Venus and Mercury blazed with light.

Note 3 --

Velikovsky, in Chapter 10 of *Worlds in Collision*, presents a listing of the anomalous spans of time that Venus was visible in the east or west, and the length of disappearances, as recorded by the *Venus Tablets of Ammizaduga*. Velikovsky uses this information to bolster the notion of an irregular orbit for Venus in 1500 BC. The *Venus Tablets of Ammizaduga* indeed prove that there was no regularity at all. But Velikovsky (or anyone) should have realized that if both the Earth and Venus were on eccentric orbits then this condition would be expected. Today Venus has the most circular orbit of any planet, and Earth nearly so, and the visibility and invisibility of Venus in the sky is thus very regular.

I should also note that the idea of "visible in the east" and "visible in the west" is an erroneous notion, since in antiquity, because of its bright coma and tail, Venus moved visibly across the skies with the Sun in the daytime (in addition to showing at night after sunset or before sunrise). What was strange to our ancestors was that Venus would periodically disappear altogether -- in passing behind the Sun or in front of it. At these times the tail would shrink also and disappear, because the plasma tail would be either directed away from the Sun toward Earth or away from the Sun while behind. This strange behavior, in fact, is why Venus was watched. It was such a peculiar object that it was not classified as a planet until after 600 BC.

Note 4 --

Normalization involves dividing data points by an associated variable, which in effect removes its influence on the data. In this case the data could be investigated without having to know (for example) the synodic period of Venus or Earth. Normalization did not supply missing data, it only allowed Rose and Vaughan to test the data against various assigned eccentricities for Earth and Venus.

The background and methods were detailed in a series of articles by Lynn Rose and Raymond Vaughan, the first of which appeared in *Pensee* in 1972 as "Babylonian Observations of Venus." This was followed by a number of articles in *Kronos*: "Analysis Of The Babylonian Observations Of Venus" (1976), "Ninsianna Update" (1980), and "Section II, The Artificial Insertion" (1980). In 1994 a summary of this analysis was presented at the "Kronia Conference" in Portland, Oregon.

Note 5 --

"When the family of the Babylonian kings died out, after 8 years of no kings, Esarhaddon the king of Assyria conquered them and held that kingdom for 13 years. (Ptolemy's, Can. Reg.) It appears Assaradinus is the same person as Esarhaddon. This is from the similarity in the names and by the word of the Holy Scripture. It intimates that he was king both of Assyria and Babylon at the same time. 2Ki 17:24 19:37"
    -- James Ussher, *The Annals of The World* (1650)

Kingship in antiquity was not assumed arbitrarily. Kings were appointed by the Gods, and kingship stayed in a family. This was recognized even by the conquerors of a nation.

Note 6 --

Assurbanipal is the third son of Esarhaddon, and is installed as king of Assyria apparently through the intrigues of his grandmother (who was Sennacherib's surviving wife, a Canaanite princess), and selected as the most able of the three sons of Esarhaddon.

By a proclamation in 672 BC, his father Esarhaddon, had ordered that on his death Assurbanipal should be crowned king of Assyria, and Shamash-shum-ukin as king of Babylon. Thus the (older) crown prince (installed in Babylon) was skipped over for kingship of Assyria. He, of course, revolts at a later date.

Under Persian rule, after another revolt in Babylon, Xerxes melted down the statue of Marduk in 482 BC. When the historian Herodotus arrived in Babylon a generation later, he climbs the 360 stairs of the ziggurat to find the chapel at the top empty.

Note 7 --

The suggestions of a world-view for the Mesopotamians is developed in the chapter "Language and Causality," under a discussion of languages and their influence on the conceptual point of view of reality for a people.

Note 8 --

The story of the Assyrians and Babylon recounted here is an abbreviated version. For greater detail see the last chapter of H. W. F. Saggs, *Babylonians* (2000). A time-line of secular and celestial events in the 7th century BC follows.

```
┌─────────────────────────────────────────────────────────────────────┐
│                 time-line of secular and celestial events            │
│                                                                       │
│       Data below are in Eastern Mediterranean chronology, and not corrected to astronomical dates. Thus 680 BC │
│       (below) will later be shown as 685 "BC" -- actually meaning -685. │
│                                                                       │
│    tablet    year    nny   events (nny = no new year)                 │
│    ------    ----    ---   --------------------------------           │
│              689           Babylon destroyed                          │
│              688     1     New Year not celebrated (see 'nny' series at left) │
│    ....... first series of the Venus Tablet data ...                  │
│    1         687     2     (Earth's eccentricity at 0.10)             │
│    2         686     3     (Earth shock recorded, Sennacherib at Jerusalem) │
│    3         685     4                                                 │
│    4         684     5                                                 │
│    5         683     6                                                 │
│    6         682     7                                                 │
│    7         681     8     Sennacherib assassinated (8th year of no temple) │
│    8         680     9     Sennacherib's son Esarhaddon becomes king of Assyria. │
│                            Venus's disappearance in the east delayed one month │
│                            Babylon rebuilt -- "Year of the Golden Throne" │
│    ....... second series of the Venus Tablet data ...                 │
│    9         679     10    (Earth's eccentricity at 0.10, but aphelion moved) │
│    10        678     11                                                │
│    11        677     12    Esarhaddon's son Shamash-shum-ukin moves to Babylon │
│    12        676     13                                                │
│    13        675     14                                                │
│    14        674     15                                                │
│    15        673     16                                                │
│    16        672     17                                                │
│    17        671     18                                                │
│    18        670     19                                                │
│    ........ third series of the Venus Tablet data ...                 │
│    19        669     20    Esardahhon dies (Earth's eccentricity at 0.0+) │
│    20        668     21    Esardahhon's son Shamash-shum-ukin becomes King of │
│                            Babylon;                                    │
│                            Marduk returned to the temple. Year 21 without │
│                            a New Year celebration                      │
│    21        667           New Year celebrated again                  │
│    ........ end of the Venus Tablet data ...                          │
└─────────────────────────────────────────────────────────────────────┘
```

Note that the year of the Earth shock, 686 BC, falls in this period, but is not an instrumental part of the calculation.

There are a number of discrepant dates, being off by one year, which may follow from the fact that Assyrian years were counted from the spring equinox (rather than January 1), and the fact that I use astronomical years as calendar years without numeric conversion. This may also suggest that the eruption of Venus may have happened directly before the rebuilding of the temple compounds. Celestial data for 680 BC shows up correctly as ephemeris information for 685 BC, Julian, however. This corrects for the four-year difference between Eastern Mediterranean chronology and actual years (the error of four years by Dionysius Exiguus), and the fact that I seem to be off by a year in the above chart. (There is no year zero in these tallies.)

Note 9 --

Except for the records detailed in the *Chilam Balam*, there are few sensible Mesoamerican details about Venus (Quetzalcoatl) in 685 BC, except notions that he set himself on fire and disappeared across the ocean on a raft of snakes. I could suggest that "the ocean" is the Absu here and the raft of snakes are seen near the equinox, similar to Scylla of the Odyssey -- except that the imagery is 1700 years late. It was more important to the people of Central America to have received the promise made by Quetzalcoatl to return and set things right. It was another salvation religion introduced to the world.

"An outstanding problem with the analysis is the eastern disappearance [of Venus] *on the twenty-fifth day of the twelfth month of the eighth year. Our model requires that the invisibility ought to have begun at least a month earlier than that."*
-- Rose and Vaughan

The month delay (before the period of the "Golden Throne") might suggest that Venus had changed the shape of its orbit, perhaps moving its perihelion to a different location along its orbit, although Rose and Vaughan claim that the orbit of Venus did not change during this period. Rose and Vaughan suggest that in this case the *Venus Tablets of Ammizaduga* might have misspelled the name of a month.

Note 10 --

Augustine quotes a lost document by the Roman Varro of the first century BC, but places the event at the time of the Exodus.

Homer makes no mention of Phaethon (except as an epithet for Helios), unless we were to understand the pouting of Achilles represents the unwillingness of Jupiter to act in response to the destructiveness of Mars (Ares) for 120 years.

Hesiod mentions Dawn as the parent of Phaethon. Apollodorus does the same in the second century AD. A document attributed to Hyginus in the same century also mentions the ride. In many instances Phaethon is equated with Saturn and, more often, with Jupiter.

Marinus van der Sluijs has compiled a collection of information from classical authors of the Mediterranean, involving the Great Year, Phaethon (which remains unidentified), comets, and planetary conjunctions in

"Phaethon and the Great Year" in Apeiron (2006). All of the information backs up the narrative presented in this text. According to vd Sluijs, what is missing in late antiquity is any clear identification of the planets. I don't have that sense.

The retelling of the Phaethon legend by Ovid (43 BC -- AD 17) is correct in detail for the nova event of Venus in 685 BC, except for the timing. Ovid has the whole of the ride of Phaethon happen in one day. But see the "Star Wars" chapter for more; this describes the movement of Venus and Mercury through the skies in accurate detail.

When Ovid and other Roman writers describe, "the Earth was burned up," as a detail of the retelling of the legend of Phaethon, they do so correctly. Other exploding blazings in the sky have sent "the fire of Heaven" (Ignis Coelis) to regions of Earth, as late as AD 900.

The "Great Chicago Fire" of AD 1871 has been attributed to Ignis Coelis. Large forest fires happened in Northeastern Wisconsin near Green Bay (the "Great Peshtigo Fire") and in Upper Michigan on the same date and on the same evening as the Chicago fire.

More recently, the patchwork of simultaneous fires in Southern California in October 2007, looks, from maps of the affected areas, to be distributed in a fashion very similar to the Great Chicago Fire of AD 1871 -- locations separated by many miles, but all along a north-south line.

Of course a long rainless season and dry tinder is a prerequisite. But the lightning strikes, which are thought to cause the ignition, were absent. Most of the 170 fires started up simultaneously on July 15. Arson has been suggested, but that would involve an amazing coordination of efforts and fails to even suggest a reason for the efforts. Similar north-south directed strings of fires happened in Greece during 2007 (June 28 and July 15) and Croatia (July 27).

Note 11 --

The *Zend-Avesta* are the sacred books of the Parsis of India, the remnants of the scriptures of Zoroastrianism (Mazdaism) at an earlier time in Persia. In 500 BC Herodotus makes indirect references to Zoroastrianism in his discussion of Persian religion.

The quotations are from the translation by James Darmesteter in 1880, and are abridged. The translator (or a later editor) notes, "Tishtrya is the angel of the star Sirius." This is a fictional association established long ago in Mesopotamia and Egypt. Each person had a star associated with their "spirit." Other quotations make clear that we are not talking about Sirius, as, for example:

"We sacrifice unto Tishtrya, the bright and glorious star, that afflicts the Pairikas, that vexes the Pairikas, who, in the shape of worm-stars, fly between the earth and the heavens, in the sea Vouru-Kasha, the powerful sea, the large-sized, deep sea of salt waters. He goes to its lake in the shape of a horse, in a holy shape; and down there he makes the waters boil over, and the winds flow above powerfully all around."

The sea here is in the cloud-bearing sky. James Darmesteter, in the introduction, writes:

"The scene of the fight is the sea Vouru-kasha, a sea from which all the waters on the earth fall down with the winds and the clouds; in other words, they fight in the sea above, in the atmospheric field of battle."

The Vouru-Kasha is in effect the Absu, imported into the hymn to Tishtrya from much older sources, not untypical of the remainder of the *Zend-Avesta*, where older "mythological" elements are incorporated in the text. Internal literary consideration would suggest that the actual written texts date from the Sassanian period of Persia, AD 200 to AD 600.

"He makes the waters boil over," is generally attributed to the star Sirius, when it would be seen at the east horizon where its path merged with the last remaining ring of the Absu. The image of the planet would flicker. This would also be true of any bright planet found on the ecliptic at the point where it crossed the remaining ring below the equatorial. This is thus a likely condition for planets in June or July, since this time of the year represents the maximum displacement of the ecliptic throughout the night, and planets will very likely be traveling through the last ring below the equatorial for some portion of the night.

Note 12 --

Velikovsky uses these descriptions as suggestions for the events of 1500 BC, but the composition of the Zoroastrian *Avesta* dates from well after 600 BC. He notes that editors other than James Darmesteter have described the hymn as a battle of Venus and the stars against the planets. I did not read that into the hymn, but it would be of revealing significance, since indeed the stars end up in complete disarray.

I should clear up some other "strange celestial events" which have come to haunt Velikovskian discussions. Astronomical information compiled by Huang Sheng (AD 1146 to 1194) includes the statement that "Once T'ai-P'ai [Venus] suddenly ran into Lang Hsing [Sirius], though it is more than 40 degrees south of the Yellow Road." But to have Venus move this far off the ecliptic (the Yellow Road), and then return, is physically impossible and represents a complete misunderstanding. The text, as it has come down to us, has to represent an emendation of earlier sources. Most likely the phrase "ran into" is an interpretation of "at the same time," not "at the same place." It is amazing that this text was copied without thought from one author to another in antiquity, including the detail of the 40 degrees between Sirius and the ecliptic (the actual separation is 37 degrees in latitude).

The "astounding event" in question is the simultaneous heliacal setting of Venus and the heliacal rising of Sirius in AD 350 (about July 10 or so) when they are only 30 degrees apart at the horizon, and after a day or so could be mistaken for each other. This is a very rare event (to be so close together just as the Sun rises), which only happens at 730-year intervals. Since this is a heliacal rising, Sirius had not been seen for months, while Venus had been moving closer to the east horizon, day by day. Just as Venus disappears behind the Sun, Sirius first shows as rising heliacally. Venus is at this point occluded by the rising Sun, and thus Sirius might easily have been misidentified for Venus, making it look as if Venus suddenly jumped off the zodiac. It happened again in about AD 1080, a century before the time of Huang Sheng's compilation, but this event went unrecorded. Sirius is the brightest star in the sky and of about the same magnitude as Venus.

Jan Sammer writes of the earlier notice of the same event,

"The same ancient tradition was [also] referred to by the early eighth-century AD Chinese astronomer Y-hang. As told by Gaubil, Y-hang wrote that 'in the time of Tsin one saw the star Sirius eclipsed by the planet Venus.'"

This is the event noted above which happened in AD 350. The Tsin dynasty dates from AD 265 to AD 420.

Note 13 --

Hercules sets himself on fire to escape a skin disease brought on by donning a poisoned garment. Mars was seen at close range through portions of the 8th and 7th century BC, and before the eruption of Venus, but did not come close to Earth again thereafter. The sightings were close enough that the Martian landscape is seemingly described by Hesiod in his composition *The Shield of Hercules*. The sight of the pockmarked and scarred lower hemisphere might have been evidence enough that the planet was suffering from some terrible disease. The later nova event of Venus constituted his funeral pyre.

[Image: Mars in a dust storm, September 2001, after NASA.]

The garment might also have been a global dust storm, which still obscures Mars today after it passes Earth and is subjected to increased plasma impinging on its surface from Earth's plasmasphere tail. (Last noted in AD 2001.)

Note 14 --

M. A. van der Sluijs, in "On the Wings of Love," *Journal of Ancient Near Eastern Religions* (2008), makes the case that the Phaethon of Hesiod is the same as Phaethon of Ovid and Nonnos. See http://www.mythopedia.info/two-Phaethons-JANER.pdf. Quoting an absolutely minimal description from Hesiod:

> *"And to Cephalus she [Eos] bare a splendid son, strong Phaethon, a man like the gods, whom, when he was a young boy in the tender flower of glorious youth with childish thoughts, laughter-loving Aphrodite seized and caught up and made a keeper of her shrine by night, a divine spirit."*

"She" here is Eos, dawn. As I have pointed out in the text, the electric impact between Earth and Mercury a year earlier (686 BC) reduced Mercury's orbit to fall close to the Sun, so that indeed he would show as the "Morning Star." Thus Mercury at this time had to be reconciled as being "new," so that calling Mercury or Phaethon "the child of Dawn" is perhaps appropriate, since Mercury would only show at dawn, briefly. Only the reference to giving birth keeps this mention from being totally enigmatic, for otherwise we would have to assume that Mercury had been in the position of only showing briefly at dawn for eons.

Van der Sluijs follows up on the earlier quotation from Hesiod with a quotation from Hyginus, 750 years later, in the second century AD:

... in his book on astronomy, alluded to what is evidently the same story concerning the anonymous Aurorae et Cephali filium, *"son of Aurora and Cephalus", whose beauty rivaled that of Aphrodite:*

"Some have said it represents the son of Aurora [dawn] *and Cephalus* [another hero kidnapped by Dawn], *who surpassed many in beauty, so that he even vied with Venus."*

Vd Sluijs elucidates "it" as "the star of Venus," but Hyginus had already identified "it" as Saturn in his text in the then current tradition which assigned "Phaethon" to Saturn or Jupiter. "It" cannot simultaneously "be Venus" and "vie with Venus." But vd Sluijs bolsters the tradition of an abducted Phaethon with other quotes from antiquity.

Knowing the placement of the planets in the sky for the years of 686 BC (after March) and 685 BC, all the various attempts at anthropomorphized rationalizations in antiquity start to make sense. It is still somewhat disconcerting to realize that Hesiod, who most likely witnessed the events of 686 and 685 BC, did not make more of it. This suggests that perhaps the mythology of the misguided "chariot of the Sun" and the death by a lightning bolt may have had its source in Asia Minor, the same region which yielded a number of religions based on the death of a Son of God, rather than Greece.

Note 15 --

James Darmesteter, in his introduction to the translation of the *Zend-Avesta*, also makes note of the lightning bolt in Zoroastrian and Vedic literature:

"Sauru, which in our texts is only the proper name of a demon, was probably identical in meaning, as he is in name, with the Vedic 'S'aru,' 'the arrow,' a personification of the arrow of death as a godlike being."

"The same idea seems to be conveyed by Ishus, 'the self-moving arrow,' a designation to be accounted for by the fact that Saru, in India, before becoming the arrow of death, was the arrow of lightning with which the god killed his foe."

Neither the *Popol Vuh* nor the *Chilam Balam* has reference to the plasmoid from Jupiter as events, but only as objects. In the *Popol Vuh* a "bundle" is identified as in the possession of the Quiche tribe by the time they receive their tribal Gods. Considering the 120-year period when the Earth was constantly subjected to lightning strikes from Mars, perhaps it could be understood that a lightning bolt from another planet might have been accepted as matter of fact. But it seems unlikely.

Note 16 --

I am basing this on timing developed in the chapters "The Books of the Chilam Balam" and "Olmec Alignments," that is, that it took 12 days to travel 484 million miles. Thus the bolt was only seen in the daytime sky as it passed Earth for two and a half days. During two half-day periods of this time the Pacific Ocean faced the traveling plasmoid. During the other times first America, then Asia, and then Europe, in that order, saw the shape in the sky as the bolt passed by. Asia and Europe only saw the bolt as it was approaching and again after it had passed by Earth.

Note 17 --

The understanding of Olmec iconography is completely submerged under ideas of depicting ears of maize as sacred aspects in a completely unknown philosophy, religion, and social structure of the Olmecs and the people of the Valley of Mexico. See, for example, Karl Taube, in *Olmec Art at Dumbarton Oaks* (2004). Certainly the Olmecs would see the metaphorical connection between flower-shaped plasma expulsions and ears of maize. The use of a tri-lobed headdress and depictions of ears of maize may have preceded 685 BC. Later Maya iconography clearly depicts the maize iconography. It is curious, however, that sprouted and ripening maize does not look like that.

What we think we know about the Olmecs is without exception completely derived by analogy from the structure of our own society. Taube suggests that it is the export of "rich agricultural abilities" and a "symbolism of agricultural fertility and wealth" which provided the exchange basis for raw materials such as jade, as if trading technology for materials. I would suggest that their main export was a religion with a claim of control over the sun and the rain.

For the jester-god see the summary of archaeological sources and iconography bearing on this in a paper by Virginia M. Fields, "The Iconographic Heritage of the Maya Jester God" (Los Angeles County Museum of Art, 1991).

Note 18 --

Almost universally all the retellings of the legend of Phaethon, from 500 BC to AD 500, add the curious detail that as Phaethon dies he falls into a celestial river "Eridanus" (a constellation), or the river Po in northern Italy (also known as Eridanus), but located northwest from Greece. His three, seven, or nine sisters, who mourn his death, are turned into poplar trees along the river, and their tears drop as amber beads into the water. The poplar is a very slim tall tree of the Mediterranean region, and perhaps apt as a representation of plasma plumes.

Amber washes up at the shores of the Baltic. The change in the axis of the Earth in 685 BC moved the Arctic Circle six and a half degrees of latitude further north, perhaps bringing the region of the Baltic into the European trade circuit. The amber beads have their source in a play on words, but also accurately reflect their source in trade from the Baltic. (Amber is found in the Po region of northern Italy also.)

Note 19 --

Chaldea was originally a nation from Southern Mesopotamia or Northern Arabia which came to rule at Babylon after 625 BC. Bishop Ussher records for 261 BC:

"Gerosus (Pliny l. 17. c. 56.) published the observations of the Celestial Motions among the Babylonians for a period of 480 years. This is the number of years from the beginning of the Epoch of Nabonassar's account [747 BC] as other learned men understand this."

Others have pointed out that there are no sensible records for the period of approximately 750 BC to 700 BC, with the exception of the *Venus Tablets of Ammizaduga*. What we have today is data only from after 650 BC.

Note 20 --

From the data of the eccentricities, Rose and Vaughan come to the conclusion that the ratio of the synodic periods of Earth and Venus was 1.63. (A synodic period is the time a planet takes to complete one orbit as seen from Earth.) This is close to today's ratio of 1.625.

Calculations are in Unix bc notation, where ∧ denotes exponentiation; the functions a(rctangent), s(ine), and c(osine) use radians; angle conversions to radians or degrees by the divisors rad=.017+ and deg=57.2+; other

functions are shown as f( ); tan( )=s( )/c( )
units: million == 1,000,000; billion == 1,000,000,000;
AU == 93,000,000 miles.

Recovering the Lost World,
A Saturnian Cosmology -- Jno Cook
Chapter 25: The Hour of Phaethon

Revision: 42.38 (hist.php)
Contents of this chapter: [Dating The Events] [Hour of the Thunderbolt]
[The Start of History] [A New Order of the Sky] [The Sky in Disarray]
[A Change in the Equinox] [Endnotes]

"From the first, humanity had to be religious. It is still so.
Further, it will be religious so long as it will exist.
Religion is ultimately hope, and humans live on hope."
-- Alfred de Grazia *The Divine Succession* (1983)

Dating the Events of 685 BC

This chapter deals with the world following 120 years of electric contacts between Earth and Mars, from 806 BC to 687 BC, and the subsequent blazing of Venus and Mercury in 685 BC. This is an era which will see the start of history, science, and philosophy, and the genesis of contemporary religions. All four are the direct result of the events of 685 BC. The quieting of the skies after 685 BC affected how humans saw the world, and we see immediate attempts to reach a new understanding, a science not based on the willful and arbitrary actions of the Gods. At the same time, a much larger religious conceptualization comes forward, based on a power beyond the observable Universe. But first, dates for the year 685 BC.

I'll briefly describe how the four dates of the events of the year 685 BC were found. The dates can all be derived from the Maya *Chilam Balam*, verified from Mesoamerican site alignments, and partially verified from information from the Eastern Mediterranean region. [note 1]

The dates, on the Gregorian calendar and all in the astronomical year 685 BC, are as follows:

- Venus and Mercury start to blaze, June 15
- Jupiter develops a coma, July 9
- Jupiter releases a plasmoid bolt, July 14
- Jupiter's plasmoids lands at the Sun, July 25

In the later chapter "Olmec Alignments," I have determined the three previous dates when the world was destroyed and recreated (in 2349 BC, 1492 BC, and 747 BC), from site alignments in Veracruz and the Valley of Mexico (alignments of the sites to a setting sun at mountains or volcanoes). For the 13 sites which were considered, 20 alignments can be assigned to September 8, 2349 BC (or the later equivalent for the setting of the Pleiades), 16 alignments can be assigned to April 19, 1492 BC, and 10 alignments can be assigned to February 28, 747 BC. This is an astounding series of coincidences -- especially since these were distributed over only 13 sites.

Thus when I started to find additional alignments to July 9 (4 or 5 instances), July 14 (5 instances), and July 25 (7 or 8 instances), they could not be ignored. Additionally, August 12 started to show up. August 12th or 13th was a retrocalculated date for the "second creation," probably first used at La Venta, and then by the very influential city of Teotihuacan, where it was achieved with an alignment of the primary axis of the site. There may be other alignments like that, but I do not have site plans for other sites. The additional alignments, by the way, occur at sites dating in their construction to after 600 BC. Details below.

The following lists the dates in reverse order, for once the concluding date is found, the other dates can be found in reference to that.

... ending date, July 25th

The first inkling that July 25th may have been an important date in Mesoamerica was the fact that the Maya celebrated the following day as "new year's day" at the time of the Spanish invasion. The date is mentioned by bishop Landa, and was apparently set at the Maya site of Edzna in the Eastern Yucatan, where a vertical gnomon has been found, set to show the overhead passage of the Sun on July 25th. Edzna is at the same latitude as the city of Teotihuacan in the Valley of Mexico, where one of the site alignments (to a mountain) is also for July 25th. The next day, July 26th, was new year's day and the start of a seasonal agricultural period.

The importance of the date of July 25th can also be suggested from the fact that Book 10 of the *Chilam Balam* makes only one error in the recollection of the 7000-year history of celestial events, and that is to force the assignment of July 25th to the event of 2349 BC (which we know as the flood of Noah), by reassigning the event to an incorrect year (actually to an incorrect Katun and Tun). The "flood" of 2349 BC, known to the Maya as the "third creation," was very important, as can be shown from the continued iconographic references in sculptures 3000 years later. Having experienced the end of an era on July 25th, 685 BC, it became necessary to prove that all previous eras had also ended on July 25th. (More on this particular quirk in the chapters "The Books of the Chilam Balam" and "The Day of Kan.")

If July 25th is accepted as the day that the plasmoid from Jupiter landed at the Sun, and brought quiet to Venus and Mercury, ending a 120-year period of high planetary activity, then other dates and time spans will segue easily to this date in 685 BC.

... start of the eruption of Venus, June 15th

The starting date of the nova event of Venus in 685 BC can be found by collation of some disparate data. My first clue was a comment by Dennis Tedlock, translator of the Quiche Maya *Popol Vuh*. He commented on a passage where the hero twins of the *Popol Vuh*, Hunahpu and Xbalanque, willingly jump into the oven of the lords of Xibalba (the underworld). In the *Popol Vuh* the lords attempt to trick the twins into jumping into an oven. The twins see through the trick, and respond as follows:

"You'll never put that one over on us. Don't we know what our death is, you lords? Watch!" they said, then they faced each other. They grabbed each other by the hands and went head first into the oven.

Little did the lords of Xibalba know that in sacrificing themselves, the twins were destined to "become" the Sun and the Moon. Mesoamerica certainly understood that both the Sun and the Moon had made their first appearances in the remote past, the Sun in 4077 BC, the Moon in 2349 BC. But connecting an event of 685 BC to events thousands of years earlier was not a problem to the Maya, especially in a popular narrative which had already existed since the Classical period (AD 400 to AD 900), as can be ascertained from depictions on vases from this period. [note 2]

In the *Popol Vuh* the twins Hunahpu and Xbalanque are understood to be Venus and Mars. This much is certain from the story of their birth, and can be collaborated from comments in the *Chilam Balam*. But this is not correct for the last instance. In actuality the two planets which were seen in flames in 685 BC were Venus and Mercury. Hunahpu definitely is Venus. As Tedlock notes, he is named after the first day of the five periodic cycles of Venus as Morning star and Evening star. Xbalanque, on the other hand, is not as easily identified. His name could be translated as "little jaguar of the night" where

"X" is a diminutive. Xbalanque is always "little," whereas the term "little" is only applied to Hunahpu in a very few instances. In the *Popol Vuh*, Hunahpu always acts in the daytime, Xbalanque acts at night. This would seem to correctly reflect on what side of the Earth Mars (and in the last instance, Venus) and Mercury primarily acted during the 60-year period after 747 BC.

In the last instance, when two planets go up in flames, the two planets are Venus and Mercury. Venus is large, and seen as large, especially with a coma, whereas Mercury is definitely small. Mercury had lost most of its atmosphere two years earlier, and looked no larger than it is today, although after June 15th it was blazing like a sun.

I am making this identification, because the confusion of the planets existed already in antiquity. For example, in the Eastern Mediterranean region it was assumed (in some retellings) that the eruption of 685 BC only involved Venus. Mercury travels so close to the Sun that it could easily be confused with the Sun if it (or both) were seen blazing in the sky, and Mercury normally could not be located in the skies during the day, unlike Venus, which was visible day or night because of its coma and tail. Mars was also in the skies at in 685 BC, close to the Sun but behind it.

Identifying Xbalanque as Mercury allows following up on a comment by Tedlock which comes some pages later after the following text in the *Popol Vuh* which reads:

And then the boys ascended this way [leaving Xibalba], *here into the middle of the light* [that is, this world], *and the sun belongs to one and the moon to the other.*

Tedlock writes in his notes:

It is not stated literally that they became the sun and moon. ... The nature of Xbalanque's lunar role is foretold by the fact that he is face-to-face with Hunahpu when they burn together, this being the position of the moon when it is full.

The comment is revealing, but the statement is wrong. This imposes our knowledge of how the Moon and Sun are related, and the cause for a full Moon. For a people to whom the Earth was flat, only a new Moon would fulfill the condition of the Sun and Moon facing each other. They had to be in the sky at the same time, and close together. In fact, looking at a graphical ephemeris for July 25, 685 BC (the ending date), Mercury is seen next to the Sun, and Venus next to the new Moon.

I thus started to look at new Moon dates in the year 685 BC. From about the time of the equinox, when Venus might have first returned to view from behind the Sun, through the beginning of July, before the concluding day of the nova event, there are five new Moons. In each of these instances the Moon would be very near the Sun. The condition I was looking for was the simultaneous close proximity of Venus and Mercury in the sky.

The following are the new Moon dates, and the location of the planets with respect to the Sun, shown in Right Ascension (hours and minutes of left-right location): A minute is 0.25 degrees. I have only listed the two instances where Venus and Mercury are close together, May 23 and June 22 (Julian).

**From east to west in the sky at noon sidereal time,
Mexico City. Right Ascension in hours:minutes.
Dates shown as Julian.**

May 23 --
       Mercury, Venus, Sun, Moon, Mars
       4:50, 4:40, 3:25, 3:23, 3:05
       Mercury and Venus are close together in Gemini.
       The Sun and Moon are close together at the east end of Taurus.
June 22 --
       Venus, Mercury, Moon, Sun, Mars
       7:20, 7:08, 5:15, 5:26, 4:29
       Mercury and Venus are close together in Leo.
       The Sun and Moon are close together between Cancer and
       Gemini.

The above dates of May 23 and June 22 qualify. In both instances Venus and Mercury are grouped close together, one almost above the other, but slightly displaced. In effect Xbalanque and Hunahpu are facing each other, almost holding hands. The Sun and Moon are nearby and in an almost identical position with respect to each other. The point of this exercise is based on the conviction that the Olmecs would have seen these conditions, and furthermore recorded them.

I picked the June date as most likely. June 22 Julian is June 15 Gregorian. The choice of June 15 was made on the basis of information from the other end of the world, from the "Tishtar Yasht" hymn to Venus, of the *Zend-Avesta*. Tishtrya (Venus) battles demons in the sea (sky) for 34 days before victory is achieved. I have noted the details in the previous chapter. Thirty-four days fits the span of time from June 15 to July 25 (Gregorian), with a few days left over, which may also be accounted for in the hymn, but not clearly.

But much more convincing is the description of the blazing of Venus in 685 BC recorded in the *Sibylline Oracle Books*, composed at a much later date in Alexandria, Egypt. The *Sibylline Oracle Books* clearly places Venus in Leo at the start of the event. In fact, as others have noted, Venus riding on the back of a lion (the constellation Leo) was regarded as a symbol of disaster in the Eastern Mediterranean.

Does this date, June 15, show up in Mesoamerican site alignments? No. I almost wrote, "of course not." It does not show up because it is the start of an event; the structure of Mesoamerican languages recognize only the completion of events, and pays scant attention to beginnings.

However, the *Chilam Balam* records a period of time when "it came about that the sun in Katun 3-Ahau was moved from its place for three months." The complete period is noted because it was a celestial disaster of immense scope. Katun 3-Ahau includes the year 685 BC. The three months (of 20 days) are counted inclusively, as are all other intervals of time mentioned in Book 10 of the *Chilam Balam*. So the actual period is two Tzolkin Uinal months. The interval of 40 days (two 20-day months) exactly spans June 15th to July 25th.

... the release of the plasmoid bolt, July 14

This date is based on an interval of 12 days which was put to use in a reconstruction of Monte Alban in 275 BC (detailed in a later chapter), the fact that July 14th is used by five sites as an alignment, and the suggestion of possible selection of the "day of Kan" associated with the end of an era -- the delivery of the plasmoid on July 25th. Additional nuances with respect to Mesoamerican attempts to forge a science from the numerology of the Tzolkin calendar, including the elusive search for the "day of Kan," are discussed in a later chapter. July 14th also represents a reasonable interval of time for a plasmoid from Jupiter to travel the 480 million miles (773 million km) to the Sun. I develop the reasoning for this date in the chapter "The Day of Kan." Since it would take a considerable amount of text to detail all this here, I will have to leave off at this point in the retelling.

... Jupiter develops a coma, July 9

This date is based solely on the fact that it first shows up at Tres Zapotes, recurs 4 times elsewhere, and represents an adequate interval for Jupiter to have been seen with overhead plasma plumes and a lower bifurcated or trifurcated body -- so that these shapes would enter Olmec iconography. This date is thus not well supported. Although the site alignments associated with this date are within two degrees of solstice alignments, it is unlikely that these represent a solstice, despite the fact that both Vincent Malmstrom and

Anthony Aveni delight in assigning Mesoamerican site alignments to Summer solstices. The later Maya (and Aztecs) had no ceremonies or festivities associated with the solstices.

Selection of this date for a sunset alignment is somewhat problematic, for "beginnings" are seldom held as significant in the Mesoamerican worldview. What could make the date of July 9 significant is the consideration that the explosion of Jupiter into a coma was a return from the dead (and thus the conclusion of a "death" period) of what would have been, at the time, the primary God, in a manner similar to the return from the dead of Jupiter in 2349 BC. This previous event was certainly remembered, and had been recorded in graphic books. The iconography of the split mountain, the Absu at the autumnal equinox of 2349 BC with an emerging and resurrected God, continues well into the future. The ballcourt imagery is based on this also.

The primacy of a chief God passes to Quetzalcoatl or to the ball-playing twins of the *Popol Vuh* after 685 BC, however. I think we need to see the July 9th alignment as one of the religious interpretations of the events of 685 BC which did not take hold in any measure.

Hour of the Thunderbolt

Mesoamerica did not see the plasmoid hit the Sun, for it happened two hours after sunset in Mexico. In the Eastern Mediterranean the flash happened two or three hours before sunrise. But in Australia it happened in full view an hour after sunrise in the morning.

The time of day can be found from an Australian Aborigine legend, called "Kirkin and Wyju," recorded by William Ramsary Smith in *Myths and Legends of the Australian Aborigines* (1930). It appears to be about Venus (Kirkin) and Jupiter (Wyju) in the winter (in the southern hemisphere) of 685 BC.

The story portrays Kirkin as very conceited and self-centered. He combs his long blond hair daily, facing the Sun, and tosses it over his head to the front at times in a vain display. (Blond hair occurs among the aborigines.) Wyju, on the other hand, is characterized as "a humble man, who did many wondrous acts." Part of the story tells of his rescue of a child who was swallowed by a God Snake. Wyju has to coax the snake into an upright position, for otherwise the local water supply would disappear. With the snake standing on the tip of its tail, Wyju sliced the snake open along its back to remove the swallowed child.

This will be recognized as an image of the polar plume, with the swallowed child as the ball plasmoid near the end. The timing is wrong, but for the sake of a moralizing story, that doesn't matter. There will be a later image of the polar plume in terms of a column of white smoke.

> *"The story of his wonderful deed reached even the conceited Kirkin, who became very jealous, and decided that if Wyju should come within the bounds of his hunting ground he would endeavour to slay him."*

Kirkin, in fact, invites Wyju to be his guest. During the evening meal Kirkin suggests they go hunting the next day for Wallows -- kangaroo rats. While Wyju sleeps, Kirkin repairs to a nearby Wallow nesting ground and places pointed sticks in the ground around a dead Wallow, with a hidden string tied to the grass and leading away from the location. Kirkin recommends to Wyju:

> *"To procure this most coveted prey no spear, boomerang, or nulla-nulla is required. You simply walk cautiously into the nesting-ground, and when you see the grass moving you know that beneath it lies the wallow, and with a mighty leap into the air straight above the prey you come down and let your feet land right upon it."*

The next day, during the hunt, Wyju does exactly that.

> *"Wuju jumped with all his might, and came down with both his feet upon the sharp spikes, which pierced them deeply."*

Wyju faints in pain, and when he comes to, Kirkin tells him:

> *"Oh my friend, when you walk upon your feet please don't forget to look me up. The sign by which you will find me is a white smoke column that rises on a still, clear day."*

Kirkin leaves, leaving Wyju to suffer and bleed.

> *"From new moon until next new moon did Wyju, overcome with pain and suffering, weep and cry unto the All Father Spirit."*

He requests having the Winjarning brothers sent. They appear at the second new moon and heal his feet. Note the *new moon* dates. The reader will recognizee the period of two new moons from the Mesoamerican *Popol Vuh* narrative.

> *"Wyju went in haste far away into the northern land, and saw a white smoke column rising straight into the clear blue sky. [He walked until] ... he came within sight of Kirkin, who was walking round and round the*

fire."

After sunrise the next day, armed with a warrior's boomerang, Wyju closes in on Kirkin, who is facing east.

"He raised his weapon, and with a mighty stroke severed the head with the golden hair from the trunk. He then committed Kirkin's body to a fire. The spirit of Kirkin rose out of the flame and entered the body of a small hawk-like bird."

I was not entirely convinced until I ran into Jupiter suffering from the spikes in his feet from one new moon to the next new moon, and then a few additional days to hunt down Venus. That matches my deduced timetable, which goes from one new moon (June 15, Gregorian) to the next (July 14, Gregorian) plus 11 more days.

The spikes in Jupiter's feet must be the "long fire-flames [which] rebelled against the Sun," as the *Sibylline Star Wars* text has it. And the blood: Jupiter's plasmasphere would have been red in color, as it had in 2349 BC. When the Olmecs start to construct pyramids, they are called "red mountains," after the image of Jupiter in 685 BC.

The Winjarning brothers seem to be the Australian version of the various celestial twins and brothers of Greece, Italy, and Mesoamerica: the Dioscuri, Romulus and Remus, Apollo and Heracles, and Hunahpu and Xbalanque of the *Popol Vuh*. Wow! That places the legend in the era of 800 through 685 BC. In Australia the boys are busy with "righting wrongs." The evil wrought in the northern hemisphere was absent south of the equator.

Wyju was initially a "half day's journey toward the rising Sun." That is about right; Jupiter stood a half-day toward the east in 685 BC.

The column of white smoke (!) from Kirkin's fire is the northern plasma plume, which would have shown up very soon after the Sun's nova event started. Even Nonnos recalled this 1100 years later. Kirkin has a fire going, which matches the various polar plasma plumes given out as "the fires of the four directions," as, for example, the four braziers of the Egyptians. Kirkin's circumambulation is the apparent traversal of the north cardinal direction at about noon during most of the 40 days when Venus and Mercury appeared during daylight hours.

The bleeding of Wyju also shows up as the bright spikes shining through the last red ring of the equatorial rings. At the latitude of Perth (the likely location of the source for this tale) the Sun, Moon, Venus, Mercury are all below the equatorial at the second new Moon, and the condition of a backlighted red ring could have been seen (the red ring would not otherwise be seen in the daytime). By July 25 (Gregorian), when the skies were identical to today, Venus was probably within that band (ready to bleed), but not Jupiter. However, Jupiter's coma would be red.

In the Eastern Mediterranean the reverse was true. Jupiter may have been high enough at culmination (36 degrees at Cairo) to be behind the red ring (at 42 degrees). But it didn't matter. Jupiter had a red coma anyway. However, the Sun, Venus, and Mercury rode high above the equatorial, and were thus clear of the red ring.

After the spikes are removed, Wyju had traveled to the northern land where Kirkin normally resided -- "in haste." Was the plasmoid mistaken for Wyju? This actually happened in India and with Mazdaism -- the lightning bolt was a separate god. I think a substitution was made in Australia also. This allows Wyju to move "in haste" and to "sneak up" on Kirkin. As the plasmoid passed Earth it would have been seen moving rapidly. Then it slowed down visually, "sneaking up" on Kirkin.

The time of the decapitation is interesting; Wyju selects the "early morning hours of the rising Sun." If correct, this could serve as an anchor for other estimates.

In Western Australia near the end of July of 685 BC, Mercury rises at 6am, the sun rises about 7am, Venus rises two hours later at 9am. (The southern hemisphere is in winter.) Jupiter will not be in sight until late in the day, near 3pm. It is obvious that it is the plasmoid that needs to be watched, not the planet Jupiter.

If the blast at the Sun happened at 9am in Australia, it would be sensed as a flash at the horizon at 3am in the Eastern Mediterranean, which would be an hour before Mercury rose, and two hours before the Sun appeared (it is summer in the northern hemisphere). If the landing of the boomerang was seen an hour later in Australia, then the last travels of the plasmoid would still not likely to have been seen, since it was still an hour before sunrise in the Mediterranean. Mercury was above the horizon but became engulfed by the flash.

I had originally estimated the night as the time of the event for the Eastern Mediterranean, based on the fact that the Phaethon legend shows no clear idea of what entity in the sky was blasted by the thunderbolt. The estimates from Australia confirm this.

Mesoamerica experienced the event at 9pm. The Sun and Venus had set. (Although in summer, at this location is near the tropics, the Sun had set at 7pm.) Mesoamerica also had no idea of what object in the skies was hit. Only knowing that Mars was located just to the west of the Sun (and also below the horizon) would give a clue. Venus has just set at the western horizon a half hour earlier. It might have been obvious that Venus was not the target. The plasmoid had bypassed Venus. But Mars had been the culprit for 120 years.

In Mesoamerica the splashdown would show as a flash at the western horizon, where the Sun was below the horizon, having set about two hours earlier. If the blast had lasted longer than 9 hours (my estimate of the splashdown time at the Sun) it would still have been seen in the east in the morning hours. Thus perhaps did Quetzalcoatl "go east and set himself on fire."

The rise of Venus after "8 days" (in Mesoamerican retellings) is equated to a canonical 8 days (for a westerly disappearance of Venus) because the skies were obscured for four days and this is what Venus was expected to do if it had been properly observed. The *Popol Vuh* mentions four days during which Hunahpu and Xbalanque appear as catfish ("seen in the river"). The catfish are likely smaller plasmoids from Jupiter which kept the turmoil at the Sun alive for these four days. This is similar to the sequence of plasmoids from Venus in 2349 BC: first a large thunderbolt, followed by lesser bolts in the following days.

I considered using a later hour (like 10am), for Wyju definitely sees Kirkin preening himself before launching the boomerang. Wyju comes up from behind, with Kirkin "facing the Sun." This is indeed the situation if Kirkin is Venus. Kirkin is east of the Sun, with its large plasma tail facing away from the Sun, and Jupiter much further east, and thus sneaking up behind him, but Jupiter remained well below the horizon. It is the plasmoid itself, as the warrior's boomerang, which is seen.

If we wait for Jupiter to show above the southeast horizon, it will be after 2pm. That invalidates any estimated times for other longitudes. I'm inclined to move the character of Wyju from Jupiter to the thunderbolt on these last few days.

Burning Kirkin's body is interesting also. It recalls the Mesoamerican Quetzalcoatl. That would also make me believe that the decapitation probably started shortly after 9am. That way we have an all-day cremation event. It is over (most of it) in a few days. The fire is likely the north polar column in arc mode at its lower portion. The fire and the column would have remained in the same location. Also, the rising of the "spirit of Kirkin" duplicates the rising up of Venus as a star ("the Morning Star") as recorded in Mesoamerica.

Some things remain unresolved, but then, I think that everywhere in antiquity there was an immediate confusion of who was struck by lightning, and who was Phaethon. Hesiod's brief description, along with Hyginus (as pointed out by van der Sluijs), has Mercury as Phaethon, the same as Nonnos and Ovid. Others have Venus. The Eastern Mediterranean actually has it more correct than Mesoamerica, for by assigning Mercury to Phaethon, there was no need for a "rising into the sky" as Mesoamerica had. After the plasmoid was delivered Mercury was no longer seen in the day skies, and was seen only at night within a few degrees of the Sun at sunrise or sunset.

The flash most likely occluded the planets near the Sun, Mercury and

Mars. Venus was some 35 degrees east (about 2.5 hours) of the Sun. It probably disappeared in the flash too. Strangely, the Sun was never the suspected target.

If the Eastern Mediterranean had seen the affair in the day sky, it would have been obvious that the plasmoid traveled past Venus, and not past the Sun, but the splashdown happened at night. That the boomerang came to a halt at the Sun should have been noted in Australia. But it was Venus which had lost its tail and coma. And, of course, the Sun just went on as if nothing had happened.

Mercury was a peculiar object in that it only showed in the day skies for 40 days during this year, and then was never again seen rising that high. It had only taken up its regular station of the true morning and evening star in the previous year.

The last piece of discrepant information is the fact that Kirkin and Mercury, in addition to facing the Sun, were said to face east -- both on the last day. Only Mercury, west of the Sun could have been in a position to do both of these. Mercury was close to the Sun, about 15 degrees west.

Let me remind the reader that we are seeing all this in the southern hemisphere so that the location of the planets would seem to be reversed from what is seen in the northern hemisphere. The Sun rises in the east, but that is to the right when facing north and facing the equator, where the path of the Sun through the sky will be.

But now consider also the fact that between about July 8 and July 11 (Julian) Mercury moved from a position just east of the Sun to a location just west of the Sun. Since Mercury during these two days rode above the Sun (by 5 degrees), the effect would have been to see its plasma tail "hair" being tossed from his back over the top and to the front of his face. This matches the description of Kirkin:

> *"Every morning he would mount a high boulder and comb his hair. Then with both hands he would bring the golden shower from the back of his head to hang in front...."*

Thus Kirkin in this last scene may be the planet Mercury. If so, then the delivery of the plasmoid at the Sun would have happened between 8am and 9am. In either case, 9am is probably a close approximation of the delivery time of the plasmoid.

The Start of History

What stands out in the period after about 600 BC, and increasingly over the following centuries, is a sudden intense interest in history, which shows up, not only in the Middle East, Greece, and Ptolemaic Alexandria, but also in China. Why this sudden flurry of research and speculation on events, and specifically only events of the recent past?

There had been over 600 years of a quiet sky, from 1440 BC to 800 BC. Then, within a span of a little more than a hundred years, Venus, Mars, and Mercury closed in on the Earth (or seemed to). The length of the year changed, Mars repeatedly cruised very close to Earth (nine times) to cause massive earthquakes and interplanetary lighting strikes which traveled across wide areas and were accompanied by hurricanes of ground-up rock, burning trees, and flaming sand. Then, just as suddenly, after the nova event of Venus in 685 BC, which surpassed the Sun in brilliance and dropped fire from heaven over wide areas of the Earth, ending with a lightning bolt from Jupiter directed at the Sun, it all stopped.

During the 8th and 7th century BC, and periodically a hundred years earlier, endless wars had raged in the whole region of Mesopotamia and the Levant, mostly involving the states of Assyria and Babylonia feuding with encroaching tribes and kingdoms from the north. Starting in about 750 BC Assyria expanded to conquer all of Babylonia, Syria, the city-states along the Mediterranean coast, and eventually Egypt.

The physical and political changes required an explanation, and the first line of inquiry was to sort out the events. A change in perspective on the progress of time took place, which resulted in the increase of the number of chronicles and records. This is seen especially with the Assyrians, who start to record all their activities -- in effect, they start to write history (as do the Babylonians). The conditions of wars and the compilation of histories is the same in China.

This was followed soon by philosophical speculation, which we will eventually understand as the start of science. It should be recognized that the people of this era were technologically quite proficient. They could measure and map the stars and planets as well as the geography of the Earth, solve for the roots of quadratic equations, and undertake massive building and irrigation projects.

Bronze metallurgy was supplanted by the technology of iron after 800 BC. The smelting methods were apparently imported from regions north of the Caucasus. The Assyrians start producing iron weapons. They also adapt the horse to warfare, forging an effective and fast moving cavalry. The same Assyrians, by their own reports, model their warfare after 750 BC on the strikes of Mars and its hordes of companions, absolutely devastating their enemies with a cruelty unequaled in all previous history.

Historians after 600 BC will divide world history into two parts, the era before 747 BC, and the era after 747 BC. The year 747 BC had seen a change in the length of the year, had thrown the lunar month out of sync with the year, and had initiated 60 years of geological and climatic disturbances (or 120 years from 806 BC). However, a more important date was 685 BC, when it all stopped.

A New Order of the Sky

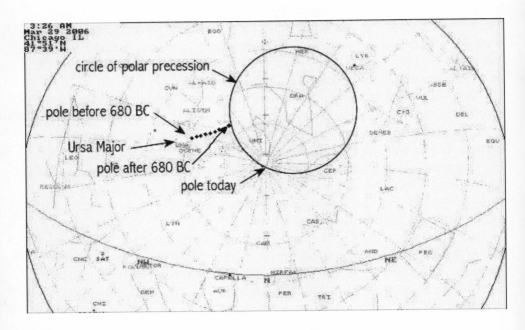

[*Image: The change in polar axis in 685 BC shown with a dotted-line. This is an approximation. The path of the polar precession describes a 30- to 32-degree circle about the location of the Sun's axis in space. Illustration by J. Cook.*]

In the seventh century BC, as noted in the previous chapter, the spin axis of Earth (the polar axis) changed to point to a new location in the sky. Greek, Roman, Egyptian, Chinese, and Indian sources, without being specific about a date, all extrapolate to the 8th or 7th century BC as the date when the axis of the Earth changed from Ursa Major (the Big Bear) to a location closer to the Ursa Minor (the Little Bear). Today the axis is located at the tail of Ursa Minor. But both the new location and the actual cause for the change elude us. Did the nova condition of the Sun affect the Earth's axis in 685 BC? I think it probably did. (The thunderbolt from Jupiter in July of 685 BC was not likely the cause.)

Seneca and others claim that the Earth's axis of rotation, that is, the place in the dome of the stars to which it pointed (today at the star Polaris in Ursa

Minor), was located in Ursa Major before the 7th century BC. Velikovsky quotes Seneca as, "And the Wain [Ursa Major], which has never bathed in the sea, shall be plunged beneath the all-engulfing waves." But this is hyperbole from the first-century AD play by Seneca, *Thyestes*. The Wain did not plunge below the waves of the Mediterranean sea at the latitude of Rome (42 degrees north) before or after the change in the sky. It still does not do so today. The tail started to just touch the ocean (the north horizon) after AD 200 as seen from the latitude of Alexandria in Egypt. All the rest of Seneca's description is just to make drama of a transformed sky. However, it is the use of a "changed sky" as a metaphor in his play which speaks to the fact that the changes were common knowledge. [note 3]

There are many other references in Roman, Greek, and Indian sources which note that the Earth's rotational axis had at one time been located in Ursa Major. There is even an old reference among the Pyramid texts, "the king looks among the stars of The Wain, to determine true north." [note 4]

The spin axis (polar axis) of the Earth points today to the star Polaris, at the end of the handle of the Little Dipper, the constellation Ursa Minor. Over the course of time the location where the axis intersects the dome of the stars is understood to move slowly on a circular path to point to different locations in the northern sky, but always angled 23.5 degrees away from a line perpendicular ("normal") to the orbital plane of the Earth (known as the "obliquity" of a planet). This circle in the sky is known as the "precessional path" of the Earth's axis, like the circle described by the top of the axis of a wobbling top. By today's observations, it takes 26,000 years to complete the wobble. [note 5]

I will propose that the spin axis moved directly and in a very short period from a location "among the stars of Ursa Major" to a new location in the sky near the current precessional path close to Ursa Minor and then halted, changed direction, and continued at a right angle very slowly. I think this happened in 685 BC during the 40 days when Venus and Mercury blazed in the sky. The nova event of the Sun would have represented an absolutely gigantic electric storm capable of twisting the Earth's rotational axis. I will thus suggest that the blazing of Venus and Mercury, and the simultaneous change in the location to which the Earth's spin axis pointed, were caused by a mass expulsion from the Sun -- a nova event. This was not a single hit, it was an expulsion that lasted 40 days. [note 6]

Attributing the cause to an electric storm from the Sun does not seem so far-fetched. I would find this an acceptable hypothesis because the effect would have represented relatively low forces extended over a long period of time. The Earth's axis, although experiencing a bending torque, did not react in the typically violent manner that a gyroscope exhibits on the application of an impact force. It is, of course, possible that there were geological effects but these remained completely hidden among the constant earthquakes experienced since the Earth shocks of 747 BC and 686 BC. Earthquakes continued at a high frequency for a long time. Eight hundred years later Rome still reports 57 earthquakes in a single year (Velikovsky). [note 8]

[*Image: The comet NEAT in 2003, meeting up with a coronal mass ejection (CME) from the Sun, a minor nova event. The larger disk blocks the Sun's corona. The smaller diameter circle represents the size of the Sun. After NASA.*] [note 7]

It could also be suggested that the current precessional path of the spin axis -- the so-called wobble which we still experience -- is the last remnant of the event of 685 BC. A "wobble" is what gyroscopes experience, but only if the applied torque persists. But since there is currently no applied force, and precession has not stopped, it is more likely that precession is caused by the Moon's travel around the Earth on a path which each month moves the Moon out of and back into the Earth's plasmasphere. The Moon is the only satellite of any planet which does this. All other satellites of all the other planets travel within their planets' plasmaspheres, except for a few satellites which remain completely outside of planetary plasmaspheres. [note 9]

The Moon leaves the Earth's plasmasphere monthly because the Moon is on an orbit much further from its parent planet (Earth) than any other satellite of any planet, excepting the few really distant satellites of Saturn (at 6 and 11 million miles). At an orbit of 250,000 miles (400,000 km), the path of the Moon extends beyond the boundary of the Earth's plasmasphere on the Sun side. The Earth's plasmasphere extends only to 80,000 to 160,000 miles (130,000 to 257,000 km), but much further on the night side -- the "shadow" of the Sun's electric field. Thus the Moon travels within the Earth's plasmasphere only on the night side. [note 10]

The entry and exit of the Moon into and out of the Earth's plasmasphere would result in electric effects at the boundary. This would affect the boundary of the plasmasphere locally with each entry and exit. The electric effects are experienced by Earth, just as the arrival of a coronal mass ejection (CME) from the Sun causes a temporary slowing of the rotation of the Earth, although the Earth always regains its rotational speed afterward. The effect of the Moon's entry and exit from the plasmasphere, however, is unlike the effect of a CME, for the disturbance is localized and always offset from the center of the rotational axis of the Earth. All exits are always at the leading edge of the Earth's orbital path.

Since precession was not noticed by the astronomers of antiquity until after 400 BC, we could reason backwards and suggest that the Earth's plasmasphere was more extensive (larger) before that time (probably before 685 BC) such that it would contain the Moon in its travels around the Earth. This would imply that the nova event in 685 BC reduced the size of the plasmasphere to where the Moon, since that time, would cut across the plasmasphere boundary. Since the size of the Earth's plasmasphere is determined by the electric field of the Sun, it suggests also that the Sun's electric field was reduced in 685 BC.

Most likely the relocation of the Earth's axis in space had a relatively quick onset and then a rapid exponential decline, so that much of the change was accomplished within the period of 40 days, but not so suddenly that the Earth would have been jolted -- as had happened frequently in the past. We have to posit these conditions because we know the change happened, and most likely happened at this time, but went unrecorded (but certainly not unnoticed), lacking violent physical effects impinging on the Earth. The blazing of Venus and Mercury and the lightning bolt from Jupiter were seen by anyone who looked up at the day sky. The rotation in the dome of the stars to a new location was noted, especially by sailors and eventually by astronomers. I do not consider it even a remote possibility that the rotational axis of Earth shifted geographically in any significant manner. The geographic location of the axis of rotation before 685 BC was at exactly the same place (the "North Pole"), as today. [note 11]

Velikovsky mentions a Vedic source which tells that the Earth "receded 100 yojanas" from its place. This is an interesting and significant data point, and turns out to be wholly correct when compared to other astronomical sources. The measurement most likely dates from after the 7th century BC, when the oral Vedic traditions were being transferred to writing in India and emendated with contemporary historical events. One hundred "yojanas" is 720 km, or 447 miles, and would represent a change of 6.5 degrees in the latitude of stars overhead.

If the Vedic source noted that "the Earth receded 100 yojanas from its place," it would indicate a noticeable single change in the skies. The wording seems consistent, because later Roman authors agree that the Earth had sunk towards the south. Pliny called it, "a slackening of creation." But this would only be noticed with a comparison of the night skies before and after 685 BC. The question becomes, "What in the skies stood higher up after the change?"

The position (or height) of the Sun would be an indication as would a change in the background stars of the polar axis. This change can only be accounted for with a change in the inclination of the spin axis to the Earth's orbital plane.

Allowing that the Indians were competent mathematicians (and they certainly were, our algebra is derived from them), it could be suggested that the 6.5 degrees (100 yojanas) represented the shift in the Earth's axial inclination in 685 BC. The axial inclination can be easily measured from the difference (before and after) of the elevation of the Sun at the winter or summer solstice (for example). That would suggest that the axial inclination of the Earth before 685 BC was 6.5 degrees different from the present 23.5 degrees -- it was 30 degrees. [note 12]

The location of stars with respect to each other in the dome of the stars would not change with a relocation of the polar axis (or even a new orbital inclination). Thus, as far as the geography of the Earth is concerned, north would still be north, and the other cardinal directions would still be where they were expected to be. The North Pole location in the sky, also would not assume a different elevation above the north horizon. Latitudes would remain the same, although they would have to be recalculated. The Sun and the planets would still travel on the ecliptic, against the same background of stars. None of the stars would shift with respect to each other.

Only the relationship of the stars to the horizon and the equatorial would change, plus the intersection of the equatorial with the ecliptic (the location of the equinox). This is what I have proposed in the previous chapter and from comparison with other data, this seems to be the case. I'll describe the change in the skies further below.

A clear indication of the changes in the axial inclination probably remains obscured as yet among Babylonian records. Velikovsky brings some of the confused records forward, but he uses these in support of other events, and nothing can be gleaned from their perusal.

The fact that the Earth's axial inclination was 30 degrees at an earlier time was verified when I started to look at alignments of Mesoamerican ceremonial centers with the surrounding mountains and volcanoes. See the chapter "Olmec Alignments" for details. The chapter titled "The Chilam Balam" includes other clear numeric instances. [note 13]

The Sky in Disarray

Even if I can only suggest the mechanism involved in these changes, I can be more certain in identifying the location in the sky to which the axis of the Earth originally pointed. There is a Lakota Indian myth or legend which states that, upon death, people enter heaven through a hole in the sky where there once was a star, located within the four stars known as "the stretcher" or "man-carrier" -- the box or pan of Ursa Major.

[*Image: San Jose rock showing Ursa Major
and Ursa Minor; courtesy of Keith Snyder.*]

Physical evidence for this, notably far from the Mediterranean where we find most of the mythology, is an undated hand-sized smooth stone found in California by Keith Snyder. The stone had drilled holes which exactly match the stars of Ursa Major and Ursa Minor. The sizes of the holes which pockmark the stone are proportional to the brightness of the stars in the two constellations. There is one additional hole in the pan of Ursa Major which is not included in most contemporary star charts of the Big Dipper. It is inside the pan (the "stretcher") and just below the line connecting Megrez to Dubhe and closer to Megrez than Dubhe (noted with the arrow in the above image). [note 14]

Going by the Lakota lore, Keith Snyder thinks it is a missing star which is now a mythological hole in the sky. Going by the Saturnian lore, I think it is the previous center of the sky before 685 BC and the location of the *axis mundi* before the departure of the Gods in 3147 BC. This spot is no longer the center of the sky.

We can plot a line, from the old location in Ursa Major to the current precessional path of the North Pole, to suggest the path of the pole in the last 2700 years. On this basis the center of the sky shortly after 685 BC, after the change of the polar axis, was most likely located about six to eight degrees above the line connecting Megrez to Dubhe, and perhaps some distance west (counterclockwise). [note 15]

This new location was between constellations -- which is why none of the sources describe the new location to which the pole moved. At the end of Ursa Minor, opposite from Polaris, closest to Ursa Major, there is a star named *Kochab*, which translates as "star" from Arabic, but has been referred to in ancient sources as the "pole star." This is the one star of Ursa Minor nearest to Ursa Major, and also the star closest to the most likely new location of the polar axis. [note 16]

When the polar axis relocated, the circle of the equatorial would have relocated. The equatorial is a projection of the Earth's equator into space. It is thus a flat plane extending above (out from) the equator. Seen from Earth it is a circle in the sky connecting the east and west cardinal locations which is tilted at an angle above the south horizon equal to the complement of the latitude where it is observed (90 degrees less the latitude). This new equatorial cut a new path through the dome of the stars. The Universe had been defaced and the constellations had moved, claimed the ancients. But what moved, or seemed to have moved most significantly, was the relationship of all the constellations and the zodiac to the horizon. [note 17]

The other circle in the sky is the path of the zodiac, the ecliptic, a circle which wobbles on a daily basis, and differently during different times of the year (because of the tilt of the Earth's axis). The overhead part of the zodiac moves up and down over the course of the year, traveling some 47 degrees up from its lowest position.

The intersection of this circle with the eastern and western horizon shifts from north to south (and in the reverse) in the course of each night, only standing still on the two nights of the equinoxes. (The location where the zodiac dips below the horizon changes much less in the tropics.) But one quickly gets used to this, even today, without the "zodiacal glow" which had clearly defined the ecliptic up to the early 19th-century AD; the location of the ecliptic in the sky can readily be found by spotting one or two of the planets or the Moon which move along the path.

If you live where the night sky is unaffected by electric lights or the pollution which enshroud our cities today, you become familiar with the stars.

When these are identified in groups, the familiarity extends to the ability to recognize a constellation on a partially clouded night from as little as two stars. As the sky rotates each night, it seems to move constellations up and down in the sky as it rotates, expanding and contracting them. Changes happen also because at different times of the year we see different portions of the dome of the stars. But, despite these distortions, constellations can be easily recognized because the changes from night to night are minor.

However, when you move to a different latitude from where you grew up, it is initially very difficult to locate the constellations with which you were familiar. Nothing looks right; all the stars are in the wrong places. And that is what happened when the night sky was "defaced" in the year 685 BC. This rearrangement of the dome of the stars was noticed even as the changes were happening. [note 18]

These were not minor changes. If, as Hindu records suggest, Ursa Major slid down 6.5 degrees, we are talking about some constellations changing their location with respect to the horizon by 13 diameters of the Moon. Constellations directly below Ursa Major (like Leo) would have seemed to move down and constellations 180 degrees removed (like Aquarius) would have seemed to move up. Constellations east or west of these would have moved less.

There are numerous references to the changes in the dome of the stars, a "defacing of the Universe." Velikovsky notes many of them, but inevitably applies them to the wrong events, or places them in the wrong era. The very fact that the changes in the dome of the stars were remembered are an indication that they refer to a late era. I would propose that all these references date to 685 BC and after. None were remembered from 1492 BC when the inclination of the rotational axis changed from 25 degrees to 30 degrees.

To date there has been not the slightest inkling among catastrophists of the event of Phaethon as described in these pages. Extra-terrestrial objects named "Typhon," "Phaethon, and "Apep" plus planetary thunderbolts are all guessed after and transformed like so much silly-putty, but nothing has been put in chronological order, correctly identified, or explained physically.

A Change in the Equinox

As the polar axis relocated, so did the intersection of the two great circles in the sky -- the celestial equatorial and the ecliptic. The two locations where these cross determine the rising of the Sun directly east on the vernal and autumnal equinoxes.

In 129 BC Hipparchus measured an annual "drift" of this intersection based on an 80-year record from a contemporary source. He found that the vernal equinox moved 46 seconds (of a degree) west each year -- west, that is, along the ecliptic, so that each later year the Sun would rise slightly further along the zodiac. This slippage has remained more or less at the same value. Today the accepted value is 49.6 seconds of a degree per year. [note 19]

As the polar axis moves, so does the equinox, slowly moving westward from one constellation of the zodiac to the next. Today the Sun rises at the vernal equinox near the beginning (the west end) of the constellation Pisces. If we calculate 2700 years back we find that the Sun rose at 15 degrees of Aries in 685 BC, which is at the center of the constellation Aries. (The "15 degrees of Aries" above is with respect to the delineation of the Zodiac in antiquity, which places zero degrees of Taurus, 30 degrees of Aries, at a location directly between the constellations Aries and Taurus.)

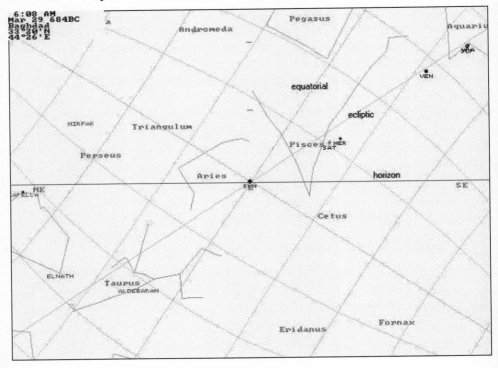

[*Image: The equinox after 685 BC at 15 degrees of Aries as measured in antiquity. Looking directly east. The horizon, equatorial, and ecliptic are marked. The date is on the Julian calendar. Illustration by J. Cook, after SkyGlobe 3.6.*]

Today the division of the ecliptic into 12 segments has no relationship to the original constellations or the measurements used in antiquity. Today "zero degrees of Aries" is arbitrarily assigned to where the ecliptic and the equatorial currently cross. This defines the first day of spring for us. This is done for timekeeping and celestial navigation. Today this is not in the constellation Aries, it is actually near the west end of the constellation Pisces. In AD 150 Ptolemy was already suggesting placing "zero degrees of Aries" at the location of the equinox -- for the purposes of astrological charts.

I contend that before 685 BC (the shift in the polar axis), the equinox was located directly between the east end of Aries and the west end of Taurus -- at the start of Taurus. There are a number of indications which all point to this. The change happened in 685 BC and was spread over 40 days. The *Chilam Balam* notes the Sun "left its path" for 40 days. The most notable record from the Eastern Mediterranean is a section of the *Sibylline Oracle Books*. Although written nearly 800 years later, it recollects events spanning the movement of Venus and the Sun over a number of constellations which would account for the same time period.

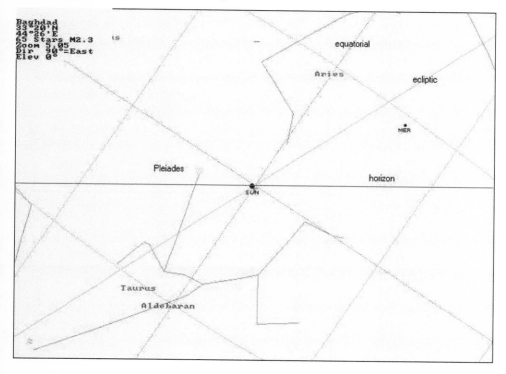

[*Image: The equinox before 685 BC. As depicted here, the horizon line should be rotated 15 degrees counterclockwise (the stars moving clockwise), which will place the Pleiades almost directly above the rising Sun. Illustration by J. Cook, after SkyGlobe 3.6.*]

But what I find more convincing, is that the Pleiades were held to be the start of spring worldwide, and if not associated with the start of spring, then the autumnal equinox, when the Pleiades culminated at midnight -- rose to the highest point in the sky -- and thus also rose when the Sun set. After 685 BC it was discovered that the Pleiades no longer signaled the start of spring and that Taurus no longer started the cycle of the year. The fall culmination of the Pleiades had moved 15 days also. [note 20]

The Pleiades are an easily recognized cluster of stars located directly between the constellations (and zodiac houses) Aries and Taurus. But if we retrocalculate the skies on the basis of today, then in 685 BC the Pleiades did not start spring, nor, for that matter, and again by retrocalculation, for thousands of years earlier. This is because a retrocalculation does not account for the 15-day jump in 685 BC. [note 21]

Zero degrees of Taurus is also the only location in the whole of the zodiac which falls exactly between two constellations. This is peculiar, but, as I surmise, it was purposeful at an earlier time. The constellations of the zodiac do not occupy equal 30-degree spaces, and the constellations assigned to any of the 12 segments ("houses") are very arbitrary. The division of the 360 degrees was probably made long before 747 BC, when the year consisted of 360 days and the Sun would move one degree each day throughout the year. The sky of 360 degrees had been divided into 12 segments to match the 12 revolutions of 30 days of the Moon during the year at that time.

The zodiac had been established in Babylon probably since 1000 BC, or much earlier, since in the *Enuma Elish*, written in 1700 or 1600 BC, Marduk had ordered the constellations of the zodiac when he recreated the world -- when they became visible after removal of the Absu (in 2349 BC actually). Although originally consisting of 18 constellations, and thus of 20 degrees each, these had been reduced to 12 constellations. [note 22]

The Pleiades are seen as a cluster of seven stars located at the leading horn of the constellation Taurus -- just east of zero degrees of Taurus (in the zodiac as in use in antiquity). The location directly at the start of Taurus places the Pleiades almost directly above the rising Sun. [note 23]

The Pleiades had been held by almost all people of antiquity (including India, China, Mesoamerica, and South America) as the first index of spring. For people throughout the world, the sight of the Pleiades in the east just before sunrise -- when they had not been seen in the skies for six months -- signified the coming of spring and the start of the new year. Hindu calendar reforms after 600 BC mention that "the people wanted to have the year start [again] at the first showing of the Pleiades."

On the other hand, it has to be admitted that the return from death of Jupiter two nights after the autumnal equinox of 2349 BC -- rising up directly below the culmination of the Pleiades -- was remembered and celebrated for thousands of years. But this was a midnight showing of the Pleiades.

With respect to the division of the year into zodiacal houses, I would suggest that long before 685 BC a system of measurements had been imposed which had purposefully placed zero degrees of Taurus (which is 30 degrees of Aries) exactly at the midpoint between the constellations Taurus and Aries, and almost directly below the Pleiades. This lines up with the edge of the first horn of the bull Taurus, and will show the Pleiades above the horizon at the equinox -- and in line with the rising Sun. I suggest this was done because this location had been the start of the year forever, and was the location from which everything else on the zodiac was measured -- in 30-degree increments, each representing 30 degrees of movement of the Sun originally. [note 24]

After the change in the heavens in 685 BC, the zodiac sign in which the Sun rose on the first day of spring was significantly different. An ephemeris program which keeps track of precession will show that, after 685 BC, the Sun rose at the equinox as the constellation Aries was at the horizon, rising at the center of Aries. This was at 15 degrees of Aries, as measured in antiquity.

A few hundred years later, in 200 to 100 BC, the Sun rose at the equinox on the longitudinal line for Mesarthim in Aries. This was identified in antiquity as "8 degrees of Aries." Retrocalculation from 200 BC to 685 BC, shows that the Sun rose 7 degrees east of Mesartim. Thus after the displacement of the pole in 685 BC the Sun rose at (7+8=) 15 degrees of Aries, as was also suggested above. [note 25]

The nova event of Venus in 685 BC moved the equinox 15 degrees. The vernal equinox thus rapidly shifted from the Sun rising at the beginning of the constellation Taurus to rising in the center of Aries. Before the changes of 685 BC, the constellation Taurus was already partially above the horizon as the Sun rose at the equinox and this had been so for centuries. The "Age of Taurus," with all the connotations attendant to the horned deities of antiquity, did not gradually slip into the "Age of Aries" -- the age of lambs and shepherds. The change came suddenly in 685 BC.

The change in the location in space to which the rotational axis of the Earth pointed is a change in the inclination of Earth's axis with respect to the orbit. After 685 BC the Earth was differently inclined toward the Sun; the climate would have changed. However, the change in the axial inclination would not significantly move the tropics or temperate zones, although it would move the Arctic Circle with respect to the pole. It would also not change the seasonal variation in climate. Climatic disturbances and fluctuations have been noted, however. [note 26]

The orbit of Earth also remained the same. Only the starting date of the year shifted -- by two weeks. A relocation of the vernal (and autumnal) equinox did not alter the calendars and would not have been of note to farmers. Farmers do not use calendars to determine the time for planting, they use the weather. [note 27]

Although the altered sky was noted by everyone, the change in the equinox was only noticed by the astrologers and philosophers of the Middle East, Europe, China, and Mesoamerica. The sky had not really been thrown into disarray, but it had been moved -- suddenly twisted -- and, as was later observed, the equinox continued to rotate ever so slowly through the constellation Aries and further away from Taurus. It invalidated the tables which were used in Babylon to determine the start of the year and the predictions of lunar eclipses. The paths of the planets were confused and those tables also had to be redone. Comments have been made by 19th-century researchers about the records left by the Chaldean astrologers from this period (after 650 BC), mostly suggesting that the astrologers were making things up and paid no attention to the actual skies. [note 28]

At Nineveh, the principal city of the Assyrian kings, Assurbanipal founded a library in the 7th century. The library collected copies of temple records throughout Assyria and Babylonia, which included topics ranging from literature to mathematics and many letters of the kings of Assyria. When the combined forces of the Medes, Persians, and Chaldeans attacked Assyria in 621 BC, and leveled Nineveh, the library burned down, turning the clay tablets to fired clay.

David Brown, in *Mesopotamian Planetary Astronomy-Astrology* (2000), has investigated the astrological (astronomical) texts from this library in light of the extended correspondence between the Assyrian kings and the astrologers and scribes in their employ. [note 29]

John M. Steele, in a review of Brown's book, wrote:

"He [Brown] *contends that all of the extant texts that are believed to have originally been written before the eighth century B.C. fit into a* [earlier] *paradigm that had no interest in predicting celestial events, and that we should see the period schemes, intercalation rules, etc. found, for example, in 'Enuma Anu Enlil' and 'MUL.APIN' as being aspects of celestial divination, not primitive or inaccurate astronomy."*

Writers in the history of science, including Brown, have dismissed documents like the *Mul.Apin* by pointing out that it was obviously written around the concept of an "ideal" year of 360 days and an equinox at the rising of the Pleiades. I would suggest, however, that the *Mul.Apin* (which mostly consists of a chart of constellations) was indeed accurate in the era before 747 BC, despite the purpose, both before 747 BC as well as after, of divination. That does not detract from the *Mul.Apin*'s status as a "scientific" source document for the Babylonians.

I suspect that lunar eclipses were not experienced at Babylon before 747 BC. Before that time the Moon's orbit was larger (30 days), and only after 747 BC, when the Moon's orbit had shrunk to 29.5 days, did it come close enough to Earth to have the umbra of its shadow show up on the surface of Earth. Even today, because of variations in the Moon's orbit (it has an eccentricity of 0.05), the shadow at times does not show.

This would explain why the first documentation of an eclipse is from 721 BC. When the eclipses started to appear sometime after 747 BC, they were frightening, especially since these earlier solar eclipses were caused by Mars -- and inevitably accompanied by earthquakes, hurricanes, and electric bolts from the heavens.

The extensive correspondence between the kings and the astrologers was for the obvious reason that the skies had changed in 747 BC and again in 685 BC. There was a sudden urgency to develop correct methods of predicting lunar and solar eclipses, which showed up two to four times per year, and were totally unpredictable. The Babylonians never did figure out how solar eclipses were caused -- and little wonder, if their data included solar eclipses caused by Mars. Ptolemy, 800 years later also never found a means to predict solar eclipses. But by about 700 BC the lunar eclipses were correctly modeled and became predictable. Then after about 686 and 685 BC the skies changed, and all the calculation had to be started over. [note 30]

There is only a sprinkling of documents from before 747 BC because only the useful documents were retained. The *Mul.Apin* certainly was one of these, even if the year was no longer 360 days. Also retained was the *Enuma Anu Enlil*, a record of observations, detailing celestial events, water levels of the Euphrates, and economic indicators (like the price of barley). The *Enuma Anu Enlil* records included the *Venus Tablets of Ammizaduga*.

Special thanks to K Snyder for pointing up the San Jose rock.
Special thanks to S Bourke, AU, for the Kirkin story.
Special thanks to J Brookes for suggesting the Moon as the cause for precession.

Endnotes

Note 1 --

A more extensive derivation will be found in the chapters "The Chilam Balam books" and "Olmec Alignments." This requires a familiarity with the Mesoamerican calendar, described in the chapter "The Maya Calendar," and Mesoamerican thinking, some of which is discussed in the chapter "Language and Causality."

Note 2 --

A distinction should be kept in mind between popular narratives about the creation of the world and actual events. The *Chilam Balam* relates the sequence of four instances of actual events of the past. But these were copied from the official records. What we see in the *Popol Vuh* is a constructed narrative, made at a time when the Maya considered all of history as repeating itself endlessly anyway, so that sequencing events separated by 4000 years was not a conceptual or philosophical problem. The authors of the *Popol Vuh* claim they had the official histories at hand, and, in fact, many details slip into the story of the *Popol Vuh* which could only have come from very old codexes.

Note 3 --

In Europe away from the Mediterranean, throughout Northern Asia, and in North America the constellation "the Wain" was known as "the Bear," apparently since remote antiquity. Only by considering the Wain as representing a bear with four long legs extending below the pan of Ursa Major could this constellation be considered as dipping into the ocean. The Romans, however, did not consider Ursa Major as representing a bear. It was a wagon which endlessly circled the sky at the location of the old polar axis.

Note 4 --

"The Wain" is here translated from the Egyptian equivalent, an ox, a mummified ox, or a mummified ox leg, graphically depicted as early as 1500 BC, with an axis piercing the body of the ox. The fact that this has remained the same suggests that there was no precession of the equinox before the relocation of the rotational axis in 685 BC.

"Looking among the stars of Ursa Major" is also described in formal texts in the temple at Denderah, which was built (or rebuilt) in Roman times -- thus some 600 or 700 years after the polar axis had relocated away from Ursa Major.

Attempts in the 19th century to date the first Chinese emperor Yao to 2350 BC, by a retrocalculation based on precession which places the Pleiades at the vernal equinox are baseless, despite the fact that the results agree with the dating estimates made during the Han dynasty, by the compilers of the *Annals of Shu*, which did not involve the precession of the equinox. The Han dynasty scribes have the Pleiades appear at the spring equinox.

Why the compilers of the *Annals of Shu* would add this strange information in the 7th or 8th century BC, (which could be suggested from the fact that other astronomical and calendrical information was added at the time of the Chou or Han), is unclear, for by today's retrocalculations, the Pleiades did not define the vernal equinox in 700 BC, or, for that matter, as early as 1500 BC. Legge notes this in his commentary on the *Annals of Shu*.

Similar retrocalculations have been made in India in the last century for the start of the current era and for the Bharata battle (and placed variously at 3037 BC and 1432 BC), based on hints from the Vedas. However, all these strange retrocalculations can be resolved. See for this "A Change in the Equinox" in this chapter.

Note 5 --

The 26,000-year cycle is based on only a few hundred years of observation, equivalent to watching the passage of about 1 or 2 degrees of the 360 degrees of the path. The rate of precession, which currently is a movement of about one degree every 72 years (since AD 1600), has been known with some accuracy since the first century BC. There have been periods of time when the precession stopped, and when the value differed markedly from today's value.

Uwe Topper in "Cataclysms are the reason for our wrong chronology" *International Meeting of Chronologists*, Potsdam, 2008 (http://www.ilya.it/chrono/pages/), notes that the historical value for the number of years per degree has varied from 50 years (some early Babylonian sources in 330 BC, although this is disputed) to an early Greek value of 100 held by Aristarchus (210 BC), Hipparchus (130 BC), Ptolemy (AD 200), and confirmed by early Arab astronomers. Later Arab and European astronomers from AD 800 to AD 1300 used a value of 66 years. The current value of 72 years has been maintained since Kepler (AD 1600).

The "wobble" of the axis is not related to the wobble a spinning toy top experiences when the upward force at the support point at the bottom and the downward force of gravity through the center are displaced by some distance, forming a torque about the horizontal center. In the case of a toy top, the precession is the result of a torque which continues to be applied. Obviously, nothing of the sort is experienced by the Earth.

Note 6 --

Electric effects such as these cannot be neglected. In the thirty years since the spin of the Earth has been measured with atomic clocks, the Earth has slowed down by 30 seconds in its rotation. This is much larger than what can possibly be accounted for under present theories of astrophysics (which, however, excludes electric considerations).

Note 7 --

"The Sun's glare prevented observers on Earth from viewing NEAT's approach. But the SOHO spacecraft, stationed between Earth and the Sun, has an instrument called Large-Angle Spectrometric Coronagraph (LASCO), which blocks the Sun's brightest light, permitting the satellite to record the comet's dramatic swing around the Sun."

"As NEAT raced through the extended solar atmosphere, a large coronal mass ejection (CME) exploded from the Sun and appeared to strike the comet. The comet responded with a kink that propagated down the tail. The disk in the center is created by the coronograph as it blocks the Suns glare."

-- From http://www.thunderbolts.info TPOD for May 26, 2005. (Image Credit: Solar and Heliospheric Observatory (SOHO)/ESA/NASA)

Note 8 --

It might be suggested that the change in the Earth's axis was due to another approach of Venus, as regularly happened at 52-year intervals (supposedly) in the remote past. Since 1492 or 1442 BC, the "52-year intervals" of close approaches of Venus have been 50 years up to 747 BC, and 52 years thereafter. See Appendix B "The Celestial Mechanics," where this information is developed.

Adding 50 or 52 years (or multiples) to the dates which could be identified as a previous approach of Venus (776 BC) does not yield a date anywhere near 685 BC.

Note 9 --

From an essay by Walter Cruttenden, "Comparison of Precession Theories: An Argument for the Binary Model" (Internet, 2003):

"It was Sir Isaac Newton, who had just developed his theories of gravity that said if the Earth did wobble it must be due to the mass of the Sun and the Moon, the only bodies considered close enough or large enough to have such an effect. But Newton's equations never did match observed precession rates."

"Consequently, the equations were substantially revised by Jean-le-Rond D'Alembert who added factors for torque and inertia, but even this effort proved a poor predictor of precession rates."

"Since then precession calculations have been continually modified and now include many factors beyond the original "lunisolar forces," including the gravitational effect of the inner and outer planets, tidal influences, effects of the 300 largest asteroids, and even a possible elliptical movement of the Earth's soft core."

"But as is apparent the calculations have become more of a 'plug' whereby inputs are gradually added or modified to fit the observation rather than being predictive or resting on solid theory."

This goes for the orbit of the Moon also. The equations describing the path of the Moon have to account for 5 separate motions, including a left-right wobble which allows us to see more than a half face of the Moon. The Moon bobs up and down also.

Note 10 --

The orbit of the Moon is 250,000 miles (400,000 km). The plasmaspheres of planets extend 10- to 20-planet diameters from the surface, thus 80,000 to 160,000 miles (129,000 to 260,000 km) for Earth.

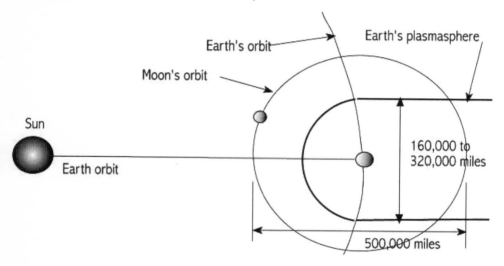

Path of the Moon during a month
The Moon spends most of its orbit outside of the Earth's plasmasphere
top view of orbits nts

Additionally the Moon's travel takes it some 20,000 miles (32,000 km) alternately above and below the Earth during the year. This affects the date when eclipses will be seen, but has little effect on its entry and exit from the Earth's plasmasphere. The actual travel around the Sun describes a cycloid pattern -- not a series of semicircles.

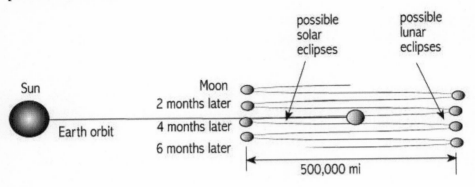

side view of orbits   nts

Path of the Moon over a Six-Month Period
The Moon follows a spiral path which reversed
in the up-down direction every six months

Note 11 --

Alfred de Grazia, in *The Lately Tortured Earth* (1983), writes:

*"Yet Velikovsky, arguing the case for axis displacement, had earlier
discussed a calculation by Weizacker demonstrating that an Earth
transaction with a strong magnetic field would affect its axial inclination
much more readily than its rotation [13]."*

The reference is to an article in *Pensee,* by William Straka, "Straka:
Science or Anti-Science," (1972). From what happened to the Earth's
magnetic field in remote antiquity, that is, before 10,000 BC (see the chapter,
"Event of the Younger Dryas), we know that this is not true. The possibility
of a magnetic couple, induced by the extreme Solar Wind passing by Earth, is
as unlikely, since the planets' magnetic poles do not coincide with the axis of
rotation. A constant applied torque is required, which calls for a force applied
off-center from the Earth's axis. See Appendix B, "The Celestial Mechanics."

Note 12 --

Although a yojana is a terrestrial land measure (distance), it can be
projected to the sphere of the stars which surrounds the Earth as a change in
celestial latitude. A north-south distance of 100 yojanas on Earth represents a
6.5-degree change in latitude. The same angular measure would apply to the

dome of the stars. A 6.5-degree change in celestial latitude in 685 BC would place the earlier location of the rotational axis of the Earth directly in the pan of Ursa Major.

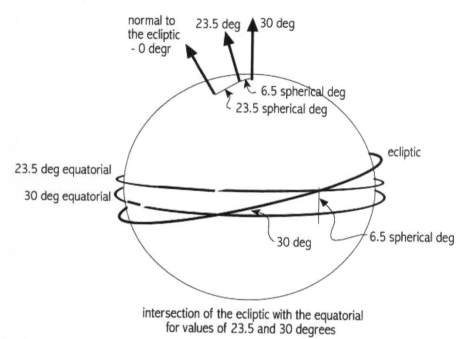

intersection of the ecliptic with the equatorial
for values of 23.5 and 30 degrees

[*Image: The intersection of the ecliptic and the equatorial, in Summer of 685 BC. Illustration by J. Cook.*]

By itself, a 30-degree axial tilt will make only a minor difference in climate compared to a 23.5-degree tilt. The Arctic Circle would move closer to the pole by 6.5 degrees.

The triangle defined by the old and new equatorial projected onto the Earth (the ecliptic remains the same) determines how far the equinox advanced along the ecliptic -- and thus how many days were lost in 685 BC. The intersection of the ecliptic and the equatorial is the equinox, and thus the start of the year. The amount that the equinox advanced along the ecliptic (from the old equatorial to the new equatorial) is found from considering the angles and spherical segments.

From the relationship for spherical triangles, **sin c / sin C = sin a / sin A**, sin c is found as:

s(c) = s(pi/2) * s(6.5/deg) /s(30/deg) = 0.226 which is 13.1 spherical degrees [as the arcsin of 0.226].

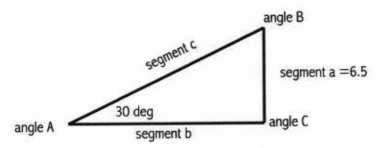

Along the ecliptic (segment c) this represents a fraction of a year of 365.24 days, thus **(13.1 / 360) * 365.24 = 13.29 days.** Thirteen days of my estimate of 15 days are thereby accounted for.

Using plane trigonometry, I calculate 14.74 days.

Note 13 --

Book 10 of the *Chilam Balam* includes three instances of spans of time, all given as so many months or years. I have not been able to make sense of any of these time spans except by recognizing that the original author in each instance counted inclusively.

The most significant statement in the text is, *"After three heaps of years it* [the sun] *will come back into place in Katun 3-Ahau."* (The use of future tense is peculiar to the translation into an Indo-European language.)

A "heap" is probably 5 (elsewhere known as a "bundle") and a "year" is a 260-day Tzolkin year. The fifteen years is another of the instances of inclusive counting for it turns out that the "three heaps of years" represent an interval of 14 Tzolkin years in the Mesoamerican Long Count calendar.

Fourteen Tzolkin years correctly states the number of days it takes for the same day-name and day-number combination to recur for a sunset at the same horizon sunset location of the Sun before and after the change from the 30-degree axial inclination to a 23.5-degree axial inclination.

This simple fact is key to an understanding, because 14 Tzolkin cycles of 260 days do not bring us back to the same seasonal day in the year, or even present the same Tsolkin and Haab day-names of the calendar. Seasonally it falls short by about 12 days. The *Chilam Balam* thus says that the Sun set at the same horizon location as in the past, but 12 days earlier. This cannot be achieved except with a change in the axial inclination of the Earth.

I should point out also that the information as presented in the *Chilam Balam* probably refers to the setting location of the zenithal passage of the Sun at some location within the range of 15 to 20 degrees north latitude.

As I point out in the chapter "Olmec Alignments," zenithal passages of the Sun were important to the ceremonial centers of Olmec Veracruz and the

Valley of Mexico. Nearly every center was aligned to have the Sun set at some mountain or volcano after a zenithal passage over the site. The difference of 12 days suggests that the information of the *Chilam Balam* was originally recorded for a latitude of 17.0 degrees (possibly Monte Alban). See the chapter "The Chilam Balam" for additional details. This is one of the clearest indications that there was a change in the axial inclination of the Earth -- in fact, from 30 degrees to 23.5 degrees.

Note 14 --

I am indebted to Keith Snyder, who found and recognized the stone, and mentions the Lakota source in Ronald Goodman, *Lakota Star Knowledge: Studies in Lakota Stellar Theology* (1990), on his website at snyder_kas.home.mindspring.com/Indian_Stones.html. If the legend is still current, the age of the drilled holes does not matter.

The missing star might not be missing. A star exists at the designated location, although dim, with a magnitude of 6.1.

Interestingly, the centroid of the stone looks to be halfway between Ursa Minor and Ursa Major, at about the star Kappa in the constellation Draco. This is about where I would expect the axis of the sky to have moved in 685 BC, before eventually settling down near Kochab in Ursa Minor.

Note 15 --

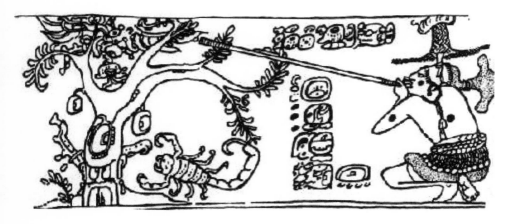

[*Image: A pottery Image: Hunahpu shoots Itzam-Yeh (Seven-Macaw). The text reads, "Done by Hun-Ahau; on 1-Ahau 3-Kankin he entered the sky, Itzam-Yeh." After David Freidel and Linda Schele "Maya Cosmos" (1993).*]

Recovering the Lost World, Volume 2

East and west in the dome of the stars is defined by the direction the stars seem to rotate. Facing south, west is to the right. Facing north, the stars above the pole star move left to the west; the stars below the pole star move toward the right, where the geographic east is located.

The original location of the axis within the pan of Ursa Major would be at 58.5 degrees of elevation, and a Right Ascension (RA) of 11.7 hours. Right Ascension is the number of degrees from the current vernal equinox, expressed in hours, where 360 degrees represents 24 hours.

One of the ball-playing twins of the *Popol Vuh*, who represent Venus in 685 BC (Hun-Ahau, Hunahpu), has to shoot down the bird Itzam-Yeh (Seven-Macaw), who had perched on top of the central axis of the sky, the World Tree, before a new creation could start. Itzam-Yeh, Seven-Macaw, today is thought to be Ursa Major. The image above describes the removal of Ursa Major as the center of the sky, but from the perspective of Mesoamerica. The bird reference, however, is to Saturn at the polar location before 3147 BC.

The scorpion below the tree is the constellation Scorpio at the base of the Milky Way. Scorpio has the same name in Mesoamerica as in the Eastern Mediterranean. There is a snake on the left (not shown here) which is the constellation Sagittarius. Therefore the North Pole is here shown from the perspective of the south, and thus is upside down. But it is seen, not from the south horizon, but from the edge of the Absu, somewhat below the equatorial. This is not really such an outrageous presentation. The jaguar paw reaching out from behind the tree trunk is often identified as Xbalanque, but it is the hieroglyphic sign for "te" (tree), and used together with the glyph "yax" on the other side of the tree trunk, identify the tree as "yax-te" or ceiba tree.

In Classical Maya cosmology the Milky Way has replaced the World Tree, which originally was the polar configuration from before 3147 BC, but forgotten by the Maya nearly 4000 years later, and only recalled from ancient graphical books. That the Milky Way is the World Tree is the opinion of archaeologists. See David Freidel and Linda Schele, *Maya Cosmos* (1993), and Dennis Tedlock, *Popol Vuh* (1985). However, the Milky Way does not intersect Ursa Major.

The date of 1-Ahau 3-Kankin is curious, for it does not match the Maya retrocalculated date of 4-Ahau 8-Cumku in 3114 BC usually listed for this event (actually as the *completion* of the previous creation). The date 1-Ahau 3-Kankin, as Freidel and Schele note, would correspond to May 28, 3148 BC Gregorian, more than a year before my date of 3147 BC. Actually it is -3148 in numerical notation, which is 3147 BC in BC/AD notation. This would suggest the point and date at which Earth was released from Saturn -- and would represent the initial location of the aphelion of the Earth's orbit (and what might be the earliest winter solstice date). I'll cover this in a later chapter.

Note 16 --

The Hindu poem *Mahabarhata* notes a number of locations for the pole star, which are all below the precessional path of the pole star as understood today. They are correct in Right Ascension for the 8th through the 5th century BC (when the poetry of the Mahabarhata was created), but too far below the path of the pole as described today. These locations would also not hold for a more remote antiquity. Backward in time from today, the currently defined path of the pole bisects the region between Ursa Minor and Ursa Major and curves toward the tail of Draco. Scholars who have analyzed the astronomical data of the Mahabarhata have taken note of the Right Ascension (before 685 BC) to place the war in 1400 BC, but have failed to take the altitude into consideration. See S.P Gupta and K.S. Ramachandran (editors), *Mahabarhata, Myth and Reality* (1976).

Note 17 --

The horizon is probably the most important anchor point in visually recognizing and locating constellations.

Note 18 --

At age 12 I moved from 55 degrees latitude to 42 degrees latitude. It took years before I could again instantly recognize constellations which I had learned earlier in childhood. And there were new ones.

Note 19 --

The Babylonians (Chaldeans) may have noticed the precession about 50 years earlier than Hipparchus. In China, Yu Hsi noted the precession of the equinoxes around AD 330. John Henderson writes:

"This discovery is traditionally attributed to the fourth-century astronomer, Yu Xi ([AD] 307-338), though astronomers as early as the Han era had noted that the winter solstice shifted with respect to the lunar lodges."
     -- John B. Henderson "Cosmology and Concepts of Nature in Traditional China" (essay, nd)

The Han spans 206 BC to AD 220. The "lunar lodges" are the houses of the zodiac.

Note 20 --

Patten and Windsor, in *The Mars-Earth Wars* (1996), similarly come to the conclusion there was no precession of the equinox in antiquity, but use 701 BC as the terminal date of that condition.

Note 21 --

In the first and second century BC it was universally accepted by all the Mediterranean civilizations that the vernal equinox was located at 8 degrees of Aries. This is actually a peculiar location, and certainly not selected by design at that time. The reader will realize that there is no way for a slipping equinox to have started at zero degrees of Taurus and have moved to 8 degrees of Aries in the span of a few hundred years under current conditions.

Note 22 --

Almost all people everywhere established some sort of division of the night sky into 12 or 13 regions of marked significant stars, all to the purpose of noting the passage of the Moon. The Egyptians at a very early time used 36 notable stars for timekeeping at night. India divided the sky up into 28 sectors (called mansions) marking the progress of the Moon. This was a system dating from a yet earlier era. The Chinese year was also divided into 28 "lunar mansions" -- long before contact with India. We know of the Chinese divisions from Shang dynasty inscriptions at least since 1400 BC.

China reduced the zodiac to 12 constellations in about 100 AD, during calendar reforms. The new Chinese constellation names were both indigenous and received from Indian sources, who in turn copied Babylonian constellation names under Alexander's Greek influences after 330 BC. The European Greeks, and eventually the Romans, did the same, substituting Babylonian names for earlier local names. Thus the entire Asiatic and European zodiac of today derives from, or was modified from, the zodiac in use in Babylonia -- but in all cases long after the constellations were named in Babylon. See calendar notes in Appendix A, "Chronology."

The earliest surviving description of the Mesopotamian constellations is the *Mul.Apin* tablet series, with the oldest dated example from the 7th century BC. "The *Mul.Apin* was not a marginal source, but probably forms our most important document for ancient Mesopotamian astrology." -- vd Sluijs. The *Mul.Apin* marks the vernal equinox and autumnal equinox as follows:

> *"MUL.MUL (eta-Tauri, the Pleiades) and GIR.TAB (beta-Scorpii) were visible at the East and West points of the horizon and also defined the Vernal and Autumnal Equinoxes."*
> -- from http://www.lexiline.com/lexiline/lexi171.htm

This has led some to suggest that the tables date from 2340 BC, on the basis of a retrocalculation based on today's skies and today's estimate for the precession of the equinoxes. This is a ludicrous suggestion, not only because of the extrapolation to such a remote date, but also because it assumes that no changes were made in the data for the next 1600 years even though the skies (on the basis of an implied "precession of the equinoxes") would have changed continuously. It cannot be believed that the zodiac descriptions remained stuck at a value determined for the year 2340 BC for thousands of years. See for instance, Werner Papke, *Die Sterne von Babylon* ("The Stars of Babylon") (nd).

Most researchers have neglected this information, and write about the *Mul.Apin* as if it represented "an idealized year of 360 days" with an equinox at the rising of the Pleiades, a similar idealization. The *Mul.Apin* certainly dates to before 747 BC, although the oldest recopied texts date with certainty only to 687 BC. By stylistic content of the dozen copies (from Nineveh, Assur, and another location), they date to perhaps 1000 BC.

About the ecliptic, and for a later date of 400 to 300 BC, Robert Powell, in "The Definition of the Babylonian Zodiac and the Influence of Babylonian Astronomy on the Subsequent Defining of the Zodiac," PhD Thesis, Polish Academy of Science (2004), writes:

"According to this original definition the zodiac is defined by the two first magnitude stars Aldebaran and Antares in such a way that each is located exactly at the midpoint (15 degrees) of their respective sign, Taurus and Scorpio. Thereby these two stars define the central axis of the zodiac, which was the primary zodiacal reference axis for all other stars."

The first part of this statement is fact; the second part is guessed after. However, selecting Aldebaran as 15 degrees of Taurus places zero degrees of Taurus within two degrees of where I suggest the division of the ecliptic started in antiquity. If Taurus was not meant to be the first constellation to show above the horizon at daybreak at the beginning of the year, why was Aldebaran selected as one of the midpoints of the ecliptic? Powell continues with the suggestion of how the sidereal ecliptic was replaced by a tropical (solar) ecliptic -- where the equinox is set at "zero degrees of Aries" -- but has difficulty substantiating his claims (which I won't cover here). He does add a note on the selection of the equinox (apparently at a somewhat later date of 200 BC):

"Note that if there was a perfect correspondence between MUL.APIN's solar calendar and the zodiac, the vernal point would have to be located

at 15° Aries, since Aries as the first sign of the zodiac corresponds to month 1 and in the Babylonian solar calendar the vernal equinox was placed on the 15th day of month 1. However, in System A of Babylonian astronomy the vernal point was located at 10 degrees [of] Aries and in System B at 8 degrees [of] Aries."

Changes were made in the Babylonian record keeping, but the reasons for the changes have eluded any contemporary analysis based on a continuation of present conditions into the past. The three values for the equinox suggest that the change in the heavens may have taken some years to subside, although all other data contradicts this.

Note 23 --

Before 685 BC both the horizon line and the equatorial would be rotated about 15 degrees counterclockwise when viewed directly east. Thus the Pleiades would rotate 15 degrees clockwise with respect to the horizon, placing them almost directly above the rising Sun.

Note 24 --

Note that the choice of a location from which the circumference of the night sky is measured does not depend on how many zodiacal constellations are identified or the number of degrees assigned to each. Thus, if at an earlier time, the Babylonians identified 18 constellations of the zodiac it makes no difference to the starting point between Aries and Taurus. We know from records of the 4th century BC, that by that time the zodiac had been divided into 12 sectors of 30 degrees each, even though the original reason for a division into 12 houses was no longer valid and the constellations for which the "houses" of the zodiac are named were a poor fit.

China was not wedded to a system which divided the night sky up into 12 equal segments of 30 degrees. The sectors of the sky were of unequal size, as little as 2 degrees, with boundaries along the longitudinal lines of easily recognized stars. Thus in 747 BC, when the length of the year changed, the Chinese had no reason not to reorganize the night sky over a full circle defined as 365.25 "degrees." This remained in use until circa AD 1400.

Note 25 --

There are suggestions that perhaps the initial displacement of the equinox was not 15 degrees, but something closer to 9 degrees. We are only certain of the complete displacement of 15 degrees in about 300 BC or 200 BC, when the equinox had moved well beyond the initial 15 degrees along the equatorial.

Velikovsky (p. 353 ff) discusses Talmudic references to calendar changes made by Hezekiah, mentioning a doubling of the month of Nisan (the post-exile name for the first month of the year) to celebrate Passover. The Talmud actually explains that this was done to adjust for the lunar year -- which lagged behind the solar year. These "corrections" would have been made after 747 BC. Hezekiah made many reforms after 747 BC, cleaning out the temple, reinstituting the priesthood, both of which had been neglected by his predecessor Ahaz.

With the Moon's period of 29.5 days, representing an odd interval of the year, which was 365.25 days since 747 BC, the religious festivals which had been signaled by visible aspects of the Moon, like the new Moon or the full Moon, now drifted around the year. Religious feast days fell 9 or 10 days behind with every following year.

This clearly shows up at least once when mention is also made in the Talmud that Hezekiah moved New Year's Day, normally celebrated at the fall equinox, back 9 days from the 10th day of the seventh month to the first. Velikovsky suggests that it was the fall equinox which had moved back 9 days. But there is no need to make this suggestion. I suspect it was a lunar adjustment, which would have failed again the following year.

Velikovsky also mentions Babylonian records of that era which at one point place the (spring) equinox at the 15th day of the month of Nisan, and on another clay tablet list it as the 6th of the same month -- 9 days difference. I suspect such differences are all due to the new orbital period of the Moon after 747 BC.

Note 26 --

Velikovsky notes for the 8th and 7th century BC (in an unpublished document at http://www.varchive.org/tac/polturm.htm, "Political Turmoil Around -687"), "*Climatic change was again very significant and oscillations of climate marked the ninety years from -776 to -687.*" This sums up information from his book, *Earth in Upheaval* (1955), where he also writes of the depopulation of regions north of the Alps.

These years include the period of frequent electric contacts by Mars, concluding with the (unrelated) nova event of 685 BC. Disturbances north of the Alps were also due to Mars when it continued to pass Earth on its orbit, which was inclined at an angle of 1.85 degrees to the orbit of Earth.

A depopulation of Europe, for that matter, is matched with similar demographic changes elsewhere. More properly, the demographic changes might be attributed to a combination of causes, involving not only climatic fluctuation, but the physical devastation due to some nine plasma contacts with Mars during this period, of which we certainly have a clear record for the cities and citadels of the Middle East.

The climatic changes were real; they are recorded in the tree pollen found in bogs.

Note 27 --

The length of the delay in the start of spring, 15 degrees, is equal to about 15 days. A degree is just short of a day. In an abridged version of James Frazer's *The Golden Bough* (Theodor Gaster, editor, 1959), a text entry reads, "The Greeks gather and press grapes in the first half of October." An endnote explains:

> *"In ancient Greece the vintage seems to have fallen somewhat earlier, for Hesiod (Works and Days, 609 ff.) dates it to the time when Arcturus is a morning star, which was on September 18."*

This would place Hesiod's composition of *Days and Works* to before 685 BC. The date of September 18 is about correct under the composition of the skies before 685 BC and with a 15-degree displacement of the equatorial. Other details of *Works and Days* place its composition to *after* 685 BC, however.

Note 28 --

There are lengthy astronomical records made by the Babylonians, starting in the eight century BC directly after 747 BC (and other records supposedly since circa 2500 BC), involving the planets, the Moon, and the path of the Sun. The equinoxes, the shortest and longest days of the year, the distance traveled by the Sun each day against the background of stars, were all noted. But most of the records we have date only from after 650 BC. It looks like in most cases the data from before 650 BC was discarded.

Velikovsky wrote that, at times, as many as three differing records were kept of the path of the Sun and planets, suggesting changes in the Earth's orbit during the 8th and 7th centuries BC. It is true that multiple records were kept in this era, in sets of three, by the Babylonians, as well as the Indians and Israelis.

But Velikovsky also added information from the *Mul.Apin* which he misunderstood. He refers to the Enlil path, the Anu path, and the Ea path as if they were separate trajectories of the Sun. The *Mul.Apin* "paths," however, are sectors of the sky concentric about the polar axis, representing the constellations rising, roughly, in the northeast, the east, and the southeast. They are named after appropriate gods, so that the Enlil region represents the "air" above the ecliptic, Anu represents the central region of the sky which includes most of the "river" of the ecliptic, and Ea represents the "waters" south of the central region.

Note 29 --

The period Brown has reference to is 750 BC to 621 BC. The correspondence with the astrologers was generated by the last kings of Assyria, Tiglath-Pileser III (745-727), Sargon II (721-705 BC), who took up residence at Nineveh, Sennacherib (705-681 BC) who rebuilt Nineveh, Esarhaddon (681-668 BC), and Assurbanipal (668-626 BC), who built the library which burned down in 621 BC.

Note 30 --

The records of Babylon were translated into Greek in antiquity (on Alexander's orders), but apparently everything before 747 BC may have been discarded at an early date as being unreliable. In fact, there is also a notable absence of records until about 650 BC. A number of people have pointed out that solar eclipses (due to the Moon) would not have been experienced in the region of Babylon during this era.

Ptolemy lists 721 BC as the first lunar eclipse seen in Babylon. The first recorded lunar eclipse in China falls in 720 BC. The Chinese *Spring and Autumn Annals*, spanning the years 722 BC to 481 BC, records 37 eclipses.

Calculations are in Unix bc notation, where ∧ denotes exponentiation; the functions a(rctangent), s(ine), and c(osine) use radians; angle conversions to radians or degrees by the divisors rad=.017+ and deg=57.2+; other functions are shown as f( ); tan( )=s( )/c( )
units: million == 1,000,000; billion == 1,000,000,000;
AU == 93,000,000 miles.

Recovering the Lost World, A Saturnian Cosmology -- Jno Cook
Chapter 26: Hezekiah and Babylon

Revision: 42.32 (star.php)

Contents of this chapter: [Jastrow: *Sun and Saturn*] [The Sibylline Star Wars] [Hezekiah and Babylon] [Philosophy, Religion, Science] [The New Religions] [Philosophy and Science] [Holding On to the Past] [The Presence of God] [Endnotes]

Jastrow: *Sun and Saturn*

The *Enuma Anu Enlil* records have been used by the Saturnians of Thunderbolts.info as one of the sources for the concept that Saturn was known in antiquity as "the Star of the Sun" and in fact was considered to be the Sun -- especially when translated as "Sun Star." Cardona and other Saturnians who have justified this position with reference to an essay by Morris Jastrow, "Sun and Saturn," written in 1910, have been faulted for ignoring some of Jastrow's comments.

To quote Leroy Ellenberger:

"According to Morris Jastrow, Jr., in his 'famous' and oft-cited article 'Sun and Saturn,' Saturn was not given a specific name until after Venus and Jupiter were named, which is surely strange if Saturn was the primordial deity described by the 'Saturnists.'" [note 1]

This sequence of naming, and similar faults, is entirely resolved if it is understood that this record (of the planets) was created in 685 BC or shortly thereafter. It explains everything. Note is made first of Mars and Mercury because of their interference with Earth since 806 BC. Venus was noted because in 776 BC it may have struck Mars (and the Moon) with a thunderbolt. Venus went nova along with Mercury in June of 685 BC. Mars and Mercury were also the two planets most frequently seen in the sky.

These planets were already in the record. Jupiter is noted next after it expanded into a coma later in July of 685 BC. Saturn, located almost twice as far from the Sun as Jupiter, was not noted until later yet, when it also developed a coma, but after Jupiter had become very prominent, or perhaps had calmed down again. Saturn thus comes last in the record because it was the last to light up.

Dwardu Cardona, in an autobiographical essay titled "The Road to Saturn" (excerpted from *Aeon*, 1988) wrote, about the revelation of Saturn as a night Sun by Jastrow:

> *"In the fall 1975 issue of* Kronos, *[Lewis]* Greenberg and *[Warner] Sizemore published a half-page article titled 'Saturn and Genesis.' In it they briefly analyzed Maurice [Morris] Jastrow's 1910 paper, 'Sun and Saturn,' in which the Assyro-Babylonian belief in Saturn as a sun that shone at night is discussed at some length. ... When I unearthed and read Jastrow's original paper, I became convinced that Saturn, despite the author's expected disclaimer, must have been a true sun of night, radiating its own light."*

Cardona takes no account of the fact that the portions quoted by Jastrow from the *Enuma Anu Enlil* date most likely to the 7th century BC, not to the era of circa 3100 BC or earlier. I would suggest that this "sun of the night" notion was an idea surviving from antiquity, and Cardona sees it this way, but understands it as contemporaneous with the "Age of the Gods," instead of an observation dating to after 747 BC or 685 BC. Its use needs to be contextualized to the era in which it was written and needs to be understood as answering to political circumstances.

I think that there would be no mention at all of a "midnight sun" unless it again became relevant in late antiquity, as in 685 BC after Saturn also gained a coma, following a much more massive and visually more impressive expansion of Jupiter. Also, I do not think Saturn was the main concern of the Babylonian astrologers, but Jupiter. It was Jupiter which had lightened the skies as the "midnight sun" for a thousand years.

It seems, from Jastrow's article, that the *Enuma Anu Enlil* has nothing to do with Saturn at the pole, since by the most generous guess the data sources only date back perhaps 1000 years before 700 BC. And I even doubt that, and certainly for the data on market prices for barley. Factoids from 3400 years previous would be useless as prognostication of current conditions to the compilers after 685 BC, in addition to the fact that guessing at the future was a recent preoccupation, dating back perhaps 500 years. Almost all of the tablets deal with the Sun, the Moon, and the weather. Only the last 20 tablets deal with planets.

The *Enuma Anu Enlil* has nothing much to do with Saturn. Jupiter is indicated when "Shamash" is mentioned, and not Saturn. "Shamash" translates as "sun" from the Sumerian glyph, Utu. And Jupiter was the most recently recognized "sun of the night," not Saturn. Additionally, Jastrow is basing his "Sun equals Saturn" identity on an offhand remark by Hyginus, made 3300 years later, and on the translation of the name Shamash from Akkadian to mean "Big Steady Light in the Sky." So, Jupiter was not big and steady?

I would suggest that the astrologers of Babylon added annotations to their tablets to make sure that their notes would not be misunderstood. Shamash was the "sun of night" and understood to be the planet Jupiter. But after Jupiter lighted up in July of 685, Saturn followed suit, and started to blaze like a sun. Although this could be called "Shamash," it needed to be distinguished from Jupiter acting in the same capacity.

Jastrow says his opinions are based also on "contextual" readings. But here is the real context: The compilations were made under pressure from the Assyrians, who revived themselves in 740 BC. So we need to look at what happened after 740 BC. Certainly older records were incorporated, but not likely much further back than about 747 BC, when the skies changed. As I have noted earlier, others have pointed out that there are apparently no records for the period of approximately 750 BC to 700 BC.

Records from 1200 BC, when attention first starts being given to omens, tokens, and magical predictions, probably were not used, unless they dealt with mundane phenomena like early morning cloud cover -- if that was available at all. The objection posed by Ellenberger to the "order of naming planets" is invalidated in their being created in the time span of 685 to 650 BC (the period after the nova event involving Venus and Mercury), and has nothing to do with non-existent "records" dating back to 3100 BC. The Sumerians were not even writing in 3100 BC, and certainly were not at that time concerned with fortune telling or what the morning clouds meant.

... Mercury

No one, in the meantime, has explained the prominence of Mercury, which is almost impossible to see in today's arrangement of the Solar System. Even Jastrow writes:

> *"On the basis of passages like these it was natural to conclude that Mercury was for some reason regarded as the planet* par excellence. *I accepted this view and for the later period it appears indeed to be correct. Traces of the special position accorded to Mercury are to be seen in the multifarious traits with which he is endowed in Greek and*

medieval astrology. He is the only one of the planets who is conceived as both male and female and embodies, as it were, a summary of the qualities of all the planets."

If this does not date these records to being very late, what will? Jastrow takes note of the lack of physical significance of Mercury, something we know already:

"On the other hand, it was difficult to find a satisfactory reason for this supposed preeminence granted to the smallest of the planets and the one most difficult of observation, whose actual role, moreover, in Babylonian-Assyrian astrology does not at all suggest that the omens connected with Mercury had any special significance."

Is this amazing? It is also a fact that many peoples (even the Celts in Roman times, 700 or 800 years later), held Mercury in great awe. It was not only difficult to find a reason, it has proven to be impossible. No archaeologist has ever figured out the overwhelming prominence of a planet that could not be seen. Since 685 BC Mercury could almost not be found. It is only seen near the horizon just before sunrise or after sunset and only for a few days in the year. Because of this Mercury is the least significant of the planets, yet in antiquity he held a position as the God of language, magic, crafts, trades, and travel.

We know of the change which removed Mercury from the heavens. Jastrow does not, and he assumes that Mercury has always been diminutive and insignificant.

... dates

I looked by chance at an essay, "History and Science" at the University of Oklahoma, concerning the *Enuma Anu Enlil* which read:

"For centuries... [they specify 1600 to 700 BC] ..., [records were kept] because the scribes provided counsel for the king...."

Never mind the rest. They did not, not during that period, only after 750 BC or so, and then the "kings" were Assyrian monarchs, the overlords of Babylon, who would impale you if you crossed them. Where does all this claptrap come from? I get the feeling that the *Enuma Anu Enlil* has been caught up in a series of misreadings spanning 2700 years.

The records in question collate information from the past, but all offer specific data only from after 650 BC. This has long been known of the

Babylonian records, although Jastrow makes the unlikely suggestion that some predate the period of Hammurabi (circa 1700 BC in the consensus chronology). In actuality, the dates do not matter, for the Babylonian astrologers were attempting to forecast events for their Assyrian overlords on the basis of desperate guesswork, using any available records whatsoever.

That, in addition to Jupiter, Saturn was also called "sun" (Shamash) is no surprise at all. Saturn indeed had been the Sun at one time -- and certainly the "sun of the night" until 3147 BC. But it was Jupiter who had been the "sun of the night" after 3147 BC and with some interruptions for a thousand years, until 2150 BC.

Some 1500 years after Jupiter had diminished in size to become a star, the Babylonian astronomers were suddenly pressed into service by the Assyrian kings, because of the destructive close passes of Mars, and then the start of the explosive nova event of Venus and Mercury, after which Jupiter -- the night Sun -- blazed again in 685 BC, and was followed soon by Saturn.

The names of the planets to be watched, which included Mars and Venus (and Mercury), were derived from a 3000-year-old tradition. In the newly developed astrological database being devised in the 7th century BC, Venus and Mars were thus named before note was made of Jupiter and Saturn -- and in that order, as Ellenberger noted.

Everyone understood that Jupiter should be called a "night Sun" if it brightened. Duplicated use of "Shamash" could be sorted out when seen in context in most cases. Some tablets, however, were annotated with indications of whether the daytime or nighttime Sun was meant, and to which planet the name "Shamash" would apply in any particular instance. Seen in this context, the *Enuma Anu Enlil* is not a good source for suggesting that Saturn had stood in the sky as a sun before 3100 BC. It mostly speaks to Jupiter and certainly speaks only to conditions after 685 BC.

... Halos and Crowns

I think a greater fault is that none of the Saturnian commentators have done anything to address some of the truly strange wording of the tablets, like:

- "Saturn [Lu-Bat Sag-U] stands in the halo of the moon"
- "The moon has a halo around it and Saturn [Lu-Bat-Sag-U] stands in it."
- "If Shamash [(An) Ut] enters into the moon...." there is a note "Saturn (Lu-Bat Sag-U?) entered the moon".
- "When the sun [Shamash] stands in the place of the moon..."

- "When a mock-sun [Rum-me, sun-circle] stands over the moon (or) under the moon..."
- "If Shamash has a halo around it, there will be rain." with the note "Shamash of the day"
- "When Jupiter [Sag-me-gar] [stands] in the sun [An-Ut]..."
- "If Venus approaches Shamash, the King will perish." with a note explaining that here by Shamash the Sun is meant.

The essay, "Sun and Saturn," by Morris Jastrow is commentary on the translations by others, by the way. The parentheses and brackets in the quoted text above are insertions by Jastrow.

[Image: Various "star in crescent" illustrations from worldwide sources; after David Talbott.]

The illustrations above are from Talbott's *The Saturn Myth* (1980), and some might date to from before 3147 BC. The star image in that case consists of plasma streamers in glow mode connecting to Mercury (thought to be Venus) from Saturn. The left-right crescents and some other forms are missing in this collection.

Some more descriptions from Jastrow:

- A "sun-crown" above Venus...
- "Dilbat [Venus] is decked with two crowns."
- "A 'Shamash' crown above the moon, is explained as 'Lu-Bat [Saturn] [standing] by the moon.'"
- "If a mock-sun stands above the moon or below the moon..."
- "If Mars reaches the road of the sun [the ecliptic] ... there will be a famine."
- "The mock-sun and moon appear together," explained as "on this night Saturn approached (or 'was near') the moon."

The first three notes dealing with crowns need some comments from Jastrow. It is a footnote which unabashedly presents this information:

[footnote 24] *"These 'crowns' above Venus, of which various kinds are mentioned in the Anu-Enlil series -- dark, white, green, dark-red, broad, small, 'rain-bow crown', 'sun crown', 'moon crown', 'Jupiter crown'* [reference deleted] -- *clearly refer to rays above Venus, the different colors being ascribed to different planets standing in front of her, green = Mars, dark-red = Mercury, while other designations, similarly, describe the supposed specific causes, a 'rain-bow' crown being due to the rain-bow, a 'moon' crown to the moon etc."* [reference deleted]

Jastrow justifies the texts of the tablets in uniformitarian terms, as with:

"Strange as it may seem to us, the planet Saturn appears to have been regarded as 'the sun of the night' corresponding to Shamash *as 'the sun of the daytime' and the cause of such light as the night furnishes. It was argued, that since there was a sun furnishing the light of day, so there must be some corresponding power which causes the illuminations of the heavens at night."*

It is difficult to conceive of a more patronizing attitude toward the "magicians and astrologers" of Babylon. To think they reasoned that there "must be" a Sun of the night, is to assume that they were no brighter than 6-year-old children.

... refraction

Besides the fact that such absurd reasoning degrades the intellectual abilities of the Babylonians, this supposition (and others about "atmospheric phenomenon") is not necessary. The "crescent of the Moon," seen below, above, even on both the left and right, or seen in multiple units, plus the various colors, is the diffraction of the light of a very bright planet on approaching the last remaining band of the equatorial rings. This had been the case since 2349 BC when the Absu disappeared, but only at this time, at the press of the Assyrian kings, was it necessary to compile all available data and try to make sense of it.

The refraction pattern would be placed some distance away, probably 1/4 or 1/2 wavelength of the striations, and thus perhaps 1/4 spherical degree to the left and right, and make it appear as if the planet were placed within a Moon. Mesopotamian "Star and Crescent" images show the star consistently well within what would be the orb of the Moon, a situation which could not happen if the crescent genuinely belonged to the Moon. The above and below crescents of the moon (a waxing or waning Moon in the first quarter or last quarter) only happen in the tropics.

The left and right diffraction, when a bright object was centered on the band of the remaining equatorial ring, would result in an image similar to the "double axe" image of remote antiquity, but on a somewhat smaller scale. Before 2349 BC the ecliptic dipped behind the intact Absu. Jupiter, with its gigantic coma, would at that time have been the candidate for the giant double axe imagery (known traditionally as a "labrys"), refracting its bright disk to the left and right as giant crescents. The refraction of light would be predominantly to the left and right because the structure of the rings of the Absu had a radial component (described in Egypt as "reeds"). The handle of the labrys axe, which is infrequently shown, is always too slim to be hafted to a large double-bitted axe head. The labrys is a ceremonial object of the Middle Bronze Age, circa 3200 BC to 1200 BC.

I should point out, however, that images of a star within an upturned crescent could date back to before 3147 BC. At that time the crescent at the bottom was the Sun-lighted lower half of Saturn. The star form consisted of plasma in glow mode impinging on Mercury in discrete bundles. Like the dark of the Moon during the day, the unlit portion of Saturn would not show up visually during the day. But the identification of specific planets in the *Enuma Anu Enlil* records argues against the notion that such imagery dates from before 3147 BC.

It is the same diffraction of any point-source light of a planet or star when behind the last of the equatorial rings which causes the depiction of planets as four- and eight-pointed figures. The refracted light would be at right angles to the pattern of the equatorial ring. Refracted light would radiate left and right from the primary planet behind the ring. If the ring had a granular structure the refracted light would more likely form a "halo." Photographers use filters with etched lines to achieve similar effects.

The use of the phrase "mock Moon" implies that the Chaldeans recognized that some of these images were not real. But they were signs in the sky, and had to be accounted for.

Jastrow and others allowed that the situation of Saturn, or another planet, might be seen above or below the Moon because the Moon frequently runs off the ecliptic by some 5 degrees. What has not been accounted for, of course, is to have the Moon's crescent appear on the top or bottom. That does not happen in real life except at the horizon in the tropics.

It should also be pointed out again that the last equatorial ring was red. It caused Sirius to appear as red when the axis of the Earth shifted. The ring was recalled as a rope in the sky by the lowland Maya -- "and blood ran through it." In the *Popol Vuh* it is called the "river of blood." This is the Uoroboros. The tablets, on the other hand, suggest many colors.

The patterns would appear where the ecliptic crossed the ring in the sky. Because the ring was located in the south below the equatorial, these events would not happen directly at the equinox location (the intersection of the equinox and the equatorial), but would have been a month or so later in fall and earlier in spring.

... Saturn in Pisces

What needs to be answered also is why the *Enuma Anu Enlil* has so much to say about Saturn. Obviously Saturn was seen frequently, and seen in a position in the sky which caused the strange appearances of "standing in the halo of the Moon."

In fact, let us consider Saturn for a moment. Saturn moves at such a slug-like pace that it is unlikely that anything interesting would ever develop in terms of its interactions with other planets. It takes 30 years to get around the zodiac, moving only 12 degrees per year.

What would make Saturn more interesting would be the occasion for it to be seen through the last remaining band of the Absu. Then it would twinkle and sparkle and cause refracted patterns. I decided to research this topic.

The orbit of Earth had stabilized in 747 BC, and since Jupiter had last blazed in 2150 BC, it could be assumed that Saturn had also come to its final orbital position a thousand years ago. Thus an ephemeris would be accurate for the time period after 685 BC (the last change in celestial parameters). It would work if Saturn would travel through the location of the last ring in its travels along the zodiac.

Well, it turns out that in the fall of 685 BC (astronomical year), Saturn is on the zodiac at an elevation (at its highest point in the night sky) of 45 degrees at Babylon, 12.5 degrees below the equatorial. This places it within the last ring of the Absu, and thus it would be seen behind an ever-changing curtain of particulate matter, causing refractions left and right and below.

This depends, of course, on my estimates of how high in the sky the last ring of the Absu appeared. I have made some estimates of this in an appendix, on the basis of numerous reports of Sirius as colored red. The data is from the current era, and spread from AD 200 to AD 570. In each case Sirius is at a declination of 16.5 to 16.0 degrees below the equatorial. In September of 685 BC Saturn was at 12.5 degrees declination below the equatorial. A width of 4 degrees is reasonable for the remnant of the Absu.

The Moon would move through this position frequently, as would the other planets. Saturn would move away from this location in a few years, after having spent more time behind the last ring of the Absu than any other planet. Jupiter would move into this location three years after Saturn, but Jupiter had already blazed earlier, starting in July of 685 BC. The red ring is, of course, the Uoroboros.

Thirty years later, in 655 BC (astronomical), Saturn would again spend some years moving through this position. And again in 625 BC. In 612 BC (in normal Eastern Mediterranean chronology) the Persians and Medes burned down Nineveh, the capital of the Assyrians. With that the astronomical records of Babylon ended.

I do not think these last two instances would have added anything to the record which was probably originally composed directly after June and July of 685 BC, for it seems 655 BC and 625 BC are much too late for a planet to still show a coma after the event of 685 BC. What we see instead is a long record all dating to the many months that Saturn had traveled through the path of the red ring in 685 BC. This would account for the many records concerning Saturn.

New Star Charts

What is also significant is how graphical star charts changed. Before 600 BC the constellations are depicted as seen from the vantage point of Earth. There was no other imaginable point of view. After 600 BC we start seeing reversed charts, and eventually globes, which require a vantage point from outside of the dome of the stars.

In time, the more subtle changes in the sky became public knowledge. It was of special significance because for most people the Earth was fixed in space, and it was the dome of the stars that revolved. The dome had been twisted and the axis had relocated. The effect of knowing that *there had been a change* in the dome of the stars would have been of much greater importance than any physical effects from the actual change. The change suggested a prime mover acting beyond the largest object in the Universe known at the time, the dome of the stars, which included all the planetary

Gods. The concept of an entity which could alter the whole Universe eventually formed the basis of most religions of the world. That this had happened in one 40-day period of a summer, accompanied by planets on fire in the sky and then disappearing, was important also.

The Sibylline Star Wars

The *Sibylline Oracle Books* are texts from the first century AD, composed in Alexandria, Egypt, in Greek. The last few lines of the fifth volume, known as the "Star Wars" text, describe the blazing of Venus in 685 BC and the change in the skies -- written nearly 800 years after the event. These lines prophesied the future or impending end of the world in terms strictly coincident with events of 685 BC. It is probably the most spectacular evidence of the religious and philosophical importance of the events of 685 BC.

Oracle Books were all the rage in the period of 100 BC to AD 400. John's *Book of Revelations* is an example of one which was accepted into the canon of the New Testament. Oracle books, or collections of visions and oracles, date back to perhaps the fifth century BC. The Roman senate employed a number of persons as keepers of *Roman Oracle Books*. They were consulted whenever difficult decisions arose. [note 2]

The *Sibylline Oracle Books* are mostly Jewish in sentiment and philosophy. They use a well-established metonymical style (substituting associated names, like "Babylon" for the Roman Empire) used by the oracle of Delphi and the prophets of Israel. A close examination establishes without doubt that the descriptions can be matched against the changes in the skies in 685 BC, not only in the movement of the planet Venus, but especially in the details of how the constellations were rearranged after a new equatorial was established, and all of it presented in poetic language. Franz Xavier Kugler examined the Star Wars text in 1927. This has been expanded upon by Malcolm Lowery and Livio Stecchini in the 1970s. An analysis, additional details, and diagrams may be found in the following chapter, "The Sibylline Star Wars."

Hezekiah and Babylon

There is a well-known promise delivered by Isaiah from God to Hezekiah, king of Judah, in about 690 BC (probably in early 684 BC). Hezekiah was sick and thought he would die. Isaiah agreed, but the same day changed his mind and told Hezekiah that he would live another 15 years. As a sign, God promised the following:

"And this shall be a sign unto thee from the Lord, that the Lord will do this thing that he hath spoken. Behold, I will bring again the shadow of the degrees, which is gone down in the sun-dial of Uzziah, ten degrees backward. So the sun returned ten degrees, by which degrees it was gone down."
    -- Isaiah 38:8

It was a rash promise, but it can be explained. Velikovsky, in an unpublished document (hezekiah.htm at http://www.varchive.org), suggests that "degrees" should be read as such (*"maaloth in Hebrew is preferably 'degrees' and more so when applied to the sundial"*). Donald W. Patten and Samuel R. Windsor, in *The Mars-Earth Wars* (1996), however, disagree and suggest it should be taken to mean "measure." I also doubt that the "ten degrees" can be understood in terms of degrees of a circle as today. We are in an era 800 years before the development of trigonometry and the measurement of "degrees." Ussher makes the point in his comments that Judah was not even using "hours" to measure the day, even after their return, much later, from Babylonian captivity.

Patten and Windsor place the "commotion of Uzziah" in 756 BC, and the "return of the shadow" in 701 BC. De Grazia places the commotion in 747 BC (-747), as does Velikovsky. Velikovsky places the return of the shadow in the year -687, on the basis of rabbinical sources, in the evening of the demise of Sennacherib's army. The rabbinical sources, however, only point to a disturbance in the movement of the setting Sun. We know about that. In -687 Earth experienced a repulsive electric contact with Mercury, detailed in the previous chapter.

If, as Isaiah suggests, the "ten degrees" were added earlier, then it might be suggested that the Earth's axial inclination to the normal of its orbit changed from some previous value and returned to 23.5 degrees in 686 BC, with the second Earth shock. I really doubt this. But the implicit suggestion of a previous event which would have moved (lengthened) the shadow, is exactly what all the catastrophic researchers from Velikovsky to de Grazia were looking for. There was no "commotion" to account for this; the reference to Uzziah is a foil. Uzziah only built the gnomon, "the sun-dial of Uzziah."

What is most likely is that the promise by Isaiah speaks only to the measured length of the shadow at the equinox. Before 685 BC the equinox fell 15 days earlier than after 685 BC, as I have related. On this earlier equinox date, March 6th, the Sun at noon reached an angle of 58.38 degrees above the south horizon at Jerusalem (31.78 degrees north latitude). After the summer of 685 BC, the Sun was lower in the sky on the following March 6th, rising only at 52.34 degrees above the horizon, and causing the shadow to be longer by a good measure on this day.

The first full moon after the equinox had traditionally signaled the celebration of Passover (on the following Sabbath). Thus it was important to know when the equinox was. This could no longer be found from the lunar calendar as in the era before 747 BC, but it could be calculated from the number of days since the last equinox and checked against the length of the shadow on that day.

But in the first year following 685 BC, the angle of the Sun at noon on March 6th was only 52.34 degrees above the south horizon. The shadow had (as a result) lengthened by one fourth of what it was earlier. This is a considerable amount, and reason enough to call it "ten degrees" or ten measures. The Sun, on what was thought to be the day of the equinox, had "gone down" some large amount. [note 3]

There was no event which returned the shadow to its proper length, only the realization by Isaiah that the day of the equinox had moved (remember, he had changed his mind). Isaiah's promise held good, because 15 days later, when the "new" day of the equinox was reached, it was again 58.38 degrees, or very close to it. The shadow on March 21, 684 BC, was again the same length that it was on March 6, of the previous year, for the angle of the Sun at the equinox depends only on the latitude, not on the inclination of the rotational axis of the Earth. Isaiah had experienced the change of the date of the equinox already in the fall, and could have made the simple guess from that data. Isaiah, like many of the prophets, was a competent astronomers.

What is interesting is that the sign from God also symbolized how many more years Hezekiah would live, for the difference between the old day of the equinox and the new date was 15 days. This is not mentioned in the Bible, but it is in line with the frequent acting-out by the prophets, as when Isaiah goes naked and shoeless for three years to demonstrate what would happen to the Egyptians after a three-year war with the Assyrians. *"This intimated that when that time expired, they likewise would be stripped of their clothes and go bare foot into captivity and bondage by the king of Assyria."* -- Ussher.

... Jerusalem moves 6 degrees south

Another discrepancy in the 7th century BC is noted by Donald W. Patten and Samuel R. Windsor in *The Mars-Earth Wars* (1996). The priests of the temple at Jerusalem permanently close the door through which, at an earlier time, the rays of the Sun would penetrate to the center of the temple on the morning of the equinox. Patten and Windsor conclude that Jerusalem moved south by 6 degrees of latitude in the 8th or 7th century BC, writing:

"On the basis of Kazmann's data [Raphael G. Kazmann, 'On the Orientation of Ancient Temples and Other Anomalies' (*Aeon,* 1990)], *the conclusion here is that the latitude of Jerusalem slipped south by a total of 6 degrees between 965 B.C.E. and 701 B.C.E. During this time span there were five Mars flybys."*

The date of 701 BC is, of course, from Patten and Windsor's narrative. The date of 701 BC marks, for them, the date when the length of the year changed -- which every other revisionist cosmologist has assigned to 747 BC. Patten and Windsor therefore conclude that the temple doors were closed after a change in the length of the year. The first temple, attributed to Solomon was oriented to face the northwest Atlantic. The light of the Sun was cast into the interior with a set of mirrors.

"If this interpretation of Kazmann's data is correct, the latitude of Jerusalem shifted southward by some 400 miles. Simultaneously the North Pole (spin axis) shifted some 400 miles in the Arctic Basin. If so, the North Pole net shift was away from Scandinavia and toward Alaska, the Yukon, British Columbia (and Seattle). As Jerusalem shifted southward 6 degrees, or 410 miles, Seattle, Vancouver, Anchorage, Fairbanks and Point Barrow shifted northward a similar distance and their climates became cooler."

I frankly cannot follow how Patten and Windsor arrive at the difference of 6 degrees in latitude. Moving a location south (or north) does not change the shadows at the equinox or the location of the rising Sun. The first temple at Jerusalem had an axis located 6 degrees west of north, pointing to the North Atlantic -- to the much earlier location of the plasma contact from Saturn.

Patten and Windsor fail to note that the temple built by Solomon was rebuilt in 516 (after the Jews' return from Babylon) but oriented to the true north-south and east-west cardinal directions. I might suggest instead that the sudden displacement of the equinox by 15 days in 685 BC and the change in the polar axis might have been an influence in correcting the notion of orientation which was already 2000 year out of date in Solomon's time.

... the latitude of Babylon

It was noted in antiquity that apparently the latitude of Babylon had shifted by about 2.5 degrees south, from 34.95 degrees north latitude to 32.55 degrees latitude, some time after 700 BC or 650 BC. That there were two values for the geographic location, that is, the latitude, of Babylon, which could be derived from recorded measurements of the longest day at midsummer, was noted by Ptolemy (circa AD 150), Arzachel (circa AD 1050), Kepler (circa AD 1600), and Kugler (circa AD 1910). The records date from 700 to 650 BC. Kugler worked from original sources.

However, there was no change in latitude; it was an inadvertent misreading at the time the inclination of the Earth's axis changed.

In antiquity the "latitude" was expressed as the ratio of the longest day to the shortest day, and rather poorly integrated into notions of the angle of the Sun and the inclination of the Earth's axis. Babylon's "earlier" recorded ratio of longest day to shortest day was 1.50.

We cannot solve this problem with trigonometry as we know it, for trigonometry dates from about AD 300. The Babylonians, similarly, would not have used trigonometry.

The latitude problem has remained unexplained for over 2000 years now. What I will suggest as a solution is that the ratio of 1.50 was erroneously derived. The following is based on how the Babylonians would most likely have proceeded.

The first date after July 25, 685 BC, that new values would be measured, would be the winter solstice. This is easily found, since the Sun would seem to be standing still, that is, not advancing along the horizon, for two to four days.

The length of the day was 9 hours and 50 minutes. Taken into a ratio of the longest day at the previous summer solstice (at that time on June 6th, equivalent to June 21 of today), 14 hours and 52 minutes, which had occurred before the change in the heavens, this would yield 1:51 -- and was recorded.

```
     ---- Babylon, ratio of longest day to shortest day ----
  axial incl   longest day   shortest day   ratio   notes
  ----------   -----------   ------------   -----   ------------
  30.0 deg     14:52 hrs      9:06 hrs      1.63    prior
  23.5         14:08          9:50          1.44    today
  ----------   -----------   ------------   -----   ------------
  measured Dec 685, compared with Jun 685:

  30.0 deg     14:52 hrs                            Jun 685 BC
  23.5                        9:50 h               Dec 685 BC
  error        14:52          9:50          1.51    in error
  ----------   -----------   ------------   -----   ------------
  measured Jun 684, compared with Dec 685:

  23.5         14:08                                Jun 684 BC
  23.5                        9:50 h               Dec 685 BC
  correct      14:08          9:50          1.44    correct
```

Six months later a new ratio of 1.44 was computed, based on the new lengths of both the winter and summer solstice.

Had the Babylonians known trigonometry, they would have realized that the latitude can be found as the complement of the height of the angle of the Sun above the south horizon at the equinox. Without this, the Babylonians had to use the solstices to properly measure the shadow.

Considering that the Babylonians were deeply involved in their revised mathematics of lunar eclipse predictions, and additionally kept multiple records of the locations of the planets, even though some were obviously outdated, it seems reasonable that an erroneous value for the ratio of the longest day to the shortest day was also not discarded. That was a mistake.

Whatever happened to the ratio of 1.63 recorded before 685 BC? It was based on a polar axis tilted at 30 degrees, taken into a ratio based on the current axial inclination. It is not just wrong, but even useless. This ratio would have suggested that Babylon was located at 40.3 degrees north, a difference of 7.75 degrees, placing Babylon in the Caucasus mountains between the Black Sea and the Caspian. No one since Babylonian days would have believed that, and if this value had been recorded it would have been held as totally erroneous. Even the Babylonians of the seventh century BC would have discarded the data.

The additional erroneously derived ratio of 1.51 was kept because it looked to be nearly correct. The Sun had moved in 685 BC, that was certain. Who was to tell how things had changed with the Earth and the stars. Pliny had described it as "a slackening of creation," as if the Earth had slipped south.

... the Babylonians visit Hezekiah

The Moon had changed its period after 747 BC, to 29-1/2 days, and thus there were now slightly more than 12-1/3 lunar months in the year, since the year had also lengthened. This would cause no end of problems, for the lunar months no longer coincided comfortably with the number of days in the solar year. But after the summer of 685, there was the additional problem that the equinox had shifted.

As a comment on cooperative calendrical efforts in the Middle East, it should be noted that the Babylonians (Chaldeans), who had apparently celebrated the new year at the spring equinox based solely on the fact that this coincided before 747 BC with a new Moon, were now at a loss to figure out the date of the equinox, especially since the phases of the Moon now showed up at arbitrary times throughout the year.

Babylon sent observers to Jerusalem, for the Israelites knew the day of the equinox, since Passover was celebrated on the Sabbath following the first full Moon after the spring equinox. Jerusalem knew how to exactly find the day of the equinox, by counting days, and by measuring the shadow of a gnomon.

The visit by the Babylonians is recorded in the Bible at 2 Chronicles 32:31.

William Whiston, translator (in AD 1737) of Josephus's *The Antiquity of the Jews* (AD 93), writes in a footnote, about the regression of the shadow of a gnomon by ten steps under Hezekiah (in 685 BC):

"... this wonderful signal was not, it seems, peculiar to Judea, but either seen, or at least heard of, at Babylon also, as appears by '2-Chronicles' 32:31, where we learn that the Babylonian ambassadors were sent to Hezekiah, among other things, to inquire of the wonder that was done in the land."

Ussher records this as:

"Now in the beginning of the 15th year of Hezekiah's reign, Merodach, or Berodach Baladan, the son Baladan, the king of Babylon, sent messengers with presents to him. They wanted to know the reason for the miraculous retrogradation of the sun which happened in the world."

The "retrogradation" is correct nomenclature. The Sun normally advances in the sky further east each following day, and further into the series of zodiac houses. What had happened is that the Sun had backed up half of a zodiac house, as noted by the end of the year 685 BC. We have to recognize (as has already been demonstrated in this text) that the prophets of Israel were competent astronomers. This is again demonstrated here, where the foremost astronomers of the whole Middle East come to Jerusalem to learn a few things.

Philosophy, Religion, Science

Venus lost its tail in 685 BC, and Mars no longer came close to Earth after 670 BC. Mercury also was not seen again anywhere near Earth. The coma of Jupiter had probably disappeared by 650 BC. The blackboard in the sky, which had taught mankind all of its conduct, had been erased. The Gods were gone. When Xerxes, in about 484 BC, entered Babylon to destroy its religious hold on the region, he found the statue of Marduk in a coffin. He melted it down.

Despite some continued local "Ignis Coelis" (fire falling from the skies), continued sightings of meteors, which slowly reduced in frequency over the next 1000 years, and the earthquakes which continued for hundreds of years, the lessons from the Gods had come to an end. In the sky only the stars and pinpoints of planets were to be found. The band of the ecliptic continued to glow like a highway until AD 1840. In the 20th-century, references to the "path of the Gods" are identified with the Milky Way instead (to confound "ancient legends" even further).

[*Image: A 19th century graphic in the style of a medieval illustration by Camille Flammarion (1888); looking past the dome of the stars. Rather than finding God beyond the dome of the stars, the viewer is confronted with an endless expanse of additional wheels and gears -- the mechanics of the Universe.*]

Yet plasma contacts between distant planets persisted for a long time after 670 BC. There are dozens of recorded observations in China, Arabia, and medieval Europe. Charles Raspil paraphrases an incident recorded in China in the 10th century AD, which caught my eye:

"On the morning of March 18, [AD] *904, Venus was observed near the Pleiades blazing like fire. The next morning, to observers, Venus appeared to have developed three horns, somewhat resembling a flower, and then began to tremble and shake.*
     -- Charles Raspil *Planetary observations of the T'ang* (1994) [note 4]

Mars and Jupiter are also noted for anomalous behavior, but many of the observations find the planets in the wrong location, and thus the anomalies can be attributed to errors in identification. Strange celestial events were frequently noted elsewhere also, as recounted in European records of "fire falling from heaven." But humanity was no longer confronted with large globes looming threateningly above the Earth during the day or night. After 685 BC the planets kept their distance.

The planets, which had previously had been seen as the Gods -- Saturn, Jupiter, and Mars -- had been identified and tracked as they receded in the sky after 3147 BC and after 685 BC. But Venus was not added to the "four planets of antiquity" until after 600 BC -- primarily because of the strange path taken by Venus in the sky. And, in fact, the clear identification of Isis, Horus, and Thoth with the planets Venus, Mars, and Mercury often remained uncertain during the prior period when the Gods raged across the skies.

They were often misnamed and misidentified, confused with each other, or associated with the names of differing Gods and Goddesses (and stars also). This was to be expected since the planets were on unpredictable orbits, disappearing towards the Sun or deep into the night sky, and then appearing inexplicably close to Earth. As long as that happened, and as long as no "model" of the Universe existed, the planets retained their anthropomorphic qualities. A science of astronomy, based on the regular traversal of wandering specks across the night sky, did not develop until after the 7th century BC. [note 5]

The suddenly cleared skies caused a second immense change in humanity's perspective on the world, not unlike the change in 3147 BC when the Gods departed, but without the attendant catastrophic physical trauma. Whereas for 10,000 years everything had been ordered by the willful and unpredictable Gods, now there was nothing to base life's decisions on.

The New Religions

We can readily trace the development of all of the modern religions to the period following 685 BC, although many have much deeper roots.

... Zoroastrianism

In the seventh and sixth century BC, Zarathustra (born in 628 BC, a date derived in antiquity), a Persian, develops a new religion, Zoroastrianism, as a composite of Vedic and Persian religious practices. He retains the essential monotheism, equating the deity Mazda or Ahura-mazda with fire, and adds prohibitions against human and animal sacrifices. He is also the first to suggest the devil as a separate God, forever in conflict with Mazda for control of the world. Zoroastrianism becomes the official religion of the Persians. It is significant not only for its monotheism, but also for the change of worship from anthropomorphic celestial deities to a worship of a conceptual God, here expressed as the element of fire. Philosophically, Zoroastrianism introduced the concept of free will. It seems almost certain that Zoroastrianism had been influenced by the fiery battle of Venus and the Sun.

... Mithraism

One of the (later) minor deities of Persian Zoroastrianism, Mithra (which translates as "contract"), becomes the God of a new religion and contract between humans and a greater God. The concept of a covenant between this new, greater, and impersonal God is offered as a promise of hope, something which will pervade all the new religions except Taoism. [note 6]

Mithraism was first noted in Parthia in 272 BC and became well established in Roman regions of Europe and North Africa by the first century AD. In a few hundred years, Mithraism spread far into Western Europe as a self-contained religion. It was a forerunner of Christianity, especially in the idea of a "new contract" between God and mankind. In the Roman cult of Mithraism, the name "Mithras" is understood to mean "mediator." Christ preached a new contract with God also, under the metaphor of God as a shepherd.

Mithraism takes on the iconography of a bull (the constellation Taurus) slain by the God Mithras (as represented by the constellation Perseus, standing above Taurus in the sky), and clearly includes a number of other constellations in the imagery. These are constellations close to the equatorial, not the ecliptic. All represent animals which one by one follow Taurus in appearing above the eastern horizon during the summer night skies.

"In Porphyry [philosopher, 3rd century AD], *for example, we find recorded a tradition that the cave which is depicted in the tauroctony and which the underground Mithraic temples were designed to imitate was intended to be 'an image of the cosmos.'"*
-- David Ulansey *The Origins of the Mithraic Mysteries* (1989)

The cave as a metaphor for the cosmos is an interesting concept, for this can be extended to having a God standing outside of the cave, outside the cosmos. We have no clear idea what the real meaning of the Mithraic iconography is, although it could be guessed that it expressed a new order for humanity and the Universe: the old gods were dead, the Son of the Sun (Venus in 685 BC) had slain the horned bull (Taurus) associated with the former Gods (and the prior start of the year), and had moved the whole sky to a new starting point for spring -- to the constellation of the Ram. The understanding was that the start of a new world order had been signaled with a sign from a God who exceeded in power all of the old deities, a God who stood outside of the dome of the stars and planets and suddenly moved it one day to a new location. [note 7]

We need to add another set of twins to the list developed in the previous chapter. The iconography of Mithraism always includes twin boys (known as Cautes and Cautopates) on the left and right of Mithra and on each side of a surrounding depiction of the zodiac. The boys are holding torches, one holds his torch high and one with his torch pointed down. Both boys have their legs crossed, each with a different leg in the front. Others have noted that the crossed legs might represent the vernal and autumnal equinox -- the St Andrew's cross of the red ring of the equatorial and the yellow band of the ecliptic, as I had also noted for Mesoamerica. In some cases the crossed legs correspond correctly to the the vernal and autumnal equinox, in other cases these are reversed.

I would also suggest that the torch held down and the torch held high represent the winter and summer solstice of the Sun respectively after the fall and spring equinox. The torch held down represents the act of relighting the torch at the winter solstice (which is normally done by grinding the lighted end against the ground). The torch held high represents the full light of the summer solstice (they might represent the equinoxes instead of the solstices). [note 8]

... Taoism

In China, Lao-tse (604-531 BC) develops the philosophy of Taoism. Lao-tse's book, the *Tao-te*, proposes to explain "the change of the path." The path, which could metaphorically be taken as "the path of life," is clearly also the path of the planets. Chinese cosmology had already advanced to imagine the Earth (although conceived of as a flat square of land) surrounded by a rotating dome of the stars. The shift in the heavens in 685 BC must have had a huge impact on the thinking of the Chinese. It was as if some giant external hand had suddenly twisted the dome of the stars. This seemed to have curtailed any further removal of the remaining "mystical" elements from religion and cosmology which had been initiated by the Chou. The power of a "heaven" was retained as a certainty, as an external force which would continue to dominate imperial politics, reinforced by later Confucian philosophy. [note 9]

We have to understand the "new religions" as having the same purpose as the "new philosophies" (discussed further below). Both sought a moral order independent of the older Gods, and both were meant to democratize thought and religious practices, in effect taking these functions away from a priestly cast. The coincidence of dates is as follows:

- Zoroaster (Zarathustra, Northeastern Persia, 628-?? BC), of the tribe of the Magi, developed Zoroastrianism (Mazdaism). Zoroaster understood the events of 685 BC as a battle between good and evil, with good eventually winning the battle, but not without continued support from the people. The Persian kings hired the Magi to officiate at their ceremonies and sacrifices. The monotheism of Mazdaism influenced Judaism during the Babylonian captivity of the Jews (597-536 BC), and spread throughout the eastern portion of the Middle East and into Arabia. It gave rise to Mithraism by perhaps 300 BC, and was a very important model for Christianity and, at a much later date, for Islam. [note 10]

- Lao-tse (China, 604-531 BC) devised the philosophy of Taoism. His existence may be in doubt, but that would serve his philosophy of restraint well. Taoism was discussed above.
- Confucius (China, 551-479 BC) extended to everyone the worship services originally only allowed to the emperor.
- Siddhartha Gautama, the Buddha, (India, 563-483 BC) founded Buddhism, one of the major influences in the reformation of Hinduism, and later a major philosophical influence in China. About the teachings of the Buddha, H. G. Wells, writes in *The Outline of History* (1961), *"It is beyond all dispute the achievement of one of the most penetrating intelligences the world has ever known."*
- Vardhamana Mahavira (India, ??-527 BC) was the founder of Jainism, with ideas partially derived from Hinduism and Buddhism.
- The mystery religions of Anatolia and Greece (the worship of Demeter, Orpheus, Dionysus) all seem to date to the 6th century BC, although some elements, as, for example, the Eleusinian rites of Demeter, may be much older and more primitive. [note 11]
- Changes in Mesoamerica are harder (if not impossible) to trace. The Olmecs seemed to have worshiped (or feared) Mars in the 8th and 7th century BC (and Venus earlier). Elements of their culture resurface in Central Mexico, but with the addition of the cult of Quetzalcoatl, the sacrificed Venus, and a cult of the dead -- actually a cult of the afterlife. New alignments to the setting or rising sun on or about August 12 become a feature of ceremonial centers after 600 BC. The definitive site was the city of Teotihuacan -- "the place where men become Gods." See the chapter "Olmec Site Alignments."

The new religions were testaments to hope -- hope for a good life on Earth, hope for the abatement of evil, hope for an afterlife, hope for union with God, hope for victory of a nation, hope for the conquest of others. The specifics vary with the politics and philosophy of various peoples. The Christians hoped for the return of their savior. Their hope lasted 1200 years. The Mexicans and Maya hoped for the return of Quetzalcoatl for 2200 years. The promise of a redemption resulting in life after death is almost universal.

I should also point out that the older Gods were not simply put aside. From a look at the history of republican and imperial Rome it becomes obvious that, certainly at the official level, the honors and ceremonies extended to the elder Gods continued unabated for the next thousand years. But it should also be noted that no new Gods were added. As Alfred de Grazia wrote:

"No new sky god has been 'invented' in any part of the world since the Martian age [after circa 680 BC]. ... *Nor did the Teutonic peoples invent new gods, try as they might, after the 'Ragnarok' or 'Götterdämmerung.' Nor did a new sky god come out of India, China, or America."*

"Whence one concludes that 'real gods' cannot be 'invented' by the human mind as a pastime, or as a cold decision. Further, the abstract God of the Jews and of Christians and Muslim, and the abstract Heaven of the Chinese, are gods of philosophy. Insofar as a tangible presence is given to them, that presence becomes manifest in the behavior, appearances, visitations, rituals and iconography of the ancient sky gods and their heavenly hosts."

Philosophy and Science

Within 100 years after 685 BC, we see the simultaneous rise of philosophy in China, India, Mesopotamia (Chaldea), Israel, and Greece. The coincidence of start-up dates is amazing. The methods of building a philosophical system differ, but everywhere the systems include a sudden interest in history and in physics. About the sudden interest in materials and basic concepts, Kelley L. Ross writes:

"The multiple points of similarity between thought of Greece, India, and China, evident in the simplest terms in their respective treatment of the physical elements, cannot be accounted for by mutual influence, which does not seem to have existed at the earliest period." [note 12]

China will retain the Yin and Yang and the "five elements" of remote antiquity, and build onto this a political and moral philosophy. Chaldea and India devise a science of astrology. Israel collates the historical facts for the Bible and adds the rituals from antiquity. The Greeks start investigations which will form the core of Western physics, and write the first histories. [note 13]

About the period of 600 to 500 BC, Irving Wolfe wrote, in 1997:

"[There is] *evidence for what I call a 'Kultursturz' or cultural crisis in which a large number of cultural elements underwent quick and sharp change within the same short period of time. These include the appearance of secular as opposed to strictly religious art, a host of new religions of a new type, new philosophies of a new type, writing, dynastic upheavals, the quick upsurge and removal of several tyrannical regimes, urbanism, new patterns of consciousness, behavior, and dreaming, new types of social organization, vast pan-Greek ritualistic athletic games, the institution of democracy and the use of money. All of these elements are totally different in spirit from those of the previous (Bronze Age) cultures."*

-- Irving Wolfe, "The 'Kultursturz' At The Bronze Age / Iron Age Boundary" *Natural Catastrophes during Bronze Age Civilizations*, SIS Conference (1997).

Wolfe continues with:

"If all of these cultural revolutions can be correlated chronologically among themselves and to scientific evidence for similar upheavals well documented in the geological, archaeological and climatological record, then we have before us the outline of a global natural event which not only ended one historical era, but led to the distinctive cultural characteristics of our modern age. After all, we are the children of this period of upheaval."

The "evidence for similar [geological] upheavals" clearly exists as part of the 8th and 7th century BC, preceding the changes of the 7th and 6th century BC which Wolfe speaks of. But the one single celestial event of 685 BC, which became the definitive opening of the new human cultural era, caused no physical upheavals.

The people of Mesoamerica also acknowledged the change in milieu, even though the written records attesting to this do not appear until nearly 2000 years later. The death of Quetzalcoatl is a concluding event in Mesoamerica, as it was for people elsewhere in the world, and no new celestial Gods are introduced after the 7th century BC. It is at this time, in fact, that we see the demise of the Olmecs and the rise of other Central American civilizations, and a Mesoamerican "physics" which becomes a system of control over the spiritual world, not unlike that of India and Babylonia. An intense interest in history also develops, soon aided with a fully developed script (after 600 BC) used to elucidate the much older graphical records painted on bark books. The interest in history at this time was worldwide.

"And here ends that interval of time which is termed mythological. From this time on history begins."

-- Varro, first century BC.

Varro is actually speaking about history after the 8th century BC, in reference to 776 BC, the first Olympiad. But prior to Varro Greek chronographers had already divided history up into two eras, the "mythological" and the "historical." The year 747 BC was the dividing line between the two eras. [note 14]

By the first century AD, historians are convinced that there is no sensible history more than a few centuries before their own time. Varro and other historians had never seen any of the wonders that the ancients talked about, nor had Herodotus in 400 BC. They considered the visits of Athena, streaking through the day skies with her long hair, or the attacks on the Earth by Ares, the bloodied stormer of walls, as "myths" concocted by their ancestors. Their attitude seems entirely modern to us. In the Greek city of Miletos, a new school of philosophy sought to explain the world in terms of what was observed rather than basing explanations on the testimony of the ancients. [note 15]

"Human beings are distributed all around the Earth and stand with their feet pointing to each other"
     -- Pliny, first century AD

Pliny's observation is paralleled by Greeks, Mesopotamians, Indians, and Chinese of the same era. "Everywhere upon the globe of the earth, men think their own place to be topmost," reads the Hindu *Suyra Siddhanta* of about the same date. Many people of this era knew that the Earth was a globe which "hangs suspended and does not fall," as Pliny wrote. Chaldeans knew that eclipses of the Moon were caused by the Earth's shadow, and could predict them. Aristarchus of Samos knew the Earth traveled around the Sun. Hipparchus (129 BC) calculated the minute annual shift in the Earth's equinox. Eratosthenes correctly found the circumference of the Earth. [note 16]

I am using these examples of a new physics of the Solar System to demonstrate that a watershed had been reached in subjective consciousness, which over the course of a few hundred years expands to an ability to incorporate observations into narratized mental spaces and explore them profitably. This particular model -- representing the Earth as a globe suspended in space -- could only be seen in the imagination.

The same is seen in China and India at about the same time, where natural history develops into "sciences," which depend on imagined mental spaces congruent with reality as observed. To explain everything, without reference to remote antiquity, it was first necessary to describe the physical world.

Not the same can be said for Mesoamerica at first glance, with its detailed congruence of real-world and spiritual-world interactions, based perhaps too much yet on the celestial observations of remote antiquity for our taste. But there was also a very different attitude toward the past. The people of Mesoamerica had complete illustrated records of the past, extending back 40,000 years, and in a uniform graphical format. Pictures don't lie; the Olmecs, Mexicans, Guatemalans, and Maya believed in the past -- unlike the people of the Mediterranean, who were always suspicious of the tales and retellings of their forebears. I think also that texts were only added to the graphic books after about 600 BC.

Considered in detail, the thought system of the Maya exhibits the same rationality in navigating this intricately detailed imagined spiritual space. It does not involve "facts" as we understand them, that is, events placed in a continuity of time and a contiguity with other observations, but is instead totally based on firmly believed interactions between the realms of the real and the spiritual. Yet it represents a way of thinking which is far removed from mere acceptance of the world. The Mesoamerican "philosophy" also dates (I suspect) to after 600 BC. It was widespread and uniform when the Spanish arrived. The histories written after the time of the Spanish of the ball-playing twins, written 2200 years after the events (and the surviving celebrations which still exist today), point to the stability of the underlying philosophy.

Some of the new science went awry, of course. The Babylonians (Chaldeans) had made astronomical observations dating back perhaps to 2300 BC. But only in the seventh century BC is this seriously developed into a "science" of astrology. This effort was a giant leap into an arena of correlation between observed celestial and earthly events which the same people had been incapable of even imagining during the previous 2000 years. What made this particular "science" valid to them was the assumption that the planets, identified with the Gods of old, still regulated the lives of men and controlled events on Earth, just as the Gods had always done.

Holding On to the Past

The ultimate effort everywhere was to explain mankind's existence and formulate a code of proper behavior. By 500 to 400 BC the Greeks had reached an intellectual level which is completely modern to us. And yet, at times the past peeks through. The same philosophers who could verbally extract the roots of quadratic equations, held fast to omens and espoused the prophesies of oracles with certitude.

The prophetess at Delphi, in effect, ruled the whole of the Greek political world for 1000 years with her instantaneous answers to questions about colonization, leaders, laws, enemies, and personal fortunes. Thucydides, writing about the Peloponnesian Wars (430 -- 404 BC), in detailing all the human failings in the course of events, never fails to append his histories with the pronouncements of Delphi to show how the prophesies had been accomplished. The *New Testament* uses prophesies in the same manner, as authentication. Plato, in his otherwise completely cynical writings, holds the Delphic Oracle in high esteem.

Omens, prophecy, and foretelling of the future remained very serious practices lasting well into the current era. (The *Sibylline Oracle Books* were still in circulation in the 16th century AD.) The concept of "free will" was developed in Greece in classical times (400 BC), but not widely accepted for another 2000 years. The Greek tragedies hold that "fate" runs the lives of men, resulting in plotlines often completely inexplicable to us as modern readers. The idea of "chance happening" does not take hold in Europe until well after the Middle Ages. [note 17]

The past maintained a particular hold on the people of South America and Mesoamerica. For Mesoamerica, the observation of Venus remained a primary theological obsession, especially for the Maya, who record yearly corrections to a base calculation of the location of Venus which comes closer in estimating its movements than the Europeans would be able to do for 200 years after they "discover" the Maya.

For the Aztec, the pacification of the Gods remains at the center of life. The Aztecs, the people of Mars, had successfully kept cosmic misfortune at bay, for hundreds of years, at the cost of many thousands of lives, when the Spanish arrived in AD 1492. Even in the last battle with Cortez's soldiers over possession of the city of Tenochtitlan, the Aztec warriors take time out from battle to drag captured Spanish soldiers to the top platform of the temple of Huitzilopochtli to rip out their hearts. The sacrifices were necessary measures as long as the return of the unpredictable Gods remained a possibility.

The Presence of God

It seems almost unbelievable that the altered night skies, and especially the rotation of the dome of the stars, would have the effect that it did in generating a half dozen new religions, initiating an historical awareness, and be the genesis of the study of physics. It is even more astounding to see these changes happening worldwide and at almost the same time -- in Babylonia, Greece, India, China, and Mesoamerica. The simultaneity of the interests in these topics is amazing, especially considering the lack of cultural contacts.

This has been remarked upon by others.

If you look for the history of any of the Greek cities, or the nations of the Middle East, or China, you will see that in most instances history cannot be traced back before 600 or 700 BC. Everything disappears into legends. It is as if the world suddenly woke up, and abstract thought was first allowed after 600 BC.

I should point out, however, that the changes in outlook did not come easily. Plutarch, writing in the first century AD, tells of Anaxagoras, after about 500 BC:

> *"Anaxagoras was the first to put in writing, most clearly and most courageously of all men, the explanation of the moon's illumination and darkness. His account was not common property, but was a secret, current among only a few. For in those days they refused to tolerate the physicists and stargazers, as they were called, who presumed to fritter away the deity into unreasoning causes, blind forces, and necessary properties."*
>
> *"Anaxagoras was accused of impiety and sentenced [to death] for holding that the sun is a red-hot stone and the moon is of earthly nature. This was in disagreement with the view that these luminaries were deities."*

By 650 BC we have a society of vagabonds and inland survivors in Greece. The coastal people had been decimated with the repeated strikes of Mars. The up-land goatherd survivors had no earthly history of more than one or two generations, no genealogy except that which linked to mythical beings, and no homes. For the mainland Greeks and those of Asia Minor, the devastations of the 8th and 7th centuries BC had made a complete break with the expectations of the past and with the conservative attitudes of the past. The time and the place were ripe for something new (de Grazia).

The fact is that far-flung regions of the world all simultaneously came to the same conclusions about the universe and the world. This suggests the possibility of something global being the cause of the new sciences, philosophies, and inquiries.

Two recent events are possibilities. The earlier instance of the "Tower of Babel" event was in 2150 BC. This was the flaming of Jupiter. A second "Tower of Babel" event is dated to 686 BC (astronomical), and seems to be universally attributed to Mercury. These later "Tower of Babel" stories are worldwide, which also suggests that the event was recent, and not 1500 years earlier. But in both cases the "event" preceded a change in the attitude and awareness of humans. The fire of Jupiter in 2150 BC precedes a jump in awareness of around 2000 BC. This date can be understood as the time when the first historical interest seems to have developed.

But in terms of a timetable for the development of philosophy, science, and religion, the date of circa 2000 BC is far too early. The electrical contact by Mercury in 686 BC happened directly before the blazing of Venus and Mercury in 685 BC. Mercury, I should point out again, is the only inner planet (besides Earth) with a magnetic field, although minor. It might be coincidence but this also preceded a jump in awareness for humans.

The other thing which stands out, besides the "Tower of Babel" event, is a change in the size of the plasmasphere of the Earth. This can be concluded from the precession of the equinoxes. Before 747 BC there was no precession of the equinoxes. This is certainly to be recognized from the multitude of data which points to the fact that the same constellations were held to be the centerpoints of the spring and fall equinox -- Taurus and Scorpio -- for the time before 685 BC, which can be extended to 747 BC. Precession was only noted after 400 BC in Asia Minor and after AD 300 in China when it became obvious. To notice the precession of the equinox requires the accumulation of data for more than a hundred years, since the rate is about one degree in a hundred years.

The lack of precession before 747 BC means that the Moon did not exit and reenter the Earth's plasmasphere in traveling "around" the Earth. Today the plasmasphere of the Earth has a dimension of 10 to 20 Earth diameters on the Sun side, thus 80,000 to 160,000 miles. The Moon today remains within this for only part of its orbit. The Moon moves outside the plasmasphere when it travels to the Sun-side of Earth, because the radius of the Moon's orbit is 250,000 miles, and the plasmasphere of the Earth is currently at best only 160,000 miles. That means that before 747 BC the plasmasphere of the Earth must have have had a dimension of some 30 Earth diameters on the Sun-side -- 240,000 miles -- large enough to keep the Moon wholly within the Earth's plasmasphere.

It is not the Moon, however, or the precession of the equinoxes, that changed our behavior. These changes are much too slow to account for the sudden changed attitudes and interests after about 600 BC. What I am suggesting here is that the Earth would have been at a much different electric potential with respect to the surrounding space of the Sun. That probably happened after 685 BC. If the Earth's plasmasphere shrunk after 685 BC, then it was because the electric field of the Sun had dropped in intensity. And this in turn might have been the consequence of Mercury moving to an orbit close to the Sun.

... lowered potential

We cannot neglect that the Sun changed its output for 40 days in 685 BC, or the fact that Jupiter released a thunderbolt. But these were temporary events. We could assume that it represented an adjustment in the flow of plasma from the Sun (the solar wind) after the change in orbit of Mercury in 686 BC. In 686 BC Mercury for the first time assumed an orbit entirely within the orbit of Venus. This must have caused a radical change in the conductive path for the solar wind or at least a change in the electric field at the exterior to the Sun. Certainly the Earth also made an adjustment in its electric parameters if Mercury, Venus, and Jupiter did so.

There might be effects on the physiology of humans resulting from a voltage difference from head to toe, but I doubt it, for this is but a small fraction of the voltage difference from ground to the stratosphere or the ionosphere, or certainly to the location of the double layer of the Earth's plasmasphere.

The only thing I can suggest is that the era before 685 BC would have experienced much more active electrical interactions between the upper atmosphere (or ionosphere) and ground level -- in terms of thunderbolts, Saint Elmo's Fire, but especially in terms of things like ball lightning. I am suggesting this last because the psychological effects are still experienced today, even though ball lightning occurs only infrequently.

I will start with a note on ball lightning as a minor version of the larger crop circles. There are similarities in that both are manifestations of moving plasma. Ball lightning is an example of a spherical plasmoid, which is self-sustaining, at least for a lifespan measured in seconds or minutes. And then they disappear. But this is actually most likely a mode change for ball lightning. The disappearance would make the original grapefruit-size ball plasmoid in glow mode into an invisible sphere in dark mode perhaps ten or twenty feet (3 to 7 meters) in diameter or larger. This could easily engulf a nearby human, resulting in a feeling of "presence" of another being (as what also happens when we sense another human or animal nearby).

Various people have expressed everything from nausea to terror in the presence of extinguished (dark mode) ball lightning but especially in crop circles. My one-time experience after extinction of nearby ball lightning was of terror, being certain that there was "somebody else" near me -- in the middle of the night, no less. As others have said, once you meet up with ball lightning, you never forget. Typically perhaps, I think people will localize such an experience (I did), so that it becomes associated with a place and a condition. Specific to crop circles, BLT Research (Internet) reports:

"A wide range of anecdotal reports exists of the effects on people. These reports have not been scientifically evaluated, but it seems clear that many people experience unusual physical effects in some crop

formations -- and most often when the crop circles are relatively new.
These effects range from the unpleasant (splitting' headaches, dizziness,
disorientation, heart palpitations, a sense of 'dread') to the euphoric (a
strong sense of 'peace,' a feeling of joy, a sense of 'oneness,' and a
feeling of love).... Many people have also experienced the sensation of a
presence of some sort -- other than their own, and invisible -- while
inside crop circles."

"It is easy, perhaps, to dismiss such reports as being due to some sort
of hysteria or over-excitement, and there seems to be no evidence of
long-term effect to either people or animals. However, the fact is that a
large number of field personnel who have spent considerable time in the
formations, as well as some of the more casual visitors, have
experienced one or several of these effects in crop circles all over the
world. The fact that most of these experiences are reported in newly
formed crop circles suggests there may be a remnant energy still present
at some of these sites, to which at least some people are sensitive. It is
most interesting that these effects do not seem to be present at all crop
circles, and that, even when some people are affected in a particular
event, other visitors will be unaware of anything unusual at all." -- BLT
Research, http://www.bltresearch.com [note 18]

Because of the life-long recurring dread or feeling of potential contact for
anyone who experienced this condition, I think it would take a generation or
two of people who never experienced this, before we would see the
intellectual effort to summarily dismiss the tales told by their parents and
grandparents. Agnosticism fills the void of missing evidence -- the missing
experiences your grandparents told you about. And agnosticism then searches
elsewhere for meaning. That certainly was the case for the Greeks, and seems
to have been the case in China and India and Israel. Nothing like it in Egypt,
of course.

What was missing then, after 685 BC, was the potent and palpable
presence of God. That was the difference, I think, between the period before
685 BC and the period afterward.

I started this text to suggest that the effect of lowering the Earth's negative
charge (or specifically, the Earth's potential) after 685 BC, suddenly made us
humans much smarter -- philosophically, scientifically, and probably
religiously also. We suddenly see a vast outpouring of literature,
philosophical speculation, historical inquiry, all starting within two
generations after 685 BC. The connection between 685 BC and the start of
philosophy and physics is startling. There is a gap of two generations -- the
time it would take for grand children to no longer believe in the old tales. But
it must have taken more than just a generational difference, for religious

traditions die hard. This change was sudden and radical. What I will suggest, therefore, is that the changes that were experienced were entirely due to the cessation of the effects of ball lightning and allied forms of plasma transfers between the Earth and the upper atmosphere and I will suggest "crop circles" instead of ball lightning as the prime agent.

... crop circles and ball lightning

The following is an example of very powerful ball lightning:

"In May or June of 1988 or 1989 around 2 P.M. CEST, Mr. Alois Fuehrer, a farmer of 38 years from Jungschlag, a small village South of Ottenschlag, Northern Lower Austria, 850 meters above sea level, returned early from fieldwork because a heavy thunderstorm moved in from the north-west. Fuehrer stood in the open on a wooden plank at the rear of the diesel tractor driven by his father."

"The vehicle had passed the last Ottenschlag houses southbound, when he noticed a falling object. It was round, 20 centimeters across, and 'seemed to come down like a toy balloon', vertical, soundless, without rotation. It was brilliant white, a steady light, and had 'something like a smoke trail'. Only 20 to 30 meters to the right of the tractor and of the road, after 4 to 6 seconds, the object hit the surface of a green summer barley field, flashed up and 'exploded with a loud, very high pitched bang.' Mr. Fuehrer said 'this was no thunder,' and noticed no heat or pressure wave. However, what he felt caused panic -- a tingling, and his hairs stood on end on his head, neck, even on his hands. He urged his father: 'Get out of here, the next one will kill us!', who also felt the electrostatic effect in the driver's cab. The diesel tractor continued to function normally."

"Arriving home, the Fuehrers still wondered what had happened and they went back to have a look on the same evening. They found a circular patch about 6 meters [18 feet] across in the impact area where green barley plants had been reduced to ashes and smoke, 'as with a cutting torch.' The burn effect was strongest in the center. The soil had not been moved."

-- From William Corliss, http://www.science-frontiers.com.

Although there is certainly a close similarity between ball lightning and crop circles, I don't think crop circles are simply the result of ball lightning (farmer Fuehrer notwithstanding). In glow mode or arc mode, these forms (the ball lightning) are tremendously variable in their amazing displays and lifetimes, but the power level is simply too low to account for the large-scale effects produced at crop circles, like leveling a 30-foot diameter circle of full grown wheat crop in under a minute. Ball lightning is estimated to require only 25 watts of power to sustain a 10-inch diameter ball in glow mode for periods of 2 to 10 seconds. That is almost nothing. Even a ball which shines at a brilliant 5000 Kelvin (which has been observed) and melts a circular hole through a window, is not exhibiting much beyond what a quartz utility-light produces -- perhaps 500 watts.

There are simply no available data on the energy requirements of a grain crop circle. It would at any rate be difficult to evaluate the forces required to heat and bend the grain in a 30 feet (10 meter) diameter circle. There is, however, one report on a temporary crop circle formation on water, at the Loosdrechtse Plassen, a series of lakes in the province of Utrecht, in Holland, in June of 2002, by Martin van Wieringen, a Ptah Foundation (World Mystery Research Center) observer:

> *"After a short trip with my boat on the Loosdrechtse Plassen at 01-06-2002 around 3:30 pm, I saw a sort of a mist on the water surface which appeared suddenly. The result was a fast rotating cylinder of water with a diameter of approximately 20 meters on the water surface. This cylinder of water was "sucked up" from the surface with a height of approximately 2 or 3 meters. The pattern of the cylinder looks similar as a vortex pattern."*
>
> *"First I thought it was a tornado, but that wasn't what causes this cylinder of water. This because the cylinder was flat at the top. The cause of this cylinder of water sprayed the water on top of the cylinder. The result looks the same as a combination of a tornado and the properties which are characterized of how crop circles are formed. After approximately 15 seconds the cylinder collapsed, but after a short break another rotating force was following a long "path" of approximately 50 meters. After this path disappeared, a new cylinder of water rises from the surface. This cylinder had a diameter of approximately 8 meters."*
>
> *-- Dutch Crop Circle Archive*, http://www.dcca.nl

At 1000 kg per cubic meter, 630,000 to 940,000 kg of water were raised two to three meters above the water level, and forced to travel in a circle for 15 seconds. That is certainly a lot more energy than what is associated with ball lightning.

I have experienced waterspouts on Lake Michigan (as a pair), but they rose into the sky as funnels; they were not flat topped.

John Abrahamson, A. V. Bychkov and V. L. Bychkov have presented a collection of ball lightning encounters (still held to be "fantasies" and "delusions" by scientists), in "Recently reported sightings of ball lightning:

observations collected by correspondence and Russian and Ukrainian sightings" (*Philosophical Transactions of the Royal Society*, 2002).

The contents of this paper reiterate what is already known about ball lightning, with the exception of the violently exploding dropped "ball of light" reported by farmer Fuehrer.

Abrahamson, with J. Dinniss, also constructed a model for ball lightning, detailed in "Ball lightning caused by oxidation of nanoparticle networks from normal lightning strikes on soil" (*Nature*, 2000), which suggest that ball lightning represents the slow oxidation of nanoparticles of silicon from soil vaporization due to high-temperature lightning strikes. Amazingly, almost all the properties of ball lightning can be ascribed to this chemical process.

Similarly, David Turner, in "The fragmented science of ball lightning" (*Philosophical Transactions of the Royal Society*, 2002), attributes ball lightning to a process of hydration of the outer shell of atoms or ions.

Lastly, and as yet another example, J.B.A. Mitchell, et alii, in "Evidence for Nanoparticles in Microwave-Generated Fireballs by Synchrotron X-Ray Scattering" (*International Conference on Phenomena in Ionized Gases*, 2007), passed x-rays through small ball lightning created and sustained in a microwave oven. The scattering pattern suggests very small "nanoparticles" internally, which would seem to confirm the work by Abrahamson and Dinniss, mentioned above.

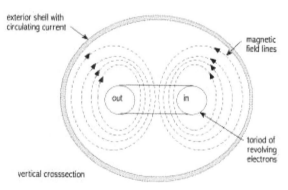

[*Image: Type structures for ball lightning; after Lars Wåhlin.*]

There are many other research papers published. Much of it comes close to the effects experienced with ball lighting, although extensive efforts are made to explain all the aspects of ball lightning chemically. (It is additionally not at all certain if "nanoparticles" exist.) An explanation for the exterior glow is generally missing, something which electrical engineers would at once attribute to a space charge (thermonic emission), often represented as a "boiling off" of electrons. The most obvious and easily recognized space charge effect is the glow of electrons surrounding the cathode of a neon lamp.

Ball plasma is also suspected of setting up a resonant space, within which the electric and magnetic fields will assume a mosaic of patterns. Since ball plasma in arc mode is generally only 12 inches in diameter (1/3 meter), they would be operating at a frequency of around 1 gigahertz (300,000,000 / 0.3). That is what is normally considered the "shortwave" or "microwave" range.

Lars Wahlin (Wåhlin), in *Atmospheric Electrostatics* (1989), a book which deals with the generation of terrestrial lightning, identifies two forms of a toroidal current or a toroidal magnetic field, each capable of producing an accompanying magnetic field or current flow. Wahlin suggests that the form with the internal magnetic field as being due to the constriction of an encircling magnetic field which pinches and cuts off a flow of current in a lightning strike. This effect has actually been observed by others. A collapsing magnetic field will induce a corresponding electric field.

The point of this is not to suggest that crop circles are degenerate ball lightning forms, but to support the fact that any moving plasma stream also produces a corresponding magnetic field. The vector product of the magnetic field and the current flow will produce a force attempting to change the direction of the current carriers -- in effect at right angles to each other. This is known as the "right hand rule" of Force, Magnetic Field, and Current (where each of these is expressed as a vector) and is the basis for the design of electric motors and generators.

... fake crop circles

Most crop circles are hopeless fakes. Even the True Believers (with apologies to Eric Hoffer) say so, and I'll buy that opinion, even if their analysis is presented in a jargon of intersecting magnetic and geodetic lines, the relationship to ancient monuments, and "remnant energies" -- with much of the geometry of intersecting lines and the feelings deduced through dowsing.

I would dismiss "dowsing" as a source of information about crop circles (or anything), but it is a fact that the same investigators report detecting the feeling of dread and nausea after entering "genuine" crop circles. If this is the "remnant energy" of a crop circle event, what exactly is felt? The word "energy" in common usage represents "potential forces, inherent powers" -- things like that, but all related to human interactions. The word "energy" in physics means something entirely different, it is "work" -- in the most basic form it is a force moving a mass through some distance.

Anyone who has taken a course in physics or mechanics would be loath to give recognition to psychological or spiritual "energies." With this in mind, the question then is, What could be felt physically after a crop circle event? The feelings of energy, dread, and nausea seem to fade with time. Humans do not react to changes in the magnetic field, or to nuclear contamination (not quickly). We do react to changes in temperature and barometric pressure, the last of which is often recognized as the dread of an impending storm. But local barometric pressure is difficult to relate to the movement of plasma, because the inflow of the surrounding air would equalize the pressure within seconds.

But what can readily be felt, almost always, is static electricity. It remains for some time and only slowly leaks away. This is most likely the "remnant energy" as well as the "dread" felt by people in recently made and genuine crop circles.

Genuine crop circles, predictably (and as readily pointed out by any number of crop circle enthusiasts), are simple designs without symbolic significance, can be placed in fields equipped with alarms, take under 2 minutes to form, mostly come into existence at the edge of night and day (this is not entirely certain), bend grain at the nodes by (apparently) softening the nodes and then bending the stalks at 90 degrees, blow holes in nodes (suspected as due to overheating of the sap with microwaves), leave scorch marks at the base of some stalks, alter the DNA of seeds and thus their genetic future, interweave grain stalks in contrary directions, pull selected exterior stalks into the circular design, deposit ferrous iron in the soil and on plants, leave behind distinct radioactive isotopes, change the local magnetic deflection by about 4 degrees (supposedly), and dry out the soil locally.

... infrequent crop circles

Real crop circles are actually very infrequent, and the number drops every year with a drop in the number of sunspots (like the auroras do also). Even the True Believers in the UK have noted that of a hundred or more crop circles appearing in a recent summer (2010), there was not likely to be more than 1 "real" one. It has also been noted that 98 percent of crop circles appear after the weekends, and after Bank Holidays. That says something!

This candid attitude of some of the UK researchers is refreshing (my source is Freddy Silva and his site http://www.cropcirclesecrets.org). But the problem I continue to have with the True Believers is that they are still convinced we are getting messages from aliens, and even see these as psychically induced in the fake crop circles. In other words, it is assumed that it takes an intelligence to produce the circles, although all we seem to be getting (in the fake circles) is a roundup of geometric forms from high-school geometry and physics text. It is the sort of thing any juvenile could do. Even the supposedly vastly clever binary encoded messages used the standard ASCII character set.

The whole idea of assuming an alien intelligence is another case of "intelligent design" as a solution to the inability to imagine long time-periods, minute small changes, and the possibility of intricate biological mechanisms, or, in this case, imagine what a self-sustained plasmoid could do.

The other thing I find objectionable is that the True Believers can only extend their imagination to contemporary wants and desires. A thousand years ago people would have suggested that aliens should bring us eternal life and gold. Today it is "advanced technology" and "new mathematical theories." I cannot believe this simplistic attitude. If I wanted anything from the aliens, it would be a deliverance from our ferociously murderous antipathy toward each other. Second would be deliverance from lying politicians and, third, greedy people.

... genuine crop circles

What I am suggesting here is that crop circles are real, although very rare (especially today), that these had probably been experienced much more frequently in remote antiquity, and that they are the result of a spherical geometry of dark mode plasmoids exiting the Earth's surface. This claim can be made despite the fact that there are many fake crop circles (estimates of 80 percent fakes by Colin Andrews in 2000, and estimated at 99 to 100 percent by Freddy Silvas in 2010).

In remote antiquity the experience of crop circles would have been much more frequent, and would have been convincing evidence of being in the presence of a God, localized to a sacred site. Entering the room where at night I once experienced ball lightning still sends shivers down my spine. Imagine being out in a field in Neolithic England and seeing grasses suddenly bending to lay down in a circular geometric formation, accompanied by the certainty of a "presence." The humans of the early Neolithic in England must have recognized the condition. Crop circles today appear with the greatest frequency where circular monuments were built in the Neolithic. God was visiting. [note 19]

... plasma defined

I think, then, that crop-circles are caused by rising elongated plasma streams in dark mode (imagine it to look overall like a giant rotating turnip or carrot), and thus of large sizes, 20, 30, or 40 feet (7 to 13 meters) in diameter. Other people have also reached the same or similar conclusions over the last decades, although some of it was given over to weather phenomena. But plasma streams and even ball lightning have only recently come forward for consideration. [note 20]

Plasma is a diffuse stream of electrons or ions (or both). If it travels down from the ionosphere or upper atmosphere it will tend to form into tightly compressed streams. In various quantities of plasma flow, these are dust devils, waterspouts, tornadoes, and, in much larger form these are hurricanes. Lightning is plasma in arc mode (from intermediate cloud layers). "Plasma" is thus a term loosely meaning a continuous flow of electricity.

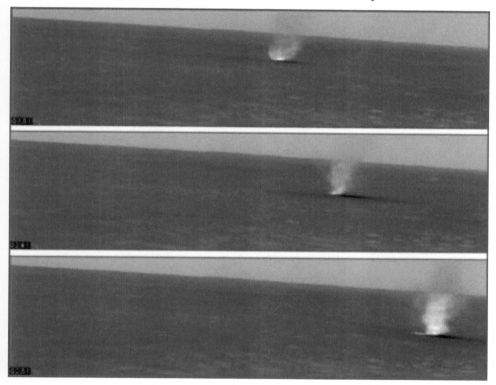

[Image: Dust devils on Mars; after NASA.]

For dust devils, waterspouts, and tornadoes, electrons or negative ions (O_2 and NO_2 anions) are moving to Earth; the flow of current is thus upward. This defines a counterclockwise circular magnetic field, as seen from above, surrounding the stream of electricity. Any ionized material near the base will try to follow the circular magnetic field lines and rotate around the center of the plasma stream. This would include dust and dirt from the surface which would be positively ionized by induction. Tornadoes are the most pesky manifestation.

Dust devils are seen on Mars, rising 300 hundred feet (100 meters) up from the surface, although there is almost no atmosphere on Mars. The tornado-like forms consist entirely of ionized dust. Electric arcing can be seen at the base where the devils touch the surface of Mars and where these cyclones concentrate current flow to arc mode. They leave behind blackened trails.

The base of a tornado is tubular, and rasps the Earth like a router. The magnetic field at the center is downward directed, and up directed at the outer edges. The loosened dirt, trees, cars, houses, and other debris are levitated electrically (aided by the upward directed magnetic field) at the outside of the funnel -- not in the interior.

As opposed to tornado forms, I would suggest that crop circle plasmoids rise out of the ground. If the crop circle plasmoid is of a limited size, then the flow of electric current will create a solenoidal magnetic field within the core of the plasmoid, and directed oppositely on the exterior of the more or less tubular plasma formation.

The travel of an electric current, which will also exhibit itself in the stems of grain crops (since the stems are conductors), will produce a force at right angles to the direction of current flow and at right angles to a magnetic field, attempting to move the conducting stems into a path at right angles to the overall upward movement of the streaming plasma. The individual blades of grass would experience this force. The flow of electricity in the grass is upward at the outer circumference and otherwise inward directed. That would result in snapping the grass blades at right angles at the nodes (a weak point), and tangentially to the radius of the crop circle. And this is the effect that is seen.

Let me add perhaps another few qualifications. First, as suggested above, the plasma streams upward, based mostly on the Loosdrechtse Plassen experience. This could reasonably be expected also from the fact that the Earth maintains a charge balance, so that, for example, charge transferred to the surface via thunderstorms or tornadoes will be offset, sooner or later, by plasma streaming away from the Earth.

Second, there is no reason to suggest that the streaming plasma could not revert to glow mode or even arc mode on moving up past the surface of the Earth. This is plasma; almost any form could be taken. There are a number of instances of observers having seen brief beams of light emanating upward from attested genuine crop circles.

The crop circles are all about that, apparently, except that the True Believer observers think that something lowers to the ground from higher up -- thus you get claims of flying saucers and extraterrestrials. I think it is more likely that these phenomena move up from below ground, since they keep occurring in nearly the same locations. The direction of travel, together with occasional observations of lighted spheroid shapes (even photographed at some crop circle locations), would suddenly account for various "UFO phenomena." UFOs almost always rise up, they are not seen to lower to Earth. [note 21]

Special thanks to R Houston for pointing out the plasma sources.
Special thanks to R Boerman for a discourse on crop circles.

Endnotes

Note 1 --

Leroy Ellenberger, "An Antidote to Velikovskian Delusions" in *Skeptic* (1995) or at http://abob.libs.uga.edu/bobk/velstcol.html. But the point of a valid criticism is entirely missed. All the Saturnian writers almost to a man have assumed without hesitation that the source data for the essay by Jastrow is applicable to the period before 3147 BC -- the "Era of the Gods" -- rather than entertaining the possibility of a very late period.

It is just insane to suggest that any people would keep such idiotically detailed records alive for 3000 years. As a matter of fact, almost all of the associated records which do not deal with planets are clearly contemporaneous economic records from the 8th and 7th century BC: the cloud cover in the morning, the prices of grain, dates, and lumber. And as soon as the Assyrians lose their control over the fortune-tellers and astrologers of Babylon (in 612 BC), the records cease. Almost all the Babylonian records date to after 650 BC.

Note 2 --

Revelations is based entirely on contemporaneous astrological concepts of the first century AD. The letters to the seven churches, which open the text, are addressed to the seven planetary Gods. The sign of the beast, 666, represents the number of years needed for a change of the equinox of one decan -- ten degrees -- along the ecliptic. The number 666 is one of the measures for the precession of the equinox current after the second century AD (66.6 years for one degree; today this is 72 years). The "beast" refers to the bestiary of the zodiac.

Note 3 --

The King James Bible quotation is awkwardly worded, "I will bring again the shadow of the degrees, which is gone down in the sun-dial of Uzziah, ten degrees backward." Ronald Knox has, "see how low the shadow has fallen, with sun-down, where the dial of Achaz [Uzziah] marks the hours! I will make it go ten hours back."

We are, at any rate, talking about a shadow which was longer than expected (it was a winter-time shadow). At a latitude of 31.68 degrees north, the Sun at the equinox assumes an angle of 58.34 degrees with the horizon (58.38 before 685 BC). After 685 BC, in 684 BC, the Sun culminates at 52.34 degrees on March 6th -- on the old day of the equinox.

The reciprocal of the tangent, **cos( )/sin( )**, measures the shadow on the ground as a fraction of a gnomon of unit height. Thus the shadow on March 6 (on the equivalent day of March 21), before 685 BC, was:

cos(58.38) / sin(58.38) = 0.615.

On March 6, 684 BC, it was:

cos(52.34) / sin(52.34) = 0.771.

The fractional difference in the shadow is:

(0.771 - 0.615) / 0.615 = 0.25,

... representing a lengthening of the shadow by 1/4th of the original length.

Note 4 --

Charles Raspil "Planetary observations of the T'ang" (*1994 International Velikovsky Symposium*). The base information is from Edward Schafer, *Pacing the Void, T'ang Approaches to the Stars* (1977). Raspil supplements it with information from European, Byzantine, and Islamic sources. Raspil writes:

"Probably because of his shock at finding so many incredible astronomical observations (for e.g., fixed stars that blink on and off, or disappear for awhile, or appear with horns or other appendages; or planets that give off ribbon or flag-like emanations), Schafer attributes to T'ang astronomers talents that suggest that their greater competence is as whimsical poets."

Raspil could not deduce a consistent pattern, except to suggest that many anomalies happened during "conjunctions." Kepler is quoted as an example of the thinking of medieval astronomers (astrologers) on conjunctions:

"experience shows that all sorts of meteors were seen when the planets were configured in aspects, whereas the air was undisturbed otherwise."

"Aspects" are the angles made by celestial objects to each other, measured across the 360 degree circle representing the dome of the stars. On March 18, AD 904, Venus was indeed very close to the Pleiades.

Note 5 --

I should note that Velikovsky may have "Venus not added" wrong. In an address by Abraham Sachs at Brown University on March 15, 1965, Sachs noted:

"In 'Worlds in Collision', p. 161, Dr. Velikovsky says that Babylonian astronomy at one time had a four-planet system, with Venus missing. For this, he refers to a book written in 1915. Not being a cuneiformist, Dr. Velikovsky cannot inspect the original text referred to in his 1915 source. I have read the text and I can report that it is quite true that Venus is missing in the text-- but so are the other four planets. Dr. Velikovsky's 1915 source mistranslated the names of four fixed stars as planets."

A transcript is at http://abob.libs.uga.edu/bobk/vsachs.html.

Marinus van der Sluijs in "gods-and-planets.htm" at mythopedia.info [since removed] provides an extensive critique of the ready willingness with which the Saturnians (Talbott, Cardona, and Cochrane) assign the Gods of the Polar Configuration to various planets (as I have done as readily). He writes, about the Babylonian astronomy after 600 BC:

"The fact stands that the Babylonians often employed the same divine names for various planets. [And, it should be noted, also mixed them with the names of stars and constellations.] *Why they did so is far from clear to us. It seems unlikely that the Babylonians of the first millennium BCE could not properly distinguish between the various planets. David Brown* [see the text] *argues that a name applied to more than one planet in the period he studies has nothing to do with confusion or unclarity on behalf of the Babylonians, but is indicative of a system whose rationale escapes us today."*

"The 'logical problem' introduced with the realization that myth communicates with us through symbols, simply forbids us to take the mythical or folkloristic statement that the gods were planets literally. If we accept that a god was Mars or Saturn because the myth says so, we ignore the principle that myth speaks through symbols. What we ought to suggest, acknowledging both the planetary association and the symbolical nature of myth, is that a certain visual prototype was symbolised by the myth-makers as the planet, because of certain similarities the planet had in common with the remembered prototype."

Myths are not "made." They are recollected history, and have no symbolic content, despite the three assertions by vd Sluijs in one paragraph. If Van der Sluijs conceives of myths and legends as "symbolism and displacement metaphors," I think he is making an enormous mistake for a self-proclaimed mythologist. I have been at pains to explain that the ancients were incapable of abstract metaphorical reasoning and symbolic notions in earlier times, and certainly did not "think" in the manner understood by us. Van der Sluijs's insistence on "symbol and metaphor" introduces an unwarranted and unneeded contemporary point of view when applied to concepts which have their sources in remote antiquity, although by the 8th and 7th century BC, the use of metaphors and symbolic reasoning was certainly in use.

By his own admission, van der Sluijs argues exclusively from the mythological point of view, not, as he states, from an interdisciplinary perspective (which would include the hard sciences), although he will readily admit that the legends and myths have their genesis in the visual effects of the polar display. Additionally he quotes extensively from older sources, none of which have considered earlier celestial catastrophes or the confused sky up to the seventh century BC as influencing the identification and naming of the planets.

In my point of view, the primary Gods to the ancients were real persons who could be seen in the sky -- as globes which today we call planets. Only after 1200 BC or so do they start to acquire spiritual qualities. To the Chaldean (Babylonian) prognosticators of the 7th century BC, the Gods had indeed become physical entities, which moved across the sky like so many chess pieces to determine the fate of nations and individuals, and had to be treated yet with respect, for the priests were in the employ of the pre-conscious Assyrians to whom the Gods were still very real personages. Contemporaneous with the Assyrians and Chaldeans, Homer treated the Gods in complete mockery.

Lastly, it has been noted that the names of the Egyptian Isis, Osiris, Horus, and Seth, the Greek Athena, Kronos, Aries, and Zeus, the Sumerian Inanna and An, the Canaan Ishtar, and Babylonian Marduk (and more) do rotate somewhat haphazardly among the planets Venus, Saturn, Jupiter, Mars, and Mercury. The correct identities are not always certain. The best test is to use the insight of the Greeks during classic times, that is, if two Gods have similar histories and characteristics, they *are the same* even though they might be known by different names in different lands.

Note 6 --

Mithra is also one of the Hindu pantheon, representing the shining Sun disk of daytime, and was also known among the Hittites of Anatolia in circa 1500 BC, as well as among the Zoroastrians. His popularization is likely due to the influence of Mazdaism at the time of the Persian Empire.

Note 7 --

See David Ulansey *The Origins of the Mithraic Mysteries* (1989). Most of what we know about Mithraism is from the writings of the Church Fathers -- Jerome, Tertulian, and others, plus a number of Greek and Roman authors. Ulansey comes to the same conclusion as I do, that is, that Mithraism is in response to a change in the equinox. Ulansey bases his theory on the suggestion that a knowledge of the precession of the equinox came to light in the third or fourth century BC, despite the fact that the iconographic references of Mithraism are to Taurus and Scorpio as the constellations of the equinoxes. Using today's estimate for the precession of the equinox, and assuming that the precession of the equinox had always been the case for Earth, this would place this configuration in about 2000 BC. This is unlikely as a remembered condition, and cannot be related to any significant event. There are just too many intervening events and religious rethinkings to make sense of this.

Ulansey equates the stance and gesture of Mithra in sculptures to the depiction of Perseus after decapitating Medusa (the Gorgon), that is, looking away. He also draws parallels between the Gorgon and the frequent depiction of a lion-headed God entwined by a snake and standing on a globe representing the Earth, or, more likely, representing the globe of the stars as seen from a remote exterior. This apparently became a standard depiction in the Middle East and Greece. Globes of the stars at this time start to show both the equatorial and the ecliptic as encircling bands.

I could add to the confusion of associated imagery by noting that the Gorgon is Venus blazing in 685 BC with plasma streamers as hair, although Perseus is nowhere nearby (Perseus is above Taurus). Additionally, the image of the Gorgon is much older than 685 BC. Medusa is one of the three sisters of the south of remote antiquity, dating to after 10,900 BC. She is the main ball plasmoid which could not be looked at -- but only because it was far too bright to endure. Peratt has suggested the brightness also, in noting that many petroglyphs were carved only where the artists would be shaded from the brightness of the ball plasmoids.

Ulansey's lion-headed God is the Sun in the constellation Leo on July

25th of 685 BC, when the plasmoid from Jupiter landed after midnight and the eastern sky blazed for nine hours. The entwining snake is (likely) the plasma plumes appearing at the north and south magnetic poles of Earth under the conditions of a radical change in the field of the Sun.

What confirmed for me the common core of this diverse and unfamiliar imagery was the depiction of the lion-headed God as item 312 in Maarten Vermaseren's *Corpus Inscriptionum et monumentorum religionis mithriacae* (1956), where the statue wears a plasmoid bolt on its chest, rather than the usual Gorgon head. This is also illustrated on page 33 of Ulansey's book.

Note 8 --

Although I guessed at this, as I found out later, David Ulansey also agreed that the boys with the torches represent the vernal and autumnal equinox, and Ulansey also admits that the symbolism is at times reversed. I did not check to see if Ulansey considered the visual crossing of the ecliptic and the equatorial or the factual crossing.

The crossing of the equatorial and the ecliptic is also notable in Mesoamerican iconography. The same symbol is used, the Saint Andrew's cross, where one of the diagonal bars crosses the other, a different configuration for the spring and fall equinox. For the vernal equinox the bar starting at the upper left crosses in front of the other. The autumnal equinox reverses this. The visual representation in Mesoamerica is based on the shadow of the Earth falling on the last ring of the Absu, which lasted well into the current era.

Note 9 --

The event of 685 BC had happened 80 years before Lao-tse was born. Reading "Tao" as the road, meaning the zodiac, and "Thien" as heaven, meaning the dome of the stars, the text, although with obvious strong philosophical rather than scientific overtones, becomes immensely elucidated. See especially the introduction of James Legge in the *Sacred Books of the East, Volume 39* (1891) and the comments on translations by Kelley L. Ross at [www.friesian.com/taote.htm].

A typical interpretation of Taoism was made by Sze-mâ Khien, writing, in the first century BC, "Lâo-dze [Lao-tse] cultivated the Tao and its attributes, the chief aim of his studies being how to keep himself concealed and remain unknown" (quoted by Legge). This represents seeking a high moral order by imitation of the still-standing and unknown quantity -- eventually identified as "Heaven" even by the Confucianists -- behind the dome of the stars which had made such a sweeping change in 685 BC.

Confucius, born in 551 BC, must have been aware of the change, even though it happened 100 years before his time. However, it is not mentioned in any of his writings. To us, the most important works of Confucius were his compilation of ancient records, his preservation of a thousand years of poetry, and his annotation of the *I Ching*. But to Confucius himself, his most important work was the compilation of a year-by-year political record of his home state of Lu, the *Spring and Autumn Annals*, covering the years 722 BC to 481 BC. He specifically noted the importance of the *Spring and Autumn Annals*, working on it until shortly before his death. This period was also a time of internecine struggles among the nearly independent states, and the Confucian Annals have given their name to this period of Chinese political history -- the "Spring and Autumn" period.

His students and followers knew how Confucius felt about the *Spring and Autumn Annals* and elevated the book to the status of one of the five Confucian Classics. Yet the contents lack any philosophical observations and the entries relate activities which are all too terse and mundane to be of any interest.

If Confucius was searching among historical data for the effect of the change in the zodiac, it does not show. An inspection of the *Spring and Autumn Annals* yields nothing of note during the years spanning 685 BC. Some 37 eclipses of the Sun are listed for the complete period, of which all except two were verified in the 19th century. Five floods are listed, four earthquakes, three comets, three lightning strikes, and many rains of excessive magnitude.

The *Spring and Autumn Annals*, and the commentary by Tso Kew-ming, the *Tso Chuen*, are instead totally absorbed with the human failings of the leaders -- issues of honor, insults, and reputations.

China at that time was an inland nation, with the coastal regions held by "barbarian" tribes. Thus China did not use the stars for navigation, as the Eastern Mediterranean did. Little attention was paid to the stars or the planets, which to the Chinese did not represent earlier Gods. For example, when a large comet appeared in 524 BC the recommendation by the priests and court historians to perform extra sacrifices to avoid disaster were ignored. An earlier solar eclipse in the same year was accompanied by similar recommendations and response (from the *Tso Chuen*).

Frances FitzGerald, in *Fire in the Lake* (1972), details the outlook of the people of Viet Nam in recent times as a conservative Confucianism with the deeply imbedded elements of the Tao. The politics and social order for the Viet Nam "way of life" -- what FitzGerald calls "state of mind" in her first chapter -- are essentially Chinese, 2000 years old, rational and pragmatic, and so astoundingly different from European and American thinking and outlook as to be virtually incomprehensible.

Note 10 --

From the introduction to the *Zend-Avesta,* by James Darmesteter, in *Sacred Books of the East, Volume 4* (1880):

"The world, such as it is now, is twofold, being the work of two hostile beings, Ahura Mazda, the good principle, and Angra Mainyu, the evil principle; all that is good in the world comes from the former, all that is bad in it comes from the latter. The history of the world is the history of their conflict, how Angra Mainyu invaded the world of Ahura Mazda and marred it, and how he shall be expelled from it at last. Man is active in the conflict, his duty in it being laid before him in the law revealed by Ahura Mazda to Zarathustra. When the appointed time is come, a son of the lawgiver, still unborn, named Saoshyant, will appear, Angra Mainyu and hell will be destroyed, men will rise from the dead, and everlasting happiness will reign over the world."

The Persians only used open fires as altars. Fire altars were in use for sacrifices to the Gods since remote antiquity in China, Central Asia, and India. These are modeled on the "fire on a platform" seen in the sky after 4077 BC when Saturn went nova. In Western Asia, Eastern Europe, Mesopotamia, and Egypt the image of Saturn in the sky is understood as a house instead, and temples are built as houses for the Gods.

Note 11 --

The celebration of Dionysus formed the basis of Grecian theater. As is noted by Alfred de Grazia in *The Disastrous Love Affair of Moon and Mars* (1984), it consisted of the introduction of a folk art form into an unformed society of survivors of the destructions of the 8th and 7th century BC.

"The theory of causation seeks evidence of abrupt takeover of a destroyed culture by marginal survivors who cast aside, or employ ceremonially, practices they do not or cannot use or understand. Then they proceed to draw from every source their new synthetic culture."
"... when the Greek theater appeared [writes Giovanni Patroni], *we find the rustic god Dionysus, with a goat-cult of dancers cloaked in skins. The poverty of the means, the few actors, the vagabond origins of the Thespian theater, all showed still, according to Patroni, that the primitive real Greek theater was not receiving the subsidies of princes, not the interest or participation of Mycenaean high society; it was left to the rural folk. ... In the general destruction of societies, the art of the survivors made its way quickly forward. The elite and its sophisticated*

art forms were destroyed; folk art (not primitive art) dominated the scene."
     -- Alfred de Grazia

Note 12 --

See Kelley L. Ross at [www.friesian.com/upan.htm]. He continues with the following (describing the transfer of ideas some 700 to 900 years later):

"The undoubted transfer of ideas between Greece and India in the Hellenistic Period, and the export of Buddhism from India to China beginning in the Han Dynasty, provides us points of comparison with what, the uninfluenced traditions, came before."

Note 13 --

For a development of Greek philosophical systems from about 500 BC to about AD 200, see the first half of Charles Freeman's book *The Closing of the Western Mind* (2005). Later chapters detail the rise of Christianity after Constantine, up through the time of Aquinas.

Note 14 --

Livio Stecchini reports that a change to a differing dating system was initiated in Greece and Rome after 747 BC without reference to concurrent changes in Mesopotamia. See *The Velikovsky Affair* (1966).

Note 15 --

"It [the Miletian school of philosophers] *set about to explain these phenomena* [lightning, earthquakes] *in terms of the same elemental processes ... as it invoked to explain the orderly arrangement of the earth and the heavenly bodies. In so doing, it implied the baselessness of the traditional Olympian religion which attributed lightning and earthquakes to whims of Zeus and Poseidon and world-destructions to battles of the sky-gods."*
     -- William Mullen, "The Agenda of the Milesian School" *Natural Catastrophes during Bronze Age Civilisations*, SIS Conference, (1997).

Thales of Miletos (640 -- 546 BC) is traditionally held as the first Greek rationalist investigator, based on his total rejection of the role of the Gods in creation, and his conclusion that everything was made from water (attributed to Thales by Aristotle). We see this as the first primitive atomic science. But consider the fact that, with this statement, Thales is repeating the oldest creation myths, which hold that everything indeed was made from water.

The measurement of the year and the rationalization of the periods of the Moon is also attributed to Thales. Apocryphally, to Thales is attributed the advice to navigators to steer by Ursa Minor, rather than the traditional Ursa Major.

Note 16 --

The circumference of Earth was found by Eratosthenes by measuring the length of a shadow in Alexandria at noon on the solstice, when it was known that, at the same date, the Sun was directly above Syene (Aswan). The distance between the two locations, at almost the same meridian, was known from Egyptian surveying records and probably accurate to within a few hundred feet. The most generous measure of his estimate for the circumference, 252,000 "stadia," based on an appropriate selection of a "stadia" (there are three differing measures for "stadia"), is 24,662 miles, which is within 198 miles of being correct -- and despite the fact that Syene and Alexandria are not at the same meridian, and that Syene is not located exactly at 23.5 degrees north. See Justin Pollard and Howard Reid, *The Rise and Fall of Alexandria* (2006). This book is a wonderful compendium of ancient science and philosophy, covering 330 BC to AD 650.

Robert Crease, a historian of science, writes in *The Prism and the Pendulum* (2003) about Eratosthenes,

> *"Eratosthenes's picture of the cosmos* [a model] *was critical to the success of the experiment. Without this particular picture, measuring the shadow would not yield the earth's circumference. For example, an ancient Chinese cartographic text, the 'Book of the Masters of Huainan'* [139 BC], *notes that gnomons of the same height but at different (north-south) distances from one another cast shadows of different lengths at the same time. On the assumption that the earth is essentially flat, the author attributed this difference to the fact that the gnomon casting the narrower shadow is more directly under the sun, and argues that the difference in shadow length can be used to calculate the height of the sky."*

This would have worked, but would not have resulted in a useful model, for the statements above are based on the concept of Earth as a flat plane.

The "picture of the cosmos" in Eratosthenes's time was derived from Aristotle: the Earth as a globe. It is one of the "narratized mental spaces" mentioned in the text, and it need not be a valid point-for-point representation of reality, as many models of physics will testify. Appropriate results from the exploration of this mental space are the only criterion for usefulness.

Note 17 --

For elements of statistics and probability theory in the context of their historical development which parallels common attitudes toward chance, see Michael Kaplan and Ellen Kaplan, *Chances Are* (2006).

The Greeks also developed the concept of the soul as a separate entity, which leaves the body on death and continues a life of its own. The concept was taken up by a number of writers and philosophers in Greece, first used in the sense of a transmigration of the soul. The idea of the existence of the "soul," unlike the idea of "free will," quickly spread to other cultures, introducing itself into the thinking of the Middle East and Alexandria, and was readily adopted by Christianity.

"Life after death" was not a common Greek concept in the period before the current era. A "land of the dead" was, however, interpolated into both the *Iliad* and the *Odyssey* after 500 BC, and achieved its modern definition with Plato after 400 BC.

The Romans did believe in the concept, and as a result developed a much higher social morality. But it was apparently already an accepted concept among the tribes north of the Alps (if we go by the medieval legends of the Celts).

Note 18 --

Not that there are not some very strange things reported by BLT Research, especially with Robbert van den Broeke.

Note 19 --

It could be suggested that adding a series of posts or megalithic stones would help in concentrating the incoming (or "outgoing") plasma to the same location, and hence the building of henges. But this contradicts my earlier supposition that the number and location of the posts or stones replicated the look of the plasma stream seen incoming from the sky overhead. Henges were mostly abandoned after 3000 BC.

Note 20 --

I have seen suggestions of "plasma" on crop circle web pages, but they are often presented as some form of air disturbance and in terms of magneto-hydrodynamic fluid flows. See an article "The Physics of Crop Formations"

(1998), by John Burke, at [BLT], which suggests plasma discharges as the cause (although Burke has not much of a handle on the mechanics of either plasma or electricity) and traces the original suggestion to George Meaden's book *Circles from the Sky* (1991). Meaden is a meteorologist and physicist.

Note 21 --

Robert Boerman, a Dutch author, wrote to me in an email in 2008:

"I have studied the crop circle phenomenon for 11 years from 1997. I visited, researched, photographed, measured and studied almost every single Dutch crop circle from 2000 to 2006, wrote two books about it, and now, after all those years of research, I don't know it anymore. The phenomenon is too complicated. What I found out is that there is a link between plasma (balls of light?) and crop circles. And I think that some of the crop circles are formed by nature itself, some by human mind, some definitely by hoaxers."

Boerman was the first to make me aware that he and other people were considering crop circles as a plasma phenomenon. See his website at http://www.dcca.nl/index.html.

Calculations are in Unix bc notation, where ^ denotes exponentiation; the functions a(rctangent), s(ine), and c(osine) use radians; angle conversions to radians or degrees by the divisors rad=.017+ and deg=57.2+; other functions are shown as f( ); tan( )=s( )/c( )
units: million == 1,000,000; billion == 1,000,000,000;
AU == 93,000,000 miles.

Recovering the Lost World,
A Saturnian Cosmology -- Jno Cook
Chapter 27: Sibylline Star Wars

Revision: 42.23 (sib.php)
Contents of this chapter: [The Sibylline Star Wars] [The Great Year]
[The Opening Text] [New Locations of the Stars] [Conclusions About Dates]
[Nonnos's Dionysiaca] [Two Meteors] [Dating the Denderah Zodiac]
[Endnotes]

The Sibylline Star Wars

The information below bears on the blazing of Venus and Mercury in 685 BC, the relocation of the polar axis, and the change in the location of the equinox. It is from a document written 800 years later, but clearly from extant sources. It is probably also the most spectacular confirmation of the reality of the events of 685 BC.

Franz Xavier Kugler, an early 20th century translator of Babylonian cuneiform astronomical tablets, in a book titled *The Sibylline Battle of the Stars and Phaethon Seen as Natural History* (1927), analyzed the ending of the fifth volume of the Sibylline Oracle Books, originally completed (it is today estimated) in about AD 115 in Egypt. He suggests that the text deals in specifics, of a yet-to-come event, for which details were garnered from older records, although in his opinion the details date from 1500 BC. In my opinion the details date from 685 BC.

The *Sibylline Oracle* books were written in Greek in lower Egypt between 100 BC and AD 200. They are mostly Jewish in sentiment and philosophy, as they are in politics. Using an established style for prophecies, as in the Delphic oracles and in the writings of the prophets of Israel, "Babylon" is substituted for Imperial Rome, while "Rome" might be a substitute for the real name of an Emperor. This makes interpretation difficult at times. The Books were still in circulation in the 16th century as manuscripts. German and English translations (from the original Greek) appeared late in the 19th century.

Livio Stecchini, in "Cuneiform Astronomical Records and Celestial Instabilities" in *The Velikovsky Affair* (1966), reiterates Kugler's idea that the Sibylline prophecies were based on extant data from antiquity. He also notes that the scientific philosophies which had developed by this time (100 BC to AD 100), required specifics in prophecies. There are additional comments by Malcolm Lowery in the article "Father Kugler's Falling Star" in *Kronos* (1977), and by Bob Kobres in "The Path of a Comet and Phaethon's Ride" in *The World & I* Volume 10, No. 2 (1995). Stecchini writes, about Kugler:

"Kugler wanted to indicate that the writers of the oracle were so preoccupied with solid astronomical facts that they described the successive phases of the episode of Phaethon according to what they knew about the position of the heavenly bodies in the several months of the year. It is his contention that the writers of this oracle, far from being maniacs breathing gibberish, were trying to make their prediction (based on a past historical occurrence) credible by framing it in an accurate astronomical timetable."

Stecchini then continues to promote his own viewpoint:

"This group of philosophers was fathering modern uniformitarianism, because they were fitting the historical tradition of 'catastrophes' into a cyclical pattern of phenomena recurring at fixed intervals of time, past and future, according to an absolutely unchangeable and predictable order of the heavenly cosmos."

That is so modern to say. The "unchangeable and predictable order" is totally missing. Just read the poem once and you will be convinced. I also disagree with the date of 1500 BC, as if some celestial disruption happened at that time, for it is doubtful if such detailed data was recorded that far back, or that it would have survived as astronomical data, when the social milieu of that remote time still held fast to attributing all such events to the Gods. And I do not think we could hope for a clear calendrical record if the land had been devastated repeatedly and the skies were obscured for years. Much more likely the specific data records the blazing of Venus in 685 BC. By 685 BC, Babylonian astronomical records had appeared and observation of the heavens was well established.

The Great Year

I should first note a related numismatic oddity among the coins of the Roman Imperial period. This involves the reverse side depiction of an upfacing crescent with seven stars above. These occur in the reigns of the Roman emperors Hadrian (reigned AD 117 to AD 138), Commodus, reigned to AD 192, and the Severan dynasty (AD 193 to AD 235) with dates late in the second century AD and early third century. These coins thus coincide or closely follow the writing of the Sibylline Star Wars text. [note 1]

I looked at hundreds of coins from the Roman Imperial era. All the coins depict a head (generally the emperor) in profile and the scene of a full-sized figure on the reverse -- at times mythological, at times as allegorical personifications (Victory, Africa), at times a temple structure or sacrificial devices. One even shows the double-ended triple-tined thunderbolt of the Eastern Mediterranean on the side of a cart drawn by four horses. There are also infrequent depictions of a star within an upturned crescent. In one case this is sitting directly above a pillar of sorts.

There are also some Parthian coins with the crescent and seven stars of the same dates. And then, after the third century AD, it fades, except for occasional uses into the current era. In antiquity Isis, holding baby Horus, is shown standing on the crescent with seven stars surrounding her head, as Mary holding baby Jesus is today.

[*Image: Roman coin of the Imperial era after Hadrian.*]

Curtis L Clay, posting at http://www.forumancientcoins.com/board, in November, 2005, writes, with respect to Roman coins with a "crescent and seven stars" design on the reverse:

Strack, noting that the same type is labeled SAECVLI FELICITAS, "The Happiness of the Age", on Eastern denarii of Septimius Severus [reigned AD 192 to AD 211], interprets Hadrian's type as indicating the return of the seven movable heavenly bodies to their original positions, signaling the beginning of a new golden age.

He cites: (1) Festus: "The mathematicians call it the Great Year when the seven wandering stars complete their individual courses and return to harmony with each other", and (2) Servius [4th century Roman grammarian] *on Virgil's* Eclogues: *"At the completion of the Great Year all of the stars return to their places and begin the next cycle of identical movements. If the movements of the stars are repeated, it follows that everything that happened will recur again, since it is obvious that everything is determined by the motions of the stars. For this reason Virgil says that the Golden Age will return and everything that happened before will be repeated."*

I cannot find the related text in Virgil. Clay continues with:

On this interpretation, we have to assume that the moon is depicted twice in the type: it is represented not only by the crescent, but also by one of the seven stars above the crescent, since it is one of the seven wandering heavenly bodies, but is also by far the most prominent of them at night, and the only one that waxes and wanes.

But I suspect that the Moon is *not* depicted twice. The upturned crescent has nothing to do with the Moon. Although the seven stars are grouped in various ways to reflect graphic convenience and representative shorthand, the crescent is always shown as upturned -- a condition which the Moon never achieves, except in the tropics.

The crescent is the backlighted portion of Saturn, last seen in 3147 BC. It has no significance for 2349 BC or 1492 BC, or for June and July of 685 BC, except to signify the endpoint or the start of creation -- the destruction of the heavens. The grouping together of all the planets was still remembered or understood as significant from before 3147 BC, although during the "Era of the Gods" the seven objects grouped together were probably the satellites of Saturn. In the third century AD these were the seven planet. The crescent below the stars is part of the standard depiction, and has nothing to do with the Moon.

This idea of "grouping together" and the start of a new epoch was reinforced at the beginning of the calendar year following the nova event of 685 BC. In spring of 684 BC, on the day of the equinox, all seven planets presented themselves in the eastern sky just before sunrise.

On March 8th, Gregorian (the equinox in the previous era), the planets extending from the east horizon were: the Sun (before rising), Saturn, the new crescent Moon, Mercury, and Jupiter and Venus (almost conjunct), then a large gap and Mars over the southwest. The first six were all grouped in two houses, Pisces and Aquarius. Geometrically the center of the distance between the Sun (at the far east) and Mars (at the west end) is located in the constellation Capricorn.

Berossus

Berossus, a priest from Babylon who moved to Greece after 300 BC, had noted that planets in Capricorn of the Great Year are associated with a deluge, and when these appeared in Cancer the catastrophe would be fire.

In the previous year -- the year of the nova event of 685 BC -- early in June (June 15, Gregorian) the planets Venus, Mercury, plus the Moon, Sun, and Mars straddled the constellation Cancer (all within 45 degrees). This was the starting day of the blazing of Venus and Mercury. This may be the reference to Cancer which Berossus had in mind. Jupiter and Saturn were nowhere near, however.

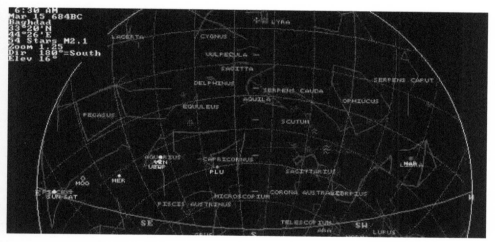

[*Image: The sky on March 15, 684 BC, Julian, the signs in the sky of the first "Great Year" after the plasmoid of 685 BC. From SkyGlobe 3.6.*]

I should note that March 8, Gregorian (March 15th, Julian), is the "old date" of the vernal equinox, which had moved to March 21 in 684 BC, as I have shown elsewhere. This was the first instance of the new date of the spring equinox (although using the old calendar date). The conjunction was also not a unique event. By the end of the same year another conjunction showed up on December 15th: the Moon, Saturn, Jupiter, Mars, Venus, Mercury (these two both in Capricorn) and the setting Sun.

The initial conjunction includes all the elements of the "Great Year" from antiquity: a long interval between catastrophic destructions of the world (or so it was assumed), the grouping together of all the planets so that they will restart their orbits, the first day (the equinox) of the first year in the new era (at the conclusion of the previous era when Phaethon was bolted by Zeus), and, lastly, the identification of the start of the Great Year with the constellation Capricorn.

van der Sluijs

Marinus van der Sluijs, in "A Possible Babylonian Precursor to the Theory of Ecpyrosis," *Culture and Cosmos* (2005), in an analysis of a Babylonian text *Erra and Isum,* suggests a precursor to the concept of a Great Year as shown in the poem's dialog between Marduk (Jupiter) and Erra (Mars). Mars has usurped Marduk's power but relents after being warned how the world will end with fire if he persists. It does, of course, nearly end with fire, although in 685 BC Marduk (as Jupiter) takes control again.

The narrative compares the "water catastrophe" of Marduk with the "fire catastrophe" of Erra -- as if these two directly followed each other. They did not, of course, as we know. The fall of the Absu in 2349 BC would be the "water catastrophe," but the Exodus event intervened.

The crucial details of a common element allowing for the comparison, and the reason for selecting the 2349 BC "fall of the Absu" event rather than Exodus, is that in both instances, 2349 BC and 685 BC, Jupiter (Marduk) is involved in an identical gesture -- he gets up from his seat, then sits down again. The moment he rises, creation starts to come undone.

"Getting up from his throne," in the *Erra and Isum* narrative is an up-country version of the same incident recorded in the Babylonian *Enuma Elish*: the disappearance and reappearance of Marduk's garment. In both cases -- in the *Enuma Elish* and in *Erra and Isum* -- this was the disappearance of the lower mountain-shaped plasma expulsion of Jupiter. In these two instances, in 2349 BC and 685 BC, as I have detailed already, there was the sudden reappearance of the lower coma expulsion or "throne" of Jupiter after the catastrophe -- as if to suggest that the act of reseating Jupiter stabilized creation. The sequence in both cases is extensive because the time lag between unseating and reseating is measured in decades or centuries, but a causality was affirmed.

This is among the details brought forward by vd Sluijs, although without reference to actual events and dates, which he is unaware of. We possess only portions of the narrative, and thus we do not know how the conflict between Jupiter and Mars was resolved, although we could guess. The *Erra and Isum* text is thought to be dated to the period of 1200 BC to 600 BC. Because of the revolt by Mars and the warning of devastation to come, I would opt for a creation date for the document after 650 BC.

What we have here is an example of myth creation (narratization) for two historic events which identify the agents involved. We know both the events and the protagonists, having met them already in the text I have so far presented. Most interesting is that the author is willing to tie together events 1500 years apart with the single gesture of the reseating of Jupiter. The reseating we know of already also. The number of years between these events is certainly much longer than the 684-year span of the Great Year as suggested directly below.

Even in antiquity (as we know from texts in the first century AD), the length of the Great Year was in question. Why this was so will soon become clear. There are some obvious values for the span of time of a Great Year which could be calculated. Some are patently obvious.

Clube and Napier

Victor Clube and Bill Napier, in *The Cosmic Serpent* (1982), use a Great Year of 684 years. It is a value based on B.L. van der Waerden's *Science awakening II: the birth of astronomy* (1974). Van der Waerden found this as a frequently encountered number in ancient Babylonian sources. Clube and Napier go to some rather extensive numerological contortions to pick up a time span of 684 years. They use the date of the second Earth shock (686 BC) identified as due to Mars by Velikovsky, along with a made-up date for the Exodus, 1369 BC, to fit the time span of 684 years (counted inclusively), and use it to suggest that the next catastrophe would be in 2 BC.

This is based on the fiction of a new date for Exodus, which, however, is not needed. The span between the more generally accepted date of 1492 BC for the Exodus, and the first "attack" by Mars in 806 BC (which Clube and Napier were not aware of), spans 686 years -- close enough to van der Waerden's (and the Babylonian) value of 684.

What is interesting, of course, is that the Babylonians were attempting to impose some order to the planets in the sky. The dreadful 120 years of assaults by Mars were real, and were remembered. So were the 684 quiet years which preceded that period. The date of 2 BC might have been viable for a long time as forewarning of another catastrophe, but apparently nothing happened.

I looked for 7-planet conjunctions between 7 BC and AD 1 (Julian astronomical dates, thus to AD 4), checking month to month during the time of a new Moon. These conjunctions are not uncommon. A list of the five found during this 8-year period is shown in the endnotes. [note 2]

I should note that likely the Babylonian astrologers did not use Clube and Napier's math to obtain the number 684. But, assuming "684" was indeed known and was correct, then adding 684 years to 806 BC (the first time Mars devastated the Middle East) will result in scheduling the next catastrophe for the year 122 BC -- when also nothing happened. But adding 684 years to 685 BC makes the next event fall in 1 BC. The dates are astronomical, so that 1 BC represents AD 4 in Eastern Mediterranean chronology. Either date will do.

Hadrian

Meanwhile, conjunctions just kept on coming, without any apparent catastrophic effects. I checked, but no conjunction happened anywhere near the death of Julius Caesar, despite his deification in response to a sighted comet. I also started to check for the time period of the emperor Hadrian from the year AD 100 on. Conjunctions of all the planets spread across the sky happen on the following Julian dates (I may have missed some).

- AD 107, Sep 19, Moon (rising), Sat, Mar, Mer, Ven, Jup, Sun (setting)
- AD 109, Oct 27, Moon (rising), Mar, Sat, Ven, Jup, Mer, Sun (setting)
- AD 115, Jun 5, Sun (rising), Jupiter, Venus, Mercury, Saturn, Mars, Moon.

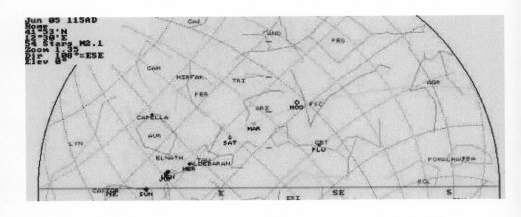

[*Image: The sky on June 5, AD 115, Julian (AD 119 in Eastern Mediterranean chronology). From SkyGlobe 3.6.*]

The last of these (AD 115) corresponds to AD 119 in Eastern Mediterranean chronology. Hadrian became emperor in AD 117, two years before this conjunction. The first coinage of the crescent and seven stars occurs in AD 119 or 120, although I have not been able to verify this from other sources. Hadrian was in Britain at this time, busy with Hadrian's Wall.

I would suggest that the frequent conjunctions were worked into the propaganda of political discourse. The Romans were acutely aware of astrology, and nothing would have been missed. Additionally, the future locations of the planets in the sky could at this time be accurately calculated in advance. [note 3]

"There was an obsession with astrology," writes Tom Buggey, "during the reign of Septimius Severus and successors, the reliance on astrology became a mania." (At http://tjbuggey.ancients.info.) Buggey means the Severan Dynasty, AD 193 to AD 235, which followed directly after the emperor Hadrian.

In AD 126 Hadrian completed the building of the Pantheon in Rome -- the temple to all the Gods, all seven -- an absolutely magnificent and sturdy building, which still stands today. On June 30 of astronomical year AD 122 (which is AD 126), there was a clear conjunction (another "Great Year" lineup) with Jupiter in Sagittarius in the southeast, Mars and the new Moon in Libra, and Venus, Saturn, and Mercury in Leo, with the Sun setting in the northwest. All the Gods stood in the sky. Perhaps dedicating the Pantheon at this time had prevented the end of the world.

Stecchini

It thus seems likely that the prophecies of the *Sibylline Books* accomplish what Livio Stecchini proposes, that is, to present a "cyclical pattern of phenomena recurring at fixed intervals of time," even though Stecchini offers no indication of the measure of the repeating cycle. Stecchini wrote, paraphrasing Kugler:

"It appeared in the east sky more brilliant than the Sun,"

He writes, additionally:

"The lines purport to describe the circumstances of the coming end of the world; they were written in the century before the birth of Christ [but collated with other texts in the second century AD] *by Greek-speaking inhabitants of Egypt, when the ancient world was agitated by the Messianic expectation of a cosmic upheaval. But the lines give an account that is so exact and technical that it must be something more than a mere mystical vision of coming destruction. Such precise astronomical details are given that, calculating by the position of the constellations around 100 B.C., the crisis began in September and reached a climax in seven months ... after the 7th or the 8th of April."*
"... According to Kugler, the crisis described as the Battle of the Stars began with the appearance in the eastern sky of a body as bright

*as the sun and similar in apparent diameter to the sun and the moon.
The light of the sun was replaced by long streams of flame crossing each
other."*

*"After the mention of these streams of flame that replaced the sun as
a source of light, there follows the line, 'the Morning Star fought the
battle riding on the back of Leo.'"*

Stecchini explains, after Kugler, that "Venus [the Morning Star] riding on
a lion" was a well known and "feared emblem for disaster" in the Eastern
Mediterranean region, and gives examples of unconnected goddesses all
depicted as riding on lions. I would point out, of course, that the "emblem"
was well known because it had been experienced in 685 BC. Phaethon
appeared not in remote antiquity, but in 685 BC. And the "Morning Star" was
not Venus, but Mercury.

In the Star Wars description we again find Jupiter (Zeus) coming to
deliver a mortal thunderbolt, as in the "legendary" event of Phaethon.
Although in our current concepts of the solar system the honor of being the
Morning Star goes to Venus, in 685 BC, and since the prior year already
Mercury was the Morning Star.

There is no question that the Phaethon legend describes the nova event of
Venus and Mercury in June and July of 685 BC, although the Roman author
Ovid (before AD 17), who narratized the "legend," places all the action in the
span of one day rather than 40 days. Some descriptive details stand out. Ovid
notes that large regions of the Earth were burned up with *"Ignis Coelis"* (fire
falling from the sky), that Phaethon had to struggle against "the whirling
poles" (which may have been a reference to a polar plasma plume) and was
swept away by the "swift axis" (the polar axis?), that the normal path of the
Sun through the skies was not followed, that the northern constellations
attempted to dip into the sea (as the equatorial moved), and ends with the note
that the Earth "sank back a little lower than her wonted place" (as
paraphrased by Velikovsky).

Plato (circa 300 BC) quotes Solon to the effect that Phaethon's ride ended
when he was hit with a thunderbolt delivered by Jupiter. Hesiod (circa 650
BC) mentions the birth of Phaethon to Eos (Dawn) and his abduction by
Aphrodite (Venus). Phaethon is Mercury. Aphrodite here is the planet Venus,
not the Moon.

A year earlier Mercury had been involved in a plasmasphere contact with
Earth which had reduced its orbit to fall entirely within the orbit of Venus.
With this in mind, his "birth" as a Morningstar -- "the child of Dawn" -- plus
his spectacular "abduction" by Venus will start to make sense.

Mercury's abduction is the near conjunction of Venus and Mercury on
June 15th of 685 BC. It was seen as an abduction (also understood as a birth)

because Mercury had previously only been seen just above the horizon before sunrise or after sunset (four times a year). It would not have been seen as traveling across the sky with the Sun, except that on June 15th, while very near each other in the sky, both Venus and Mercury started to blaze like suns during the day.

The two planets looked like comets, with shafts of light streaking across the sky -- directed both toward the sun and away from it, and likely at right angles as well. This is what comets do under the electric stress of approaching the Sun. Later astronomers, inspecting ancient records, came to the obvious conclusion that comets are generated when planets meet in conjunction. This opinion was held from Roman times through the Middle Ages.

A Starting Date

My estimate, made before I ran across the text by Stecchini, was also of an initial appearance in the east and a course of 8 months. Originally I selected a period starting at the earliest in March/April and lasting to January of the following year (rather than Kugler's September to April of 100 BC). At the first writing of this text I had no idea at all of when Venus would first have started to blaze, and used the first date of its appearance in the east, going by ephemeris information. Only in early 2008 did I manage to derive a reasonable set of dates for the event, based on diverse records. At this time I would hold that the blazing of Venus started on June 15, Gregorian, and ended on July 25th Gregorian (June 22 to August 1, Julian). The general details of these two dates were presented in a previous chapter. (Fine detail is presented in the chapter "The Chilam Balam Books.") Finding these dates simplified a reading of the *Sibylline Oracle* texts, which I will address below.

What is of greater interest are the specifics of the prophecies, not the dates. I disagree with Stecchini's evaluation (after Kugler) that the information "is so exact and technical that it must be something more than a mere mystical vision." I should explain that Kugler sees the progression of the Sibylline description as simply recording the path of the Sun through the constellations between September and April, and that this becomes the basis for his assumed Phaethon event of circa 1500 BC by inference (which was actually the Typhon event, and points up how little is really known of the Exodus).

What I see, instead of a play-by-play, is an opening and closing statement which encloses a long list of damages in terms of relocations of the constellations, which range over all except a few of the zodiacal constellations. The effect is not unlike the trail of constellated animals which follow the depiction of the killing of the bull (Taurus) in the temples of

Mithras, or the list of celestial damages presented in the play *Thyistes* by
Seneca. Both of these are contemporaneous with the Sibylline prophecies.

There is an opening statement: the account of the visionary, how the star-
war progressed (at which point dates come into use), what the main weapon
was, and a summary of the lasting damages. At the end of the text we find a
resolution and a windup signifying the end of creation. Enclosed by these is a
long list of alterations in the constellations of the zodiac (and some others),
which are neither complete, nor make all that much sense except when the
new skies are compared with the old skies -- the dome of the stars before and
after 685 BC. But I suspect that the list was not meant to be complete; the
main purpose was to suggest the utter derangement and confusion of the stars
resulting from the battle.

For Kugler to have used 100 BC is reasonable, since in 1927 it was the
best guess for a date for the Fifth Book, and since Kugler only sees an
association with the normal path of the Sun. I will not pursue this. I am more
interested in obtaining data for the actual event of 685 BC. I will thus shift
attention to an ephemeris for the year 685 BC.

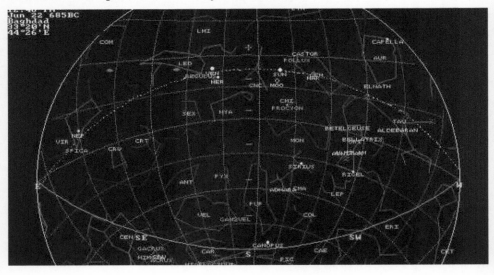

[*Image: The sky on June 15, 685 BC, Gregorian. Looking south, at
noon, a day of the new Moon. Venus and Mercury are in Leo, to the east
of the Sun and Moon, which are in Cancer (CNC). (Not corrected for the
change in the Earth's axis.) From SkyGlobe 3.6.*]

The location of the planets and the constellations with respect to each
other remains the same before and after 685 BC, but the polar axis and the
equatorial both shift. The constellations all appear in the skies in the wrong

places, that is, in the wrong locations with respect to the horizon and the zenith of the earlier ephemeris. Additionally, the starting date of the year (the vernal equinox) after 685 BC had shifted 15 days into the future.

The Opening Text

The text in question, representing lines 688 through 711 of Book Five of the *Sibylline Oracles*, is from a translation by Milton S. Terry in 1899. The text starts with: [note 4]

"I saw the threatening of the shining Sun
Among the stars,"

"and in the lightning flash
The dire wrath of the Moon; the stars travailed
With battle; and God gave them up to light."

It is the Sun which is threatened by another body or bodies. The "travail of the stars" involves the relocation of the constellations of the zodiac after the battle is done. This becomes fact only after the 40-day battle is completed. More on this below.

"I saw ... in the lightning flash, the dire wrath of the Moon." The author here jumps to the climax of the event, the delivery of the plasmoid lightning bolt of Jupiter on July 25th. Before July 25th (Gregorian), Europe and Asia had seen the bolt approaching from Jupiter for days. The bolt had passed directly by Earth on the day side, but only Mesoamerica had witnessed it at full size. On the 25th of July (August 1, Julian) the bolt was seen approaching Venus and the Sun.

As night fell, and Europe turned away from the path of the plasmoid in the day sky, nothing was seen except the Moon standing in the south, in its first quarter, probably after 9pm in the evening (it set at 1:30am). With the plasmoid traveling at an estimated speed of 40 million miles per day (64 million km per day) it would have reached the Sun in a half day after it disappeared from view to Europe. That is when the plasmoid hit the Sun. It would have been 3am in the Eastern Mediterranean.

The Sun rose the next day at 5am, engulfed in a cloud of plasma (to last an additional 7 hours as the 15-million-mile (24-million-km) long plasmoid crashed into the Sun), which also occluded Mercury, Mars, and perhaps Venus. Venus rose late, but may have lost its coma already, in which case it was not likely to have been seen.

I have previously proposed that the plasmoid would have had a diameter of perhaps 1.5 million miles (2.4 million km). That is twice the diameter of the Sun. The plasmoid would have engulfed the Sun. At an estimated length of 15 million miles, the flash of the first contact might have lasted 9 hours. The *Popol Vuh* suggests that additional smaller plasmoid bolts continued to arrive from Jupiter for four days.

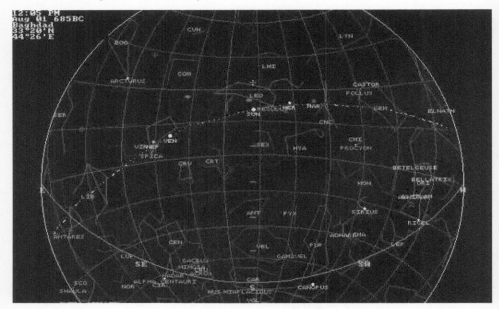

[*Image: The sky on July 25, 685 BC, Gregorian (August 1, Julian), the concluding day of the blazing. The Sun is in Leo, Venus is in Virgo. From SkyGlobe 3.6.*]

It must have been seen all around the horizon, and the Moon, rising the next day in the east after 3pm, while the Sun was still engulfed in plasma, would have lit up spectacularly. This describes the concluding event.

"God gave them up to light" obviously is meant to poetically tell that the battle happened during the daytime, which agrees with ephemeris information, or that a lot of light was produced for days. The narrator now drops back to the beginning of the battle.

"For long fire-flames rebelled against the Sun;
Lucifer treading upon Leo's back
Began the fight; and the Moon's double horn
Changed its shape;"

The starting position is now indicated as defined by the text, "Lucifer treading upon Leo's back." This was "Venus riding on a lion," the well known and "feared emblem for disaster" in the Eastern Mediterranean region, as per

Kugler. On June 15 (June 22, Julian), Venus and Mercury are in Leo, to the
east of the Sun and Moon, which are in Cancer.

The "long fire-flames" are the plasma tails of Venus and Mercury. Not
unlike some comets, there may have been multiple tails which crossed each
other (appropriate for Venus which does not have a magnetic field to coerce
its plasmasphere tail into a cohesive bundle). The "long fire-flames" also
might have extended both away from the Sun and toward the Sun, as well as
at right angles to these. This has been seen for comets. [note 5]

Before and after sunrise the "flames" would reach up from below the
horizon. Stecchini writes of the plasma plumes as "long streams of flame
crossing each other" (quoted from Kugler). Rising up from the horizon where
the Sun has set, these are the pointed sticks planted in the ground by Kirkin
(Venus). Jupiter (Wyju) jumps into the same section of the horizon about 6
hours later with both feet.

Almost at once after mid-June, Mercury starts to move toward the
position of the Sun, and passes it by July 3 (July 10, Julian). At that point
Mercury, also ablaze, might have sent streams of plasma directed at Earth, for
being in front of the Sun, its plasma tail would have pointed at Earth.

The coma, the plasma expulsions, and the distorted view of the plasma
tail of Mercury when it extended toward Earth (easily confused with the Sun
which Mercury was close to), are described by Isaiah and Ezekiel.

I would also suggest, in fact, that if the two inner planets were in flames
and Jupiter reacted similarly a half month later, then certainly the Earth also
would have been subject to such a condition. Plasma expulsions from the
Earth may have been seen moving up into space. In a previous endnote I
wrote:

"... the Earth also would have ended up erupting, but because of the
Earth's magnetosphere and enclosing atmosphere, the Earth might have
been spared the creation of thousands of electric burn craters, as on
Venus and especially Mercury. There is the contemporaneous statement
by Assurbanipal, king of Assyria, about Ishtar (Venus) 'raining fire over
Arabia.' Later Roman writers make the same claim of the Earth burning
up because of the close approach of Phaethon, as does Plato."

The Moon (at night after June 15) would be lighted by the Sun, and the
bright Venus and Mercury, so that its crescents ("horns") would be misshapen
from its normal form. The Moon would normally have had sharp waxing
horns after June 15. Now, with the blazing of Venus and its extended light,
the horns might have reached further around the edges of the Moon, or the
opposite edge of the Moon would have been lighted, "the Moon's double horn
changed its shape."

During the days of the late summer, with the steep gradient of the zodiac, the plumes would point down at the horizon, since Venus would be below the Sun most of the day. Only late in the day would the flame become horizontal. After nightfall a stream would come up from below the western horizon at a 45-degree angle, lighting up a large portion of the night sky.

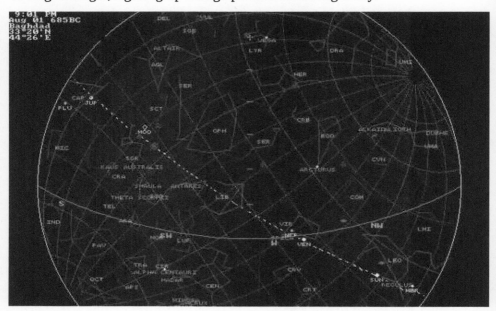

[*Image: The sky on July 25, 685 BC, Gregorian (August 1, Julian), the concluding day of the blazing, after about 9pm. The Sun and Venus have set. Sun in Leo, Venus in Virgo. Not shown is the plasmoid arriving from just below the western horizon. From SkyGlobe 3.6.*]

The image above is for 9pm of July 25 (Gregorian). It is the early night sky of the concluding event, as seen from the region of the Eastern Mediterranean. Jupiter's plasmoid lightning bolt is headed for the western horizon. In the diagram above the plasmoid travels along the circle of the ecliptic. As Europe turned toward the night, the bolt was seen approaching Venus -- thought by some to be the errant Phaethon -- to strike him down. In actuality the bolt passed by Venus and struck the Sun, but the contact was not seen. The plasmoid landed at the Sun at about 3am. The morning would see the Sun, Mercury, and Mars all engulfed in a haze. The *Popol Vuh* claims the turmoil lasted four days.

It is quite possible that the people of the Eastern Mediterranean got it right, and knew the thunderbolt struck Mercury, who was primarily identified as Phaethon. But an error remains, for the target was the Sun, not Mercury, which was within 11 degrees of the Sun. By next morning Venus and Mercury must have quieted down, although the skies remained obscured for days. [note 6]

Mesoamerica did not see the massive explosion at the Sun either, because it happened a few hours after sunset. It was assumed that the bolt was destined for Mars, standing just to the right (west) of the Sun (about 30 degrees). The explosion at the Sun would have visually engulfed the location of Mars in the sky, as well as Mercury. The next day the Sun was still in place, so it was assumed (at least by some of the many literate people of Veracruz and the Valley of Mexico) that Mars had been hit. Mars did not again come close to Earth, but primarily because the orbit of the Earth became nearly circular (as noted by Rose and Vaughan) before the time that Mars might have returned again. (Assigned to 670 BC, in Eastern Mediterranean chronology.)

The Maya *Book of the Chilam Balam* states that the Sun left its normal path for three Uinal months of twenty days. This is counted inclusively, however. The actual period would be 40 days -- June 15th to July 25th, Gregorian. The *Chilam Balam* also places the arrival of the lightning bolt from Jupiter, which ended the affair, exactly on July 25, 685 BC (Gregorian), which may also be calculated (from the same text) from the last close pass of Mars 520 days earlier.

From the *Sibylline Oracle* it might be suggested that the end of the drama happened with the Sun and Venus both in Capricorn, which would have been January of the next year. The *Sibylline Oracle* reads:

"Capricorn smote Taurus's neck;
And Taurus took away from Capricorn
Returning day."

But this might also simply suggest the most obvious aspect of the list of changes which will have been wrought with the war -- the change in the equinox. Jupiter was in Capricorn when the plasmoid was released. So it was Capricorn (in the typically displaced wording of prophecies) that "smote Taurus's neck." The phrase "returning day" is the fact that Taurus has been shifted to below the horizon at the vernal equinox with the change of the zodiac, thus giving up some 15 days.

That prediction will be true for the coming years. Taurus's neck was broken, it would no longer be the constellation that the Sun rose in at the equinox. In the typical stylishly metonymical metaphor of the Sibylline Oracle, whatever "Taurus," the constellation, took away from "Capricorn," Taurus was giving up -- calendar days.

The wording, "smote Taurus's neck," is reminiscent of the Tauroctony of

Mithraism, the slaying of the bull Taurus, depicted as having its throat cut. In antiquity the constellation Taurus was depicted only as the head of a bull, not the complete body, as is done today, which is also how the constellation was first depicted in the temples of Mithra circa AD 100.

Before 685 BC, with the Sun rising between Aries and Taurus at the vernal equinox, it is the head of the bull which was already (or soon was) above the horizon at the equinox. After 685 BC, with the Sun rising at 15 degrees of Aries at the vernal equinox (using the divisions of the ecliptic of antiquity), the head of Taurus no longer appeared above the horizon as the Sun rose to announce spring. His throat had been cut.

Capricorn is here the agent of change. Jupiter is in Capricorn throughout the 40-day period. In early January of the following year the Sun and Venus were also both in Capricorn. By this time the blazing of these two planets had subsided long ago, and this condition probably has nothing to do with the lines about Capricorn (and despite my earlier note about Berossus).

The *Sibylline Star Wars* document is obviously based on an ordered record of changes, and the travels of Venus, but that is no guarantee that it correctly incorporates the starting and completion dates. [note 7]

The display in the sky is nicely wrapped up in the closing lines of the poem (I'll detail the center section below):

"And the strength of the mighty Shining One
Aquarius kindled. Uranus himself
Was roused, until he shook the warring ones;
And being incensed he hurled them down on earth."

"Shining One" translates to "Phaethon," and thus refers back to Mercury or Venus. But if it is Aquarius (the constellation) who "kindles the strength," then it was Jupiter who was invigorated. However, Jupiter is not in Aquarius during the 40 days of battle. In July Jupiter was in Capricorn, the next constellation to the west of Aquarius.

This is the same displacement we see for the record of the Sun and Moon on June 15th. They are not in Cancer, but somewhat west of Cancer. Likewise Venus and Mercury are not exactly riding the back of a lion, but just west of Leo.

Then "Uranus," who is Jupiter of the family of Uranus, entered the fray, and throws both the Sun and Venus to Earth, that is, below the horizon. It is possible that Saturn is meant by "Uranus." Saturn is the son of Uranus. (The planet we have named "Uranus" since AD 1781 has nothing to do with the identification of planets in antiquity.)

The oracle (which is a vision of future events) claims that then the world will be set on fire, and the stars will disappear:

*"Then swiftly smitten down upon the baths
Of Ocean they set all the earth on fire;
And the high heaven remained without a star."*

We should be able to imagine what this looked like. The "baths of Ocean" is the zodiac or the region below the zodiac, but also might be the actual ocean, the Mediterranean. In most of the retellings of late antiquity, which all apparently take some 5th century BC play or tale as their source, possibly a lost play of Aeschylus, *The Heliades* ("Daughters of Helios"), Phaethon falls into the river Eridanus, which was identified as a constellation at an earlier time. [note 8]

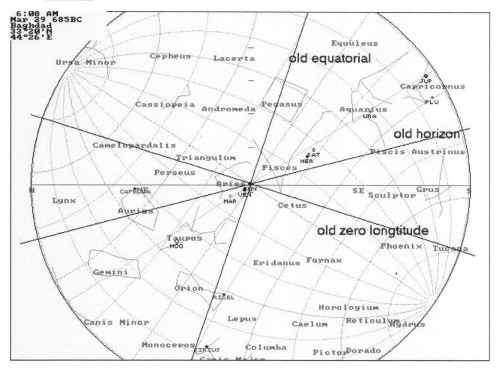

[Image: East hemisphere of the sky, after 685 BC. From SkyGlobe 3.6.]

But in the later retellings Eridanus is simply localized in the west, in the land of the Celts, also often identified as the Po in Northern Italy (which was under Celtic occupation in the early days of Rome), or in Spain, another well-known Celtic region. A location in the west would have been correct, for the splashdown of the plasmoid of Jupiter would have happened after the Sun had set north of directly west, and would have brilliantly lit up the western skies for hours. Setting the world aflame and the disappearance of the stars is also correct, for the stars would have disappeared in the light of the nine-hour-long flash.

New Locations of the Stars

The intervening lines of the text deal with the new locations in the sky of the zodiacal constellations plus Orion, Draco, and the star Sirius. All the changes relate to the location of the ecliptic, the equatorial, and the horizon. The change in the starting point of the year was probably noted by the next year, 684 BC. But the change in the location of the polar axis was noticed immediately. The change would move some constellations up in the sky and would move others down. Two lines indicate this clearly:

"Draco disavowed his zone."

Draco, a circumpolar constellation, before 685 BC chased the tail of the Big Bear, Ursa Major, where the polar axis was located. When Ursa Major suddenly dropped "down" by 6.5 degrees, Draco, the most noticeable northern constellation, started to rotate about another space away from Ursa Major. Today it revolves around the star Polaris of Ursa Minor.

"from the Sun's flame Sirius slipped away"

As I noted in prior text, Sirius was formerly located very near the equatorial -- about 2 to 3 degrees below. (See Sirius at the bottom of the diagram above, almost directly on the old equatorial.) After the change Sirius had dropped some 18 degrees below the equatorial. The "slipping away" of Sirius also reveals that it failed to rise or show in June, as it had in the past, and rose instead a month later. Sirius had been the primary star used as a celestial marker for ocean navigation, rising and setting almost directly east and west.

"Orion would no more
Abide his yoke"

In November Orion is seen in the southern sky with Gemini and Taurus above his shoulders. This did not change after the polar axis shifted, except in the spacing of these three constellations as seen in the sky. The equatorial cut across the bottom stars of Orion before 685 BC and through the top stars after. (Today it passes through the center of Orion.) The "yoke" might refer to the belt of three stars.

*"the lot of Gemini
Did Virgo change in Aries;"*

"Virgo" here is "the virgin," an almost universal appellation for Venus in the Eastern Mediterranean region ("the maid"), who changed Gemini's lot by being in Aries. Gemini's lot would have been to be suppressed further below the horizon at the start of the year. I am either reading this incorrectly or it is recorded incorrectly, for it would suggest a time of the year when Venus appeared in Aries. Otherwise by "Virgo" the constellation is meant.

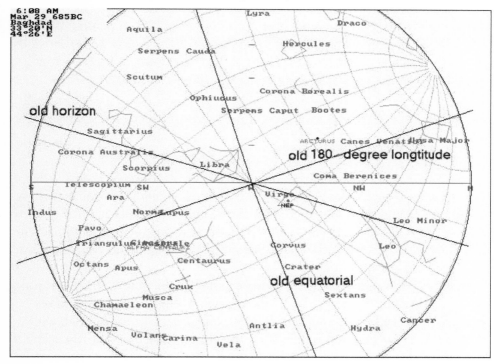

[*Image: West hemisphere of the sky, after 685 BC. From SkyGlobe 3.6.*]

The translation may, in this case, have reversed two constellation names, for at the concluding date, July 25 (August 1, Julian), Venus ("the virgin") was in Gemini, which implies that it was the lot of Aries that had changed. Aries's lot, of course, was to be the opening constellation at the start of the year -- at the new equinox -- noticed the following year when the Sun rose at the midpoint of Aries, rather than at the start of Taurus.

I should point out also that it was this phrase which led Kugler to the conclusion that the *Sibylline Star Wars* only described the path of the Sun starting in September, when the Sun is in the constellation Virgo (in 100 BC).

I read this differently.

> *"no more shone*
> *The Pleiades;"*

The above line is another clear reference to the change in the location of the equinox. With Taurus below the horizon at the start of the year, the Pleiades, located at one of the horns of Taurus, would no longer announce the start of spring and the start of a new year.

All the constellations moved, not with respect to each other, but with respect to the equatorial and the horizon of the Earth. The equatorial is a circle in the sky connecting east and west which is tilted at an angle above the south horizon equal to the complement of the latitude where it is observed. Thus the stars moved with respect to the horizon and the top of the sky.

> *"Down into Leo's girdle Pisces went.*
> *Cancer remained not, for he feared Orion;*
> *Scorpio down on dire Leo backwards moved."*

Scorpio did not move backwards. But any review of the zodiac at a later time might note discrepancies which should not be there if the constellations had been designed by God. Scorpio is placed below the ecliptic, as is Sagittarius, and Leo is off the ecliptic in the opposite direction. Both of these locations remained the same before and after. The ecliptic did not move with respect to the constellations.

Cancer (as well as another half-dozen constellations) moved up in the sky, while others sank. "Leo's girdle" is the belt of the equatorial. It should be remembered that both the ecliptic and the equatorial were still strewn with dust in 685 BC. The "zodiacal light" of the ecliptic lasted to AD 1840. The dust of the last ring of the equatorial (the remnant of the Absu, the Uoroboros) probably lasted to AD 400 or 600.

Conclusions About Dates

As I have pointed out elsewhere, these were not minor changes. It is for this reason, plus the lighting up of the day sky by the nova event of Venus and Mercury, plus the enormous flash on the 25th of July, that the event was understood as a war among the stars. When it was over every constellation had moved -- to where it should not be.

After blazing up in 685 BC, and then failing to disappear in front of the Sun in the west (in late December), Venus showed again as the Morning Star in early January of the next year. So say the *Venus Tablets of Ammizaduga*, or, as Mesoamerica has it, "Quetzalcoatl rose in the east as the Morning Star."

I have no question at this point that the shift of the polar axis and the change in the equinox happened, and happened suddenly, especially when combined with such comments from other sources.

I will maintain that the main "event" concluded on July 25th of 685 BC, with a plasmoid strike from Jupiter. I have detailed the derivation of this date in earlier chapters. The Guatemalan *Popol Vuh* suggests that the ecliptic remained obscured for four days after Hunahpu and Xbalanque jumped into the oven of the Xibalbans. Ovid suggests that the Sun did not show for a day (but then, Ovid places all 40 days in one day).

The descriptions of the phenomenon as a "throne," as a "horse without hips," or, as in Ezekiel's vision, of "brass glowing like fire in a furnace" and a "fire with encircling radiance," all speak to a display with much shorter plasma outpourings ("flames"). This would be the condition of Mercury as it reached inferior conjunction with Earth, and its plasma stream was directed towards Earth, and therefore visually foreshortened.

The *Chilam Balam*

An accurate Mesoamerican source, the Maya *Chilam Balam* books, reads that the Sun "moved from its place for three months," in Katun 3-Ahau (688 to 668 BC) and would return after "three heaps of years," or at least by the end of Katun 3-Ahau, that is, before the end of a twenty-year Katun period.

As I have pointed out, all five time spans recorded in Book 10 of the *Chilam Balam* use inclusive counting. So the "three months" represent a span of two Mesoamerican Uinal months of 20 days, a total of 40 days. From the *Popol Vuh* it is obvious that Venus and Mercury need to be close together in the sky (they hold hands) at the start of the nova event. June 15 (Gregorian) qualifies, and is, in fact, 40 days before July 25th.

The second remark in the *Chilam Balam* (about three heaps of years) reads as follows:

> *"After three years* [three heaps of years] *it will come back into place in Katun 3-Ahau. Then another Katun will be set (in its place)."*

We do not really know what "heaps of years" are, but I would guess that they are groups of five, as used on Maya counting boards, and further, that these are Tzolkin cycles of 260 days, and therefore we should count an interval of 14 (three times 5 less one), not 15 (three times five).

The "place of the Sun" would be measured by its setting location along the horizon and matched against calendar records of when and where this was expected. After the disturbance of the orbit of Earth in 685 BC, and after quiescence had returned, the Sun would rise and set again where expected, that is, on the proper date of our calendar, but not on the same date on the Mesoamerican Tzolkin calendar. But it turns out that 14 cycles of 260 days are exactly correct in "returning" the zenithal passage of the Sun to the same Tzolkin calendar day name for a latitude of 17 degrees north. What was important for Mesoamerica in this instance was the fact that the Sun obeyed the Tzolkin.

Of course, the Sun did not return to its proper horizon setting location on the same dates. Normally with the Mesoamerican calendar, the same Tzolkin day-name and day-number corresponding to the same Gregorian calendar date only after 20 Tzolkin rotations. Fourteen rotations will be 12 days short. It did return to the same horizon locations for zenithal passage over the sites in Mesoamerica, from which we receive the fiction perpetrated by the Olmecs that the Sun had returned to its proper place. I discuss this in the chapter "Olmec Alignments."

Nonnos's *Dionysiaca*

The writers mentioned above who have commented on Kugler's work have gone on at some length about the fact that Kugler's book does not reach the conclusion it might have originally intended to have. The book is, after all, about Phaethon. Kugler does not place the appearance of Phaethon in 100 BC, but only suggests by the accuracy of the description that we should not neglect the "legends" from circa 1500 BC, or what is thought to be 1500 BC -- that is, the Exodus of 1492 BC.

In fact Kugler supplies a series of sources for the dates of the fall of Phaethon which solidly place the event at the time of Moses. I have no disagreement with this as long as it is recognized that the events at the time of Moses (that is, in 1492 BC) are described by the Typhon legends, not the Phaethon legend. But what we also see, of course, is the Typhon legend reworked to fit the later event of 685 BC. The Star Wars prophecy is not the only instance. Another instance used by Kugler is the *Dionysiaca*, written another 300 years later, in circa AD 450, under the name of Nonnos.

This is a poem detailing the complete adventures of the God Dionysus, composed in the antique style of Homer and Hesiod (as was the style in Greek literature). Book 38 has a description of the Phaethon legend, which again describes changes in the sky overhead, with claims of all the constellations moving to different locations. The details of the description are almost incomprehensible in terms of an exact reading, unlike the *Sibylline Book*, with the zodiacal animals growling and clawing at each other, but the concluding lines are of interest. It reads:

"No longer did the stars in the Bear, moving in a circle fastened around his hips, dance up high near the northerly pole, but moved to the southwest and wet their dry feet in the Lake of Hesperia at the unaccustomed Oceanos."

Hesperia is a mostly fictitious ocean in the sky, probably based on the Absu, and adjacent to the river Oceanos, which is probably the last red ring below the equatorial. These particulars are mostly a poetic formulation. But more important, here we have the Phaethon legend tied to the change of the dome of the stars, like in the *Sibylline Book*. This is preceded, earlier in the description, with:

"Even the axis, which turns in the centre, began to totter through the whirling ether."

And:

"But winged Virgo sped past Arcturus, approached the Axis and collided with the Wain. The Morning Star sent erring rays to the western rim, and was even then pushing away the Evening Star, which stood opposite."

This actually describes the concluding dates of the event. Venus (Virgo) stood in the sky below Arcturus, maybe 17 degrees further west, while, with the Sun set already, Mercury (now the Morning Star west of the Sun) was already below the horizon and indeed stood opposite Venus (now identified as the Evening Star, for it followed the setting Sun).

Two Meteors

Kugler sees in the *Sibylline Star Wars* a description of the arrival of two meteors, but takes this information no further, perhaps suggesting that these phenomena would have disappeared in a few days. Malcolm Lowery wrote:

"Kugler recognizes in lines 512, 513 and 515 a description of the arrival of 'two enormous meteors of the apparent size and form of the sun and the moon . . . with their characteristic accompanying features', but is happy to leave them out of the further action, accepting them, presumably, as no more than the excuse the ancients needed to write a poem about the events following."

I would suggest that the blazing Venus seen next to the blazing Mercury would be sufficient to explain "two enormous meteors," especially if they are suggested to be of the same size as the Sun and the Moon (the Sun and Moon are the same apparent size). There are Chinese sources in antiquity which recall that at one time "two Suns" were seen battling in the sky.

Dating the Denderah Zodiac Ceiling

(May 2007) The temple of Hathor at Denderah in southern Egypt contains a very unusual circular zodiac ceiling panel in one of the auxiliary buildings. The temple was rebuilt under Roman rule sometime in the first century. The zodiac panel may have been started under some of the Ptolemies, perhaps a hundred years earlier.

[Image: Denderah zodiac ceiling; Approximately 8 feet (2.5 meters) across. Collection of Louvre Museum.

Since its discovery in 1799, various researchers have attempted to determine what date might be depicted by this star chart. The zodiac of the

Denderah ceiling is not very accurate, however, as others have noted. But accuracy was never an issue in Egyptian depictions of the stars. It was all about religious symbolism. The iconography of the zodiac is solidly Ptolemaic Greek, however. It politically gives recognition to earlier Egyptian astronomy with an outer border of decans. Decans are a series of stars that rise every hour at night, marking time. There are 36 for use throughout the year, one every ten degrees.

I am using a portion of the locations of planets as determined by Julie Gillentine in "The Zodiac of Dendera" (*Atlantis Rising,* 2001), and Joanne Conman in "The Round zodiac Ceiling of the Temple of Hathor at Denderah" (*The Secret Chambers of the Sanctuary of Thoth,* 2002, on line).

Gillentine made the selection without recourse to the identification of certain figures as planets, so that, for example, I disagree with her selection of Jupiter and Saturn. I selected the duck between Sagittarius and Capricorn as Jupiter. The duck has always been identified as Ra, and Ra is Jupiter.

Conman identifies a number of figures with Gods and Goddesses of southern Egyptian nomes, which I do not think is called for. This is a notion first brought forward in the 19th century. This is just unlikely. There are many more nomes than there are figures in the ceiling zodiac. And it certainly also does not apply to the figures of the decans, for these were well established, and had nothing to do with local temple concerns.

The time depicted by the zodiac chart would be about midnight, with Jupiter almost directly south and the full moon in the south-southwest. Sirius (the ox in the boat) is shown directly north, but this would be below the Earth and only rotate into the daytime as the skies turned.

From the ceiling zodiac the locations of planets can be read as presented in the text below. Some of the constellations have been turned, shrunk, or dislocated, however. The example which everyone will recognize at once is that Aries is reversed, facing Taurus, and looking over his shoulder toward the west. Some of the planets are erroneously or haphazardly placed. Mars, for example, seems to be placed early in Gemini, away from where it ought to be in Cancer. But Sirius is also below Cancer, which cannot be, because Sirius and the constellations are immovable stars. Sirius belongs below Gemini.

Finding the year and date for this configuration of planets is thus problematic, but it can be done. If Saturn is in Pisces, there are only two or three years which need to be inspected out of every thirty years to find Jupiter in Capricorn. In all cases the month of July or August has to be selected, since the Sun must be in Leo. Mercury will be there also, and Venus should be close by. The appropriate year can be located from the requirement of having Mars in Gemini or between Gemini and Cancer.

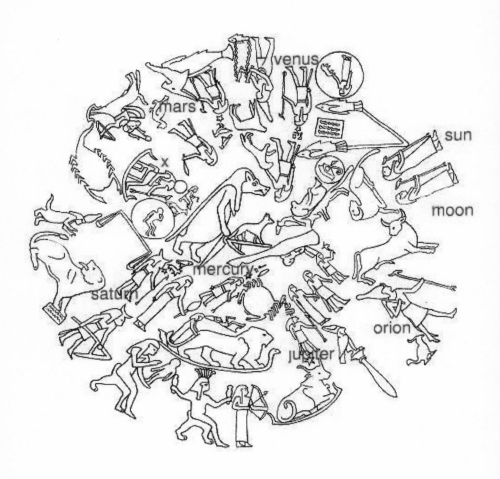

[Image: Figures with Was scepters at Denderah, incorrectly attributed to planets. Decans not shown. Original after Conman.]

There is a question as to which figures constitute the planets. There is a set of standing figures which each hold a *Was* scepter, which normally indicates their status as Gods. (One remains unidentified in Scorpio, plus Orion is likewise equipped with a *Was* scepter.) These are held to be the planets placed in their governing house, that is, each is located in a zodiac sign of importance to that particular planet. The concept that every zodiac sign has a "ruling" planet which has particular potential in those locations has come down to modern times in astrology, and is called the "exaltation" of the planets. The genesis of this is a complete mystery. It was already established in Babylonian times.

The location of the exaltation of the planets does not constitute a plan for a date for the zodiac, since Mercury (in particular) is much too far removed from the (assumed) location of the Sun in Aries. Mercury is located three or four zodiac signs away in this schema -- the Sun is not in Aries. I wanted to point this out.

If we are to look for another indication of a date, we have to look at a more correct set of symbols which encode planet names and locations. These are listed below.

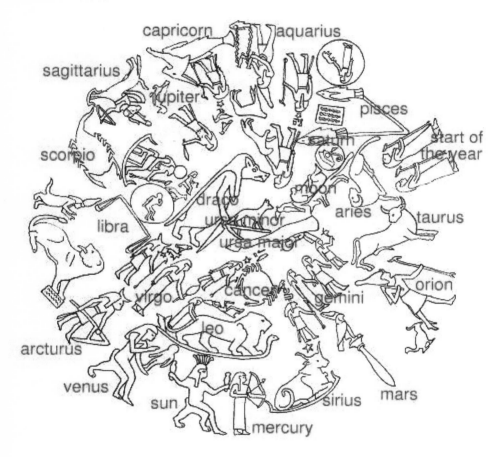

[Image: Figures as planets and zodiac signs at Denderah; Decans not shown. Original after Conman.]

- "Venus in Virgo" -- Venus (Isis) with Horus on her hand.
- "Sun and Mercury in Leo" -- Mercury to the west, shown as an archer, the Sun holding two jars, and with a plumed head dress.
- "Mars in Cancer or Gemini" -- This is the crowned falcon on the papyrus plant. He is shown below Gemini, but should properly be below the adjacent Cancer.

- "Moon in Pisces" -- The Moon is the baboon above the Eye of Ra.
- "Saturn in Pisces" -- the figure of the *Eye of Ra*.
- "Jupiter in Capricorn" -- The duck ("Ra") between Sagittarius and Capricorn.

It is this last, the duck as Ra and Ra as Jupiter, which has consistently sabotaged all efforts at determining a date, or even a coherent listing of planets, for everyone holds Ra to be the Sun, whereas for 3000 years Jupiter was identified as Ra. And all too many researchers have thought that the duck in this zodiac is just decorative, like the corresponding *Eye of Ra* in Pisces. The *Eye of Ra* is not decorative, it is Saturn.

Now to determine a date. In the time span of the half millennium preceding the first century BC, when the zodiac ceiling was installed, only three events stand out as universally significant. The first was the lengthening of the year in 747 BC. The second was the Earth shock by Mercury and the burning tower of Babel in 686 BC. Both of these were spring events, with the Sun in Aries.

The third event was the delivery of the plasmoid of Jupiter at the Sun on July 25, 685 BC. I only reached a conclusion about this date when I realized that the baboon in Pisces was a well-established symbol for Thoth, but by Roman times Thoth had migrated its planetary association from Mercury to the Moon. Mercury had all but disappeared from the skies 460 years before the Roman rebuilding of the temple, and the assignment of the messenger of the Gods had passed to the Moon. The Moon should be in Sagittarius on July 25th. It would be in Capricorn two days later, in Aquarius in four days -- roughly two days of displacement for every zodiacal house. The Moon reached Pisces in six days. Here it is the baboon above the *Eye of Ra*.

This extension of six days after the actual delivery of the plasmoid (on July 25) reflects how soon the skies cleared of plasma at the Sun, and accounts for further events, including the delivery of subsequent smaller plasmoids.

The *Popol Vuh* suggests that the ecliptic remained obscured for four days. About the blowgunner twins, Hunahpu and Xbalanque, who had just been burned up and their ground-up bones cast in the river, the *Popol Vuh* reads:

"And on the fifth day [after] *they reappeared. They were seen in the water by the people. The two of them looked like catfish when their faces were seen by Xibalba."*

The blowgunner twins of the *Popol Vuh* were seen as catfish. You will find later in the Chapter "The *Popol Vuh*" my comments:

"Catfish were seen, but these are more likely additional minor plasmoid bolts from Jupiter. Since these would have traveled in the ecliptic, they might easily be mistaken for Venus and Mercury, especially when it was unclear where these planets were. The catfish were seen while the day and night skies blazed with the reaction of the Sun to the initial plasmoid strike from Jupiter."

Selecting the baboon as the symbol of the Moon, places the Moon in Pisces. That would bring the close of the event to July 30, Gregorian. The close of the event was the beginning of a new creation. There were no further interferences by any planets after this date. The following spring showed all seven planets in a line in the sky -- the start of a Great Year.

Endnotes

Note 1 --

A number of numismatic sites with an interest in astronomy have suggested that the seven stars might represent a conjunction of all the planets in the sky. It is also suggested that the seven stars represent either Ursa Major or the Pleiades. And, in fact, the earliest coin of this nature dates from AD 76 and is clearly marked TRIO, short for Septentriones, a name for the seven stars of the Wain (Ursa Major) and generally meaning "north."

Note 2 --

Some conjunctions only last a day, some last a week. The location of the Moon is not hard and fast, since it moves 12 degrees per day.
Oct 5, 7 BC, Sat, Jup, Moon, Mar, Ven, Mer, Sun (setting)
Jul 5, 6 BC, Sun (rising) Mar, Ven, Mer, Jup, Sat, Moon
Apr 6, 4 BC, Moon, Jup, Mar, Mer, Sat, Ven, Sun (setting)
Mar 7, 2 BC, Jup, Sat, Mar, Ven, Mer, Moon, Sun (setting)
Oct 27, AD 1, Sun (rising), Jup, Mar, Ven, Mer, Moon, Sat

Note 3 --

To get a glimpse at how easy it is to calculate planet positions in the past or future, take a look at how Patten and Windsor make these calculations in *The Mars-Earth Wars* (1996), reaching back 2300 years. Patten and Windsor use data listed to many decimal places, but this would not be much different from what was available in antiquity, which had already accumulated 600 years of data by AD 200.

Note 4 --

The complete Sibylline text follows. I have broken it up into sections to clearly indicate the composition. Line numbers are in brackets.

The opening lines:

[689]"I saw the threatening of the shining Sun
Among the stars, and in the lightning flash
[690] The dire wrath of the Moon;"

The battle:

"the stars travailed
With battle; and God gave them up to light.
For long fire-flames rebelled against the Sun;
Lucifer treading upon Leo's back
Began the fight; [695] and the Moon's double horn
Changed its shape;"

The lasting change:

"Capricorn smote Taurus's neck;
And Taurus took away from Capricorn
Returning day.

The changes in the sky:

"Orion would no more
Abide his yoke; the lot of Gemini
Did Virgo change in Aries; [700] no more shone
The Pleiads; Draco disavowed his zone;
Down into Leo's girdle Pisces went.
Cancer remained not, for he feared Orion;
Scorpio down on dire Leo backwards moved;
And from the Sun's flame Sirius slipped away;"

The closing passage:

[705] "And the strength of the mighty Shining One

Aquarius kindled. Uranus himself
Was roused, until he shook the warring ones;
And being incensed he hurled them down on earth.
Then swiftly smitten down upon the baths
[710] Of Ocean they set all the earth on fire;
And the high heaven remained without a star."

Note 5 --

The spikes in four directions from the two planets, but especially Mercury, would likely result in the later claim of the crucifixion of Mithra.

Note 6 --

I have made this statement before, that Venus would have lost its tail and large coma at this time, but this is not at all certain. Only by the time of the writings of Aristotle (384 BC to 322 BC) do we see a definite attempt to separate planets from meteors and more ephemeral phenomena (which last are classified by him as "weather"-- meteorology). Stecchini writes, "It is significant that, after having described the general topic of meteorology, Aristotle begins the treatment of it by refuting those who say that 'the comet is one of the planets'." The "comet" here is Venus.

Note 7 --

In fact, I have not been able to pinpoint a closing date. The document clearly records all of the travels of Venus between an unexpected blazing in June and (perhaps) the subsequent easterly reappearance -- except that there was no westerly disappearance of Venus. On this occasion, as an ephemeris will show, Venus rode about 8 degrees above the Sun as it was setting in the west, and reappeared the next day in the east at sunrise.

This would explain the missing data at the close of year eight of *The Tablets of Ammizaduga*. I would suggest furthermore that Venus may have changed its orbit with the relocation of Mercury in the previous year. That, in turn, explains perhaps the fact that Venus set a month late, as noted by Rose and Vaughan, and which remained inexplicable to them. Normalization of data does not tell one anything about orbits.

The closing date indicated with the Denderah Zodiac ceiling is five days later than August 25. See further text below.

Note 8 --

The constellation Eridanus is identified as a series of stars hanging from the left foot (Rigel) of the constellation Orion and reaching the horizon -- like a river -- even with Orion high in the sky. In July of 685 BC Orion and Eridanus are both west of the Sun and below the horizon at nightfall, but they rise in the east 4 hours before sunrise. Eridanus is located well below the ecliptic and the equatorial. The star Rigel is at the same relative altitude (44.5 degrees at culmination for Cairo in 685 BC) as Sirius (42.1 degrees). The start of Eridanus, which dips down (toward the southern horizon), would thus be located behind the last red ring of the original Absu which also gave Sirius its red color. The blood in this river -- backlighted perhaps by the flash at the Sun, below the horizon -- would be convincing evidence of the death of Phaethon.

Recovering the Lost World, A Saturnian Cosmology -- Jno Cook
Chapter 28: Language and Causality

Revision: 42.35 (lang.php)
Contents of this chapter: [Consciousness] [Becoming Human]
[Language Development] [Boat People] [Languages and Texts]
[Subjective Consciousness] [Advantages] [Disadvantages] [Children]
[Endnotes]

> Primates learn from their peers, not from adults.
> -- Sherwood Washburn, [note 1]

Consciousness

And now for something entirely different: Let me introduce *subjective consciousness* at this point, and language and texts as a secondary topic. The reason for presenting this material is two-fold. First, I need to point out that an understanding of events in the remote past is never modulated by abstract metaphors, something we today do with great fluency. The events of the distant past are facts, they never "stood" for something other, excepting perhaps in the use of similes. Secondly, I need to point out how grammar effects the understanding of the world for different people, how it completely and radically changes concepts which we take for granted. This is particularly relevant to an understanding of the following chapters which deal with Mesoamerica.

Subjective consciousness is not biological. It is a learned faculty, like language, and is thus dependent on contacts with other people and includes within its structure the ability to promulgate its use to others by purposeful example. To become *subjectively conscious* means to learn how to *teach subjective consciousness* to others, and thus keep *subjective consciousness* alive. This is no small task, yet we constantly perform the task of teaching through our dialogues with others and we do it automatically.

Even the most ardent micro-evolutionist will have to admit that language and speech were probably not available to humans before about 40,000 BC. (John Halloran at [www.sumerian.org/] believes 10,000 years ago to be more accurate.) And much, much later came consciousness as we experience it today. Of course, our experience of consciousness is so entwined with our identity, and seems so overwhelmingly innate, that anything suggesting differing conditions, like the notion that our experience of extended consciousness -- *subjective consciousness* -- is not biological, but is cultural, will bring most people's reflection on this topic to a complete halt. It comes as an immense shock to realize that *subjective consciousness* is only a very recent development.

We are here not talking about consciousness, self-consciousness, or self-awareness. These are qualities possessed by all animals. It allows them to identify themselves, allows them to associate past experiences with their peers and mates, allows knowledge of the thousands of details of a wide-ranging geography, and allows the incorporation of learned experiences. We do all that too, and mostly without thinking about it.

And we point fingers, and understand others when they point. As Malcolm Gladwell notes in *Blink* (2005), "... interpreting a pointing gesture requires, if you think about it, that you instantaneously inhabit the mind of the pointer." Most animals don't get it. Animals do not seem to do well with questions either, which represents a similar displacement into the mind of another person. [note 2]

I will describe *subjective consciousness* as distinct from *consciousness* further below. At this juncture it might be more instructive to list some examples of people who, for any number of reasons, have remained *pre-subjectively conscious*. These include people who are very accomplished, for example, musically, but have never composed anything new or even improvised, people who can draw or paint with mastery but only derivatively and have never produced a new image. Or the person who keeps asking you and others for advice on some question, yet never acts on it. Here there is a failure of imagination, or as others have suggested, a failure of judgment, although I would hold that we are dealing with both the inability to imagine and to make judgments based on what was imagined. This is a poor integration of functions which the left-brain is capable of with the remainder of mental activities which we would call "thinking."

Of course it is possible to get through life without ever accessing or exploring the analogical vistas of the imagination, just as is it possible to converse without ever using metaphors. Such conversation, or such thinking, can certainly present the complexities of relationships, the gripping realities of emotions, and the humor of situations. And we can still fill a dialog with lies and falsehoods, just as we can deliver biting sarcasm. What can't be done easily is to present or suggest a situation to the recipient of our dialog which is composed, not of reality, but of a what-if situation -- an analogical reality, offered to the hearer for his personal exploration.

The lack of metaphorical thinking in remote antiquity is critical to understanding what we are told by our forebears. The languages in which the first observations of the heavens were rendered were specific and concrete -- as Jaynes suggests -- "end to end." These people were not creating symbols or dealing in mystical religious philosophies; what we are told of was exactly what was seen and experienced.

This is, in fact, what Jaynes proposes, that metaphorical thinking dates only from after 1000 BC. Jaynes demonstrates this through examples and details from the earliest historical texts and through an analysis of cult objects of Mesopotamia and Egypt. Of course, nothing is proven, for nothing can be proven about the mentality of an era we did not participate in. But enough striking examples are brought forward to suggest that his hypothesis might very well be correct. I should point out that Jaynes was completely unaware of any of the catastrophism developed in this text.

What is more significant is that Jaynes's concept of *subjective consciousness* is based on a working model of the mind which has very large predictive value. This is also why there has been no follow-up to Jaynes's model. Besides stepping away from academic mainstream psychology in writing *The Origin of Consciousness in the Breakdown of the Bicameral Mind* (1976), Jaynes's model, which locates consciousness exclusively in the left hemisphere of the brain and delegates volition to the right half, in effect closed the door to further research, despite the fact that vast behavioral areas remained to be explored, for the basis of the model was largely philosophical, it was not clinical. But it works!

Current stock psychological research, as with neurological research, is based entirely on stringing together data from endless clinical studies. It also tends to be very reductive, equating conclusions from clinical data to elements of computer models and electrical circuitry, despite the fact that the interrupt-based methods of computer processing are not equivalent to the simultaneous capabilities of the brain -- the only true multi-processing system.

You will also see a reductiveness to named parts of the brain as if "firing order" and "activity" are causally meaningful. They are not. The dependence of the limits of clinical data is equivalent to the stalemate reached in the study of language some decades ago -- a reduction of words to sounds and phonemes without a single notion of how to jump from there to syntax.

But despite the turn by professionals to the academic minutia of clinical studies, the broad concepts of separate left and right brain are alive in popular culture. Separate qualities are often ascribed to the two hemispheres, which are, however, generally totally wrong. To say that the left hemisphere is capable of speech, for example, is completely correct, for we are aware of this faculty. To say that the left hemisphere is logical and the right hemisphere is intuitive is completely bogus. Nothing which may be accomplished by the right hemisphere is accessible to consciousness, so that nothing can be said about the workings of the right hemisphere except by inference. And the inferences come from feelings, from reminders and admonitions (often inappropriate) which spring to mind, and from images that impose themselves on consciousness. [note 3]

Malcolm Gladwell, 2005

A book by Malcolm Gladwell, *Blink* (2005), relates the ephemeral nature of the communication of the silent right brain with the conscious left. The book opens with attempts of the Getty Museum in California to verify the authenticity of a Greek statue, a kouros, dating from 500 BC which had been offered for sale to the Getty. The investigation, which included stylistic considerations, the provenance of prior ownership, the source of the material, and the evidence of 2000 years of aging, took 14 months.

In 1986, at the completion of the investigation, the kouros was viewed by a number of experts in ancient Greek sculpture. Frederico Zeri (on the Getty's board), stared at the kouros;s fingernails when unveiled -- they looked wrong. Evelyn Harrison (an independent curator) felt something was amiss and recommended against purchase. Thomas Hoving (Metropolitan Museum of Art, NY) recalled that the word that jumped into his mind at the first sight of the kouros was, "fresh," hardly appropriate for a statue reputed to be 2500 years old. Hoving also recommended against purchase.

The Getty shipped the kouros to Greece and called a conference of experts. Here are additional responses: George Despinis (Acropolis Museum, Athens), to quote Gladwell, "took one look at the kouros and blanched." Georgios Dontas (Archaeological Society, Athens), saw the statue and felt cold, he felt, he said, "as though there was glass between me and the work." Angelos Delivorrias (Benaki Museum, Athens) felt a wave of "intuitive repulsion" at the first sight of the sculpture.

The experts were eventually vindicated; the kouros was indeed a fake. But now look at the broad base of opinions of the experts: All of them made up their mind within one or two seconds after first seeing the kouros. Not one of them could articulate the reasons for their opinion or "revulsion." Note that the feeling of incorrectness seemed to be universal, but also note the words which entered their minds, and the image of the glass. These were all articulate people, yet they were stumped to explain their "feelings."

What is most amazing is that the inarticulate part of the minds of these six curators managed to come to identical conclusions in under two seconds each, when the Getty had managed to get the wrong answer after 14 months of expert investigations. The speed is phenomenal, but the inarticulateness and terseness of communication between the silent right brain and the conscious left mind is a definite drawback.

Gladwell, following current theories, writes, *"The part of our brain that leaps to conclusions like this is called the adaptive unconscious, and the study of this kind of decision making is one of the most important new fields in psychology."*

Daniel Goleman, 2006

As a second example of the reduction of Jaynes's left rear and right rear hemispheres to smaller constituent parts of the brain, consider Daniel Goleman's book *Social Intelligence* (2006). Goleman uses both sociological and neurological clinical sources in an attempt to define social interactions as dependent on pattern recognition. Here the high-speed recognition, which he calls the "low road," at least has a clear method of communicating its findings to the conscious left brain. On recognizing an emotion in others, the observer will duplicate this in his own body. Goleman calls it "emotional contagion."

"Emotional contagion exemplifies what can be called the brain's 'low road' at work. The low road is circuitry that operates beneath our awareness, automatically and effortlessly, with immense speed. Most of what we do seems to be piloted by massive neural networks operating via the low road -- particularly in our emotional life."

The "high road," writes Goleman:

"... in contrast runs through neural systems that work more methodically and step by step, with deliberate effort. We are aware of the high road, and it gives us at least some control over our inner life, which the low road denies us."

The "immense speed" of the low road, however, is relative. The brain can operate at an immense speed with familiar material. All of us have been looking at faces and associating facial expressions with emotions since we were a month old. The same operation "beneath our awareness" takes hold in typing or playing a musical instrument. But ask yourself a difficult question, and it may take weeks or months before an answer "pops into your mind" based on all the information you had already gathered. It is the "unaware" right brain which will have reviewed all the relevant data that you have consciously accumulated, perhaps over a lifetime.

Goleman lists (after Matthew Lieberman) some brain areas involved in processes which escape conscious awareness, as the amygdala, basal ganglia, lateral temporal cortex, ventromedial prefrontal cortex, and dorsal anterior cingulate cortex. It is a long list.

I would be more comfortable with Jaynes's model, which posits a fully functional second mind, but one which has almost no control over speech, and whose operation remains completely inaccessible to consciousness. It is equivalent to being inhabited by another psyche, one who is smart, fast thinking, correct in most situations, but, as has been observed, also willful, impatient, and quickly annoyed.

Michael Gazzaniga, 2008

The third example is a book by Michael Gazzaniga, *Human: The Science behind What Makes Us Unique* (2008), which discusses split-brain (commissureotomized) patients. "Being inhabited" is a concern specifically addressed. Gazzaniga writes:

> *"Why don't split-brain patients have dual consciousness? Why aren't the two halves of the brain conflicting over which half is in charge? ... Are consciousness and the sense of self actually located in one half of the brain?"*
> [note 4]

Yes, Jaynes would say. Gazzaniga points out that attention remains fixed on a single spatial location after the brain has been split, as if the two halves were still working together. (Of course this is a fiction. We cannot tell what the right brain is concentrating on.)

He also notes Paul Broca's research (in the late 19th century) which located the center for speech on the verbal left hemisphere, writing, *"A split-brain patient's left hemisphere and language centers have no access to the information that is being fed to the right brain."*

Thirty years earlier, Jaynes wrote about that also. Information can visually be fed separately to each hemisphere by showing separate images to the left and right eye. (There is some loss of informration, since the optical nerves of the eyes each split the field of view between the left and right hemispheres.) Under this condition the left and right hemisphere can be asked to respond appropriately to the separate images, and this will be accomplished, for both the left and right brain can understand speech. Since the hands and fingers are almost totally under control of either the right or left brain, the response (like picking an appropriate object) will reflect the decisions of a single hemisphere. This has led Gazzaniga to some conclusions about the separate hemispheres, as follows. (I'll note the right as silent, the left as verbal in the following.)

"Although the [silent] *right hemisphere remains superior to the isolated* [verbal] *left hemisphere for some perceptual and attentional skills, and perhaps also emotions, it is poor at problem solving and many other mental activities"*

This badly short-changes the right brain. Goleman, in the previously quoted book, in essence suggested that the silent right brain, or the parts of the brain unavailable to consciousness or introspection, is superb at gauging emotions. Gazzaniga calls it "face recognition." The silent right is also capable of completely logical analysis of data, unlike the left brain which tends to make up even incorrect theories, as the author points out. Gazzaniga writes:

"The [verbal] *left hemisphere, on the other hand engages in the human tendency to find order in chaos and persists in forming hypotheses about the sequence of events* [in this example] *even in the face of evidence that no pattern exists: slot machines, for instance."*

The use of the phrase "human tendency" takes us beyond speculation. Now calling the left brain with its apparent inherent need to come up with theories, "the interpreter," Gazzaniga finishes his analysis on a poetic rather than a scientific note:

"How is that two isolated hemispheres give rise to a single consciousness? The [verbal] *left-hemisphere interpreter may be the answer. The interpreter is driven to generate explanations and hypotheses regardless of circumstances. The* [verbal] *left hemisphere of split-brain patients does not hesitate to offer explanations for behaviors that are generated by the* [silent] *right hemisphere. In neurologically intact individuals, the interpreter does not hesitate to generate spurious explanations for sympathetic nervous system arousal. In these ways, the* [verbal] *left-hemisphere interpreter may generate a feeling in all of us that we are integrated and unified."*

The waters have been seriously muddied. Jaynes covered all this 30 years earlier, and without recourse to vapid generalizations about consciousness or "human tendencies." Let me start at the beginning, and review what we know.

Becoming Human

As a brief summary: Humans were not always *subjectively conscious*. The nature of *subjective consciousness* was explained in the text. As *subjectively conscious* humans, we are at best 3000 or 4000 years old (2000 to 1000 BC), with a "recorded" pre-history dating back 5000 years (to 3000 BC), and not the slightest significant amount more. All history starts there. There are objects and constructions from before 3000 BC, but they are certainly not "ours" -- not the work of *subjectively conscious* humans. Neither is much of what can be dated to before about 1000 BC. We owe our humanness, like the genesis of Earth's biology, to the "Gods of Creation" -- the planets, and their catastrophic interferences with Earth.

It might have gone another way. *Subjective consciousness* could have never happened. We could still be chipping flints, as Homo erectus did for a million years without improving on their one stone tool. Even today there is a great diversity of *subjective consciousness* in the world, a clear indication, I think, that it is not a biological function. Our humanity is something we have to actively work on. We are a gregarious species, a social one, and, as a group, look to others for authentication and authority. That is dangerous because this particular behavior is biological, and represents a fallback position when *subjective consciousness* falters.

We are animals, although we like to think we are different. Our biology is fully integrated into the domain of the mammals. We may have a few features not shared with other mammals, but most are shared. Primarily, like other mammals, we give birth to immature young and need to spend a long time teaching them. All mammals teach their young and that is crucially important to humans. This teaching is overwhelmingly biologically driven, and a subject often completely neglected by anthropologists and archaeologists, for it is "women's work" -- like spinning whorls or all those Venus Figurines. It does not deal with weapons, hunting, or economics. [note 5]

Becoming "human" -- that is, *subjectively conscious* -- was a chance event. There is no biological cause. Language is a prerequisite, but language has the same status -- it also has no biological basis and has to be learned. There are, however, some requisite mechanisms for language which are biological. We have to have a voice box located high in the throat and nasal cavity large enough to produce a range of sounds and we need a brain set up to allow lateralization of the speech center. (Some brain functions are lateralized in other mammals also.) There are other prerequisites which are shared with mammals, like the ability to learn rapidly, especially at an early age, and parents willing to teach what they in turn have learned.

The cat brings a live mouse back to its litter of kittens. They play with the mouse, eventually kill it and eat it. The kittens have learned about mice, about the chase, about killing mice, and eating them. When the kittens grow up, they bring mice back to their own kittens. That they also learned.
   -- observation, 1983

Language Development

The structure of languages, their redundancy, variability, and complexity of expression are all at the service of teaching -- and not just teaching children, but adults also. The same is true of *subjective consciousness*. Whenever we engage with others, we are constantly proposing a new consciousness with our expressed thoughts about areas of interest. These are proposals for alternate and new mind-space scenarios. They are new -- to the other person -- because what we express is our own, and seldom the mental experience of the other person. Teaching never ends.

The enormous number of constantly changing languages and the vast differences in grammars are proof enough that languages are not biologically mandated. The versatility of humans allowed languages to develop. However, although the existence of humans -- hominids -- stretches back millions of years, languages are not thought to be much older than about 40,000 years.

As a species we are deprived of a number of communication possibilities that are well-developed in other species. We have language because we happened to have made use of what we had: a voice box which can make very complicated discrete sounds, the ability to identify sequenced sounds, an inventiveness -- you might even say, playfulness -- beyond anything seen in two million years, an unlimited food supply, and lots of free time. Altogether, language seems to have little purpose until recently, when it became the basis for *subjective consciousness*, and looks more like an accident than an adaptive evolutionary trend with some survival purpose. It looks, in fact, more like a game that was played among humans, something which we readily acknowledge in our casual banter with others. [note 6]

All mammals communicate, and gregarious mammals do so in complex ways which remain mostly outside our ken. And it is all about food, sex, and young, and territory and enemies. Dogs, originally as wolves (100,000 to 60,000 years ago), are gregarious, and they growl, howl, and grunt, and have a dozen barks. They also use body language and facial expressions, very similar to us, to communicate. (Dog gestures are easy to learn, by the way, and can be used effectively to "talk" to dogs.) So far, so good. We do all that. We can communicate with grunts, talk with our hands, and express ourselves with facial gestures. And, as such, we need nothing beyond hand waving and a few grunts for communal food gathering, or raising children. [note 7]

But dogs (wolves) also communicate in ways completely beyond our abilities. They live in a Smell Universe which is absolutely amazing and unknown to us. A wolf (dog) rolls its back on a killed animal and carries the smell back to the den -- often dozens of miles away -- to identify the prey by species, age, health at the time of death, and the age of the kill. The route to the kill is attached to the reporting wolf like a map of smells so that the home wolves need not be guided. They know what landmarks were trotted past, how far to go, and can home in on the prey during the last part of the trek. They are not led by the wolf who brings back the news.

Dogs (rats also) have a bundle of nerves connecting the smell centers of the left and right hemispheres of the brain which is 10 times the diameter of our left to right speech connection. That means a circuitry 100 times more abundant in neural connections than what we use for speech. These animals have an integrated brain capacity dedicated to smell which is thousands of times larger than our capacity altogether for vocabulary, grammar, speech, and memorized names and phone numbers.

You cannot play "peek-a-boo" with dogs, as you can with small children. You will continue to "be there" for a dog even though you cannot be seen. The three dimensional Smell Universe has a fourth dimension in time. When I come home with my dog, she sniffs the stairway space to determine if any occupant of the house has gone upstairs, and (I suppose) when. Dogs also read the emotions of other dogs (and humans) by smell in addition to using visual signals.

Dogs are carnivores, and are attuned to the sounds, smells, and movements of prey, and thus are very aware of the same among each other. We (or related ancestor species) have been scavengers and predators for about 2 million years, maybe more. We certainly should also be attuned to sights, smells, and sounds, and thus we could be expected to have developed a language made up out of these senses.

But we have no left-right connection in our brain at all for smell. In fact our sense of smell is the only one which does not cross over in the brain, unlike all others (sight, hearing, touch, as well as all motor and autonomic nerve control). Our sense of smell is very rudimentary. That leaves us with sight and sound. And here is where things get complicated. We have areas in the rear brain which are able to make minute differentiations of sounds, and especially time-separated sounds. The area makes a slight impression on the skull (or the skull accommodates) and this is suspected as being in development with Homo erectus and Homo neanderthalensis.

At that point in our development, we could tell bird calls apart, but, aside from identifying animal calls, sound identification was useless to us in hunting. We were by design a species which roamed the edges of the savanna (supposedly) where our visual acuity (and our ability to run after a gazelle until it fell down from exhaustion) was much more important than sound. We moved from the savannas to forests and rivers where sound plays a minor role for us. Our visual acuity, however, exceeds that of dogs and wolves. We gathered food, whether plants or fish or large animals, by sight, not by sound.

Yet we have a well-developed capacity for differentiating sounds. We can tell *where* a very small object falls on a hard floor from the sound. Dogs will smell for it. We do not know the genesis of our enhanced hearing abilities, but most likely it served as a monitoring sense in communal groups. We have been gregarious forever. We have always lived in groups. We can follow a single conversation in a babble of talking voices. Eyes and hands could be used to pay attention to one task while hearing kept us aware of the activities of the group.

Our acute hearing is also of significant utility in child rearing. Our hearing is acute enough to spot the emotional content of a baby's voicing by the inflections. We can differentiate between degrees of displeasure and degrees of joy, and the whole range of other emotions and needs. (Dogs can do this also.) Our young are born in a most inept state and we need to care for them for a very long time. Next to eating nuts and berries and bringing home game, caring for children is the most time-consuming activity we ever undertook as a species. Child-rearing has probably always been a communal activity, but there are other things for the community to do as well, and since you cannot watch children constantly, sometimes you have to listen for them instead.

I don't think the start of language involved some spear-carrying Cro-Magnon coming home and having to invent the phrases, "Me-kill. Caribou. Come-with. Slice-up. Bring-home." It probably originated while watching and listening for kids, and sitting around in the spare time making up jokes, "Tickle, tickle, ha ha ha." [note 8]

Children have to be taught everything. Children learn through repetition, and humorous situations are the ones they would like to repeat or re-live. Whacking a child for stealing meat out of the pot, or shushing them away from hot coals, is not the type of activity adults and children would repeat just for the fun of it. But jokes and funny situations are. They are repeated and re-lived voluntarily.

If, in fact, there is anything "primitive" in language, it is humor. It runs consistently through all languages and through the speech of normal adults as well as brain-damaged people. My mother-in-law, with complete loss of expressive language and a severe impairment of receptive language due to two strokes, would still react to a funny situation appropriately.

And, additionally, there is nothing as universal as the ability to make puns. Puns come out of nowhere. They seem to arrive from some very primitive speech level. Puns seem to implicate the fun intellectual relationships between words of a basic vocabulary listing which exists in the mind. Even reasonably intelligent dogs invent jokes, but they cannot conceive of puns.

Language is not necessary to obtain food. We lived in a veritable pantry for tens of thousands of years. A sparsely populated world provided nothing but food for omnivorous humans. I believe that we developed language to entertain ourselves in all our free time, as we played. Play is a common characteristic activity of all mammals, and for children (as for all young mammals) play is learning.

It only takes two or three people to start an attempt to repeat and recall a funny situation. It takes very little to come up with a few nouns and verbs, and then you are off and running. A child moves from one-word sentences at 18 months to fully developed 4- and 5-word sentences in the span of a few months. Children who are never taught language will learn at any age, and within a few months.

A few adults can "invent" language in the same span of time. And with children around it will propagate generationally. Since it is a learned activity, it will incorporate its own teaching methods. We so readily teach children language because we ourselves have learned to teach language from our parents.

Language also propagates geographically. When talkies meet a non-talking group of people, the non-talkers will be talking in short order. This has been experienced repeatedly when signing deaf people have been introduced to groups of non-signing deaf people. They invent a common speech (differing from the signing originally used by the signers!) in a matter of weeks. [note 9]

The largest mystery of human language is that it is only about 40,000 years old (or much less), whereas modern humans have been around (by inference from rates of change of mitochondrial DNA) for 100,000 years. In itself that would tell you something: neither language nor grammar are biological. It is not like an appendix. It didn't "evolve" as a brain function or some neurological structure, not, at any rate, as part of the biology of our species. It evolved culturally. The rapid changes still seen in many languages today, and the enormous diversity of "grammars," also point to cultural evolution.

The biological structure needed for speech includes, besides a voice box of the proper dimensions, the enlargement of nasal passages. We don't see this in Neanderthals, but we see them fully developed in the first moderns of the archaeological record. From that point on our voicing and sound-recognition went hand in hand.

The Cro-Magnon types existed for 60,000 years (as in the Levant) using only the primitive Mousterian toolkit developed by and used by Neanderthals. And then, suddenly, about 40,000 or 50,000 years ago, we see the Cro-Magnon toolkit spring to life in southeastern Central Asia and the adjacent western Central Europe region, along with pierced shells and beads, carved ivories, limestone statues, bone needles and other household and hunting implements, decorated spear throwers, and, in Southwestern Europe, the first painted caves. None of these had ever been produced by any other hominids during the previous 3, 6, or 12 million years. [note 10]

The suggestion is that language suddenly developed 50,000 to 40,000 years ago. Wherever it developed, it would have spread like wildfire through adjacent populations of humans. It would have been the coolest thing next to pressure flaking. Language might have been the more easily taken up if the main attraction was the material culture of the nearby talking Cro-Magnon tribe. [note 11]

You have to admit that techniques like making buttonhole borers, detachable harpoons, or pressure-flaked serrated knives are not biological "evolutions" -- they are cultural evolutions. The sudden development and variety of Cro-Magnon's toolkit is *absolutely astounding* compared to the million years that Homo erectus used a single general-purpose bi-faced hand-axe as their only tool, or the uniformly sized flint "side scrapers" fabricated by Neanderthals for 200,000 years.

There are other parallel developments that are less easy to trace. Making cords, knotting nets, spinning, and weaving -- all point to a genesis in remote antiquity of about the same date. Mixing and compounding colorants were definitely within the scope of Cro-Magnon, as witnessed by the decorated caves of France and Spain and elsewhere. The first pottery dates from about the same time, in Japan. [note 12]

You would expect that language had something to do with that, but it is nearly impossible to describe in words how to knap flint or proceed with pressure flaking. In fact, language is not needed to pass on the knowledge of flint manufacturing or spinning but rather language is used to come up with the ideas for the uses of flint or threads. Language is descriptive, and any one description develops another, by way of metaphorical extension.

> *"The grand and vigorous function of metaphor is the generation of new language as it is needed. ... "*
> "[Metaphors] *literally create new objects. Indeed, language is an organ of perception, not simply a means of communication."*
> -- Julian Jaynes

From language came ideas -- suddenly and in wild profusion. That is where all the new tools came from. They were "made to order." A single human with language is capable of generating and specifying a range of ideas far beyond anything the whole rest of the mammal world was able to think of collectively in a billion years -- or Homo erectus was able to generate in over a million years.

What we have to conclude is that about 40,000 years ago humans came to a new beginning. With the addition of language, the world was totally modern. Soon all the edible plants had been named, all the huntable animals had been identified, every cave had been explored and decorated. Although language is not needed for demonstrating household tasks, naming a plant is a lot easier than locating the plant as an example. Language introduced new possibilities across the board. Anything could be invented which could be described -- tools and techniques were invented as needed.

And language allowed telling stories. We don't really know much about the stories; we only have the numerous instances of rock carvings and the painted caves which may point to such activities. When a painted cave depicts a herd of deer swimming across a river, it would certainly suggest a story activity to us, as do the cliff wall drawings in the Sahara of cattle roundups and dancing, although these last may be much later.

The Cro-Magnon toolkit coincides with the start of the last major glaciation (in Europe). Anthropologists insist that Cro-Magnon grew up during the severe cold of a major glaciation. I think that they grew up in a mild climate south of the northern glacier. More likely they had purposefully entered Europe as new hunting territory. But with the end of the glaciation it got colder and the migratory herds started to relocate northeast into Central Europe and into Northern Asia. The Cro-Magnon followed, now equipped with an advanced lithic technology for efficient hunting, portable kitchen utensils, a knowledge of the constructing of shelters, and of boats, rope, netting, and clothes, and very soon the techniques of spinning and weaving. It was language, also, which supported the social order needed for the Cro-Magnon trek eastward into Asia. [note 13]

Distance was no barrier in antiquity, as others have noted, and especially for hunters. By 35,000 years ago moderns had moved from Asia into all the continents faster than any species had ever spread, and in some cases much earlier. Australia was reached by 60,000 years ago.

Boat People

People spread out to get away from each other, and migrated to new areas to feed an expanding population, and this spread ideas widely. There are some clear signs of immensely wide contacts. Spinning and weaving, for example, are a very ancient practices, and spinning whorls are found worldwide and are identical everywhere. And finally there is the racial demography of Asia, with its parallel bands of three or four distinctly different human "types" from north to south, an indication of distinct groups all traveling east (or west, at an earlier time) to populate new territories -- and meeting the coastal populations which had arrived 20,000 years earlier. In the Americas we see the same bands -- linguistic in this case -- running in a north-south direction, an indication of arrivals of distinct groups via the Pacific coast.

At the U. C. Berkeley, Johanna Nichols has, for 15 years, classified languages by grammatical similarities to come up with relationships, rather than using the traditional language trees built on vocabularies. After 150 years of studies, finding relationships of vocabularies has only reduced the 5000 or more languages of the world to some 300 primitive types, with no indication of a connection between them.

The use of grammar as the connecting thread makes sense. All versions of pidgin English are identical in that the speakers use an English vocabulary overlaid on their native grammar. Grammar is very conservative, and it changes only slowly compared to words. The most astounding result of Nichols's work has been the identification of core grammars which spread up the east coast of Asia and down the west coast of the Americas. [note 14]

> "In Nichols's mind, the picture is clear. An enormous and sustained wave of human migration started about 50,000 years ago somewhere in Southeast Asia. Over thousands of years, successive bands of people spread out from the region. They could move relatively quickly because they were coastally adapted -- they knew how to make simple boats and make a living from the sea. Over thousands of years, some carried their languages south and west through coastal New Guinea and into Northern Australia, while others moved clockwise up the coast of Asia, across the Bering Strait into Alaska, then down the west coast of North and South America."
>
> -- Bob Adler scicom.ucsc.edu/SciNotes/9901/echoes/echoes.htm

"Simple boats" is contemporary chauvinism. It also seems clear that the trek along coastal South America was north from Antarctica. With the withdrawal of ocean water by glaciation, the coasts were cleared to reveal the plains of the continental shelves. Oceans may have been calmer. The course of travel would have been from river to river along the coasts. There are rivers every 25 miles (40 km) or so mostly everywhere. Humans stuck close to rivers because, like all primates, we require enormous amounts of drinking water. The rivers additionally were the routes inland.

Languages and Texts

In previous text I have offered snippets of historical documents in evidence on the presumption that our forebears at least had the wits to be able to keep records, even if they didn't develop particle physics or historiography. But these records and many of the later narratives cannot be read directly from our cultural perspective, which introduces the bias of modern values and the world-view derived from our particular grammars and what we think we know. It is critical to have an understanding of the worldview of the people who wrote the records of antiquity, and for this a look at the languages of those records might be useful.

I am no linguist, so this overview will be fairly brief and may not be accurate. In most instances I have only discussed some aspects of texts. This may shine some light on the underlying languages and grammars.

The language base is what forms the cognitive processes used by a people in their perception of the world. The Indo-European languages are solidly based on the concept of time as a series of "events" which flow from the future to the past through the present. The verb forms and their declensions certainly show this. We face the future. "Time is like a river," said Heraclitus, facing upstream, "you cannot step into it twice."

However, this is not true for most languages. Many languages do not require people to recognize "time" as a flowing substance or for time to have significance. There are large differences between languages, which cause different speakers to use entirely different analytical methods in reaching an understanding of the world. There is certainly an ongoing convergence among the radically different viewpoints on the world (which can be seen as early as in Mesopotamia) and today more so with increased contact between people with differing languages.

... American Languages

Overall concepts of time are cultural (so is the "value" of logic, by the way). This was pointed out by Edward T Hall in books on cultural differences (*The Silent Language* (1959), *The Hidden Dimension* (1966), and others), dealing with personal space, the concepts of self as related to the body, and, most amazingly, difference with respect to an understanding of time.

Some of this was based on earlier observations by the linguists Edward Sapir and Benjamin Whorf of two North American Indian languages. Whorf pointed out that the first concern of Hopi is actuality, and of Navajo, the type of activity. Hopi belongs to the Uto-Aztecan language family group which includes Nahuatl, spoken by the Mesoamerican Aztecs, and the *lingua franca* of the Classical Era Maya. The language group is found in the Western United States, away from the coast, along the west coast of Mexico, and into Nicaragua, interspersed with other language groups.

The Sapir-Whorf Hypothesis (as it is known) suggests that language affects how people perceive their reality -- the content and structure of a culture is directly related to the content and structure of a language, that is, of the grammar of a language.

"The commonly held belief that the cognitive processes of all human beings possess a common logical structure which operates prior to and independently of communication through language is erroneous. It is Whorf's view that the linguistic patterns themselves determine what the individual perceives in this world and how he thinks about it."

"The -- for us -- self-evident distinction between past, present and future does not exist in the Hopi language. It makes no distinction between tenses, but indicates the validity a statement has: fact, memory, expectations, or custom."

"There is no difference in Hopi between 'he runs' 'he is running, 'he ran,' all being rendered by 'wari' -- 'running occurs.' An expectation is rendered by 'warinki' ('running occur [I] daresay'), which covers 'he will, shall, should, would run.' If it is a statement of a general law, 'warinkiwe' [sic?] ('running occur, characteristically') is applied (La Barre, 1954)."

"The Hopi 'has no general notion or intuition of time as a smooth flowing continuum in which everything in the universe proceeds at an equal rate, out of a future, through a present, into a past.' (Whorf 1952)"

"Instead of our categories of space and time, Hopi rather distinguishes the 'manifest,' all that which is accessible to the senses with no distinction between present and past, and the 'unmanifest' comprising the future as well as what we call mental."

-- originally at newciv.org/ISSS_Primer/

From the same source, on the Navajo, and their primary concern with the type of activity:

"Navajo has little development of tenses; the emphasis is upon types of activity, and thus it distinguishes durative, perfective, usitative, repetitive, iterative, optative, semifactive, momentaneous, progressive, transitional, conative, etc., aspects of action."

Writing in *Language, Thought, and Reality* (1956), Benjamin Whorf states:

"We cut nature up, organize it into concepts, and ascribe significances as we do, largely because we are parties to an agreement to organize it in this way -- an agreement that holds throughout our speech community and is codefied in the patterns of our language. The agreement is, of course, an implicit and unstated one, but its terms are absolutely obligatory; we cannot talk at all except by subscribing to the organization and classification of data which the agreement decrees."

Hall, writing in *The Hidden Dimension* (1966), comments on the fact that Whorf became fluent in the Hopi language, which he studied for years, but with some effort. About Whorf's efforts, Hall writes the following:

"Whorf discovered part of the difficulty when he began to understand the Hopi concepts of time and space. In Hopi, there is no word which is equivalent to 'time' in English. Because both time and space are inextricably bound up in each other, elimination of the time dimension alters the spatial one as well."

He quotes Whorf as:

"The Hopi thought-world has no imaginary space ... it may not locate thought dealing with real space anywhere but in real space, nor insulate space from the effects of thought."

Hall concludes:

"In other words, the Hopi cannot, as we think of it, 'imagine' a place such as the missionary's heaven or hell."

I am quoting Hall here to show how divergent the reality of the Hopi might be from a reality based on the Indo-European grammar of tenses. The failure in being able to imagine a place which could only exist in the mind, which Hall suggests above, seems like a failure of *subjective consciousness,* but this statement is hardly adequate evidence.

Following chapters will need to deal with translations from the Mayan and these will point out the very apparent lack of concern for sequences in time, although "history" was certainly understood. There will also be an inexplicable certitude of time existing in a rotating series with a scale of no more than 250 years. And where we would attempt to establish causal connections between events through their apparent contiguity in time, the Maya feels the need to establish events as the actions of some agent -- to the point, at times, of making up names. Both of these are pointed up above for the related languages of the Hopi and Navajo.

"I mentioned in relation to the units of measure that the Mayas did not seem to have the same concept of time as ours. This would seem strange if we take into account an overwhelming majority of inscriptions which have relation with records of periods of time. However, in the Maya language there does not exist the word 'time.' The most common expression is 'kinil' meaning in relation to the sun, or days."
   -- Nexus Tzacol, from Project Ahau (Internet).

   Keeping this in mind will help with understanding, even though the Mayan texts I have accessed are only available to me through translations, at times through two other languages. More on Mesoamerican texts further below.

... Sumerian texts

   Neither Sumerian nor the later Akkadian is an Indo-European language. Akkadian is, in fact, a Semitic language (today classified as part of "Afro-Asiatic" which includes Arabia and North Africa). Sumerian does not seem to be related to any other language, although I have seen suggestions including Hungarian, Basque, Dravidian, and Georgian. The Akkadian speakers had enormous respect for the Sumerians, whom they succeeded, and they long used Sumerian as their official language. But we know next to nothing about Sumerian. In Sumer and Akkad there was a sense of time somewhat similar to that of the Indo-European language in that they had a past tense and a combined present and future tense -- actually a *perfect* and *imperfect* as in Arabic. But there is a notable difference in the point of view.

   "... from the perspective of a Babylonian [Akkadian, Sumerian] *the past lay before him or "faced him," while the future was conceived as lying behind him. ... the attention of Mesopotamian culture was directed towards the past and thus ultimately towards the origins of all existence."*
   -- Stefan Maul (1997) [note 15]

   The sense of "the flow of time" is thus reversed in Sumerian and Akkadian from how we assume time to flow. The Mesopotamians "face the past," and are propelled backwards "into the future" -- a cognate of the word "back" in Sumerian, by the way. The beginnings were the only reality. All the innovations of civilization had been delivered by the Gods at the beginning of time. It allowed the Gods to retain their nearly three-thousand-year stranglehold on Mesopotamia.

... **Egyptian texts**

Old Egyptian is a distinctly African language (At one time called Hamitic), the language group of much of Northern Africa, and of the same family as Semitic Akkadian and others in the Sub-Saharan region. But a conservatism even stronger than in Mesopotamia shows in their lack of any need to present narratives. Although there are some chronological narratives written quite late, there seem to be no early "narratives" such as we have in Sumer, Akkad, and Babylon starting after 2000 BC. There were tabulation of kings and annual records, as elsewhere, dating to the 5th dynasty which records kings dating back to 3050 BC. But narratives seem to have developed only during the Middle Kingdom (ending in about 1500 BC), and are quoted in inscriptions in tombs for a 200-year period early in the New Kingdom (after 1327 BC) -- in a quaintly "antique" language, that is, in the style of the Middle Kingdom.

Yet Egypt, which obviously and insistently looked to the past as the only reality -- the "First Time" -- also looked forward to the pharaoh's meeting with Re, the God of creation, as a completion of the pharaoh's earthly existence. I suspect reality was understood as a cycle of existence where time revolved, and perhaps continually repeated the past. Time did not move, as it does for us. However, it is uncertain what the worldview really was, or how it could be explained in terms familiar to us.

We know more about the Egyptian attitude towards words and names. Certainly they believed in the efficacy of ceremony and the force of words. From the spells used in the tombs, and from some later tales about the use of names, we sense that for the Egyptians *words by themselves* represented a powerful magic. The preparations for burial were entirely enfolded in magic, with absolute certainty of the results -- the continued life after death -- proven, as Jaynes explained, by the voices of the dead which continued to be heard.

What seems to be lacking in ancient Egypt is our understanding that a simile is not an identity. Books about Egypt which speak of this or that "representing" something or other, are mistakenly imposing our sense of metaphorical equivalence on their use of language. The pharaoh did not represent Horus, he *was* Horus. The multiple statues of the king in his funeral temple were not representations, they actually *were* the king -- all of them. The curious identity of images with what they "represented" is probably best demonstrated by the fact that in tombs the hieroglyphs which used images of birds or animals were faced away from the coffin (or had their legs removed graphically) so they could not advance on the coffin -- to keep the pharaoh's body safe from attack. Although this is totally foreign to us, the Egyptians had no room for metaphors.

... Chinese texts

China has a "saved" literature from 2300 BC to 700 BC, collated sometime after 500 BC. It is presented as factual, and the earliest record is a compilation, the *Annals of Shu* by Confucius, of odds and ends of surviving documents of the Shang dynasty and earlier. The first two sections of the Shu (covering dates back to 2357 BC) are clearly noted as later recollections. These start with, for example, "Examining into antiquity, we find that... ." Only the remaining sections were written at the time of the events which are described. The Shu is history.

There are, in addition, "legendary histories" of China, which are not part of the coda of the Classics. These legends and mythologies were not committed to writing until a later date (after AD 200 or 400), when a story-telling literature had become well established.

The Chinese languages do not have a "tense" associated with verbs, although there are clear indications in the texts of "when" actions occur which is fully congruent with the great complexities of Indo-European verb declensions, such as the "future past perfect." The script is ideographic, which makes it useful over different languages and more stable over time than phonetic scripts, but it is open to questions of exact meaning. Additionally, the media was impermanent -- bamboo slivers, cloth, and paper. Thus the coda of older documents has required constant transcription and has been open to endless emendation. This has left no actual documents contemporaneous with historical events, only later compilations. Additionally the script was not unified until about 200 BC under the Chin, the same dynasty which purged China of nearly all books in 213 BC. Many of these were reconstructed from memory and hidden books -- but not until much later.

The other influence on the compilations after 500 BC was the humanist and realist philosophies of the Confucianists (Confucius, 551-479 BC) and the earlier Taoists (Lao-tse, 604-531 BC). Here we are in an era of classical philosophical development. We see efforts to tame and explain the world in terms of basic forces of nature (as the yin/yang and material elements), not unlike the contemporaneous Greek efforts to displace the Olympian Gods with rational thought. This had an impact on the records which are forwarded to us, for they have been cleaned up and emptied of mythical and legendary elements. The texts were edited to be in the service of the imperial aristocracy, and only examples of virtuous deeds have been retained. The Chou had already removed many of the ancient religious specifics. The

Confucianists retained only the veneration of ancestors, plus a concept of heaven as the source of all authority. The Shu is history, however, and can be believed. It is not legend, it is fact. [note 16]

> *"It was philosophers of this period* [the third dynasty, the Chou, 1027 to 221 BC] *who first enunciated the doctrine of the 'mandate of heaven,' the notion that the ruler (the 'son of heaven') governed by divine right but that his dethronement would prove that he had lost the mandate. The doctrine explained and justified the demise of the two earlier dynasties and at the same time supported the legitimacy of present and future rulers."*
> -- www-chaos.umd.edu/history/

In part the proof of legitimacy for any dynasty was the creation of a compendium of the activities of the previous dynasty to demonstrate how the previous dynasty had gone awry, and thus lost the mandate to govern the world. Thus we have very detailed (although terse) historical records from after about 200 BC, and some from 700 BC.

... Mesoamerican texts

Mesoamerican written texts were almost totally destroyed by the Europeans, and only partially reconstituted after AD 1500. What we have are four Pre-Colonial codexes of an astrological nature, with no "historical" content except as might be inferred. There are a number of Colonial period narrative texts, but they tend to be jumpy -- they do not convey the sense of the progress of time as we would expect, despite the occurrences of finely detailed counts of years in some texts. The *Codex Chimalpopoca,* for example, proceeds to list ages into the past but it seems to be mostly number magic rather than historical fact. [note 17]

That the Mesoamerican narrative texts are formulaic, stylized, fantastical, and lack a cohesive narrative development may be due to the fact that the language structure does not require it. Mesoamerica presents a very large set of seemingly unrelated languages whose only structural affinities seem to be a highly developed sense of action (in verb use) and very weak tenses. Even the verb "to be" seems to be missing. But there is a strong sense of spatial relationships (topography), to be expected of a people who managed to make sense of the Tzolkin and Haab calendars as if they were spreadsheets.

Both the *Popol Vuh* and the *Annals of Cuahitlan* use a list of only "12 ancestors," which would amount to a time span of about 300 years, and use the movement of the tribe from a location of origin to a final location as the complete history of the recent world. It is the act of migration which is important, not the details, and the search for a new homeland is the only event of significance. The "history" texts of other tribes in the same region of Central Mexico also use this formula of a migration. Descriptions of epochs before the migration and arrival in a new homeland tend to be spectacular -- and may be assumed to represent celestial events rather than tribal events.

We know from the Maya that time was held to be circular, or rather repetitive. The numeric values of dates -- every day was individually named and numbered, and imbedded in a deep series of cycles -- loom as large as events. In fact, all events were placed on a rotating platter of time, and fitted in with predictability. Human events occurred because they had happened before, and human destiny was to repeat them, with the requirement that they do so properly. This sense of repetition is the cognate of a causal model of reality which, although mostly unintelligible to us, is not different from the status of prophecy in Greek antiquity or Christianity. [note 18]

The Maya and Mesoamericans assumed the existence of a spirit world which ordered all things to happen at the right place in time in the material world. The Mesoamerican concept of reality involved action. All successes and failures of the physical world were caused by the actions of the Gods of a parallel spiritual world, and for the Maya (and presumably for all the peoples of Mesoamerica) the spiritual world was completely dependent on actions performed in the physical world. Man maintained the spiritual world which was in turn responsible for all causation in the material world. This was a circular arrangement where each world upheld the other and presented a chain of causation which could not be broken.

Suzanne D. Fisher, in an introduction to an English translation of Antonio Bolio's Spanish translation of the Maya *Chilam Balam*, writes, about the spiritual nature of the Maya:

> *"As provider of nourishment for divine beings, man has in his hands the existence of the world, which is created and maintained by the gods. In this sense neither men nor gods are perfect, since both are mutually dependent upon one another; both are insufficient unto themselves, but the dynamic harmony they constitute gives them sufficiency."*

This philosophical outlook in Mesoamerica might explain the calendars with their unwieldy complexities of a dozen meshing cycles. Since the spiritual world remained essentially unknown, an almanac constituted the only clue as to what actions to take in the future. Once a small set of events was discovered to form a coincidence on the wheel of time, the concept of repeatability would yield an understanding of the relationship between the two worlds. I suspect this first happened after 2349 BC when Venus struck four times at intervals of 52 solar years. This was taken very seriously by the

454   *Recovering the Lost World, Volume 2*

Olmecs. Then when, after 1492 BC, Venus again appeared at a 52-year interval (but in a "Tun-year" interval), disaster was averted, not by chance it seemed, but by human intervention in the spiritual world. If the intervention involved bloodletting and human sacrifice, then the pattern was set. [note 19]

Such at least seems to be the world-view of the Maya, and by extension the world-view of all of Mesoamerica. The religious culture seems to be uniform up to about 600 BC, and over a large geographical area. There were apparently differing interpretations after 600 BC, but mostly consistent among the Maya.

Mesoamerican histories do not yield any information about the remote past which is sensibly ordered in time. The *Popol Vuh* groups similar actions together by location without regard to their sequence, making the book difficult to read for Westerners who expect a listing of events to follow each other chronologically. In the *Popol Vuh* the celestial ball-playing twins are repeating, with more success, the adventures of their twin fathers. It is the activity that counts, not the sequence. The *Popol Vuh* is discussed in a later chapter. Some books of the *Chilam Balam* are a notable exception to the lack of chronological order in narratives.

With Mesoamerican sources you have to search among strange descriptions and senseless concerns to find information coincident with Mesopotamian and Egyptian sources. There is plenty of solid information to be found, although nearly everything celebrates celestial events in 2349 BC and 865 BC, and much reads as magic run amok.

One exception is Book 10, the "Creation of the World," a section of the *Book Of Chilam Balam Of Chumayel.* "The Creation of the World" is very specific and recalls events dating back to 5800 BC without references to the metaphorical and allegorical twists of the Classical era. All except one event is dated correctly, that is, to the same dates as can be gleaned from Eastern Mediterranean sources, by Katun periods of 20 years. See the chapter "The Chilam Balam" for more details.

With some effort three additional sections can be read as accurate descriptions of events dating back to 2349 BC (the "third creation"), to circa 10,900 BC (the "survey of the world"), and possibly to 30,000 or 40,000 years before the present. See the chapter "The Olmec Record of the Past" for more details.

The *Chilam Balam* is also one of only three historical documents of the Maya, the others being the *Popol Vuh* and the engraved texts at Palenque of circa AD 700. Some of the text of Palenque points to events in the 24th century BC, which can be aligned with what we know from other sources.

Subjective Consciousness

What I have tried to show above is the variation in languages of different peoples (their grammars), which would have had a direct impact on their understanding of the world. Yet all of them used language to achieve *subjective consciousness* -- some earlier, some not until very late.

I have introduced the concept of *subjective consciousness* as culturally acquired in earlier text, and made reference to Julian Jaynes. Perhaps a very brief review of his work would be called for here.

I would urge anyone to read Jaynes, at a minimum in order to reach an understanding of *how* we think -- through metaphors, narratization, and spatial fantasizing -- and also how many judgments and solutions to problems are reasoned out without conscious awareness, that is, without what we would otherwise consider as "thinking." As noted by Jaynes, actual "conscious thinking" represents a thimbleful of the gross volume of all that we would consider as "thoughts."

Jaynes spends the first chapter of his book in telling what consciousness (*subjective consciousness*) is not. It is not a copy of what we experience; it is not the source of concepts; it is not needed for learning; and it is not necessary for thinking or reasoning. It is a difficult chapter, for much of what we hold dearly as the core of our innermost mentality is removed as support of consciousness.

... Basis of Consciousness

Language is an absolute prerequisite for *subjective consciousness*. Language is a system of naming which begets other names. It is ever-expansive, especially because the names for anything new are metaphorically related to things already known (and named).

But language is not enough for consciousness. After all, many animals use languages but can only conceive of the present tense and the near future. "Let's eat; let's play; let's screw."

"Arf arf, arf arf arf,
the mailman is at the door,
he is going to kill us all."
    -- the dog

Here the dog, in her limited consciousness, is imagining the worst for the next few moments, as dogs have done for 100,000 years, be it marauding bears invading a campsite or evil mailmen tampering with the mailslot. But the imagined future for a dog does not extend much further ahead. We, on the other hand, can displace our "thinking" far beyond the present or into the past, reconstructing remembered or imagined spaces. But most importantly, our minds can race through many alternatives (of "who is at the door?") and make rapid evaluations -- all based on placing a substitute for ourselves into these alternative spaces.

But what are these mental "spaces?" The spaces of *subjective consciousness*, like language, are also created metaphorically. The general metaphor in use here is the *analog,* where every part of the "real world" is represented by a corresponding part in the model -- the mental space of *subjective consciousness*. It is like a map: the map reduces real world geography to marks on a paper, and the map in turn can be inspected to determine spatial relationships of the real world.

These spaces are constructed and "observed" by us, as if we are situated within them, and are thus inhabited by a copy of ourselves, an "analog I." You can even step back to see this "I" from some distance as an "analog me." So, to complete the definition of *subjective consciousness*, it requires the individual creation of an "analog I" in the expanded mind space. It is a facility so familiar to us that it difficult to think of yourself actually engaging in "subjective consciousness." "Subjective consciousness" is to be distinguished from "self-consciousness" or "self-awareness" which is observable in many animals.

Now we have *subjective consciousness* as we understand it: a focus on the specifics of a space or an action, seemingly located in the mind, specifically in the left hemisphere, and using an "I" which is able to move about through actualities and possibilities and evaluate alternative courses of action based on probable outcomes. And in these spaces we can shift time. We can determine future actions (as yet uncompleted) and also review past actions (making up the elements of an operating space called "memory"). These evaluations are the level of "judgment" of which the verbal left brain is capable -- and at which it is very good.

Subjective consciousness is a focus which completely knits over the chasms between spatial locations (and times, also) in your mind -- to make it seamless to the point of not ever being able to be conscious of not being conscious. It reorganizes memories to make them seem like "looked at spaces," rather than actual sensory impressions. It forces you to "remember" anything you have done by taking an exterior spatial view of the activity. Even mathematical concepts are evaluated as spatial relationships. Jaynes claims there is no *subjective consciousness* except that which is represented by imagined spaces accompanied by the analogs of normal human actions --

we view, review, fit, weigh, and manipulate concepts, and all as actions. Time is also viewed spatially, as a continuous space of differing gradations. [note 20]

Subjective consciousness is a focus which only occasionally actually includes awareness of sensory experience. Not that you cannot shift your consciousness to something that catches your attention or become acutely aware of some part of your body -- but it is another (unconscious) part of the brain which tips you off, and then you shift to inhabit an "analog real space," moving your "analog I" to just behind the eyes. [note 21]

More importantly, and despite what you think occurs in your mind, *subjective consciousness* excludes the formation of concepts, so-called reasoning, and most judgments about physical objects and other people. There is no recollection, for example, of how you managed to drive your car home, and there is awareness, but no "thinking" involved in panic reactions. A later review of a newly constructed memory will add all the "reasoning" that determined your actions. All immediate "thinking" is done in the background, unconsciously, and by the right brain. You don't have any awareness of this until the conclusions are transmitted to the *subjective consciousness* of the left side. [note 22]

We only apply logic (as "reasoning") after the fact. Similarly, ask any artist where ideas come from -- they appear out of thin air. Ask Einstein where his concepts came from -- they came from no-where, usually while shaving. Einstein remarked that he shaved very carefully, for new ideas would pop into his mind and often startle him. This happened during other mundane activities also.

"I thought of that while riding my bike."
    -- Albert Einstein

None of consciousness is anything like what a wolf does to chase down an elk, which is totally automatic, involves quick judgments and pre-guessing the moves of his prey, and who knows what else. If you or I did something as wild as that we would make all the right moves and never "be conscious" of them. What we *would* be conscious of is the overview of the real space we would be operating in (chasing an elk), but seen as if we were watching a movie, with ourselves simultaneously as actor and viewer.

Our "consciousness" could be elsewhere while we were chasing the elk. This condition is easily recognized in driving a car, where we make all the right adjustments to traffic, yet are "lost in thought" most of the time, lost that is, in the musings of our left-brain consciousness. We could be considering the opening notes of some piece of music. The car trip (or elk chase) would still be completed with the same efficiency -- our body would still make the correct decisions on how to move, where to turn, when to stop. And none of it would involve "thinking" as we commonly understand it.

The right brain can perform any "learned" activity blindly, like playing a piano, or driving a car. But it has trouble with new situations. Evaluating anything new is the task of *subjective consciousness*. In fact, *subjective consciousness* will hinder automatic activity. Try becoming aware of your fingers while typing. You will start making mistakes or even come to a halt. Become aware of someone looking at you while you are walking and your step will falter and your shoes will scuff the ground.

Development of Subjective Consciousness

What Jaynes next suggests is that *subjective consciousness* is learned by children at about age 7 or 8. It involves recognizing themselves as seen by others -- an "analog I" which is then internalized and placed into the space of the imagination. This analog can move around, perform actions, evaluate results, and can even vault through time. Parents constantly guide small children through numerous "what-if" situations and badger them with metaphorical constructions and reminders of remembered events, in effect *teaching them subjective consciousness*. Part of this is to teach to the child what others might be thinking. Since *subjective consciousness* is learned, it is cultural, not biological. And, Jaynes claims, because *subjective consciousness* is language-based, it is easily learned by children as soon as they gain some facility with the expansion of language into metaphors. [note 23]

Subjective consciousness is deeply imbedded in the teaching of *subjective consciousness*. It is as if we could say that "the expression of subjective consciousness" is "the teaching of subjective consciousness." In this respect it is no different from our teaching of language skills.

Historically, Jaynes places the creation of the "internal I" after the development of written texts. It was also in response to a population expansion of the Middle East, because the other source of *subjective consciousness* is meeting new people -- not those familiar to us. For the most part we don't look at those familiar to us, nor do we question how they see us. Having to meet strangers causes you to wonder how they are seeing you and this results in the creation of an "analog I" as the way you imagine others see you. By reflection this then becomes the way you imagine yourself. [note 24]

The quality of *subjective consciousness* changes over time. Since it is cultural, there is no biological evolution involved, but *subjective consciousness* does evolve. Jaynes has documented the radical changes over the span of a few hundred years during the first millennium BC in Greece and the Levant, and noted the changes in South America over the span of a few months. The quality of *subjective consciousness* will be different from one person to another, although any social group with the same language and a common culture will for the most part share a common *subjective consciousness*.

Both the left and right hemisphere of the brain can understand speech. However, only the left brain can speak. The right brain specializes in seeing objects in context and has a sense of spatial relationships. The left brain concentrates on specific objects but is able to apprehend and order linear patterns, including, of course, speech and stories. [note 25]

That is a sort of shorthand, for the right hemisphere is also involved in speech -- operating the mouth and vocal cords. And the right brain can talk to the left brain in "voices" which are either heard silently in the consciousness of the left hemisphere, or pass right through and are spoken. You will see yourself doing this, for example, in greeting familiar people, but you will also find yourself mouthing off at the most inopportune moments.

The "voices" from the right brain are the remembered admonitions of your parents, and later, your superiors. It is your right brain that brings to mind such things as "it is time to go," or "close the door." It is the right brain that always has the seemingly appropriate solutions, for it sees things in an overall familiar context and knows what to do in any situation which is not novel. It is also the more creative -- solutions to many "computable problems" come from the right.

The left brain concentrates on individual objects often to the total exclusion of context, but works easily in linear format -- like remembering phone numbers as one unit (which is but a larger decontextualized object), remembering songs and stories, and placing all the words of a sentence in the right order when you speak. The left is verbal, linear, and, because of the imagined spaces that can be examined, analytical. But in actuality it probably spends most of the time just meandering. The only conscious "thinking" we do is musing and reflecting -- always by means of imagined actions in imagined spaces. The right brain often gets annoyed with the left, and you will hear yourself muttering comments on your lack of directed thinking or your behavior.

Jaynes points to the left brain as the center of our consciousness: we are "aware" of left brain activities, but never of the right-brain. When the left brain gets into a bind on a problem, it is the right brain which often spits out an answer to the left-brain's consciousness -- "It popped into my mind."

In an age before written texts, or before reflection on the self as seen by others, the right brain "spoke" -- actual words were heard by the left side. We still hear these admonitions today, but mostly silently, "close the door." The wonderfully common-sense right hemisphere at times has to warn the left half of something, or get its attention. Jaynes suggests that using heard speech might have been a shorthand used by the right brain because the rear commissure connecting the two halves is only a few millimeters in diameter. By comparison, the olfactory commissure (which we do not have at all) in dogs and rodents is, as I mentioned, 10 times that diameter, thus 100 times the area. These animals integrate left and right brain functions surrounding smell much better than we integrate our verbal functions.

Our right to left communication today is often in visual concepts (I suspect), rather than words, although we still hear our mind "say" things -- quietly. It can be guaranteed that almost all statements of "correct behavior" which jump out of our mouth are initiated in the right brain. However, frequently they are inappropriate. The right brain does not deal with anything novel and cannot analyze the nuances of a new situation and peruse the alternate possibilities which the conscious left brain can imagine. Often you will find yourself saying, "My first thought was ... but upon further consideration...."

... Instructions from God

Throughout the "Era of the Gods" and for 2000 years after, these instructions from the right brain were "heard" as the voices of the Gods: instructions on crop management, irrigation, and whatever else was appropriate for daily life of a community. There were many thousands of people in Mesopotamia and Egypt involved in agriculture, distribution, and trade. These were also the first large populations to do repetitive backbreaking communal tasks. Grain production requires that type of work, but it was done without reluctance because the Gods were held as real, superior, and absolute in power, and a slave mentality developed. Society was to continue as it was: with people sowing and reaping the fields of the Gods. Early inscriptions insist on this.

Jaynes points out the "authority" of spoken words, and he supplies extensive data from schizophrenics and commissureotomized patients. The right brain under these conditions issues commands, not solutions or suggestions. This is not different, he claims, from what was experienced by the people of Mesopotamia and Egypt up to about 1000 BC.

It is the development of written texts (claims Jaynes) which opened up a new vista: the possibility that words could be independent of a person and thus "voice" could be abstracted into silence. This is an amazing concept which filtered down into society over the next few hundred years as parents modeled such silent consciousness to children. And with that the voices disappeared. [note 26]

... Differences

As examples of the differences in consciousness of vastly different people, compare the war edicts and bragging of the Assyrians with the contemporaneous "Spring and Autumn" Wars being waged in China. The wars were no different -- and the same example of the warring Gods stood before both groups in the skies overhead. But the attitudes were completely different. The Assyrians were bellicose and cruel and insisted on devastating the peoples they had conquered -- always over matters of tribute. [note 27]

> *"Throughout the Assyrian war records runs the monotonous mantra. 'I destroyed, I devastated. I burned with fire'. No hint of mercy or pity here; but ... repetitive and total conquest. Assyria, often likened to the Nazis, was a thoroughgoing military nation, highly disciplined. Her characteristics were destructive invasion, deportation and taxation."*
> -- Originally from CIAS at specialtyinterests.net.

The Chinese states went to war over the same sort of resources, but the tactics of war and settlements took a different course. By 400 BC there was already a conscious effort to view tactics philosophically and write about them, as follows. The Chinese in fact have never favored warfare.

> *"In general, the method of employing the military is this: Preserving the [enemy's] state capital is best, destroying their state capital is second best. Preserving their army is best, destroying their army is second best. ... attaining one hundred victories in one hundred battles is not the pinnacle of excellence. Subjugating the enemy's army without fighting is the true pinnacle of excellence."*
> -- Sun Tzu, opening lines *The Art of War* (circa 400 BC).
> [note 28]

... Points of Disagreement

For many people language is so obviously and unquestionably innate that the book by Jaynes will make absolutely no sense at all. And without the idea that language could have evolved culturally, you cannot understand the idea of a cultural evolution of *subjective consciousness*. Growing up bilingual helps, for it provides some perspective. But most of us fail to examine even our own "word-thinking" and the language of others. Another contributing factor is the incredible chauvinism we have adopted to separate ourselves both from animals and from the past.

Other people will dismiss Jaynes over the details of the *Iliad*, which he uses as his start-up example of a change in consciousness. The objections involve arguments about when the *Iliad* was written, whether Troy existed at all, and how a group of Greek pirates could possibly wage a ten-year war. Also, since Jaynes is using 1100 BC for the Trojan war (a date first suggested by Herodotus), he is forced to assume that the transmission of details of the epic was via some sort of semi-conscious bards. This follows a theory of "bardic transmission" dating from studies of Balkan epic poetry earlier in the 20th century, but the exact transmission from bard to bard has since been disproven. [note 29]

I have other differences with Jaynes myself. I object to Jaynes's insistence on the need for kings and leaders. It seems to be a peculiarly Western outlook that you cannot have a village of 200 people without some sort of control, much less a city of 10,000. Often he slips into generalization like "the mechanism of social control." Archaeologically, it appears that there were no leaders, kings, or pharaohs in control before 3100 BC. However, we do not need to look among antique or primitive societies alone for egalitarian societies. The precursor of the Dutch Republic, a collection of city-states, managed adequately without promoting anyone to absolute power for several hundred years. Humans will cooperate -- it is natural for us as a gregarious species, although it is also natural to demand leadership in times of social stress, as happened after 3100 BC. The idea of "individuality," which today makes us almost perversely independent and uncooperative, is a very late concept in Europe, probably dating to well after the 16th or 17th century AD. [note 30]

Jaynes uses the idea of "social control" to suggest how the voices of the Gods -- which most definitely occurred -- might have started and been located in the right hemisphere of the brain. He resorts to the suggestion of an "evolution by natural selection as a method of social control." But this is an unclear concept. I would suggest that "natural selection" is not an issue, primarily because the need for "social control" is not a fact.

I would suggest, instead, that the structure of the mammalian brain is already lateralized for spatial and linear functionality, respectively in the right and left hemisphere. This is in itself enough to naturally place speech functions -- which require linear order -- on the left. In addition, the speech functions are fluidly relocatable, which I think would argue against an evolutionary mandate. Some people have speech functions located on the right, as with those who suffered left hemisphere damage at an early age, and with some left-handed people.

What Jaynes, publishing in 1979, was not aware of was the research by Talbott in 1980, and the subsequent expansion on this over the next twenty years, showing the enormous cultural influence of the planets standing in the sky close to Earth, which were universally understood as the Gods who directed all human activities -- the very Gods whose voices Jaynes places in the right hemisphere.

Jaynes instead uses marked graves in the Neolithic (from 7000 BC), the rather occasional extravagant graves of "kings" (which may be the misdated Sumerian pit graves of 800 BC), and the display of the skulls of the dead in homes (and later temple structures) in various locations in the Middle East, to suggest that the hallucinating voices of the dead continued to be heard. In Egypt during historic times it was certainly held true that the voice of the dead pharaoh remained to be heard to advise and direct. But this period follows directly on the prehistoric era when, for a thousand years or more, mankind was confronted by the image of a large head looming constantly above the north horizon.

We have no idea of the function of all the variously displayed and decorated skulls. In the era before 3100 BC, the skulls might have been honored dead relatives, parents, or they might have been enemies or sacrificial victims. The images in the sky after 4077 BC must have had an enormous influence on humans, and humans, as ever, imitated what they saw. The exact measure of this is not revealed until after the head in the sky had disappeared. If anything induced the "voices of the gods" to be heard via the rear commissure between the right hemisphere and the left, it would have been this constant thousand-year image of a globe in the sky.

Advantages

We could ask, What is the advantage of subjective consciousness? Obviously, in the remote past, it was used to get through change, whether cataclysmic change or the need to live through social change. But, we could ask, what is the utility in today's milieu?

From my perspective, *subjective consciousness* allows traveling through time, visiting distant places, and imagining cosmic relationships. It also allows navigating the complexities of relationships, imagining technology not yet in existence, and selling products to those who do not need them.

We should also not neglect the possibility that the *subjective consciousness* of the left brain aids the normal background processes engaged in by the right brain. Certainly we know that the right brain knows whatever the left brain knows, and is able to work out solutions to questions that the left brain just cannot handle. Einstein's care in shaving is an example of the startling revelations which can come to consciousness as if out of nowhere. Einstein's brilliant ideas certainly were not limited to parental admonitions.

I suspect that a salesman who has gone through attempts to enter the mind

of his customers will have offered all of these scenarios to his right brain.
They will be stored somewhere and can be accessed as needed. The best
approach for a particular customer will be selected and presented to
subjective consciousness as if out of nowhere -- based on an almost
instantaneous analysis of the customer's psychological state. Considering the
speed with which the right brain can operate, this certainly is a more likely
process than having to wait for *subjective consciousness* to take the time to
trip through a number of imagined scenarios. Everyday speech and the
creations of poets and artists must be generated like this. I also suspect that
the right brain today, rather than using speech to alert the subjective
consciousness, as was traditionally done, might also use images to a greater
degree. But of course how *subjective consciousness* operates, and what its
particular qualities are, depends completely on how a person is brought up in
a particular social context, including the qualities of a particular language and
grammar. We don't all think alike.

Disadvantages

We can also ask, What have we lost by giving up the bicameral paradigm?
Jaynes addresses this in the third section of his book, "Vestiges of the
Bicameral Mind in the Modern World," specifically under the topic of
schizophrenia with the subtopic "The Advantages of Schizophrenia" (page
426).

What is interesting here is that Jaynes very convincingly equates
schizophrenia with a complete loss of subjective consciousness: the loss of
the inner space of the imagination, the loss of the self reflective 'I', the loss of
the ability to narratize. It is a reversion to the pre-conscious bicameral
paradygm.

> *"Another advantage of schizophrenia, perhaps evolutionary, is
> tirelessness. While a few schizophrenics complain of generalized fatigue,
> particularly in the early stages of the illness, most patients do not. In
> fact, they show less fatigue than normal persons and are capable of
> tremendous feats of endurance. They are not fatigued by examinations
> lasting many hours. They may move about day and night, or work
> endlessly without any sign of being tired. Catatonics may hold an
> awkward position for days that the reader could not hold for more than a
> few minutes. This suggests that much fatigue is a product of the
> subjective conscious mind, and that bicameral man, building the
> pyramids of Egypt, the ziggurats of Sumer, or the gigantic temples at
> Teotihuacan with only hand labor, could do so far more easily than*

could conscious self-reflective men."

Thus schizophrenia provides a window on the behaviour of humans of before 1500 BC and much later in some other regions.

All indication are that this condition of hearing the voices of the gods generated by the right hemisphere of the brain was in effect understood as the ability at language. Jaynes places that in the Upper Paleolithic. The current estimates by linguists place the genesis of language at about 40,000 BC. John Halloran, an expert on the Sumerian language, convincingly suggests a range of 9,500 to 8,000 BC. See Halloran's site at [www.sumerian.org].

Children

Lastly, let me add some notes on children and *subjective consciousness*. Children learn language from adults who, on meeting a child, always test the level of the child's language abilities and then switch to a "caretaker language" to continue conversing. A "caretaker language" is grammatically slightly advanced beyond the level of the child. We have all learned this teaching technique, and we use it automatically with children. People who "baby-talk" to children are those who have made no effort to gauge the child's current abilities. [note 31]

What Jaynes suggests is that *subjective consciousness* is learned similarly to the way in which language is learned -- parents teach children *subjective consciousness*, and have done so actively since about 1000 BC. In the interaction with parents (*subjectively conscious* parents) children are constantly confronted with snippets of real and imaginary situations which, over the course of years of exposure, and graded to their mental abilities, suggest the possibilities of imagining what they might do under a proposed situations. What is always suggested to the child is what actions they might take -- because all "thinking" in the mind involves an analog of actions in the real world. Thus both the analogical "spaces" and the actions to be performed in them are constantly put forth to children, and this is done by us with the same lack of awareness that we use with a graded caretaker language. This process also forces upon a child the recognition that others (mainly their parents) see them in their mind. We often identify the age of seven or eight as the first glimmer of "consciousness" in children. It is, in actuality, the first glimmer of their awareness of *our* consciousness. [note 32]

It is instructive to observe children 4 to 7 years old, although the state of *subjective consciousness* depends very much on their verbal abilities and the interaction they have with their parents and other adults. There seems to be a difference also between girls and boys, perhaps because girls (in our society) are more engaged in person to person relationships by their mothers. Pre-conscious children have recognizable behavior patterns which might be reflected in the following to various degrees. The following notes are my observations. (They are not from Jaynes.)

- They lack any clear memory of the past except for events they have been told about and some critical events which may have been reenacted mentally. Pre-language "memories" of events are almost entirely absent in everyone, for most memories are "constructed" by a subjective consciousness. (As I have pointed out, this is not true of spatial memories.) This obviously also goes for events before the age of 7 or 8.
- They show little of the self-consciousness which would result in being able to see yourself from an exterior perspective -- in effect as being seen by others. Children are self-aware, as all mammals are, but are unable to displace this to an exterior perspective. Their behavior is simply regulated by parental admonitions and the parental controls of shame, guilt, or embarrassment.
- The imagination of a child, as exercised in play, is often unbounded by reality and often lacks a measure of time. Importantly, the play space often lacks themselves as an involved actor. Older children will often "correct" the play fantasies of younger children, in effect mimicking parental teaching of *subjective consciousness*.
- They are often very opinionated, blurting out the opinions of their parents in lieu of any original "thinking" on a subject, a trait which often carries far into adulthood. Original thoughts on a particular subject would involve being able to create imagined spaces for action in the mind and walking an "analog I" through these spaces to evaluate alternative outcomes.
- They will interrupt adult conversations with non sequiturs, for there is no ability to narratize the present as a mental space in which they can fit themselves and observe the (real) space as if from afar (that is, in the mind), and to narratize into that mental space what others might hear or might be thinking at the moment.
- They often have hopelessly inadequate concepts of space and travel time ("Are we there yet?"). Children experience a dilation of real time which adults do not notice. Children (young children, especially) do not have access to the musings of *subjective consciousness*, with which adults fill real time to replace the second-by-second experience of actual time.

Yet children are fully functional. They learn to read and do math. They learn skills. They learn how things work, and how to interact with others. They can create and appreciate jokes. They know who they are. But the guide to their actions is the voices of parental admonitions and attitudes which were heard, remembered, and recalled. It is, in fact, the right hemisphere which does this for any predictable situation.

Endnotes

Note 1 --

Sherwood Washburn is paraphrased by Edward T. Hall, in *Beyond Culture* (1976), from S. L. Washburn, "Primate Field Studies and Social Science," in Nader and Marettzki, *Cultural Illness and Health* (1973). He is talking about primate young (as an area of study), but this could be extended to adults also. Adults also learn from their peers.

Note 2 --

That is not entirely true. Pointer dogs point with their nose and tail, and the young will learn from older dogs. I have only taught one Rottweiler dog to follow the direction of a human's pointed finger.

Humans understand and answer questions by 18 months.

Note 3 --

The following are from an Internet source which I have not tracked. Obviously the original author has just split up mental functions by opposing approaches, which, however, has little to do with what seems to be happening in actuality. The qualities listed below are almost all incorrectly assigned, the case being that either the two are reversed from inferences we can make, or both qualities belong on one side. I'll note the obvious reversals below (marked "rev"), followed by some comments.

Consciousness is located in the verbal left hemisphere, where speech generation is also found, and which operates the right hand. The silent right hemisphere is mostly incapable of speech although it can understand language. It operates the left hand. But the silent right is capable of close reasoning, data evaluation, and rote endeavors. It can type without thinking, operate a car, play music, unlock the door. There are 15 items listed at the original; I'll go through these by relisting them as follows:

```
        LEFT                    RIGHT
1       uses logic              uses feeling
2       detail oriented         "big picture" oriented
```

(1), (2): **uses logic/ uses feeling;** and **detail oriented/ "big picture" oriented** -- Animal studies indicate that the right hemisphere, not the conscious verbal left, uses "logic," is "detail oriented," and bases decisions on "fact" (see below). "Detail oriented" is, however, also a left brain function since consciousness can only focus on one thing at a time.

```
        LEFT                    RIGHT
3       facts rule              imagination rules
```

(3): **facts rule/ imagination rules** -- This is certainly reversed. The verbal left brain operates entirely in the realm of the imagination. The right does not. The right operates on facts.

```
        LEFT                    RIGHT
4       words and language      symbols and images
```

(4): **words and language/ symbols and images** -- The verbal left brain is the only one that can speak, but certainly the right brain also understands speech. The status of "symbols and images" is ambiguous, since some of the back communication of the right brain may be in imagery, but it can also be in words that pop into your head (and at times into your mouth), as it can be in sweeping feelings. "Symbols" I am not clear on. Symbols are abstractions, and thus probably in the domain of the left brain, which uses abstractions to jump through mental spaces which would be too time consuming to traverse in detail.

```
        LEFT                    RIGHT
5       present and past        present and future
```

(5): **present and past/ present and future** -- It is the future which is accessed by the conscious left brain, as well as the past, including the imagined past or future -- especially this last. The silent right brain deals with the present, and with the past only in that current action is based on what was learned in the (real) past.

	LEFT	RIGHT
6	math and science	philosophy & religion

(6): **math and science/ philosophy & religion** -- Math and science are created and manipulated in the space of the imagination, and thus represent left brain activities. But philosophy probably belongs there also. Religion (but not theology), in that it is unsupported by any reason, belongs on the right as accepted dogma. This suggests that science, if it is learned as handed-down dogma, also is a function of the right brain, and exhibits itself in the manner of unreasoned value judgments no different from what has been learned to be acceptable in social exchanges, or as religion.

	LEFT	RIGHT
7	can comprehend	can "get it" (meaning)
9	acknowledges	appreciates

(7), (9): **can comprehend/ can "get it"**; and **acknowledges/ appreciates** -- I'm not sure what to do with these. All of these are mental judgments, so that I would probably attribute them to the operation of the conscious left brain. The right brain is not judgmental, nor does it form meta-theories about knowledge. Not, at least, without your asking it to do so.

	LEFT	RIGHT
8	knowing	believing

(8): **knowing/ believing;** -- knowledge is securely lodged in the verbal left hemisphere in that an analysis has been performed which supposedly lines up the elements of a syllogism to support the "facts." But almost always knowledge is generated by the silent right brain. Belief is a matter of conviction and has no more status than fantasy.

	LEFT	RIGHT
10	pattern perception	spatial perception

(10): **order, pattern perception/ spatial perception** -- The verbal left brain deals with order, as in the word order of speech, and this could be extended, along with pattern recognition, to the mental arrangement of external objects or events, although, I should warn, this is dependent on the grammar in use. That would by default assign "spatial perception" to the silent right brain, but this might be an inference based on the absolutely amazing speed with which familiar situations are evaluated, plus the ability to review all the relevant data of a field of study.

	LEFT	RIGHT
11	knows object name	knows object function

(11): **knows object name/ knows object function** -- Probably correct, in that it has been repeatedly shown that the silent right brain has difficulty naming objects, although it will recognize their use.

	LEFT	RIGHT
12	reality based	fantasy based

(12): **reality based/ fantasy based** -- This is exactly reversed. It is the conscious left brain which deals in fantasies, whereas the right brain remains rooted in reality. But because it bases actions on learned situations of the past, the right brain becomes deadlocked in new or unfamiliar situations, whereas the conscious left brain can work through possible solutions of how to handle new situations.

	LEFT	RIGHT
13	forms strategies	presents possibilities

(13): **forms strategies/ presents possibilities** -- Both of these are functions of the conscious left brain. The right brain does not deal with options.

	LEFT	RIGHT
14	practical	impetuous

(14): **practical/ impetuous** -- This is also reversed. The active imagination -- what I have elsewhere identified as *subjective consciousness* -- makes the conscious verbal left brain "impetuous" while the right brain remains "practical." But because of the speed with which the right brain arrives at a course of action, it might be inferred that it is acting impetuously.

	LEFT	RIGHT
15	safe	risk taking

(15): **safe/ risk taking** -- Again, the applications are reversed. The conscious left brain takes risks often based on flimsy theories of how things work. The theorizing (tracking possibilities) is so much part of what we perceive as "consciousness" that we just cannot ignore it. We tend to think of these theories as "reasoning" and value them as the highest order of mental activity. This is how gamblers lose, and how bad investments are made.

Note 4 --

The quoted text is from an article adapted from the book which appeared in *Scientific American Mind*, June/July 2008, "Spheres of Influence" by Michael Gazzaniga.

Note 5 --

Our main distinction as a species is that we are strongly neotenized, which doubles our lifespan and flattens our face. Cats are also neotenized, living twice as long as a cat-sized mammal normally would. We also lost our fur, our tail, and the ability to produce vitamin C, but have gained our longevity for the sake of our oversized and helpless babies, and to allow for their long period of learning. The other outstanding difference -- bipedalism -- is certainly common among birds, marsupials, and dinosaurs. What we hold as "racial" distinctions (body size, hair, skin color, nose and eye shapes) have generally been held to be the result of 30,000 years of environmental isolation. For paleontologists only the inside slope of the front teeth is a clear racial distinction.

Note 6 --

Steven Mithen, in *The Singing Neanderthals* (2006), attempts to make a case for the evolution of language based in part on music and dance. The book involves a lot of guesswork and unfounded suppositions about prior hominids in an attempt to build the case for a slow evolution from natural selection. There is no "slow evolution."

Jaynes also attempted to make a case for how language might have developed, but too specific to Cro-Magnon, guesses about the effect of the European climate, and "selective pressures" to make much sense.

Alfred de Grazia, I feel, is closer in observing:

"Here is an area where evolutionary thought is especially self-contradictory and, consequently, slippery and evasive. It can only get from one small change to the next but cannot get from the beginning to the end; it can explain some intra-species changes, like horse-breeding and the Beltsville turkey, but it cannot explain a major development. No known mechanism directs a long string of slight modifications in the germ plasm. Even if we were to concede that the jump from hominid to human were only apparently large but was biologically small, human genesis would admittedly be a hologenetic occurrence; when it occurred, hominid life changed drastically; it speciated."

-- Homo Schizo, Human and Cultural Hologenesis (1983?)

Note 7 --

About gestures, Edward Sapir, in 1972 wrote: *"... we respond to gestures with an extreme alertness and, one might almost say, in accordance with an elaborate and secret code that is written nowhere, known by none, and understood by all."* Quoted by Tim Friend in *Animal Talk* (2004).

About dogs, R.A. Fonda, in "Speculation on speciation" originally at rafonda.com, writes:

> *"In East Asia, by a hundred thousand years ago, casual scavenging of predator kills had developed into systematic exploitation of the wolves' capacity to pursue fleet game. That led to domestication of dogs, who were, themselves, differentiated from wolves by neoteny. They matured into an amenable creature that could pattern on humans as pack-alphas, and behave with 'puppyish' submission even when mature."*

Fonda is perhaps too glib about dog behavior. Domesticated dogs are still carnivores and wild animals, and they are certainly not neotenized. Their submission is not all that puppyish, but only as it benefits their own pack-member priorities. Their benefit to humans comes from their carnivore brains which are able to almost instantaneously reach conclusions based on integrating many diverse small environmental cues, and as a result of great value in hunting. Dogs can also "read" humans with amazing proficiency as a result. But most behavior is still all about search, chase, bite, rip, and eat. Don't get your hand caught in that sequence.

Note 8 --

From various considerations, John A. Halloran thinks that the Sumerian language was invented as a game by women, around 10,000 BC. That would place the genesis of language at the leading edge of the first settlements dedicated to mixed gathering/hunting and farming. He identifies some base words with earlier building structures in Iran and at Catal Huyuk. See [www.sumerian.org/prot-sum.htm]

Note 9 --

Halloran has suggested that the Indo-European language group is a secondary effort, that is, a language based on the active implementation of the "concept" of a language, whereas Sumerian shows the signs of a language invented from meanings associated with the voicing of vowels and consonants. In his study of Sumerian, he has shown that the basic words of that language originate from the meaning inherent in the sounds and the shapes formed by the mouth and tongue. Sumerian thus may be an original "proto-language."

"Biological forms must be descended from ancestral forms. This cannot be true for languages for an infinite time depth. The method of glottochronology must break down when it reaches the event horizon at which a population went from nonspeaking to speaking. In some cases, just the concept of speech will have inspired a population to invent their own language. In other cases, a population will have built their new language upon a repertoire of elements taken from an existing language."
      -- John A. Halloran, at [www.sumerian.org/prot-sum.htm]

Studies of the basic meaning of words of Indo-European languages show little or no relationship to the physiological content of the mouthed sounds. It would be suspected that the prototype Indo-European language was created much like Northern European alphabets, in that they were derived from the *concept* of writing, and not in imitation of Mediterranean alphabets. The glyphs used by the Romans or Greeks, like "alpha, beta, gamma, delta," originated from "ox, house, camel, river mouth" -- named objects signifying the sound of the letter. The Northern European alphabets do not show a derivation of glyphs from named objects.

Note 10 --

There are some Cro-Magnon-like developments at a much earlier period (70,000 ya) in South Africa. They are typically Cro-Magnon-like in that they seem to represent short-lived local fashions without any notable utility.

Note 11 --

Language is passed with ease to people who do not speak because the whole structure of language is imbedded in the task of teaching language. Without this our children would only learn with difficulty.

Note 12 --

Woven fabric dates from 25,000 BC (Germany). Colorants used by Cro-Magnon in decorating caves were most likely also used as makeup. Baskets derive from cording, and can be made waterproof by lining them with leather-hard clay. That is one step away from fired pottery.

Note 13 --

The "migration" of Cro-Magnon into Europe, or anywhere else, has not been firmly established, in that, for example, the expanded lithic industry does not start at some one location to spread out from there. Different aspects of the "cultural package" of the Cro-Magnon appear at diverse locations, representing, as James Shreeve writes in *The Neanderthal Enigma* (1995), "a complicated mosaic of mini-explosions that resemble one big explosion only when you stand back and take a long look at the whole."

This becomes an argument against the biological genesis of language, if we at least can accept that the use of language lies at the base of the cultural explosion in the Upper Paleolithic, for it would assume that humans all over the planet "evolved" nearly simultaneously. Of course a thousand-year lag looks instantaneous from our perspective.

Note 14 --

This presumes that North America was invaded from Northern Asia. But it is clear that most of North America was populated from South America via the Caribbean, originally some 30,000 years ago, and again after 9000 BC. The west coast regions may indeed have been populated from Asia also after that date. We have no records, since the general rise of the oceans after the glaciers melted has destroyed evidence of coastal settlements.

Note 15 --

"In our own modern conceptual world, the opposite seems to be self-evident: we look into the future, while the past lies behind us. Continuing with this line of thought, we might say that while we proceed along a temporal axis "headed towards the future," the Mesopotamians, although they also moved on a temporal axis in the direction of the future, did so with their gaze directed towards the past. The Mesopotamians proceeded, so to speak, "with their backs forward," that is, facing backwards into the future."

-- From Stefan Maul *Die altorientalische Hauptstadt -- Abbild und Nabel der Welt* (1997) translated by Thomas Lampert

See also Nicholas Osler, *Empires of the Word* (2005), for more details on Sumerian, as determined from Akkadian sources.

Note 16 --

Do not confuse the insistence of the *Annals of Shu* on the existence of Yao and Shun with "legend," for they are not identified as "Emperors" (or "legendary emperors" as western commentators would have it), but are clearly identified as "Gods" -- a perfectly legitimate term for the two planetary apparitions. See James Legge, translator of *The Sacred Books of the East, The Shu* (volume 3) (1879). Legge's translation and notes still stand as a classic.

Note 17 --

The Mesoamerican *Annals of Cuahitlan* claims we are living in the 5th age with no reference to the start of the current age. The first four ages are 676, 364, 312, and 52 years long. From what we know we could place the end of the 4th age in 1440 BC. Together that places the first creation in 2896 BC, or about 200 years after 3100 BC, only about a hundred years later than the recovery period for other people after the flood at the end of the "Era of the Gods." Interestingly, the first age ends in 2168 -- about the time of the demise of the Old Kingdom of Egypt.

This may be coincidence, however, since the ages are obviously numerologically constructed and based on the later importance of the numbers 52 and 13. The second and third ages together equal the length of the first age, 676 years, with 52 as the difference between the two (which is the length of the fourth age). All the numbers are multiples of 13.

Note 18 --

Ralph L. Roys, in *The Book Of Chilam Balam of Chumayel* (1933) writes:

"A Katun of the same name recurred after approximately 256 years, consequently at the end of that time history was expected to repeat itself. The events recounted in the Maya Chronicles found in the Mani, Tizimin and Chumayel manuscripts [The Books of the Chilam Balam] *offer excellent grounds for believing that this belief was so strong at times as to actually influence the course of history. A surprisingly large proportion of the important upheavals in Maya history appear to have occurred in some Katun named either 4 Ahau or 8 Ahau."*

In a footnote he adds:

"Katun 8 Ahau recurred approximately every 256 years, and for a thousand years every time a Katun of this name occurred, the Itzá were driven from their homes, no matter where they were living at the time. Late in the Seventh Century A.D. they were expelled from Chichen Itzá after their first occupation of that city. In the middle of the Ninth

Century they were driven out of Chakanputun. At the end of the Twelfth Century they were again driven from Chichen Itza by Hunac Ceel. About the middle of the Fifteenth Century Mayapan was sacked and destroyed; and strangely enough it was again in a Katun 8 Ahau at the end of the Seventeenth Century that the Spaniards conquered the last Itza stronghold at Tayasal, which was the end of this remarkable nation."

Schele and Freidel (in *A Forest of Kings*) similarly relate, about the meek acceptance of Christianity by Can-Elk, the last of the Maya kings, in AD 1697:

"This fatalism was part of the legacy of the Classic-period attitude toward history and its relationship to cyclic time and supernatural causality. Classic-period scribes emphasized the connectedness among the actions of their living kings, the actions of their ancestors in the historical and legendary past, and the actions of gods in the mythological past. ... The result of this type of thinking, transformed by the exigencies of the Collapse and then the Conquest, became predictive history.

Note 19 --

The 52-year interval after 2349 BC was in solar years, which were "Tun years" in the records of the past. The interval after 1492 BC was also 52 "Tun years" on the Tzolkin calendar, but represented an interval of 50 solar years. See Appendix B, "The Celestial Mechanics," the "52-year cycle." I discuss the Mesoamerican calendar in the chapter "The Maya Calendar."

Note 20 --

Most of our memories are constructed, or rather reconstructed, by us if they involve action, for we fill them out with the appropriate details, to the point of making up dialogues. Which is why memories reported as evidence in courts are suspect. Of course we do have other memories too. You will probably remember the layout of your house at age three, even though you do not remember a single event or action from that age. All animals are capable of memories involving the geography of their environment, and often with astounding accuracy.

Note 21 --

The shift of attention is managed by the "reticular formation" (Jaynes) or the "amygdala" (Goleman) or some other primitive element located at the base of the brain, with connections to sensory and motor areas of the brain and the spinal cord, which has the purpose of awakening certain parts of the nervous system while suppressing others on sensing external stimulations which require attention. How this is judged is beyond me.

Note 22 --

Hollis Frampton, in *Circles of Confusion* (1983), reports on the interview of the holder of the world's land speed record at Bonneville Salt Flats, Craig Breedlove, after he had lost his brakes and parachutes at the end of a test run -- flying off the end of the course at 620 miles per hour (1000 km per hour).

"The car went out of control, sheared off a number of telephone poles, topped a small rise, turned upside down, flew through the air, and landed in a salt pond."

Breedlove survived without a scratch. Frampton listened to a taped interview started immediately after the wreck, and wrote:

"Breedlove delivers a connected account of what he thought and did during a period of 8.7 seconds. In the course of the interview, Breedlove everywhere gives evidence of condensing, of curtailing; not wishing to bore anyone, he is doing his polite best to make a long story short."

Frampton notes that the tape ran one hour and 35 minutes, a 650 fold expansion of experienced time.

A similar incident is recollected by Walter Shapiro, in "The Washington Post Magazine" (November 9, 1980), about a Navy test pilot, Major Russ Stromberg, whose plane lost power on takeoff from an aircraft carrier. In 8 seconds before ejecting he tested the controls, judged the consequences, and determined when to eject without either landing on the deck or at the site of the crash. It took him 45 minutes to describe the 8 seconds. (cited by Edward T. Hall, in *The Dance of Life*, 1983.)

Note 23 --

There is obviously more to learning "what others might be thinking" than what is suggested here. Sarah Blaffer Hrdy writes:

"The reason our species has managed to survive and proliferate to the extent that 6 billion people currently occupy the planet has to do with how readily we can learn to cooperate when we want to. And our capacity for empathy is one of the things that made us good at doing

that."

"Predators from gopher snakes to lions have to be able to anticipate where their quarry will dart. Chimps and gorillas can figure out what another individual is likely to know or not know. But compared with that of humans, this capacity to entertain the psychological perspective of other individuals is crude."

-- "Mothers and Others," *Natural History* (2001).

Note 24 --

The reflections occur in everyday conversations. It is not unusual to hear someone say, "I did not want you to think that I thought you would think that I thought ... so and so." Convoluted on close analysis, but perfectly understandable to the parties involved.

Note 25 --

In referring to the "left" and "right" brain we are talking primarily about the speech centers -- Broca's area and Wernicke's area. The abilities of the right and left hemisphere listed in the text are abbreviated for the sake of this text. To gain an appreciation for the incomprehensible complexity of mental functions, see the classic book by Oliver Sacks *The Man who Mistook his Wife for his Hat* (1970) which deals with dysfunctions of the right hemisphere. These right hemisphere abnormalities are not noticed by the subjects, whereas left hemisphere dysfunctions are experienced and can be described by patients.

Note 26 --

"Modeled such silent consciousness," is a sort of sudden jump in the narrative on my part. It may have come later and taken more time.

At the close of the age of the prophets, the time from Elijah to Zechariah, Bible texts start including admonitions against hearing voices and talking in tongues. That is after 620 BC.

The Inca seemed to have learned in only a few months.

Note 27 --

See also the writings of Edward T. Hall and any number of academics (and non-academics) who have taken up these topics. The principles first expounded by Hall are today used in international marketing.

Note 28 --

Sun Tzu *The Art of War*, translated by Ralph Sawyer (1994). Admittedly, the texts, as they have come down to us, were edited and collated as late as circa AD 1000.

Note 29 --

I am more inclined to view the *Iliad* as fiction purposely crafted "in the style of" an earlier period or a lost earlier literature, or possibly carried forward from a remote time, not as history, which is a substrate added over time, but as a tragedy. The *Iliad* spans only some two months, and is not about a war, but about the effects of the anger of Achilles and his reluctance to initiate action.

There is no archaeological evidence for an extended war at Troy and the city has not been located or identified. The hill at Hisarlik is too small to serve as the citadel of Troy, it is not in sight of the sea, and was repeatedly destroyed by natural disasters, and at the wrong times. But by the sixth century BC, as the Asiatic Greeks faced their defeat by the Persians, the *Iliad* became the favored epic of the heroic forebears of the conquered Greeks. Everyone believed that the war had happened. Greeks on both sides of the Aegean traced their linage to the heroes of the *Iliad*.

There is not a single mention of texts in the *Iliad*, even though these were already in wide use in Mycenaean Greece (supposedly by 1200 BC, and certainly by 900 BC). The tradition in antiquity, that Homer was blind and therefore could not write, points to a purposeful falsification also, and lends an aura of authenticity to the epic.

But the final composition of the *Iliad* has to be placed in the 7th century BC when the Greeks possess an alphabet. The poem selectively picks details from an imagined past. The battle tactics are wrong, as is the armor, and the funeral customs are foreign. There are anachronistic references to the Olympic Games, and the Gods are mocked -- suggesting a composition after perhaps 650 BC.

If the *Iliad* had achieved status as a classic at an earlier time, the vocabulary should have been recognized as archaic by the Greeks of the third century BC, since language conforms to classics. Alfred de Grazia suggests that the "heroic diction" was a purposeful amalgam of dialects of a late date.

Jaynes also forgets (perhaps) that events which are discussed and recounted will be remembered. This is true for early childhood experiences, and ought to be true of pre-subjectively conscious people also. Jaynes places the *Iliad* too close in time to his date for the change to *subjective consciousness*, and thus has to conduct an argument from an indefensible position.

It is quite possible that the whole of the *Iliad* (as Talbott has claimed) is but a retelling of the "War of the Gods" of 3147 BC. It strikes me, also, as a purposeful creation -- in a purposeful "antique style." If so, it is all the more marvelous that the *Iliad* passed through Jaynes's analysis transparently.

What we are seeing perhaps is the embellishment of memory on a grand scale, although the rigidity of the underlying structure of the *Iliad* argues for a conscious composition. But the *Iliad* was also extensively edited and codified after about 600 BC by others.

The *Iliad* was written with clear intent, as was certainly understood since the 19th century AD by literary critics -- Guy Davenport in 1954 wrote, "Not a line ... can be put out of its place" -- and with a clear political balance between the egos of the Asiatic and the European Greeks. But the facts of a detailed fiction along with an adopted diction has little to do with Jaynes's analysis, which deals with the use of body-part nouns for feelings and emotions and the actions initiated by the Gods. There is no need to consider the historical dimensions of the *Iliad*. Jaynes makes this clear in the closing paragraphs of his investigations of the *Iliad*, and I certainly agree with his conclusions.

Note 30 --

In *Collapse* (2005), Jared Diamond writes about communal decision making in the highland communities of New Guinea, still in practice after the arrival of Dutch and Australian colonial government in the 1930s:

"Decisions were (and often still are today) reached by means of everyone in the village sitting down together and talking, and talking, and talking."

And, he notes, this happens today to the extreme frustration of New Guinea government officials. As I note elsewhere, the same process of reaching complete consensus through endless talk was used by the much larger groups of Plains Indians, in the 19th century AD, to the frustration of US treaty negotiators.

Note 31 --

How can Steven Pinker, popular author of books on language, all based on the notion that language is an inherent function of the brain, evolved over millions of years, be so wrong? (*The Language Instinct* (1994) and other books.) My first clue was his complete misunderstanding of "baby talk." He understands it as functional. I understand it as a completely disinterested attempt to communicate with children. I finally verified what I soon suspected, that Pinker has no children and has thus never had the opportunity to closely observe children in the acquisition of language abilities over extended periods of time.

Note 32 --

But note that, despite the shorthand of this statement, what we are talking about is *subjective consciousness*, not *self-consciousness*. I have seen people dismiss Jaynes by noting that chimps show signs of self-consciousness. Well, so do my dogs. Animals certainly know who they are and are able to reflect on themselves. But no chimp has ever escaped a zoo. That would require a measure of *subjective consciousness*.

Added note: In 2006, a chimp escaped from a zoo in the US.

Revision: 42.29 (maya.php)
Contents of this chapter: [The Beginning of Time] [The First Calendar] [An Intermediate Calendar] [The Tzolkin Calendar] [Modification of the Tzolkin] [The Haab Calendar] [The Long Count] [The Katun Cycle] [The Four Ages] [Endnotes]

The Maya Calendar

The Mesoamerican / Maya calendar contains cycles within cycles, all of which are held as significant to some degree in determining the "quality" of any day in time. Many of the cyclical features look like remnants of earlier calendar systems which could not be discarded, but were carried forward in time as each change in the calendar was forced upon the users with a change in the structure of the Solar System. I would thus suggest that the current calendar -- because of its inclusion of these arcane, and in some cases near-useless, features -- shows faithful and careful adjustments to changes in the number of days in the year over a very long period. I'll suggest, in fact, that the current calendar can certainly be traced back to the era starting in 3147 BC, and likely a prior tally used solar years before 3147 BC. I think this is clearly shown by the remnants retained at later times. In fact, a page of the *Chilam Balam*, which deals with the events of 2349 BC, specifically states, "And then days of the year were introduced." But this is the addition of a round of 13 numbers superimposed on the original "monthly" calendar of 20 named days.

- The initial period when the southern plasmoids showed up started in 10,900 BC.
- In 8347 BC, as the 13th Baktun (400 year periods) on the ongoing yearly calendar was completed, the first era of the plasmoids came to a close, and a new count was started, at least of Baktuns, Katuns, and

Tuns. 2553 solar years had lapsed since 10,900 BC.

- The fact that 13 Baktuns were completed was long remembered. In fact two of the inscribed Long Count series of glyphs are counted from this date when the earlier period ended in 8347 BC. (At the Temple of the Cross at Palenque, and at Stela C at Quirigua. So says Sylvanus Morley in the 1915 Smithsonian Institution Bulletin 57 of the Bureau of American Ethnology, *An Introduction to the Study of Maya Hieroglyphs*. J. E. Thompson confirmed this in 1950.)

- In 3147 BC, by coincidence, again as a 13th Baktun on the ongoing calendar was completed, the "Era of the Gods" came to an end. A new count was started of Baktuns, Katuns, and Tuns. This time a rotation of days was instituted, amounting to a rotation of 20 named days. These repeated 12 times to account for the 240 days of the year. The 12 may have rotated at the same time as the 20 named days.

- In 2349 BC this was augmented with a rotation of one extra day, a total of 13 numbered days (which also represent a half period of the Moon) simultaneously with the 20 named days. This is called the "Tzolkin," and consists of a total of 260 distinctly identified days (named and numbered) before repeating again, and exactly filling the year of 260 days.

- In 1492 BC another calendar was introduced, called the "Haab," consisting of 20 numbered days rotating through 18 named "months," which totaled 360 days.

- The Haab was adjusted in 747 BC to add 5 extra days (a short month), so that the calendar then totaled 365 days.

- An accurate count of days was also established in 747 BC, with a system called the "Long Count." The Long Count tallied days, "months" of 20 days, years (called "Tuns") of 360 days (not 365), double decades of 20 Tuns (called "Katuns"), and a measure of 400 years, called simply "400," or, in the nomenclature of archaeologists, "Baktuns."

It is also certain that there was a calendar, in the sense of a count of years, going forward from (the retrocalculated year of) 3114 BC, since the Maya *Chilam Balam* correctly places the earliest event of the current era in the properly named double-decade Katuns.

Also, some count of years, or spans of time, was recorded since circa 41,000 bp. One of the pages of the *Chilam Balam* specifically deals with this.

I should also note that the Baktuns and Katuns were probably in use by 10,900 BC, for the *Chilam Balam* has reference to this in Book 11 which details (what we would call the start of) the "first creation" of 10,900 BC. In 8347 BC, with the end to a period of about 2500 years of the southern ball plasmoids, the count of years had reached 13 Baktuns, and the year tally was reset to zero.

It happened again in 3147 BC, with the collapse of the "Era of the Gods," that 13 Baktuns were reached. Thus in 3147 BC the Baktun measure of the calendar was again reset to zero. This marks the termination of the "Second Creation" of the Olmec and Maya, marked especially since it was accompanied by the worldwide flood. Meanwhile, Saturn had started to blaze in 4077 BC.

Note that the "Creations" are not clear-cut episodes separated by definitive collapses of celestial conditions. For example, the date of 4077 BC, when Saturn blazed up in a nova expulsion, is not accounted for. It makes one suspect that the whole idea of various numbered creations might be a constructed effort of a late date.

[*Image: August 13, 3114 BC, day "zero" of the Maya calendar. This reads, "13 Baktun, 0 Katun, 0 Tun, 0 Uinal, 0 Kin, 4-Ahau 8-Cumku, was seen the image." After research.famsi.org.*]

... preliminary observations

With the institution of the Long Count in 747 BC, the Olmecs were able to calculate backwards into the past to determine the exact names and numbers of the days on the Tzolkin calendar and Haab calendar. When the completion of the previous era was reached in 3147 BC (which they and we calculate as 3114 BC) -- the Tzolkin day was 4-Ahau and the Haab day was 8-Cumku. The Peten region Maya were very proud of this feat of retrocalculation and had reference to it constantly in their standing stone monuments.

As interpreted by archaeologists, the Long Count used August 11, 3114 BC, on an equivalent Gregorian calendar as a starting point. Because there is a two-day difference in calendars between early Olmec (and current Guatemala) and the calendar of the Maya (and Aztecs), the other widely accepted date is August 13, 3114 BC. In both cases it is assumed that the year has always been the same length as today -- 365.2422 days. The Classical era Maya (AD 400 to 700) also used this measure, arrived at independently, to suggest a series of days which never varied, and retrocalculate the Tzolkin and Haab day names and numbers at the beginning of the current creation -- even though they are incorrect. There were records involved in the recall of history, but they were not accurate.

The archaeological count of days (which match the Maya Long Count against our own erroneous string of calendar days) starts at August 11, 3114 BC. This was first derived by Joseph Goodman in 1905. Juan Hernández in 1926 came up with a calculation of August 12, which was followed in 1927 by John E. Thompson's calculation of August 13. In 1935 Thompson revised his calculation to August 11. As the dean of Maya archaeologists, Thompson's estimate is generally used today, although any number of researchers think that the date of August 13, 3114 BC, is more likely to be correct.

"Overwhelming support for the precise placement of the Thompson [August 11] *correlation number came in the 40's and 50's, when newly discovered calendar counts still being followed among the Quiche, Kekchi and Ixil of Guatemala all supported the* [August 11 date].*"*
    -- John Major Jenkins at fourahau2.htm.

The above "correlation dates" are on the equivalent Gregorian calendar, converted from a measure known as the "count of Julian days" used by astronomers since the 16th century AD. The "astronomical year" for 3114 BC is -3113, based on recognizing a "year zero." The Gregorian calendar will match solar years under the assumption that the length of the year has not changed.

The Julian calendar, in use from about 40 BC to about AD 1500, and not to be confused with "Julian days," is based on a year of 365.25 days, and thus the Julian year is slightly longer than the Gregorian year of 365.24 days. By 3114 BC the Julian calendar places dates about 13 months (numerically) further into the past than the Gregorian calendar.

There have been suggestions that the Maya made a two-day correction at some time in the past, and that this accounts for the difference of two days between the Long Count notation found on monuments in antiquity, and in the continued use of the earlier Tzolkin among contemporary tribes.

In fact, Vincent H. Malmstrom, writing in *Cycles of the Sun, Mysteries of the Moon* (1997), suggests that this happened in circa 48 BC -- that the Maya in effect skipped two days, thus setting the calendar ahead by two days. Malmstrom sets out when and where this would have happened, and the reasoning behind the change, but admits that his "story" is pure conjecture.

A "correction" carries with it the suggestion of an absolute and uniform use of the Tzolkin and Haab calendars by many tribes spread over a large area since remote antiquity. The concept of uniform agreement doesn't work among humans. I think it should be considered that by 747 BC, when the Long Count was devised, there were already some diverse regional opinions on the concept of when one era ended and another started -- a question about the existence ("completion") of two days which had not been seen in progress. Considering that the 2000-year-old Tzolkin was in use among many diverse tribes, it is likely that some stubborn local opinions prevailed. But there might be other reasons, too.

The "August 11" calendar reaches further into the past by two days. It correctly fits the start of the Long Count on February 28, 747 BC, and accounts for later retrocalculations of some past events by the Olmecs. But it was supplanted by the "August 13" calendar because the "August 13" calendar "correctly" fit what was thought to be the quality of a number of important dates in the year 685 BC, and in 1492 BC. (Discussed in the chapter "The Day of Kan.")

My sense is that in the Valley of Mexico, and perhaps also in the Olmec coastal region, the "August 11" calendar was replaced by the "August 13" calendar by 400 BC, but long after the use of the "August 11" calendar had been exported and adapted by tribes in Southern Mexico and Guatemala, where it has been retained in the same form to today. (Some researchers have suggested that the calendars may have started in Guatemala.)

It should also be pointed out that August 11, 3114 BC (or August 13), is not the start of the current era, but is the end (the completion) of the previous era. The texts at Palenque, for example, make this clear when it is read:

"And then the past epoch ended. On 4-Ahau 8-Cumku [presumed to be August 13, 3114 BC], *13 Baktuns were completed."*

The transliterated text reads:

"(And then) there was an event / (on) 4-Ahau / 8-Cumku / were completed / 13 Baktuns"

There can be little doubt, no matter how it is translated, that this phrasing speaks to the completion of a previous 13 Baktuns -- 5200 solar years. It points directly to an earlier calendar which would have started in 8347 BC. Occasional stelae specify the placement on the day 4-Ahau 8-Cumku of "the three stones" or alternately the first "image of the turtle." The references here are to a day in the year 3147 BC, but the day name and number are known only because of a retrocalculation by the Olmecs or the people of the Valley of Mexico in antiquity, probably after 600 BC, which found this day name and number for the restart of the calendar in 3147 BC, even if incorrect. It is, in fact, incorrect since the three stones or the turtle were seen to be placed in 10,900 BC.

Support for a correlation based on the date of August 13 (for the year 3114 BC) comes from the record of eclipses, which cannot be off by a day. My observation is that the starting date of February 28th, 747 BC, Gregorian, corresponding to the Long Count date of 6.0.0.0.0, can only be upheld with an "August 11" correlation. This matches the start of the Era of Nabonassar in the Eastern Mediterranean region (the evening of February 27, 747 BC) and the start of the Roman calendar (the day after February 28th). I think the arguments among archaeologists and historians may be meaningless. It should be recognized that there were two Long Counts in use, and that they differed by two days. [note 1]

The first Tzolkin date inscription was in use at the Zapotec site of San José Mogote in the Oaxaca region in about 600 BC. By 400 BC the Tzolkin and Haab calendars were in use at Monte Alban in Oaxaca.

In 1939 the earliest engraved Olmec Long Count was discovered and depicted on Stela C from Tres Zapotes as 32 BC (Julian). Malmstrom notes that this stele celebrated a total eclipse of the Sun as it rose out of the Eastern Gulf of Mexico, if the August 13 Thompson correlation is used. Otherwise it would be off by two days. Malmstrom notes a transcription error in the stele (carving three bars rather than two to accompany the three dots for the "kin") and then writes about the eclipse:

"... whose path ... passed right over the Olmec ceremonial center of Tres Zapotes at dawn on the morning of August 31, 32 B.C. A more

frightening celestial event can scarcely be imagined, for the sun rose out of the Gulf of Mexico totally black except for a ring of light around its outer edges. [It was] described as an annular, or ringlike, eclipse, and subsequent calculations at the U.S. Naval Observatory have revealed that the disk of the sun was 93 percent obscured (personal communication). Surely, a 'day without a sunrise' is not likely to have gone unrecorded by the Olmecs!"

He concludes with:

"... therefore, the inscription of Stele C, erroneous though it seems to be, appears to confirm the accuracy of the original Thompson correlation value [August 13] *between the Olmec calendar and our own."*

Malmstrom also identifies a much later eclipse seen at Copan (Copán) on June 29, AD 763 (9.16.12.5.17 6-Caban 10-Mol), and suggests that it had been predicted. Again, the date agrees with a lunar eclipse only if the "August 13" correlation is used. The date was recorded on a half dozen stelae. Archaeologists have not as yet accepted this. (Surprise!)

It should be obvious also from many inscribed stelae that it is the completion of a time period that is celebrated, not the start. The event of 3114 BC (actually 3147 BC) is known as the end of the "second creation," which is inferred from the fact that the event which we know as the "flood of Noah" is consistently called the (completion of the) "third creation." The reason the "second creation" of 3114 BC ended with the completion of 13 Baktuns (the count of years then went to zero Baktuns), is that the predecessors of the Olmecs had already been counting years (solar years) from much earlier than 10,900 BC. In 8347 BC 13 Baktuns had been reached.

In that the Sumerians managed to have a count of years (in days) from 4077 BC, it is reasonable to suggest that the Olmecs or their predecessors were also perfectly capable of this. "Counting," after all, must have been one of the high sciences even for the slightly more remote Cro-Magnons.

The Beginning of Time

The phrase of "the image" is completed by some stelae as "the image of the turtle." As a turtle this would represent the appearance of the southern plasmoids, actually, the last appearance -- the completion of this event. We could most likely place the first showing of Peratt's southern plasmoids in 10,900 BC, the year of the first contact with Saturn at the start of the Younger Dryas which destroyed North America.

It has always been strange to note that the "zero" number for the Baktun at the start of the current era (the Maya retrocalculated 3114 BC, although actually 3147 BC) actually has a value of 13 Baktuns. Also, the date of the start of the "first creation" is not the nova event of Saturn in 4077 BC, which the *Popol Vuh* describes as the "dawning of the light," but an event 4000 years earlier -- the last instance of the showing of the southern ball plasmoid.

Here are the four creation periods:

- 8347 BC, end of the first creation
- 3147 BC, end of the second creation
- 2349 BC, end of the third creation
- 1492 BC, end of the fourth creation

The last period is questionable, it might not be over yet.

In the iconography of the Maya, the "turtle," which appeared in 10,900 BC, at the start of the "first creation," is often combined with the appearance of Jupiter ("Hun-Nal-Ye") as the "First Father" in 2349 BC, at the end of the "third creation." Just like the second and third southern plasmoids would seem to have appeared out of the carapace of the "First Turtle" soon after 10,900 BC, so First Father is shown to rise out of a turtle carapace in 2349 BC, assisted by Hunahpu and Xbalanque (from the era of the 7th century BC, no less). This scene is repeatedly shown on bowls and vases. And this is how the mythological history of the Maya advanced.

In *Maya Cosmos* Freidel and Schele present the imagery of a painted pot showing six Gods in council with a elderly seventh God. The council is urging the seventh god to "bring into existence" and "put in order" the place called "black is its center" -- a fit description of the deep shadow at the center of the Absu which changed size and shape over the year. It suggests that the dark doorway of the Absu was hiding something.

The elder God (God L) of the painted pot is easily identified as Jupiter as well as First Father. The six Gods have various names, of which some are easily identified. God "Three Born Together" is obviously the three plasmoids of the south and God "Nine Footsteps" is Mars. Subtracting God "Three Born Together" of the south leaves five Gods all associated with the polar configuration of the north. This is the same number as listed in the *Popol Vuh* (see the chapter "The Popol Vuh" for details). These are Uranus, Neptune, Saturn, Mercury, and Mars, all of which were easily distinguished in the earliest time after 9500 BC, although some disappeared behind (or above) each other by 5800 BC. And Mercury is misnamed for Venus, which probably did not exist as early as this council is meant to depict. God L (Jupiter) is here distinguished from the polar configuration planets, and it is a rare insight to suggest that indeed at the time of the council, sometime before 8347 BC, Jupiter had been known and seen for eons, and therefore was properly represented as very old.

This illustrated pot also points up the Mesoamerican concept of the simultaneity of time. The council of the six Gods happens after the start of the "first creation" period after 10,900 BC as told by the *Popol Vuh*, resulting eventually in the creation of the Sun -- the lighting up of Saturn. But the disposition of the dark spot -- the cleft -- in the Absu, in fact the whole of the Absu, is not tackled until the end of the "third creation" of 2349 BC. Most of the six Gods had long since disappeared from view by then. Archaeologists today think that the "dark spot" is a dark area of the cloud of stars of the Milky Way.

The other (and more common) image which is often represented as first appearing on 4-Ahau 8-Cumku, is the setting of the three hearthstones in the sky. These have been identified by Schele as a star of the belt of Orion and two of his feet (Alnitac, Rigel, and Saiph). The cluster M-42 is enclosed in this triangle, like a fire at the center of a three-stone hearth. The constellation is below (slightly east) of the intersection of the equatorial and ecliptic, and removed from the brightness of the Milky Way. In fact, these stars first showed up in 2349 BC, the date of the end of the "third creation," at a location known as "Lying-down-Sky" which must represent the gap in the Absu during the equinoxes. Other names for the shadow gap in the Absu are the "Earth Partition," "Black is the Center," and "Cleft Sky" -- the name for Yaxchilan. Where the Earth shadow fell on the Absu, no stars would have been seen in the dark area (excepting a few very bright stars).

Since the skies have been invariant since even before 10,900 BC the three hearthstones could not refer to the end of the second creation ending in 3147 BC, but to the first creation ending in 8347 BC. As stars, these three stones were not placed; they were always there, although not seen until some time after 2349 BC. This would suggest to me that the "setting of the three stones" probably refers back to the "first creation" when the three southern plasmoids appeared in the south -- set beneath the "mighty stone" (Saturn) of the north, as the *Chilam Balam* relates in Book 11.

The date of 3147 BC is actually a reasonable estimate for the start of the near-current era, that is, as the date for the close of the "Era of the Gods" and the end of the second 13 Baktun cycle of sets of 400 years (5200 years). The Olmecs must have had a record of the number of solar years which had lapsed since various worldwide events, and were certainly able to place events in named year tallies after 3147 BC. The records of the *Chilam Balam* books of the colonial-period Maya are accurate to the Katun (20-Tun period) after 3147 BC, allowing for some slight-of-hand by the 16th-century-AD Maya scribes, who made some unwarranted "corrections" to the chronology.

Time spans between "ages" (after 3147 BC) show up in later Mesoamerican legendary histories and are correct or nearly correct, and match the records of other civilizations. No clear record of events or time spans shows up among the sparse Mesoamerican records of the much earlier period before 3147 BC, except as might be inferred from their calendar measures.

When the Long Count was established in 747 BC by the Olmecs, they added six Baktuns (2400 Tun years) to a starting calendar date of 0.0.0.0, based on the assumption that the year (the Tun) had always consisted of 360 days. This was correct at that time, because the year had indeed consisted of 360 days since the establishment of earliest Olmec ceremonial center after 1500 BC (San Lorenzo). Thus the Olmecs also removed from the Long Count calculation the five-day correction that was added to the annual Haab calendar in 747 BC -- the "years" in the Long Count are based entirely on the earlier 360-day intervals, not on 365-day intervals. The rather arbitrary addition of 2400 Tuns (six Baktuns of 400-Tun years) to the Long Count would bring the actual "zero" date to 3147 BC, off from the archaeologically and Classic Maya retrocalculated date of 3114 BC year by 34 years. [note 2]

A "Tun" is a year. Before 3147 BC (the thousand years of the "Era of the Gods" and the 4000 years before that) the Tun was 225 days (I have assumed). After 3147 BC (the worldwide flood) the Tun was 240 days. After 2349 BC (the "flood of Noah") the Tun was 260 days. After 2193 BC (the fall of Akkad and the Old Kingdom) the Tun was 273 days. After 1492 (the Exodus and the fall of the Middle Kingdom) the Tun was 360 days -- and at this value it remained in its Long Count use, even though 5 additional days were added to the year after 747 BC when the year changed to its current value. Although the earlier "years" were shorter, the effect of adding 2400 Tuns (6 Baktun) was to have a calendar which reflected solar years, and is thus nearly identical to the accepted (scientific) chronology -- which assumes that all years in the past were Gregorian years of 365.2422 days.

When researchers calculate backwards to 3114 BC, using an actual count of days, they use a 365.2422-day Gregorian year. The researchers and archaeologists thus end up being able to place events in certain "years" which will match the intent of the Olmec and Maya Long Counts. Both are in error in terms of the actual number of days before 747 BC, but both are nearly correct in terms of "years" if these represented solar years. Both are in error because the later Maya also ignored the fact that the Olmecs knew the length of the year had been 360 days prior to 747 BC, and, in fact, designed the Long Count to tally in 360-day Tuns, not 365-day Haab years.

I have no problem with the suggestion that history might have been remembered from long before 3147 BC, or that some aspects of the Mesoamerican calendar date back to 2349 BC, and the count of years dates from before 10,900 BC. After all, in Northern Mesopotamia people had been accounting for trade products since about 8000 BC, and kept track of the number of days since 4077 BC. [note 3]

Mesoamerican iconography seems to spring to life sometime around 1500 to 1200 BC without any sign of a developmental phase. These are the dates of the first images carved in stone or engraved on celts. This suggests that the stone carvings were preceded by a long period of works in wood and other perishable materials, a period possibly lasting thousands of years. As an example of how long records could last, note that the *Dresden Codex*, a book on plaster-coated tree bark, was transcribed in about AD 1200 from material dating to before AD 700. It was sent to Spain after AD 1550. Such long endurance of books suggests the possibility of other records dating from more remote antiquity -- including, of course, chronological records.

Over the following few paragraphs I will speculate about possible early calendars, although after 2349 BC the use of a day and month calendar is certain. In circa 2350 BC Yao, the first "emperor" of China corrects the calendar. In the *Enuma Elish*, dating from Babylon sometime after 2000 BC, but detailing events in 2349 BC, the God Marduk does the same. Both of these instances assume there was an earlier calendar.

The First Calendar

I have estimated that before 3147 BC the year was 225 days long (see Appendix A, "Notes on Chronology"). A very simple but sophisticated calendar system could have been in use: the year was divided into 9 groups of 25. Fingers of one hand could be used to count up to 4. When 5 was reached the other hand closes a finger -- representing 5. Thus the other hand could hold a total of 25 units. The "Nine Lords of the Night" rotated nine times through the sets of 25 to count to a total of 225 days.

I am using the five fingers because both Olmec and Mayan ciphers were represented in base 5. The "Nine Lords of the Night" were still being counted 5000 years later, and still rotated endlessly through nine names. [note 4]

The "Nine Lords of the Night" together with the 25 "day numbers" (or more likely "day names") would produce 225 unique names for the days of the year. This sort of system would constitute a calendar which might have been a model for the later Tzolkin, which rotated 13 numbers against 20 names.

Who the "Nine Lords of the Night" were, or what they represented at the time before 3147 BC, is unknown. I suspect, on the basis of other sources, that the "Nine Lords of the Night" represented Jupiter and the eight nearest satellites, visible at close range after 3147 BC. Jupiter was known as "The Nine." See the chapter "The Chilam Balam" for this.

The "Nine Lords" might also represent an assignment of nine gods to the nine rings of the Absu -- the House of Nine Bushes. These would show at night (and not likely be very bright during the day).

left hand: 1 through 4
right hand: 5 through 25
9 Lords of the night (9 x 25 = 225 days)

An Intermediate Calendar

Of course, the previous is speculation. But for the period after 3147 BC, we can be much more certain of a calendar. After 3147 BC the year was (I suspect) 240 days long. The 240 days could be counted as multiples of 20 and could be made to fit 240 if 12 sets of 20 were to be used. A lunar calendar might be suggested for this era, with the period of the Moon at 20 days, but there was as yet no Moon. There is not a single suggestion of lunar calendars anywhere in the world before 2349 BC. It is more likely that the 20-day periods represented agricultural periods. It is possible that the 20 "day names" were rotated against 12 "day numbers" -- which would give 240 unique date-names to the year. [note 5]

The Mayan word for the 20 days is "uinal" which translates as "moon" and means "month." It also means "person," since a count of 20 day names could be understood as addressing all a person's fingers and toes. This person became personified as a "time-lord" who brought in the month as a parcel. Because of some such metaphorical construction, the continuity of time for Mesoamerican people was never a certainty (as it is for us) -- the bearer of time might not arrive with his burden.

The "Nine Lords of the Night" -- whatever their value might be -- remained in use.

A Person: 20 digits and toes (day names)
12 Day Numbers (20 x 12 = 240 days)
9 Lords of the Night

The Tzolkin Calendar

After 2349 BC the year went to 260 days. At this point speculation stops, although I have reached a year length of 260 days by somewhat of a circular argument (in Appendix A, "Notes on Chronology"). A line of a page of the *Books of the Chilam Balam*, dealing with the events of 2349 BC, reads:

"And then days of the year were introduced."

There certainly was a calendar in use, dating back some 3700 years, as the *Books of the Chilam Balam* show. This calendar consisted of a rotation through twenty named days. Only the preexistence of the twenty named days makes sense in the subsequent introduction of the Tzolkin calendar.

The count of days, the 260-day calendar known as the Tzolkin, as instituted in 2349 BC, was a lunar calendar. The Moon was intercepted in or after 2349 BC (see the chapter "The Day of the Dead"), and was probably in a stable orbit within a few years. Mesoamerica started to rotate 13 new "day numbers" against the existing 20 "day names" to yield 260 uniquely named days constituting a year. Brilliant! Every day of the year was individually identified and each was different from the others.

Imix   Ik   Akbal   Kan   Chicchan

Cimi   Manik   Lamat   Muluc   Oc

Chuen   Eb   Ben   Ix   Men

Cib   Caban   Etz'nab   Cauac   Ahau

[*Image: 20 Day Names of the Tzolkin Calendar. After Linda Schele and David Freidel "A Forest of Kings" (1990).*]

It is unlikely that the period of the Moon was 20 days at this time, or that there were 13 months to the year. More likely the number 13 is a count of a half moon period -- from a new moon to a full moon, and back. Thus the period of the Moon was likely 26 days and there were 10 lunar months of 26 days in the year, and 20 half months of 13 days.

Typical of Mesoamerican thinking, it was the completion of a change to a full moon or the finish of the waning to a new moon that counted -- 13 days for each. Thousands of years later, the Maya still call the 20-day period a "month," and a "moon" -- but not the 13-day period. This actually seems strange if the Moon's period was 26 days.

Anyway, each of the twenty days of the Tzolkin "moon period" had a separate name -- Imix, Ik, Akbal, Kan, etc. The glyphs for the day-names are unique from other glyphs in that all twenty are graphically represented as figures of some sort within the frame of an escutcheon seated on three feet. Some of the glyphs have not been recognized, which probably speaks to their extreme antiquity, as does the whole of the arcane nature of this calendar system. Glyphs which are known include tropical plants and animals as the environment of the location where these names were first selected. It has been suggested that these escutcheons are equivalent to the Egyptian name-cartouche used for the names of pharaohs and Gods. The three feet below the frame have been identified as a rope knot (Morley). Thus the escutcheons date from 2860 BC, and can be equated to the "shen" form in Egypt.

This system of a day count which rotates endlessly through 260 number-name combinations is actually the best evidence that an earlier calendar had existed. If the Lords of the Night were kept in use since 3147 BC, then there was probably a similar pressure to retain the day names after they became obsolete because they had constituted the base of a previous calendar.

Today the Tzolkin (which is still in use) shows no concern with time as a linear progression, only as a repeating cycle. This is endemic to the Mesoamerican languages, which understand time in topological terms, rather than a linear and endless series. An "historical awareness" in terms of understanding time as a linear progression does not take hold for another 2000 years. Mayan words for time involve references to round things, circles, and cycles. The future is expressed as going from here to there, as if invoking geography. We do this also, mentally, but our geography of time is a single line with no beginning or end.

The Tzolkin calendar makes no sense to us, who are used to a completely different method of tallying days. But it fits in with the suggested earlier calendar which rotated the "Nine Lords of the Night" against day names. The strangest aspect of the Tzolkin is that the 13 numbers are rotated against the 20 names, rather than "numbering" each of the names in a sequence of 1 to 13. Perhaps stranger still is that any group of 20 are known as a "month," although this may be because of the design of the later Haab calendar.

The languages of Mesoamerican people did not use tense (serial time) in verbs, but only the sense of "on-going" and "completed." In this manner the cycling of 1-Imix, 2-Ik, and 3-Akbal makes some sense, because to count 1-Imix, 1-Ik, and 1-Akbal would leave the moon-period uncompleted until the 13th count was reached. Similarly 1-Imix, 2-Imix, etc., seems to repeat the

Imix day pointlessly. The point was to reach 13, when the Moon would have become full, or new, and simultaneously keep up a rotation through the twenty day names, each of which attributes some quality to the particular day. The result, at any rate, was to have a calendar with 260 separate names for each day of the year.

A Person: 20 digits and toes (day names)
13 Day Numbers (20 x 13 = 260 days)
9 Lords of the Night

The question also occurs, why was this 260-day calendar kept in use when the length of the year and the period of the Moon changed one hundred and fifty years later in 2193 BC, and again in 1492 BC, and then in 747 BC? There could be a number of reasons, but primary is the fact that the Tzolkin calendar, and the later Haab calendar, do not function as we would imagine a calendar to function, that is, as a sequence of numbers which have a one-to-one correspondence to the sequence of days, and are discarded just as the days are irretrievable once they have moved into the past. The Tzolkin has a different function to a people whose language base does not include a strong sense of time as a path, but who do have a heightened sense of space and geography. In Mesoamerica, time had a spatial quality, and the Tzolkin functioned as a map to the domain of time.

I also think that the Tzolkin was kept for the same reason that the *I Ching* in China (dating from the Shang era or before) was never abandoned, even surviving the book burning of 213 BC. If the Maya or Olmec were at all like other people throughout the world, they would believe that all their fortunes and failures in life were predetermined. The only glimpse into the future was to "read" the qualities of each day, for like fate, each was different from any other (and Tzolkin/Haab day-name combinations do not repeat for 52 years). Using the Tzolkin as a guide to life was not unlike contemporaneous Chinese use of the *I Ching*, or Mesopotamian and Indian astrology. Even if the number of days in the year changed and a more rational calendar were to be adopted, the Tzolkin would have to remain in use without interruption.

Modification of the Tzolkin

After 2193 BC the year went to 270, 275, or 280 days. The Tzolkin could easily accommodate the 280-day year by adding an additional rotation of 20 days. I suspect, however, that the year changed to 273 days. By chance, the Tzolkin could also accommodate a year of 273 days, since it would only slip behind by a count of 13 days every year. [note 6]

That the calendar fell out of sync with the Solar year did not matter as long as the Tzolkin's primary purpose was to determine the quality of the days of the year. Consider also that the rotation through the twenty day-names had already been in use for 800 years. Certainly, too, it was kept because it represented high science to the Olmecs.

This science of the Tzolkin was used in the control of the Gods and spiritual powers. Specifically it was eventually used to control the travels of the Sun. This theme resounds through all of the history of Mesoamerica, and was repeatedly proven in the future to be correct and effective.

I suspect another cycle which has come down to us, a count of 819 days assigned in rotation to each of the cardinal points, was added in this era. Researchers have been unable to make anything of this cycle, except to note that 819 is the product of 7, 9, and 13. The period of 819 days revolved through the four cardinal directions.

Linda Schele and David Freidel, in *A Forest of Kings* (1990), note that in Maya texts the God K (also identified as God G-II), who clearly is Mars, is associated with the four directions. We therefore need to look to Mars.

First, let's note that 819 days happens to be exactly three times the length of the year (273 days) at this time (**3 * 273 = 819**).

The orbital period of Mars was 720 days. This has been proposed by Donald W. Patten and Samuel R. Windsor, in *The Mars-Earth Wars* (1996), for the purpose of their model, and as related to the period before 747 BC. From my use of this orbital period value, it appears to be correct.

In the era of 3147 BC to 2349 BC, the synodic period of Mars would have been **(720 * 240) / (720 - 240) = 360 days**. Thus Mars would show up in the same location of the sky every three years of 240 days, **2 * 360 - 3 * 240 = 0** (and once every year and a half). This three-fold repetition of the calendar year is, of course, also reflected in the mysterious 819 days, as already noted.

Let me suggest the following as a history of this: After 3067 BC (when Mars first started to appear near earth), with the year at 240 days, the reappearances of Mars were marked, correctly, at 3 intervals of the 240-day year, 720 days. This was the index of possible catastrophic interactions with Mars, which was good until about 2750 BC, after which Mars no longer was seen near Earth.

After 2349 BC, when the year went to 260 days, three of the 260-day periods were used instead, 780 days. This was incorrect and may have been useless in predicting catastrophes, but that did not matter, for Mars had disappeared from consideration some 400 years earlier, and by the end of the previous era it was probably no longer recalled why Mars had been assigned to one of the cardinal directions at intervals of three calendar years.

After 2193 BC the year went to 273 days. The assignment of Mars to the four cardinal directions was accomplished on a rotation of three years of 273 days, adding up to 819 days. Even if nothing happened, it did not matter. The interval of three years, tied to the four cardinal directions and the planet Mars, was a formal part of calendar computations, and had nothing to do with the close appearances of Mars.

The predictive value of the 819 day cycle was still correct when in 1935 BC Mars again made a series of destructive approaches. We could guess that, because of the circular nature of orbits, the interval was still 15 or 30 years, but of course years of 273 days. Mars would cruise close to Earth after every 5th interval of 819 days.

What then happened at 819-day intervals after that? It may have been kept at the value of 819 because in 1492 BC and 1442 BC a different planet, Venus, started interfering with Earth. The Mars cycle of 819 days remained unchanged. The next opportunity would have been in 1492 BC when the length of the year changed again. But no changes were made.

A Person: 20 digits and toes (day names)
13 Day Numbers (20 x 13 = 260 days)
819 days rotated against the four cardinal directions
9 Lords of the Night

The Haab Calendar

After 1492 BC the year changed to 360 days, and the period of the Moon changed to 30 days. This is certain from many sources throughout the world. A solution would have been to add five additional sets of 20 "name day" rotations ("months") to the Tzolkin, or to add five more numbers (from 13 to 18). But this would have been completely unacceptable, for the Tzolkin had to remain as it was, and as it had been for 1500 years. To extend the count would have been equivalent to changing our 7-day week to 9 days.

The only solution was a parallel calendar of 360-day period. This was done by starting a rotation through the names of 18 "months" (Uinals) of 20 days each, called the "Haab." Seven hundred years later this was augmented with 5 more days. Now for the first time we see a calendar instituted which has a familiar sensibility, like the numbered days of our months. The 18 months were separately named, but only 20 days were assigned to each month. The glyphs for the months are completely different from the Tzolkin glyphs and have the characteristics of the later development of the written language. A number of them also simply translate to "first," "second," etc. But the "months" -- that is, the Uinals -- still were 20 days long as they were previously, and were called "months" -- that is, a word meaning "moon." [note 7]

Pop	Uo	Zip	Zotz'	Zec
Xul	Yaxkin	Mol	Ch'en	Yax
Zac	Ceh	Mac	Kankin	Muan
Pax	Kayab	Cumku	Uayeb	

[*Image: The eighteen months of the Haab calendar plus the additional five-day period of the "sleep of the year," Uayeb. After Linda Schele and David Freidel "A Forest of Kings" (1990).*]

The 20 day **numbers** were most likely modeled after the 20 day **names** of the Tzolkin. The 360-day calendar of 18 months of 20 days also makes no sense, since the actual (lunar) months were 30 days long, but it neatly filled the year, and every three calendar months (60 days) coincided with two rotations of the Moon.

The Tzolkin remained in use, arcane as it was, to determine the quality of any day, and, nearly 3000 years later, as used by the Aztecs, determined the lot in life of a person named for a particular number-name day on which he was born.

The two calendars were entirely different, yet both were kept in use for the next 3000 years. (In some regions of Guatemala and Mexico they are still in use today, even in printed form.) In the Classical era of the Maya, the days were identified as the number-name of the Tzolkin, followed by the number-name of the Haab. The two calendars of 260 days and 360 days would not repeat a combination of two names for 13 years.

A Person: 20 digits and toes (day names)
13 Day Numbers (20 x 13 = 260)
18 months of 20 days (18 x 20 = 360) (13 year cycle)
819 days rotated against four cardinal directions
9 Lords of the Night

The Haab Revised and the Long Count

After 747 BC the year changed to 365 and 1/4 days. The Olmec correction, like almost everywhere else in the world, was to add 5 unnamed days at the end of the year. For the Olmecs this was a 19th short "month" Uayeb of five days, called "the sleep of the year." Actually this would shift the year one day backwards in the solar year every 4 years, for it did not account for the quarter day left over. The revised calendar in Peru actually added a leap day every four years. Mesoamerica through Classical times did not, with the exception of the Zapotecs at Monte Alban (after about 400 or 200 BC).

In 747 BC the Olmec also started to count days, perhaps to recalculate the length of the year after the Earth shock of 747 BC. This is known as the "Long Count" which was carried into the future without interruption for the next 2700 years, but was mainly used by the Maya until about AD 900. The count started on February 28 of 747 BC (actually the Julian year of -748) with all measures set to zero -- zero days (Kins), zero months of 20 days (Uinals), zero "double-decades" of 20 Tun years (Katuns), and zero years of 360 days (Tuns). In our notation of these Katuns, Tuns, Uinals, and Kins, the Long Count is rendered as 0.0.0.0 February 28, -748.

This is also the date of the start of the Babylonian "Era of Nabonassar" (which starts at nightfall of February 27th), and the same calendar day after which the Romans restarted the year since the 8th century BC. [note 8]

A larger unit, called a "Baktun," consisting of 20 "Katuns," (400 Tun years of 360 days) was added at the same time or at a later date. A starting "Baktun" value of "6" was assigned to February 28 of 747 BC. The official Long Count date for February 28 -748 (using our dotted notation) thus reads "6.0.0.0.0 11-Ahau 8-Uo," where "11-Ahau" and "8-Uo" are the day names in the rotating Tzolkin and Haab calendars. (This is based on the August 11 correlation of Thompson.) The odd day-names, both located in the middle of the Tzolkin and Haab calendars, confirm that the Tzolkin and Haab were already rotating simultaneously before this time.

It might be possible to estimate from this when the Haab was first instituted, or what the general plan for the Haab was. Others have suggested that it is likely that the summer or winter solstice was used to celebrate the start of the year. But this notion reflects our contemporary reductionist calendar concepts. It also reflects our thinking that calendars should start at the first day of the first month. That is not at all certain.

Some people in Guatemala celebrate the New Year at the winter solstice, or at Christmas. This is when the Haab recycles for them. But it is the 9th month of the Haab. But it is also possible, as I pointed out above, that the Haab calendar and its later extra 5-day "month" were instituted without regard for an elegant design, and was arbitrarily added to the existing Tzolkin. [note 9]

What is of greater interest is to know how soon the Haab was corrected by adding 5 additional days. By the 18th month (of 20 days) after February 28, 747 BC, it would have been obvious that the year was now longer, and a 19th short month should be added. But since the Olmecs kept track of the setting position of the Sun by days of the Tzolkin and Haab, it is likely they had a much earlier indication of how many days the year had slipped behind.

The intercalated 5 days were added probably as soon as the first one of the longer years was about to pass. The traditional use of the Haab in the Classical era adds the extra five days after the 18th month, Cumku. In fact it was added at the end of the first new longer year, as can be confirmed from the current usage by the Chiapas (see below). Otherwise there would not have been the amazing simultaneous coincidence with the start of the Era of Nabonassar.

Verification that the 5 days were added after only one of the old years had lapsed, comes from the practices of contemporary upland Maya in Chiapas, Mexico, who retain a form of the Haab calendar today. The contemporary Haab calendar, in this instance, starts directly after Christmas, that is, a few days after the winter solstice. No accounting is made of the fact that the calendar will slip backwards against the Gregorian calendar. Somehow an extra day is added every four years.

The year starts with a Haab month which, from its name, is the equivalent to the ninth month of the older Haab of antiquity, and continues in sync with the Haab of antiquity. The second month of the contemporary calendar is the 10th month of the old Haab, etc. There is one exception. The intercalated 5 days are placed after the third month (of 20 days), not after the last month. The third month of 20 days ends on February 24. The intercalated days start on February 25 and conclude on the day after February 28. [note 10]

The use of the Long Count, and especially the starting value of 6 Baktuns, shows that an historical awareness had developed by 747 BC. Six Baktuns represent 2400 solar years stretching back in time to 3147 BC. The Olmecs figured the past on the basis of 360-day years, but the actual length of the year does not enter the basic calculation of when the current era started. A Tun was a solar year; the length did not matter.

The Long Count rotates through Tuns of 360 days (18 times 20), and all the future uses of the Long Count disregard the 365-day Tuns, and counted instead in 360-day Tuns. This is rather amazing, and probably confirms that the Long Count was started simply to measure the new number of days in the year.

Of course what we do is to use 365.24 days as the length of the year, and simply count backwards by days (called the Julian day count). Within a few hundred years after 747 BC, the Olmecs ended up doing the same thing, that is, using 365.24 days. The prior year length of 360 days used by the Long Count was ignored or forgotten.

That the Long Count was started in 747 BC is apparent also from the fact that 6.0.0.0.0 of the Long Count falls on February 28, 747 BC, but also from the fact that this date completes a Katun 11. Katuns are named after the last Tzolkin day of a Katun; in this case the day 11-Ahau. This last is significant when we know from the 16th century AD Maya *Chilam Balam* that all of prehistory always was assigned to Katun 11-Ahau.

Some 1400 years later, in circa AD 700, the Maya at the site of Palenque retrocalculate dates 3000 years earlier, and list them according to the notion that the past -- all of the past -- consisted of 365 day Haab years, not 360 day Haab years. The Maya (or their Olmec predecessors) also retrocalculated back to the very beginning of the current era (the "second creation") to find that the initial Haab and Tzolkin days name and numbers were 8-Cumku and 4-Ahau. This works for both the "August 11" and the "August 13" concordance.

What does not work in this retrocalculation, is finding a Katun 11 ending for the previous era. The previous era ends in 4-Ahau, and thus the previous Katun is named Katun 4-Ahau. Despite this, when the *Chilam Balam* (in Book 10) recounts events from before the start of the current era (before 3147 BC, but thought to be 3114 BC), they are listed as happening in Katun 11. The notion obviously is from the time in 747 BC, when the Long Count was instituted as a Katun 11 had just ended. See the chapter "The Chilam Balam Books."

A Person: 20 digits and toes (day names)
13 Day Numbers (20 x 13 = 260 days)
18 months of 20 days (18 x 20 = 360 days)
19th month of 5 empty days (= 365 days)
819 days rotated against four cardinal directions
9 Lords of the Night

Of course the rotating calendars make no sense. Only the Long Count makes sense. One could tell how far in the past an event had happened, but only in terms of months (Uinals), which fell short of a cycle of the Moon, and years (Tuns) which fell 5 days short of the solar year. A relationship to the solar year could be kept by celebrating New Year at the summer (or winter) solstice, although solstice dates are not easy to determine. In fact, none of the people of the Central Valley of Mexico or the Maya of Mexico or the Guatemalan Peten celebrated or marked a solstice date, with the exception of the Chiapas mentioned above who remodeled their calendar to fit a Christian liturgical feast day near the winter solstice.

The actual day-name and day-number of a New Year day would change with each year. In the Yucatan the Maya of the Classical era celebrated the new year on July 26, when the Sun passed directly overhead at the site of Edzna, as did the people of Teotihuacan in Central Mexico (circa AD 200).

The simultaneous rotation through the 260-day cycle and the 365-day cycle would repeat every named day combination only once every 52 years (actually 52 "tun years"). That was of course significant in that it reflected the "traditional" possibility of reaching the end of creation (the so-called "52-year Venus cycle"), as was initially determined in the period between 2349 BC and 2193 BC.

The 365-day year, without leap days added, also kept exact pace with the synodic period of Venus, which was probably much more important than any other considerations. As long as there was a strong interest in the movements of the planet Venus, it would make sense to not add the leap day, and retain the traditional calendars. The complex Tzolkin and Haab calendars spread everywhere in Mesoamerica, but the Long Count only saw wide use by the Maya.

The Katun Cycle

After circa AD 900 the Maya give up on the Long Count which had reached back 1500 years (4000 years if retrocalculated), and continue to use only a short cycle of Katuns -- 20 years of 360 days, about 19.7 solar years total for each Katun. Consecutive Katuns were collected in a repeating series of 13 Katuns (rather than the 20 Katuns constituting a Baktun), because the ending day-names of the Katuns repeat after 13 Katuns.

The cycle of 13 Katuns is approximately 256 solar years. This series is all the Maya retain of their calendar, 600 years after the collapse of their kingdoms -- plus, of course, the endlessly repeating assignment of days to the Tzolkin, the Haab, and the "Nine Lords of the Night."

Consecutive Katuns always are listed as starting with Katun 11, named after the last day, 11-Ahau, and are followed by Katun 9, etc., with the series of declining even numbered Katuns after the last of the odd-numbered Katuns, Katun 1. This is seen in use in the 16th century AD Maya *Book Of Chilam Balam*.

Others have suggested that this is because Katun 11-Ahau **begins** with 1-Imix, the first day of the Tzolkin. But in fact it is because a Katun 11-Ahau **ends** on February 28, 747 BC (-748), when the Long Count (6.0.0.0.0) was instituted (using the "August 11" correlation). Katuns are named after the name of the last day of the Katun period, not after the day with which they start (as *we* would do). It was always the completion of a time period, not the beginning, that mattered. For the Maya, unlike for us, a period of time did not **exist** until it was completed; it also did not exist yet while it was still ongoing.

The Four Ages

The concept of "suns" or "sun ages" was recognized throughout Mesoamerica by various peoples, as well as by people in many other parts of the world. (And has become a big deal among catastrophists.) These ages are meant to represent various creations of the world, or recreations after a catastrophic destruction. In Mesoamerica four ages were recognized by all except by the Toltecs and the Aztecs, who claimed that the world had been recreated five times. Both of these people held their own invasion of the Valley of Mexico as the last recreation of the world.

The creations and recreations can be pinpointed, but the series of dates runs into conflict with various concepts of what constitutes a new age.

The Olmec and Maya Long Count calendar starts the "current creation" in (the retrocalculated year of) 3114 BC. This date does not count the two destructions of the Earth since that time, but only recognizes that conditions on Earth and in the skies were completely different before and after. This was known as the "second creation," and from this two ages are recognized.

Book 10 of the Maya *Chilam Balam* books places creations or recreations after floods, and thus recognizes three eras, the periods before and after 3114 BC, and the period after 2349 BC, this last started with an event known as the "third reign" or what would be the "third creation." But the dark skies after 1492 or 1440 BC are also dealt with as the start of a new creation. It is not surprising that this confusion exists, since Book 10 of the *Chilam Balam* is obviously derived from diverse sources.

The concept of "four ages" is a satisfying shorthand if we associate a change of the length of the year with each of the ages, and especially if these events can be associated with some worldwide catastrophe. But it does not work out that way. What can be gathered from the most reliable source, the *Chilam Balam*, is the following:

- There was a very early age, suggested in the *Popol Vuh* and detailed in Book 11 of the *Chilam Balam* -- the long period before the darkness of the Younger Dryas. And then followed the lighting up of the southern ball plasmoids in 10,900 BC. That was the start of the "first creation." This ended in 8347 BC, and marks the ending of the "first creation." This particular time period is generally not recognized at all by most catastrophists.
- The "second creation" ends in 3147 BC. References to it are only implied in the text of the *Chilam Balam* from the fact that the "third creation" ends later, in 2349 BC. The second age is thus the era between 8347 BC and 3147 BC, and includes (as the last thousand years) the "Era of the Gods."
- The end of the "third creation" is the event we know as the "flood of Noah." Book 10 of the *Chilam Balam,* however, places the "third creation" (incorrectly) in Katun 9-Ahau ending in 2266 BC. It should properly be placed in Katun 4-Ahau ending in 2345 BC.

The fall of the Absu, the end of the "third creation," is noted as "the second baptism" with the implication that the first is the flood of 3147 BC (which is also mentioned). The *Chilam Balam* also implies the start of a new calendar. In this it parallels the Chinese *Annals of Shu*, as well as the Babylonian *Enuma Elish*.

- Despite the fact that Jupiter had burst into flames and lost its coma, disappearing from the skies in about 2150 BC, Jupiter remained the ruling God. Likewise the change in the Earth's orbit in 2193 BC was not an event which defined a new era. The era of the "third creation" continued.
- The electric contact by Venus in 1492 BC starts yet another age, the fourth. In fact the *Chilam Balam* notes that Venus "rubbed the Earth" in Katun 9-Ahau ending in 1486.2 BC (corrected), although this was likely the view of the Van Allen belts in glow mode. A new creation is also to be inferred from the mention of the establishment of the trees of the four cardinal directions. This is the third reference in the document to these trees, noted previously after 3147 BC and 2349 BC.

There is also a reference to "walking in darkness," which can be identified as the 40 years or so after the contact by Venus in 1492 BC. The Israelites also "walked in darkness."

"Then they perceived that the world was being created. Then creation dawned upon the world."

The reference to creation is suggested for 1492 BC by its placement in the texts, but could also refer to the 200-year climatic downturn experienced worldwide after 2193 BC.

- There are no further ages referenced. The year 747 BC, which occluded the Sun for two days and changed the orbit of the Earth, had no bearing on the list of ages. The Earth shock of 686 BC could have represented the start of yet another age, but the *Chilam Balam* specifically states that this was not to happen (a retrospective comment). Similarly, the nova event of 685 BC is mentioned but not counted as a new era. In actuality, the understanding was that the world was rescued from Mars by Jupiter.

I suspect that the *Chilam Balam* was transcribed from books indigenous to the Peten and Yucatan Maya. The story of these books may have differed from the records kept among the Olmecs of Veracruz and in the Valley of Mexico, which have not survived.

But we can count four ages from Olmec sources under a completely different paradigm: the site alignments used in the Olmec coastal area since 1440 BC, and in the Valley of Mexico since about 600 BC.

These horizon alignments for sunrise or sunset reference four dates. First, starting at San Lorenzo and followed by almost every later site, the date of April 19, 1492 BC is recalled in the alignment of the setting Sun to some mountain or volcano. Apparently when San Lorenzo was established, the horizon location of the setting Sun for that date was known.

Similarly, at La Venta the alignment for February 28, 747 BC was also known, since it was experienced. After 747 BC the date of August 12, 3114 BC, was calculated with the aid of the newly developed Long Count. Various dates centering on July 685 BC, were also experienced and incorporated into the alignments of sites after 685 BC.

Last, in about AD 200, and at some locations, both since before and directly after 685 BC, the setting of the culmination of the Pleiades is used to signal the event of 2349 BC. These alignments show up at all later sites. The alignments are discussed in the chapter "Olmec Site Alignments."

Endnotes

Note 1 --

The dotted notation, used by archaeologists as a shorthand to identify the Long Count, consists from left to right of measures known as Baktuns, Katuns, Tuns, Uinals, and Kins.

These are thus written in modern form as as Baktun (dot) Katun (dot) Tun (dot) Uinal (dot) Kin. A dotted notation is always followed by the Tzolkin day number and day name combination plus the Haab day number and month name combination.

- Baktuns are sets of 20 Katuns, or 400 Tun years, representing 400 years of 360 days (surprisingly, not 365 days). A Baktun represents about 256 years of our calendar. The word "Baktun" is an invention of archaeologists. The Maya simply called it "400" in representing 20 times 20. The count goes from 1 to 13.
- Katuns are double decades, representing 20 of the 360-day Tun years. The count goes from 0 to 19. This is about 19 years of our calendar.
- Tuns are "years" of 360 days. The count ranges from 0 to 19.
- Uinals are "months," where each count represents 20 of the day counts. Uinals range from 0 to 17. On reaching 18, the next higher number (the Tun) of the dotted notation is advanced one. 18 Uinals thus represent a Tun year of 360 days.
- Kins are days and count from 0 to 19. On the 20th count, the next higher number (the Uinals) of the dotted notation advances one. Kins (days) thus count up to one Uinal "month" before advancing the next higher count.

Note 2 --

For Long Count dates which were retrocalculated by the Maya in circa AD 700 at Palenque, as well as the correction of the Katuns (where I have supplied the Baktun) of Book 10 of the *Chilam Balam*, a correction should be used. This will be based on the suspicion that there did not exist a record in actual Long Count days for events before 747 BC, but only a listing by Katuns and Baktuns. This correction is easy to do: Since 6 Baktuns were added to the dotted date of 0.0.0.0, the starting date of the current era would have been 2400 years earlier (6 times 400), and thus 747 BC less 2400 years: 3147 BC.

The start of the yet earlier era would be 3147 BC less 13 times 400 years:

8347 BC.

For the inscriptions at Palenque the correction should be based on the fact that the Olmecs knew that the era prior to 747 BC represented years of 360 days, not 365.24 days. But this was long forgotten 1400 years later when the Maya of Palenque start carving monumental inscriptions. Our calculations and those of the Maya of Palenque are based on a 365.24-day year, and would be off by 5.24 days per year before 747 BC, that is, the dates we use are placed too far into the past. The correction is **(3114-747) * 5.24 / 365.24 = 34 years.**

So, for example, when in AD 700 the Maya at Palenque retrocalculated a date of 2360 BC for some event listed among the inscriptions, it was based, like our calculations, on a 365.24 day year, and would be too far into the past by **(2360-747) * 5.24 / 365.24 = 24 years.** The date should be 2336 BC.

The Maya were perfectly capable of calculating backwards, and making allowances for the extra 0.24 day of the year. Anthony Aveni, in *Skywatchers of Ancient Mexico* (1980), notes a number of instances among Maya inscriptions (at Copan) where successful attempts were made to indicate the length of the tropical year. The Maya ended up with a year of 365.2420 days, only 0.0002 days different from the current value of 365.2422 days.

Note 3 --

See the chapter "The Chilam Balam Books" for a retelling of the creation of the world which dates back to thousands of years before 3114 BC and was apparently transcribed from Maya tree-bark codexes. Other pages of the *Chilam Balam* describe the darkness of the Younger Dryas (10,900 to 9,000 BC), and hint at yet earlier ages dating to the equivalent of the European Magdalenian period (17,000 to 14,000 years ago) or earlier (I suspect to 41,000 years ago).

Note 4 --

The Maya (and Olmecs) used a base-20 in their commerce, but it is difficult to maintain that they also did so with their calendar, as is often maintained. The "units" of the Long Count do not all advance as powers of 20, since the Uinals advance when reaching 18, not 20. Baktuns cycle at the number 13. The number 20 just happens to be a larger unit to count in, like our dozen or hundred. The glyphic representation is certainly in base-5.

Note 5 --

Although some of what I have suggested is conjecture, I should note a remarkable similarity of the Mesoamerican 20 day names and 12 day numbers to the calendar of the Chinese Shang dynasty, after about 1400 BC, which rotated 10 "celestial day names" (instead of 20) against 12 "earthly day names" to produce a similar calendar (of 60-day periods), elements of which lasted well into the current era. The Chou dynasty extended the rotation of 60 day names to the names of years. This last persists today.

Although the Shang dynasty is much later than the period under discussion here (before 2349 BC), it would not be at all surprising if the Shang calendar represented a holdover from an earlier period, when the 240-day year was divided into four seasons of 60 days each, thus a total of 240 days. China experiences four distinct seasons; Mesoamerica experiences a completely different cycle of seasons. The Shang, at any rate, added the lunar month days to the 60-day periods to furnish nearly accurate calendar dates during the year.

Note 6 --

I suggest a year of 273 days, based on conjectures developed later in this text. Since 273 is 13 days more than 260 days, the Tzolkin could have been expanded by adding one round of 13 numbers, or the calendar could have been left to slip backwards 13 days per year. The reason for selecting the second might have depended on an initial attempt to keep the calendar in line with the half-moon periods of the previous era. This did not work out, for the Moon changed to a period of 27 or 28 days after 2193 BC, which we know from (later) Shang oracle records.

Note 7 --

It is possible that the Haab was devised separately by a people different from those who devised the Tzolkin, and the two calendars were kept after a cultural merger after 1500 BC.

Note 8 --

According to Ussher, the era of Nabonassar starts at noon of February 26th, thus actually on the 27th. Ussher writes:

"From twelve o'clock, on the first day of the Egyptian month Thoth, from Wednesday, February 26th, in the evening, in the year 747 BC, all astronomers unanimously start the calendar of Nabonassar."
    -- James Bishop Ussher, *Annals of the World* (AD 1650)

Additionally, because of the Mesoamerican concepts that a day does not exist until it is completed, the Long Count use of "day zero" actually signifies the first day of the new era, so that the actual era-ending date is February 27th.

Note 9 --

The short five-day month can be neglected in any retrocalculation here, because it was instituted in 747 BC. If we take a hint from how the Olmecs dealt with other calendar adjustments, it would suggest that the Haab was instituted the day after the completion of the cataclysm of 1492 BC. From an earlier chapter we know that this happened on a Gregorian equivalent calendar date of April 19. (Bible tradition, for the start, is April 17th.)

On February 28, 747 BC, the Haab day fell on 8-Uo. This is the 29th day of the Haab. Thus, in 747 BC, the annual secular calendar, which starts with 0-Pop, had started 29 days earlier in that year, equivalent to January 30 on an equivalent Gregorian calendar. Thus, between April 19, 1492 BC and February 28, 747 BC the Haab had slipped 80 days backward, which is four 20-day Uinal months. This number is not in any sense meaningful.

Alternately, taking into account the fact that before 685 BC the winter solstice fell some 15 days earlier, on December 8, the Haab would have restarted 53 days after the winter solstice. Except for the fact that 53 days represents a 52-day interval, this also is such an arbitrary figure, that it can only be suggested that there was no relationship between the Haab and either the winter or summer solstice.

Vincent H. Malmstrom, in *Cycles of the Sun, Mysteries of the Moon* (1997), dates the first use of the Haab to 1324 or 1321 BC, based on placing the day 0-Pop (the first day of the Haab) at the summer solstice. The calculation would only be in error by 8 years, since the extra five days have to be subtracted from the Haab for the period before 747 BC. But also it is absurd to think that a beginning date (0-Pop) would be at meaningful in Mesoamerican chronology.

The usage of the Chiapas (see other endnote below) might bear out Malmstrom's conjecture that the New Year (the start of the Haab) was celebrated at the summer solstice, even though the Chiapas today start the year with the winter solstice (actually at Christmas), for they start with the ninth month (Uinal) of the traditional Haab calendar. The name of the month which starts the Haab is clear from the fact that the names of the first few months of the Haab translate to "first," "second," "third," etc. That would place the beginning of the Haab 160 days before Christmas (8 completed months). This is not at the summer solstice, but 24 days later, on July 18.

When New Year is celebrated is a local option. The Maya, as with Teotihuacan, used July 26. In colonial times the Aztecs celebrated the start of the new year on February 26. (There are some discrepancies with respect to this particular date, however. See the endnotes to Appendix B, "Celestial Mechanics.")

Note 10 --

See Gary H Gossen, "A Chamula solar calendar board from Chiapas, Mexico," in, Norman Hammond, editor, *Mesoamerican Archaeology* (1974). Although the Tzolkin was held as sacred, the Haab was apparently adjusted to start as convenient by various tribes.

Calculations are in Unix bc notation, where ^ denotes exponentiation; the functions a(rctangent), s(ine), and c(osine) use radians; angle conversions to radians or degrees by the divisors rad=.017+ and deg=57.2+; other functions are shown as f( ); tan( )=s( )/c( )
units: million == 1,000,000; billion == 1,000,000,000;
AU == 93,000,000 miles.

Recovering the Lost World,
A Saturnian Cosmology -- Jno Cook
Chapter 30: The Maya Chilam Balam

Revision: 42.30 (chil.php)

Contents of this chapter: [Introduction] [The Katun Cycle]
[The Start of History] [Author's Introduction] [The Thirteen: Saturn]
[The Nine: Jupiter] [Nine Lives: Mars] [The Four Trees] [Katun 9-Ahau: Ten-Sky] [Katun 7-Ahau: Venus] [The 2349 BC Event] [The Moon] [Katun 5-Ahau: Jupiter Returns] [The Burning Tower] [The Planted Timbers]
[Katun 3-Ahau: the Sun] [The 8th Century BC] [The day of Kan]
[The Flowers] [Saturn] [Jupiter] [The End of History] [Recap of Book 10]
[Endnotes]

Introduction

The *Chilam Balam* books are a collection of post-colonial (16th century AD) native manuscripts in the Mayan languages, using the Latin script, which recorded histories and prophecies, many dating back with certainty for hundreds of years, while Books 10 and 11 plus some single pages recollect events dating back thousands of years. All of it is presented in terse and obscure language.

I am tempted to repeat the statement by Hertha von Dechend about "the annihilating recognition of our complete ignorance" for I was struck with the same feeling on first reading the *Chilam Balam* -- I could make absolutely no sense of any of it. It took me six months of daily application to digest Book 10, and much longer to unravel Book 11.

Book 11 recalls events leading to the creation in 10,900 BC of the ball plasmoids of the south. This is the "first creation." Book 11 may include events dating back to circa 30,000 or 40,000 BC. A separate single page of the *Chilam Balam* specifically recalls the "survey of the world" in the period after 10,900 BC, while yet another single page recalls the fall of the Absu in 2349 BC. These additional texts from the *Chilam Balam* will be presented in the chapter "The Olmec Record."

What follows below is an attempt to "read" Book 10 in terms of the chronology of celestial events which I had already established on the basis of information from the Eastern Mediterranean region, India, and China. Book 10 deals with the "second creation" and subsequent events, including the "third creation."

The Book Of Chilam Balam Of Chumayel was translated into English by Ralph L Roys in 1933, based on original sources, and compared to other extant documents and other copies of the *Chilam Balam*. It is not easy to read, even though the text is supplemented with extensive footnotes and added commentary. One of the stumbling blocks is the mention of many Maya Gods which are still obscure and difficult to identify today. A copy of *The Book Of Chilam Balam Of Chumayel* is on line at [www.sacred-texts.com/nam/maya/cbc].

I first looked at the *Chilam Balam* after I had written most of the text of these pages. In Book 10 of the *Chilam Balam,* in a section labeled (by Roys) "The Creation of the World," I ran into a phrase which caught my attention:

"Then there came great misery, when it came about that the sun in Katun 3-Ahau was moved from its place for three months."

If there is one thing for certain, it is that since the Sun first appeared, it has never moved, acted up, or changed its look in human memory -- except, of course, in 685 BC, as I had already established. Could this be a record of the nova event of the Sun and the blazing of Venus and Mercury of 685 BC (680 BC in Eastern Mediterranean chronology), when the polar axis relocated, the dome of the sky twisted, and the vernal equinox moved suddenly to another zodiac sign?

A calculation showed that the first 20-year Katun 3-Ahau period after 747 BC started in 687 BC (6.3.0.0.0), two years before my estimate for the nova event of 685 BC, and ended about 20 years later. A closer reading of the remaining text soon convinced me that this Book retold other events dating back to before 3100 BC. And ends, as does everyone else's record of the catastrophic past, in 685 BC.

The clearest indication of these events were descriptions of interactions between Jupiter and Saturn (and their satellites) which can be placed for certain in 3147 BC. It is described with uncanny accuracy -- if we are allowed to transfer the names of two sets of obscure Gods, "The Thirteen" and "The Nine," to Saturn and Jupiter. The remainder of the text of this chapter provides the details. This portion (called a Book) of the *Chilam Balam* recounts what is known among the people of Mesoamerica as the "second creation" and subsequent events of the "third creation" and a possible "fourth creation" through 685 BC.

The Katun Cycle

First a word should be said about the cycle of 13 Katuns in use by the Maya at the time of the Spanish invasion. After Classical times (circa AD 900), the Maya dropped their "Long Count" dating and reduced their calendar to a repeating cycle of 13 Katuns (which was in use already long before AD 900). Each Katun consists of twenty Tuns, that is, twenty 360-day years (not the 365-day Haab years) and thus 19.71 of our Gregorian years, each named after the last day of the period in the Tzolkin day nomenclature. This, as it turns out, is always one of the day-numbers 1 through 13, followed by the day-name Ahau. The Katuns are named, in order, 11-Ahau, 9-Ahau, 7-Ahau, etc., skipping a day-number for each consecutive Katun. The complete cycle of 13 Katuns is approximately 256.26 actual current years.

Because of the Maya philosophy of cyclic time, only this single cycle of 13 Katuns was recognized, and all events were placed within a listing of this cycle, although at times other Books of the *Chilam Balam* texts will list Katuns as a series extending over many cycles. But often events separated by 256, 512, or 1024 years are all listed for the same Katun. Thus when an event is said to occur in Katun 4-Ahau, it could have happened in any 256-year interval of the past, or even be a prediction for the future. It is, in fact, the predictive value of this calendar that forced the Maya to consider that all events of the past had been accomplished in a single repeating cycle, and would happen again. [note 1]

In the text below, I have added corrections to the (retrocalculated) Gregorian years to show solar years, based on the indication that the Long Count was started in 747 BC, on a day matching similar efforts at calendar reform in the Eastern Mediterranean. The Olmecs added 6 Baktuns to a count set at 0.0.0.0 on February 28, 747 BC (the completion of the disturbance). Thus to correct for our insistence in calculating backward in time under the assumption that the year was always 365.24 days (as the Classical Era Maya also did), we can place the Long Count date of 0.0.0.0.0 at 6 Baktuns before 747 BC, at 3147 BC.

The corrections are then made by counting forward in time with **3147 - 400 * Baktuns - 20 * Katuns** up to 747 BC (even though the year 747 BC on which this is based is actually -747).

Retrocalculation for dates from the sculptures at Palenque (circa AD 700) require a different method. This has been covered in the chapter "The Career of Jupiter," and takes into account the difference between 360 and 365.24 days in the year. The recalculated dates in this chapter match the corrected Eastern Mediterranean chronology, with some exceptions, which can be attributed to the attitudes of the Maya to the very concepts about time, and which will be explained below.

Katun 11-Ahau: History Starts

Bishop Diego Landa destroyed hundreds of Maya glyphic manuscripts in the 16th century AD, but it is likely that many remained, for even 100 years later missionaries were reading prophecies from original bark books (as, for example, the Spanish missionary Avendaño, in AD 1696).

The *Chilam Balam* books had a different status than the original bark books. Written by the Maya in European notebooks, in the European script, but in the Mayan language, these formed a greatly condensed record of the histories, rituals, and prophecies from the time before the invasion of the Spanish in AD 1517. It was an efficient method of keeping in touch with the past. The books were kept from the Spanish priests, recited at village meetings, and copied and recopied for 300 years. The readers knew the context of the information of these notebooks, although likely this was slowly lost over the next few hundred years. [note 2]

The *Chilam Balam* books all insist that the cycle of history starts with Katun 11-Ahau. Although Maya history recorded on monuments does not reach back before AD 300 or 400, their calendar was in universal use throughout Mesoamerica probably since 600 BC or earlier, and the predecessors to the Maya, the Olmecs, were probably responsible for the concept that history started with Katun 11-Ahau. Roys claims that this is so because the first day of Katun 11-Ahau starts with the day 1-Imix which is the first day of the 260-day Tzolkin cycle of naming days. But in the grammatical construction of Indian languages, a date (or Katun) does not exist until it is completed, which is why Katuns are named after their last day, not the first. [note 3]

My thinking initially was that the reason for starting history with Katun 11-Ahau is that the ending of a Katun 11-Ahau might have coincided with the calendar change in 747 BC, when calendars were changed worldwide, and in many cases initiated. It turned out that this guess was correct, a Katun 11-Ahau **ended** in 747 BC, in fact, on February 28th. This is the ending date also for the Roman annual calendar. And also the day before the start of the "Era of Nabonassar" used in the Babylonian Chronicles, and presented by Ptolemy in about AD 150 for his list of Kings of Babylon and his list of eclipses. This is the date that the year changed from 360 days to 365.25 days. The Babylonian day started at nightfall, so that the era actually started on February 27th.

All of this is not just a coincidence. The odds of a single 20-year Katun, out of a cycle of 13 Katuns, ending in the year 747 BC, is small. That it should fall exactly on the date before the start of the "Era of Nabonassar" is astounding. That this date would be represented by the Long Count of 6.0.0.0.0 is beyond belief.

Considering that the nova event of Venus in 685 BC also coincides with a Katun period of the correct name, I thought that perhaps some faith could be placed in these Katun dates, although I expected much of the information to be out of place. In fact, as I read through the text, I realized that most of the very old events were arbitrarily assigned to Katun 11-Ahau. I did not initially expect any of the other celestial events to be placed in Katuns which corresponded with known dates from the Middle East. But at the conclusion of investigating this text, it looked like all except two of the events were correctly placed. One was, I suspect, a transcription error, and the second was a deliberate change made during classical times (or earlier) to make the date of an important event coincide with a certain day-name of the Tzolkin (July 25th).

Many of the events recorded in Book 10 of the *Chilam Balam*, however, seem to be in the wrong order in going from one event to the next. It is as if some canonical source was misread, perhaps reading the left page before the right page from a book meant to be read from right to left (which, in fact, was the case for the Maya codexes). It would seem that in some cases only the information of single sentences occupied a full page of the original. That suggests an illustrated codex with an appended text in glyphs.

Additionally, it looks as if the author had accessed three or four separate original sources, which do not match in format, although none of the events are repeated. I will indicate the suspected shifts from one source to another where I have become aware of them. [note 4]

As you can imagine, the *Chilam Balam* represents a giant sequencing puzzle, both because of the obscure sequencing of history and because of a few errors which were incorporated by the original copyist. It took me six months to get through the text initially, and I had to make a number of changes afterwards. Often a resolution of textual elements involved attempting to place myself in the position of a copyist who is earnestly trying to make sense of a document which related events from thousands of years ago.

But thanks to a cultural continuity, we can identify elements which were actual and which (from our point of view) had shifted to become metaphors. The greatest help in this was reading Linda Schele and David Freidel's book *Maya Cosmos* (1993) prior to tackling the *Chilam Balam*, for the authors identify many elements from the Classical Maya era, 1500 years ago, which still appear among the contemporary practices of Maya shamans. (I also was involved as equipment consultant for Peter Thompson's film *The Shaman of Oxkintok* about Don Chabo, a Maya shaman, in 1992 -- 1993, but known as

El Movimiento when completed in 2001.)

In *Maya Cosmos* Schele and Freidel were eventually forced to consider the stars as a major element in Maya cosmology and show that this is part of religious practices of the Classical era and is still in current use. Thus when I ran into the "timbers at the crossroads" and the "precious objects," the equivalent in our terminology instantly jumped to mind, and without question. It has likewise been shown by Schele and Freidel that many concepts and ideas, it would be more proper to say "images," of the 16th century AD Guatemalan *Popol Vuh* were already being depicted in Classical times.

In the following I have kept the *Chilam Balam* text in the same order as it exists, with a few alternate readings by Bolio (see below), and some footnotes by Roys, added. That makes for a thoroughly confusing sequence, but I thought it more important to follow the original order of the text, rather than to make repairs which would only add to the confusion. As a reader you will thus be treated to constant interruptions, where events are taken up, interrupted by other unrelated events, and continued a paragraph or two later. Overall, however, the *Chilam Balam* sticks to a consecutive narrative. That will help.

The specificity of Roys's translation can be compared with a more recent translation by Suzanne D. Fisher, made from an earlier translation into Spanish made in 1930 by Antonio Mediz Bolio. Bolio has the distinction of speaking one of the Mayan languages, but this earlier Spanish translation by Bolio seems to be a composition based on the assumption that the original was written in similes and metaphors.

In a preface to a translation of Bolio's text into French, J. M. Le Clézio wrote, *"At times ... he seems to prefer the beauty of the expression to the literal meaning, which results in a profoundly emotional and poetical version."*

At times the Fisher translation after Bolio parallels the translation by Roys and is much more readable, but often it is altogether different. Thus the sentence I quoted above, about the Sun:

"Then there came great misery, when it came about that the sun in Katun 3-Ahau was moved from its place for three months. After three years it will come back into place in Katun 3-Ahau."

This is rendered by Bolio as:

"That is what is coming, when three moons have fallen in the time of the 3-Ahau Katun, and after three portions of years, trapped within the 3-Ahau Katun; ..."

Bolio, in the text shown directly above, assumes that the original is a comment on the sense of a previous sentence, which speaks to the coming of an "unending bitterness." Roys assumes the sentence starts with the mention of the "great misery" and places the agent in this phrase. Both the sense and the punctuation have been rendered completely differently.

At cause is the original text, where there is no indication of the starting and ending of sentences or paragraphs. Both Roys and Bolio had to guess at the implied punctuation. Bolio has the advantage of speaking Mayan, and often he has polished the text, but I too feel he has frequently lost the specific details. In Roys's translation, on the other hand, the tense and number of the verbs and nouns often bounce back and forth unpredictably. I will use Roys's text and augment it with the Bolio text as needed.

A copy of Book 10 is available locally at [saturniancosmology.org/book10.htm] which collates the text by Roys with some rephrasings by Bolio, some of the material from Roys's footnotes, and a few additional insertions, but without my extensive comments. I have added the numbered Katuns. The 16th-century scribe started in Katun 11-Ahau and continued in order through Katuns 11, 9, 7, 5, [8, 2], 3, 1). After Katun 5-Ahau, two even-numbered Katuns are inserted, Katun 8-Ahau and 2-Ahau. The sequence of even-numbered Katuns is skipped, but the text ends in repeating Katuns 13-Ahau, 11-Ahau, and 9-Ahau.

The Author's Introduction

Book 10 of the *Chilam Balam* is the history of the "second creation" of the world, and the appearances of the planetary Gods. With some exceptions, the information never deviates from the purpose of this presentation. The text is introduced by the original copyist with a note of urgency. The information is presented in the context of the new Christian God:

> *"It is most necessary to believe this. These are the precious stones which our Lord, the Father, has abandoned. This was his first repast, this wine, with which we, the ruling men, revere him here."*
>
> *"Very rightly they worshipped as true gods these precious stones, when the true God was established, our Lord God, the Lord of heaven and earth, the true God."*

This section of the *Chilam Balam* is distinct from all other texts of the books in offering an introduction. The comment about the "precious stones" suggests that stones were used to represent events and represent the gods. The first Christian missionaries also told that the Maya "worshipped stones." The author here turns the "stone worship" of the Maya into a misdirected earlier effort. It might also be suggested that the Maya knew very well that the planetary Gods which were worshipped were indeed nothing more than large rocks. The close passages of Mars would have demonstrated that. In Book 11, "The Ritual of the Angels," a Maya author has the Christian "God the Father" emerge from one of the "holy stones" seen in the sky. Bolio in that case interprets "tun" as a "holy stone." It might serve the reader to think of "tun" or "stone" not as material ("made of stone") but as a shape, form, or container. [note 5]

The author continues with the introduction: (I have broken up Roys's long paragraphs throughout.)

> *"Nevertheless, the first gods were perishable gods. Their worship came to its inevitable end. They lost their efficacy by the benediction of the Lord of Heaven, after the redemption of the world was accomplished, after the resurrection of the true God, the true Dios, when he blessed heaven and earth. Then was your worship abolished, Maya men. Turn away your hearts from your (old) religion."*
>
> *"(This is) the history of the world in those times, because it has been written down, because the time has not yet ended for making these books, these many explanations, so that Maya men may be asked if they know how they were born here in this country, when the land was founded."*
>
> NOTES:
> - () insertions by Roys in the translated text,
> - [] insertions are by me from footnotes or from Bolio.

The writer acknowledges that his sources are other books. He then proceeds to list events, starting, naturally, with Katun 11-Ahau, where the cycle of all history is understood to start. The first few lines relate events which happened before 4077 BC and in 3147 BC. He then progresses through additional Katuns in turn, but only up to Katun 3-Ahau, which Roys thinks is an interpolation (in this particular version of the *Chilam Balam*). He then very briefly speaks of the miseries of Katun 13-Ahau and touches again on Katun 11-Ahau and Katun 9-Ahau as a recitation of more recent history. This is followed by portraits of Saturn and Jupiter as the two ruling Gods. Here is a list of topics, in brief outline:

- Katun 11-Ahau - The Bee Gods and The Thirteen; the fire, the rope; the capture of The Thirteen by The Nine; Nine-Lives escapes; flood and fallen sky; four trees (the period of 4077 BC to 3147 BC).
- Katun 9-Ahau - Ten-Sky appears (3067 BC to circa 2700 BC);
- Katun 7-Ahau - Uuc Chek-nal comes; Earth and Heaven touch (1492

BC).

- Katun 7-Ahau - A new world created (after 1442 BC).
- The "third creation," the Moon rules all of Earth (wrong Katun?).
- Katun 2-Ahau: Jupiter seated, gravediggers, crossroads revealed (2349 BC).
- Katun 8-Ahau: fire on high (2150 BC).
- Katun 3-Ahau - The Sun leaves its path (685 BC).
- Katun 13-Ahau - Misery, foreigners.
- Katun 11-Ahau - Nine-Lives shows (776 - 747 BC).
- Katun 9-Ahau - Nine-Lives descends, flowers (747 - 727 BC).
- Fall of the Absu (placed in 2250 BC, wrong date).
- The rulership of the Thirteen.
- The rulership of the Nine.
- The return of Kukulkan.

At first I was not always certain of how some of the descriptions translated to the chronology I had set out earlier in these pages. But allowing for the author's error in reading the order of the original texts, the insistence of sorting events by Katuns, and the additional quirk of failing to note repeating events, all of it eventually fell into place. What I am certain of is that very little is metaphorical. Much of it is simply descriptive, even though the language is one of the Maya's environment of stones, trees, flowers, and plants.

The distinct advantage to us of the *Chilam Balam* as a source for a history of the "Era of the Gods" and the period following, is its insistence, based in the original Mayan language, of describing actions rather that static states. In contrast, Egyptian or Mesopotamian sources deal almost entirely with static states.

The Thirteen: Saturn

The following are the first lines. The author starts at the very beginning, the first clear sight of Saturn in 4077 BC. I am translating "Oxlahun-ti-ku" as "The Thirteen" on the basis of Roys's footnotes. From the remaining context it is obvious that "The Thirteen" is Saturn, just as "The Nine" will turn out to be Jupiter. Together with the next few lines, we have here a condensation of the 3000 years of history of the Saturnian apparition to a few lines:

"It was (Katun) 11-Ahau when the Ah-Mucenca [the bees] *came forth to blindfold the faces of the Oxlahun-ti-ku* [The Thirteen]; *but they did not know his name, except for his older sister* [Uranus?] *and his sons* [the other planets?]. *They said his face had not yet been shown to them also."*

Only after reading ahead did I realize what was happening here. First, about the bees. "Ah-Mucenca," Roys relates in a footnote, are supernatural bees or bee-Gods. In conjunction with the following lines, these are likely to be satellites of Saturn, buzzing around the hive like bees. (These bees, and the hive, occur elsewhere in the *Chilam Balam* when much earlier history is being discussed.) [note 6]

"Oxlahun-ti-ku," Roys notes, *"literally the Thirteen Gods, are probably the gods of the thirteen heavens of the Maya cosmos, but they are usually treated as a single god."*

I would suggest that "The Thirteen" is Saturn, represented by the seven most prominent satellites which could be visually distinguished because of the proximity to Earth, plus the count of Uranus, Neptune, Saturn itself, Venus, Mercury, and Mars (a count of six). All of these planets are recognized on other pages of the *Chilam Balam* as part of the stack of planets seen since long before 10,900 BC, and noted also in the *Popol Vuh*. If Uranus is his sister, then perhaps the other planets above and below Saturn would be his sons. [note 7]

"The Thirteen" may also represent (as Roys notes) the thirteen levels of heaven imagined to be located physically above the Earth in the Maya cosmology, although I think this is likely a more recent addition to the theology. That the upper reaches of the sky are assigned to Saturn would follow from the fact that Saturn had stood above the Earth for six thousand years. On the other hand, Jupiter (known as "The Nine") is assigned to the nine levels of the Underworld, for he was only seen on the ecliptic, and thus dipped below the Earth each night.

The arcane text about "not knowing his name" may relate to the fact that a theology of these Gods was never adopted by the Maya. It has been noted (Schele and Freidel) that the earliest archaeology of the Pre-Classical Maya shows no signs of the Gods of the (later) Classical era, but I am not so sure what that means. It is clear (at least to me) that by classical times the Saturnian planets were incorporated in the theology. A look at the "altars of the cross" at Palenque, erected in circa AD 690, show that the concern was entirely with the most recently active planets: Jupiter, Venus, and Mars. At this time Saturn had been reduced to an old man. [note 8]

Similarly the concern with directional trees (see the text further below) has been found as four trees set in sockets at the top platforms of the earliest temple platforms of the Maya dating back to 200 and 100 BC. The iconography of the four trees first shows at Olmec La Venta, circa 650 BC, carved as four small sprouts surrounding a central figure, although archaeologists tend to identify the four sprouts as corn seedlings. In terms of the *Chilam Balam*, this would signify a continuation of Gods, for the directional trees are part of a mythology or history stretching back to 3100

BC -- some 1500 years before the Yucatan was first populated.

It should be recognized that the Maya, like the surrounding peoples of Mesoamerica, were "converted" at some point after 600 BC to the philosophy (and history) expounded by a set of graphical books which were obtained from centers in the Valley of Mexico, Veracruz, or Oaxaca. This was absolutely convincing, since the books so obtained matched their own recollections and records. I'll expand on this in following chapters.

Back to the bees: I assume here that "they" means the sons and sister, not the bees. This is consistent with the information of the *Popol Vuh*, except that Saturn itself is counted.

Bolio assumes that The Thirteen did not know the name of the Bee God (which he has as singular). The "older sister" is likely to be the much larger Uranus, which was involved with this configuration from the very start, and would look to have long hair because of the outpouring of plasma from its horizontally located south magnetic pole, where the other pole only showed a beak-like plasma in glow mode.

The north magnetic pole plasma outpouring was not identified as a bird beak, as in European Upper Paleolithic and early Neolithic iconography. It may have been identified as a nose of the figure. It may account for the facial disfigurement practiced by the Maya.

The "sons" would be the other planets which traveled with Saturn. If these, together with Saturn, add up to six, then Venus would be included among them. Thus we can date this description to after 4077 BC, since Venus would not show up until after 4077 BC, although the wording here seems to be speaking of an earlier time.

That the Ah-Mucenca bees blindfolded Oxlahun-ti-ku, Saturn, is not as curious as it might seem at first. The writers of the *Chilam Balam* had determined this from an inspection of a book of ancient history, composed entirely of graphical images. It suggests a coma occluding Saturn, and perhaps the other planets, which, by the way, other peoples have noted also.

The text continues with the obvious, declaring that this time is already after the creation of Earth, that is, the world. I should point out that the Olmecs were certain also of an earlier creation, a "first creation," which is detailed in Book 11. The purpose of the book considered here (Book 10), obviously is to provide the history of the Gods which were honored in Classical times, and thus will describe the "second creation" (ending in 3147 BC) and the "third creation" (ending in 2349 BC). Other pages or books of the *Chilam Balam* will also separately describe the "first creation" and again the "third creation."

"This was after the creation of the world had been completed, but they did not know it was about to occur."

Strange as the tense of this sentence is, it seems to say that something "unknown" preceded the existence of Oxlahun-ti-ku, Saturn. This is not unlike the myths of other people where we see "creation" proceeding from a misty chaos in the sky. The *Popol Vuh*, the story of the ball-playing twins, written in Guatemala at about the same time as the composition of the *Chilam Balam* books, describes the second creation as the undifferentiated mass of water or mist of the "chaos" found in other creation myths elsewhere in the world.

The blindfold stretched across the face of Oxlahun-ti-ku, Saturn, is possibly the creation of the rings in 4077 BC. At that time the satellites (the Bee Gods) would be clearly seen only if Earth were mostly below Saturn at that time. The problem with these texts is that we have no idea of what times in the past these snapshot images refer to.

However, to see the rings as a blindfold would place Earth mostly laterally with respect to Saturn. That also allows all the associated planets to be seen.

If this description were presented from sources in Mesopotamia or Egypt, I would immediately suggest that the "creation of the world" as mentioned above would be in reference to the "land" of Saturn -- Upper Earth. But I never get a sense of the stupendous object in the north skies being equated to anything other than a god-person -- with the exception of an equation of directional bees and a bee hive or pot of honey at the island of Cozumel in Book 11 of the *Chilam Balam*).

As I mentioned earlier, it is possible that the scribe here is relating the coma which was seen after the 2500 years of shadow of the Younger Dryas had lifted. This would suggest that the bees were seen at that time. The coma would have been in place since 10,900 BC and lasted to 4077 BC. The line of text about the blindfolding is, at any rate, a curious statement. But it is also not at all untypical of the *Chilam Balam* to sum up thousands of years in a single sentence.

"Then Oxlahun-ti-ku [Saturn] *was seized by Bolon-ti-ku* [Jupiter]*."*
    "Then it was that fire descended, then the rope descended, then rocks and trees descended. Then came the beating of (things) with wood and stone."

Jupiter (Bolon-ti-ku, The Nine) is introduced here, but his mention seems out of place (Jupiter appears again a few lines later). It is possible that we are being notified of an agent involved in the sudden nova event of Saturn in 4077 BC. That suggests an earlier electric collision with Jupiter started the mass expulsion and explosive plasma discharge of Saturn, although I doubt it.

- *First the fire, then the rope* -- This is in the correct order. After the extinction of the plasma flow in arc mode, Saturn would have switched to continue the discharge in glow mode -- the "rope." The "rope" will continue into post-Classical times as a symbolic connection to heaven which delivers grace and other celestial dispensations to the Maya. The concept is still in use today among Maya shamans.

I have not made much, in the text of previous pages, of differentiating the extreme arc mode plasma discharge from the glow mode plasma, since there is no indication of how long the arc mode plasma lasted. Both are recorded in the petroglyphic records from remote antiquity, although apparently most, if not all, the petroglyphs are in reference to an earlier south polar column.

- *"Trees and rocks"* -- Here I am again beset by the fact that repeatedly the order of things seems reversed in lines which follow each other. The "trees" is a phenomenon associated with the plasma instabilities during the time of the "descent of fire," that is, a plasma stream in arc mode (but also associated with high-level glow mode). The "rocks" are also likely a plasma stream disturbance but could also be the descent of Mars and his followers during the lowering of "the rope." Of course I am reading these lines as sequential because they appear in the text as one following the other. But a story with an orderly sequence in time was never a strong concern of the Mesoamerican languages. Richard Luxton, in *The Book of Chumayel* (1996), has "sticks" for "trees."
- *"The beating of things with wood and stone"* -- The "wood and stone" appear again later in the text in a description of the rulership of Saturn, and obviously refer to Uranus as the wood and Venus as the stone. Both might be seen as flailing about Saturn if the rotational axis of Earth and Saturn did not line up. Saturn would have been seen revolving (or rocking) in the sky. Vedic sources state that Saturn "rotated without cease." The *Chilam Balam* will address this perambulation later in the text, in a description of Saturn's rulership. What we have here, however, is a description of the visual effect of the rotational axes of the two planets not lining up. The "things" being beaten are the rings which would seem to wobble as seen from Earth. In the *Popol Vuh* the wood and stone are the magical gardening tools of Hunahpu and Xbalanque. [note 9]

In Classical times rulers are shown holding a "Venus scepter" -- a puppet-like head crowned with a jester headdress of three points and with the tail of a snake. The spikes of the headdress were recorded at other times, as in this example, from the Tang dynasty of China:

"On the morning of March 18, [AD] 904, Venus was observed near the Pleiades blazing like fire. The next morning, to observers, Venus appeared to have developed three horns, somewhat resembling a flower, and then began to tremble and shake."
-- Charles Raspil *Planetary observations of the T'ang* (1994)

The three spikes are a cone of plasma extending from the pole of a planet, shaped sort of like a chalice. Only the outer edges of this shape are seen, where the plasma is visually more dense in profile. The third spike is a stream of dense plasma central to this. The plasma flowers will show mainly at the north magnetic pole. The problem with this reading of the "three horns" from the T'ang is that Venus does not today have a magnetic field which would be needed to support such a display. [note 10]

The "wood," is Uranus, seen beside Saturn, and is probably represented by a jade god-face hung by a chain from the rear of the belts of the rulers in Classical times. Notice that many features of the Saturnian Polar Configuration, such as Uranus in this instance, are differently interpreted in different instances in this text, an indication that the scribe may have been looking at illustrations which were not captioned.

The Nine: Jupiter

The next line again introduces Jupiter. Saturn is attacked by Jupiter, so we are now in 3147 BC:

"Then Oxlahun-ti-ku [Saturn] *was seized by Bolon-ti-ku* [Jupiter]."

This line exactly repeats one of the lines above, which I noted as being out of place. If so, it is an old transcription error.

"Then Oxlahun-ti-ku [Saturn] *was seized, his head was wounded, his face was buffeted, he was spit upon, and he was (thrown) on his back as well."*
    "After that he was despoiled of his insignia and his smut."

About the above text Roys notes:

"Bolon-ti-ku, or Nine Gods, appear to be treated as one god. We find them represented in the inscriptions, and it seems likely that they represent the nine underworlds and correspond to the Nine Lords of the Night of the Mexicans."

"The inscriptions" mentioned by Roys are probably the *Dresden Codex* and other glyphic books which had come to light before 1930. The Nine Gods is Jupiter plus its visible satellites (eight seen before the 20th century AD). [note 11]

Jupiter rises in the east from the Caribbean, sets west in the Pacific, and travels through the sky almost overhead because the Yucatan is at a latitude of 18 to 20 degrees. Jupiter thus seems to travel in a circle over the Earth and underneath. The Maya conceived of the world as floating on water, being aware that they were bordered by the Pacific and almost surrounded by the Caribbean. And they specifically noted water welling up from below in the subterranean limestone caves and surface cenotes. The region below ground became for them the Underworld, as nine levels below ground, each level controlled by one of nine Gods. See also my notes further below on the Absu, the "House of Nine Bushes."

- *"Oxlahun-ti-ku* [The Thirteen] *was seized"* -- Saturn came into close proximity of Jupiter, 6 to 14 million miles (10 to 23 million km). This actual close contact between Saturn and Jupiter would have lasted very little time. The shock of the electric forces was attractive because of the much greater positive charge of Saturn. This is how Saturn was "seized" by Jupiter. The attractive force would have stopped very quickly with a change in the induced voltages, followed by a charge equalization due to electric arcing, and the separation of the planets. "Seized" also likely describes an extension of plasma as lightning reaching from Jupiter to Saturn.
- *"... his head was wounded, his face was buffeted"* -- This is the initial plasma interaction, probably in large sheets of plasma impinging on Saturn in visible glow mode, or as contacts in arc mode. Jupiter at this point, moving beyond its original orbit at 0.7 AU, was in need of electrons, but Saturn still had its positive charge and needed electrons even more.
- *"... he was spit upon"* -- As Saturn distanced from Jupiter, the plasma connection initiated by Jupiter would have switched to long-distance plasmoid strikes. It might have looked like spittle, since these would take time to travel through space. Egyptian legends make this image into the sperm of Seth (Jupiter) and Horus (normally Mars, but here probably Saturn). When some of the predynastic "kings" of Egypt take on names like "Crocodile" and "Catfish-Chisel" we are seeing similar interpretations from the other side of the globe. Plasmoid bolts look like catfish or like crocodiles with open jaws.
- *"... he was (thrown) on his back as well."* -- At first the spectacle would have been viewed in the north skies, since Earth was still below Saturn

by some 3 million miles (5 million km), and probably over 4 million miles (6.5 million km) below Jupiter. But as Earth was released to travel its own path around the Sun, the orbit of Earth would be lifted to have the Sun again be one focus of the orbit. At that time the perspective of the two battling planets would have changed and they would have been seen on the ecliptic with Saturn viewed edge-on -- equivalent to having been thrown on his back.

The earliest Egyptian mention of Osiris and the account of his death (Saturn here) is found among the fifth dynasty pyramid texts of Unas (2345 BC), where it is related that Osiris died by falling on his side -- at the river bank. This is not the Nile river, but the river of the ecliptic.

- *"After that he was despoiled of his insignia and his smut."* -- "Smut" is the face paint used by priests during a period of fast and consecration, Roys notes, although Bolio reads it as plumage, which is perhaps correct, as detailed below.

Roys has extensive footnotes on "the despoiling of the insignia," relating the insignia to "something held in the hand" -- a scepter carried by rulers, in the form of a dragon or manikin with a snake tail. The name of the "canhel" scepter translates as "dragon" or "serpent." "Something held in the hand" is most likely Venus connected to Saturn with a plasma trail. This is the scepter held by Maya rulers. This shows up also on the predynastic tags of grave goods of Egypt as the cudgel wielded to strike enemies. Some writers have simply equated "canhel" to Kukulkan, the plumed serpent Quetzalcoatl. Which is correct.

Bolio translates the line as:

"And their [The Thirteen's] *Serpent of Life, with rattlers in its tail, was stolen and with it was taken its quetzal plumage."*

The "quetzal plumage" of Bolio comes close to referencing the "insignia" to Quetzalcoatl -- the "feathered serpent" of the Mexicans, known as Kukulkan in Mayan, and identified as Venus. The "Serpent of Life" scepter is Venus, as Schele and Freidel have noted. [note 12]

The Maya purposely avoided any reference to Quetzalcoatl (or Kukulkan) in the *Chilam Balam* books, for the Spanish priests were on the lookout for references to Quetzalcoatl, whom they considered as possibly the chief object of idolatry among the Maya, based on their experience with the Aztecs. Other books of the *Chilam Balam* specifically blame idolatry on the Itza who had moved into the Yucatan 800 years earlier and at some point supposedly brought the worship of Quetzalcoatl from Tula. But Venus (Kukulkan) had already been part of the Maya sacred iconography in Classical times as the Vision Serpent and the double-headed serpent bar. [note 13]

Nine-Lives: Mars

Next, and still in Katun 11-Ahau, we are introduced to "Nine-Lives" -- actually, the first "Nine-Lives." This paragraph is clearly out of place for the text describes events before the close of the "Era of the Gods" in 3147 BC, which termination was related above.

> *"Then shoots of the yaxum tree were taken. Also Lima beans were taken with crumbled tubercles, hearts of small squash-seeds, large squash-seeds and beans, all crushed."*
>
> *"He wrapped up the seeds (composing) this first Bolon Dzacab* ["Nine-Lives," Mars], *and went to the thirteenth heaven."*
>
> *"Then a mass of maize-dough with the tips of corn-cobs remained here on earth."*
>
> *"Then its heart departed because of Oxlahun-ti-ku* [The Thirteen, Saturn], *but they did not know the heart of the tubercle was gone."*

Roys translates "Bolon Dzacab" as "nine generations" and suggests it means "forever." Bolio translates "He who is eternal." Fisher's text has a parenthetical insertion which reads, "Yax Bolon Dzacab -- Great Nine-Fertilizer." "He," at any rate, seems to refer to "Nine-Lives," Mars, not some other undefined God. Schele and Freidel also identify Yax Bolon Dzacab as God GII of the Palenque Triad, which is Mars. In footnote 11 to Chapter 2 of *Maya Cosmos*, Freidel and Schele identify (on a somewhat different matter, and as a verb form) "Bolon Tz'acab" as possibly meaning "nine manifested" which makes a lot more sense.

- *"... this first Bolon Dzacab"* -- Without a doubt Nine Lives is Mars. Like Horus of the Egyptians, who is called "the first Horus" when he is listed among the first gods, Mars is here called "this first Bolon Dzacab." He is also called (or implicitly regarded as) "eternal" for he will reappear for ages to come. Although the Sumerians and Egyptians counted repeated visitations of Mars as repeated incarnations, the Maya neglect repeated visits in the record of the *Chilam Balam*, both for the period before and after 3100 BC and for the later 8th and 7th century BC. It is likely that the "nine" of "Bolon Dzacab" should tell us that this event happened nine times -- one more than the Sumerian "kings before the flood." For the Mesoamerican writer there was no reason to tell of repeated visits of Mars. Additionally, it is perhaps the nine risings up to Saturn which are counted here, not the eight lowerings, as in Sumer. (The *Dynastic Chronicle* from Babylonia lists 9 kings before the flood, however.) [note 14]

- *"Then shoots of the yaxum tree were taken ... etc.,"* -- and other assorted small granular matter. On the one hand, the look of a planet wrapped in squashed beans and seeds would be the look of the lower half of Mars which is pockmarked with craters. But I will suggest another understanding further below.

- *"Then a mass of maize-dough with the tips of corn-cobs remained here on earth."* -- This obviously has reference to the "creation of humans" events recorded in the *Popol Vuh* and other sources, when humans were fashioned by the Gods out of maize dough. Bolio makes it read as, *"And then his* [Mars's] *skin and the tips of his bones fell here on the land."*

If what is described here records the descent of Mars before 3147 BC, then the "skin and bones" would represent the massive uprising of water in the North Atlantic or the inverted dome of plasma (at the same location) which is featured as a mountain in other creation myths. The Yucatan is located ten degrees further from this site than Mesopotamia or Egypt. The clouds reaching beyond the stratosphere, would easily have looked like a mountain of corn mash. This is also the location of the "Seven Caves," which repeatedly show up in other Mesoamerican creation myths down to the time of the Aztecs (as well as the Incas), where humanity originated. [note 15]

- *"Then its heart departed because of Oxlahun-ti-ku* [The Thirteen]." -- Both translators have the heart of Mars depart for the highest heaven. Bolio has: *"... because the Thirteen gods* [Saturn] *did not want his heart and seed to be gone from them."* This is the departure of Mars from Earth, and seemingly composed of the image of Mars climbing up the plasma stream in the era before 3147 BC. If this is so, then the "shoots of the yaxum tree, etc.," mentioned above, might also represent nodes in the plasma stream which seem to follow Mars on the returns. This was noted by Talbott at the 2001 conference.

Note that the Mars events described here are out of place. The return of Mars to Saturn happens before 3147 BC, not afterwards. In fact, the visits of Horus which the Egyptians experienced after circa 3050 BC are missing here, although they are described further below.

The close of the drama of 3147 BC is the second battle described by Hesiod. This probably took place within 200 years. The four planets retreating from the inner reaches of the Solar System had to move through the asteroid belt, with the consequence that asteroids were "attacked" with plasma strikes -- with plasmoid bolts by Jupiter, as would be likely under the circumstances of enormous amounts of ionized material and increasing amounts of fine silicate dust in the ecliptic at the location of the asteroid belt -- formed by the plasmoid bolts of Jupiter (and the other three giant planets). Plasmoids can travel millions of miles through space.

"After that the fatherless ones, the miserable ones, and those without husbands were all pierced through; they were alive though they had no hearts. Then they were buried in the sands, in the sea."

Roys notes that two other *Chilam Balam* versions read "fell to pieces" for "pierced through," an expected breakup of asteroids, although it is difficult to imagine how this could have been seen from Earth. Perhaps comas greatly enlarged the sizes of the asteroids. I doubt if the "fatherless ones" might have been asteroids large enough to be distinguished. That too is hard to believe, except that when individually surrounded with a coma they could perhaps be seen from Earth. Alternately it might refer to Saturn, Neptune, and Uranus receding through the asteroid belt.

The "sea" is the whole of the southern sky below the equatorial, identified as the Absu by the Sumerians and the Duat by the Egyptians -- alive with glowing moving concentric wavy rings of particulate matter looking like a sea.

The "sand" (strand) is then the edge of this sea, or the glowing ecliptic, (which dips into the Absu for part of its length). The ecliptic would start to glow as the dust of plasma contacts from Jupiter (and the three other giant planets) started to accumulate. It was yellow like sand and called the "Yellow Road" in China.

"Have you no fear of me?" says the Lord; "will you not shudder before me, before me who made the shimmering sand to bind the sea, a barrier it can never pass? Its waves heave and toss but they are powerless; roar as they may, they cannot pass." -- Jerimiah 5:22

From what God has just said, it looks as if the outer ring of the Absu was yellow or buff colored and understood as a strand -- a barrier between the celestial sea and the sky above it. Both the Bible and the Quran identify the barrier as a strand -- a beach.

"There would be a sudden rush of water when the theft of the insignia of Oxlahun-ti-ku [The Thirteen] occurred."

The narrative has backed up a page. This is the massive worldwide flood which I have placed in the year 3147 BC in the narrative, the flood of Gilgamesh (as I happened to have named it). It would, in any event, happen immediately after Earth was released from the gravitational hold of Saturn. Again we have here, as above, a dislocation of the order of events, as if, as I have suggested, the folio pages of a book were read in the wrong order.

"Then the sky would fall, it would fall down upon the earth, when the four gods, the four Bacabs, were set up, who brought about the destruction of the world."

Here the "fallen sky" is related to the time directly after 3147 BC. I presume that this mention is not more of the "rush of water," but represents what the Olmecs understood as a collapse of the sky above Earth, perhaps a darkened sky as later recollected from 2193 BC when Akkad and Egypt both collapse economically. This, too, seems out of place.

The four Bacabs are the gods of the cardinal points. They will hold up the sky, and set up four trees holding up the sky. These trees now hold up the dome overhead and the northern stars -- something perhaps never seen before. The following text will also repeatedly note that the four trees are set up as "a sign of the destruction of the world."

The First Four Trees

The text here launches into a description of the four colored trees which are set up at the cardinal points, each surmounted with a bird (of the same color), and also a green central tree. We should welcome this side-trip into geography. Mapping the Earth is a very central element to the Mesoamerican (and American Indian) conception of the world, and as a result we have details not available in other parts of the world. Besides, the "trees" were absolutely huge -- the largest entities ever seen in the skies.

"Then, after the destruction of the world was completed, they placed (a tree) to set up in its order the yellow cock oriole."

"Then the white tree of abundance was set up. A pillar of the sky was set up, a sign of the destruction of the world; that was the white tree of abundance in the north."

"Then the black tree of abundance was set up (in the west) for the black-breasted pi¢oy to sit upon."

"Then the yellow tree of abundance was set up (in the south), as a symbol of the destruction of the world, for the yellow-breasted pi¢oy to sit upon, for the yellow cock oriole to sit upon, the yellow timid mut."

> *"Then the green tree of abundance was set up in the center (of the world) as a record of the destruction of the world."*

My first inclination was to suggest that these trees were versions -- real or not -- of the tree seen in the north, connecting Earth with the Saturnian planets. Saturn at the top would look like a bird, for the equatorial outpouring of plasma (the rings) of Saturn (before 3147 BC) might have looked like the plumage of a bird. The ball-shape of Venus connected with a long thin swirl to Saturn (as in the Egyptian "Eye of Ra") could pass as the head of a bird (as could Uranus). Additionally, the plasma connection had been seen as a tree at times -- a discontinuity of the stream with toroids forming at intervals along the stream. These would flatten and the edges would turn up, making the plasma stalk look like a plant, complete with leaves and a circular form at the top like a giant flower. Images of this strange plant are still shown on Sumerian seals of 2350 BC. But these trees are not mythological substitutes -- these trees were real.

When the tree of the north with Saturn on top disappeared after 3147 BC, another stellar bird appeared in its place, the constellation Ursa Major, with the location of the axis of the sky piercing the center of its body.

At a later date the Maya substituted the Milky Way for the "white tree" of the north. The Milky Way rotates through the night sky on a daily basis, starting off at different angles at different seasons, standing as a tree in the sky at the solstices, stretching from north to south horizon (more or less), and is described in Classical times. (See especially the book *Maya Cosmos* by Schele and Freidel.) The Milky Way does not intersect the bird form of Ursa Major, today or at any time in the past.

Others have suggested that these four directional trees are imaginary markers, implicit in the solstitial rising and setting of the Sun, some 25 degrees north and south of the east and west cardinal directions. That would be a ludicrous suggestion if it were not for the fact that creation ceremonies of Maya shamans today use these cardinal points.

However, in previous text I have already presented details of the four trees (under the subject heading of "The Return of the Axis Mundi"). The north and south trees can be described as plasma plumes. These match the descriptions of a bird at the top, as seen here in the *Chilam Balam*, and from illustrations of either a manikin or a ball at the end of the bent-over plume from Mesopotamia and Egypt. These are locations 20 degrees further north, and thus the plumes were even more bent over.

Initially, after 3147 BC, the white tree of the north was probably the most significant as well as the most prominent plasma plume. The first tree of the north is mentioned in the sculptures at Palenque, and held at equal value with the end of the previous epoch, and the appearance of the planetary Gods (their births) 700 years later.

In a footnote Schele and Freidel translate the inscriptions at Palenque for the event of 3112 BC (a year and about six months after the start of the present epoch), of "Wacah chan xaman waxac na GI," to "raised-up-sky north-eight-house GI," but also translate "Wacan chan" as "six-sky." The "raised-up-sky" is based on reading "Wacan chan" as "Wac ah chan." Schele also identifies "raised-up-sky" as the Milky Way. "GI" is Venus, but GI may be a typo for GI-prime.

If "wacan chan" is read as six-sky it would fit the practice in the *Chilam Balam* of prefixing celestial objects with the number of their appearances in 3000 years of history. "Six-sky" would have appeared six times, if the plasma column were to be generated with the six known changes in the Earth's orbit (3147 BC, 2349 BC, 2193 BC, 1492 BC, 747 BC, and 686 BC). But add the change in the electric field of the Sun of 685 BC, and there are seven. Or add the possibility of two additional, but unnoted, changes between 2349 BC and 2193 BC, and there are 8 instances again, justifying a reading of "north-eight-house." North, as opposed to south, is a clear indication that we are here dealing with one of the two polar plasma plumes. This last is also better supported by the name given to the north tree at the ballcourt markers at Copan -- "Nine Successions." [note 16]

The "raised-up-sky" "north-eight-house" (also called "edifice") of Venus (GI) was dedicated a year and a half after the start of the current era, as retrocalculated by the Maya. It is within expectations that it would take perhaps a year to develop a plasma stream in glow mode in response to a change in the electric field surrounding the Earth's plasmasphere. The event is noted here (and in other records) because the raised-up-sky north-eight-house must have been much larger than anything else ever seen in the skies up to this point in time. It rose far above the previous polar location of Saturn. Seen from Mesoamerica, the Saturnian planets had hovered only some 20 degrees above the north horizon. "Saturn entered the sky," is noted because the planet had now moved (within a year and 9 months) across the sky and to the south. This had to be established first (in the Palenque text) because otherwise Saturn (God GI-prime of Palenque) would not have been able to construct his edifice. [note 17]

The Green Tree of the Center

About the tree which "was set up in the center," Roys writes, "This last tree was remembered by the Maya." The green celestial tree is the massive outpouring of plasma from the south pole of Jupiter, which I have noted in earlier texts. This was seen directly after 3147 BC, and again twice after

Jupiter had passed through the asteroid belt, although at these later times the "mountain" had turned red. There is a fourth appearance in 685 BC. Note that "green" is not one of the directional colors of the Maya. This "tree" is not located at one of the cardinal points.

Initially the green tree of Jupiter with its lower plasma outpouring was seen between 3147 BC and 2880 BC, before Jupiter entered the asteroid belt. The mountain was topped by two owl-like eyes peering out from the top of the head of the coma, and a beak-like form below it. These were recorded in profusion at this time -- carved on the interior walls of barrows, as petroglyphs, and carved as amulets. Also notice that the green tree did not include a bird.

> *"Peratt ... identified the 'eye mask' as a 'low opacity torus' or thick ring, seen from a vantage point substantially off-axis, not too far from the plane of the torus."*
> -- Talbott and Thornhill, *Thunderbolts of the Gods* (2004)

In the first hundred years or so after 3147 BC, the planet Jupiter is here the green tree of the center, whereas in later text Jupiter and its lower plasma expulsion are specifically noted as being red. Both the green and red colors can be generated by excited hydrogen ions at diffuse densities.

In Egyptian funeral imagery Osiris is almost always shown as a mummy wrapped in green. In early Egyptian iconography, and in phrases recorded in the Egyptian *Book of the Dead*, Jupiter is identified as Osiris (since the fifth dynasty).

Jupiter's green lower plasma expulsion is designated as the "tree of the center" because it was first seen in the east, and then moved, over the course of some months (in addition to nightly), past the south to diminish again in the west. The tree was obviously "in front of" the trees of the east, south, and west -- which did not move through the night or over the seasons. It was the brightness of Jupiter's coma that convincingly made it look as if it moved "in front of" the other trees.

The image of a tree of the center will reappear in later Olmec iconography, as seen at La Venta (circa 650 BC). There Jupiter, which developed another plasma outpouring in 685 BC, will be shown with a headdress of three flower-like petals, and legs composed of the open jaws of a crocodile. The crocodile form is the much more extensive plasma at the south pole of Jupiter (which is its north magnetic pole).

In much later Classical-era Maya imagery the "tree of the center" (at that time represented by the Milky Way) is frequently transformed into an upended crocodile with its jaws at the bottom and with branches at the top sprouting from its tail.

The East and West Trees

The east and west trees are very likely the toroidal belt of trapped particles (the Van Allen Belt) above the Earth's equatorial. Viewed directly overhead this would be nearly invisible because the toroidal Van Allen belt surrounding the Earth would be viewed as larger and more diffuse -- it would disappear. Seen toward the east or west, it would be much more substantial. In the east and west the edges of the toroid would be seen to rise up from the horizon, as two parallel lines or a uniformly flat strip, with a circle shape at the top, looking not unlike the ball plasmoids at the ends of the polar plumes -- but without the three-pronged extensions. The east and west trees also did not move.

At the latitude of the Yucatan these would rise almost straight up into the sky. The repeated phrase of the text, *"set up as a record of the destruction of the world,"* suggests, however, that the trees appeared suddenly. This would certainly be true for the polar plumes, which would switch from dark mode to glow mode suddenly. This also suggests that the toroidal Van Allen belt also was in glow mode.

It is possible to take a hint that this might be so from Egyptian sources, as from an illustration of the *Book of the Dead*, where four lights or plumes with the required bent-over shape are carried by four persons. There is also a glyph, known as "Khet," depicting a bent-over plume coming out of the top of a form which is otherwise identified as a lamp or brazier. [note 18]

Implicit in the imagery of the four trees at the cardinal points is the fact that they were established to hold up the dome of the sky and the stars. They (or the four Bacab Gods responsible for the cardinal points) last without harm through various destructions of the world.

The four trees were represented in Maya temples before the start of the Classical era in AD 300 or 400 as actual tree trunks socketed into the upper platform of temples (as at Cerros before 50 BC). At the close of the Classical era, in AD 900, these had been replaced by stelae (**te-tun** -- tree stones), then associated with the commemoration of the passage of time and with the celebration of various rulers.

By the time of the Spanish invasion the trees signify the geographical division of the land into four quadrants, and define the local domain of individual rulers. The trees also came to represent the winds from the four directions. The Gods of the four trees are all named after the God of rain, Chac. These Gods held up the sky in the form of an altar. Maya shamans today still construct these altar tables in "creation ceremonies." The imagery dates from the Olmec era, where gods appeared out of a cave set below the edge of the 6-foot-high stone tables. The cave will be recognized as the dark doorway which normally appeared nightly against the equatorial rings. Although this had not happened since 2349 BC, the imagery remained to show up on altars at San Lorenzo. That the sky is intended with the table-like altars is obvious from the typical Olmec "sky monster" glyphs appearing at the top edge of some of the altars.

At Potrero Nuevo near San Lorenzo, two dwarfs hold up the altar like atlantes. The table edge is carved with cloud glyphs.

A listing of the directional trees, or the colors of the cardinal directions, occurs three times in the text. Each happens (as we shall see below) at a new creation, signifying a radical change in the skies, or a renewed sky.

Mesoamerica uniformly professed a belief in four creations, called "suns," except for the Aztecs who counted their own arrival at the Central Mexican plateau as the fifth creation. If the "creations" are equated with the appearance of the Sun, or a renewed Sun, then the "first creation" started in 10,900 BC, as the creation of the southern ball plasmoids, the "second creation" is the following period, ending in in 3147 BC, and the "third creation" ends in 2349 BC, and a fourth may have been attributed to the 1492 BC. (This assumes the "creation" periods are consecutive.)

I am suggesting 1492 BC because it is the third time the trees show up. The cardinal direction trees and colors are invoked three times in the *Chilam Balam*, each time when a new sky is established, after 3147 BC, after 2349 BC, and after 1492 BC. I will return to the question of ages and eras below.

This concludes the events of Katun 11-Ahau. I don't doubt the veracity of these sources, even though presented in somewhat disorderly fashion, and describing events much older than the earliest recognized archaeology of the Maya or the Olmecs. This is not unexpected, since, as recounted (or hinted at) in the *Popol Vuh*, individual tribes acquired their own copies of the history books which had been kept at certain important sites.

In the text of the following Katuns additional details are developed, which again, with some extension of the strange names we are presented with, can be matched to worldwide catastrophic events we know from other sources. But the following events are more difficult to sort out. Whereas events before the start of the current era (3147 BC) are all listed as happening in Katun 11-Ahau, the text which follows reads as if events separated by a thousand years or more are simply listed by the Katuns during which they might have occurred -- Katun 9-Ahau, 7-Ahau, 5-Ahau, and 3-Ahau. Following these are two sections separately describing the rulership of Saturn and Jupiter.

Katun 9-Ahau: Ten-Sky

The next Katun in order, Katun 9-Ahau, is introduced. This is the next Katun in order only if we adhere to the logic that Katun 9-Ahau is the next after Katun 11-Ahau. The period before 3147 BC does not end in a Katun 11-Ahau, but in Katun 4-Ahau. Philosophically, however, the Maya could only place "prehistory" in Katun 11-Ahau (Since a Katun 11-Ahau had ended on February 28th, 747 BC.)

By coincidence, Katun 9-Ahau is actually the fourth Katun after 3114 BC (four times 20 years: Katun 2-Ahau, 13, 11, 9), thus completing the 80 years of "negotiation" which the Egyptians claim as the delay before Horus/Mars takes control of Egypt. Counting 80 solar years forward (as Katuns) from the date of 3147 BC, reaches 3067 BC as the ending date of Katun 9-Ahau. This is also the most likely date when Mars first shows up in Egypt.

"The plate of another Katun was set up and fixed in its place by the messengers of their lord."

The "plate" is often used to reference a Katun together with "cup," as in, "nine was its cup, nine was its plate," used to describe Katun 9-Ahau, and similar readings in the "Chilam Balam" for other Katuns. Tedlock reads "plate and cup" as the dedicatory vessels used at shrines.

At this point the four trees of the cardinal points are introduced again. I don't know why. We have just seen the trees that appeared right after 3147 BC. The trees are here out of order, and very likely the source pages are being read out of order. This second set of trees has to follow rather than precede the notes about Venus (Ah Uuc Chek-nal, further below, after my notes on Ten-Sky).

"The red Piltec was set at the east of the world to conduct people to his lord."
   "The white Piltec was set at the north of the world to conduct people to his lord."
   "Lahun Chaan was set (at the west) to bring things to his lord."
   "The yellow Piltec was set (at the south) to bring things to his lord."

In the third line quoted above, "Lahun Chaan" (Ten-Sky) is not one of the colored trees of the cardinal points, but is Mars. So thinks Roys, who writes, in a footnote on this matter:

"Lahun Chaan is doubtless the same as the 'Lahunchan' described by

Cogolludo as an idol with very ugly teeth. 'Lahun' means ten in both Maya and Chol, and 'chan' means sky, heaven, and serpent in Chol. The Maya word for sky is 'chaan'."

He continues at length, and adds:

"We recall that a fleshless jawbone is one of the symbols of the number ten on the monuments; but the figure appears to be the regent of the second Venus period in the Dresden Codex, *and the regent of the first of these periods in the Mexican Codex Bologna also has a fleshless lower jaw. Since the above passage in the* Chumayel *implies that Lahun Chaan was set in the west, the translator is inclined to believe that this god was closely connected with the appearance of Venus as an evening star."*

I doubt that "Ten-Sky " is a reference to Venus, for Venus is seen both in the east and in the west as well as traversing the whole of the sky during the day, as Roys's insertion suggests. Mars is seen crossing the night sky. The phrase "at the west" is, however, an insertion based on the fact that a tree of the west is not mentioned. The line actually reads, without the addition by Roys:

"Lahun Chaan was set to bring things to his lord."

I think "Ten-Sky" is Mars. We see nothing else of the repeated close calls by Mars during the period of about 3100 BC to about 2700 BC except the title "Ten-Sky." From Egyptian and Mesopotamian records it appears that Mars/Horus cruised close to Earth some ten times after 3100 BC. My estimate for the first appearance of Mars/Horus is the year 3067 BC. The Katun 9-Ahau period -- when "Ten-Sky" first appeared -- ends in the corrected date of 3067 BC.

To "bring things to his lord" is mentioned for all four (or three) trees here, but not for the other instances of these trees elsewhere in the document. The question then is, Who is the "lord"? Since we know already that during the first 150 to 300 years when Mars drew close to Earth, Jupiter stood in the sky as a globe on top of a green mountain, after which it entered the Asteroid Belt (and the mountain form disappeared), it is likely that the "lord" is Jupiter. His reign is attested to elsewhere (as the "second reign"), but here (for this Katun) there is no other mention of Jupiter.

In the *Popol Vuh* the celestial twins Hunahpu and Xbalanque defeat the mountain giant Zipacna directly after they remove the Celestial Bird of the North Pole. Mars, known as Earthquake in the *Popol Vuh*, is their third target. He will be tricked, drugged, hog tied, and buried alive.

Katun 7-Ahau: Venus

The next lines are without question about Venus. Since no notice of a change in Katuns is given, this should be a continuation of Katun 9-Ahau, which dealt with Ten-sky. But instead the record now jumps 2000 years ahead to a Katun 7-Ahau which ends in 1478 BC, and spans 1507 BC to 1487 BC in corrected notation. This thus spans 1492 BC, the electric contact by Venus (and the Exodus). This arbitrary grouping of events by Katun names, even when they are not really consecutive, is typical of the other books of the *Chilam Balam*. The *Chilam Balam* continues:

"But it was (over) the whole world that Ah Uuc Cheknal was set up. He came from the seventh stratum of the earth, when he came to fecundate Itzam-kab-ain [the Earth], *when he came with the vitality of the angle between earth (and) heaven."*

Roys translates "Ah Uuc Chek-nal" as "he who fertilizes the maize seven times," which suggests that "Ah Uuc Chek-nal" appeared seven times. I suspect "Ah Uuc Chek-nal" is Venus.

"Itzam-kab-ain" is the Earth, the whole Earth, designated as a "crocodile-footed whale." The Maya conceived of the Earth as floating on water, and as supported by a giant whale-crocodile creature. Bolio translates this passage as:

"At that moment, Uuc-cheknal came from the seventh layer of the sky. When he came down, he trodded on the backs of Itzeam-cab-Aim, so-called. He came while the earth and sky were being cleaned."

The imagery is not far removed from a "close passage" of Venus, except that Venus would never have come close. The phrase "while the earth and sky were being cleaned" suggests hurricanes and tsunamis, which would certainly have been experienced on the four or more approaches by Venus between 2349 and 2193 BC and again in 1492 and 1442 BC. The first approach (2349 BC) involved the fall of the Absu -- the "flood of Noah" -- but this is handled separately and out of proper sequence further below.

If this, as I suspect, represents the contact of 1492 BC, the compressive contact would have been in the Pacific, and immense amounts of water vapor would have been carried into the atmosphere. The path of arcing would have angled up (because of the Earth's gyroscopic reaction), swung through the Indian Ocean, the Mediterranean, and angled southwest again through the Atlantic. The experience of Mesoamerica would have been two-fold, first a Pacific tsunami from the west, followed by billowing clouds from the east, the last arriving less than a day later. Attributing these to a celestial interloper is fully within the realm of what other people did. The planet was seen -- as if approaching -- and the local effects were interpreted as if Venus were close by.

Roys suggests another translation of *"when he came with the vitality of the angle between earth and heaven,"* which reads, *"then he descended while the heavens rubbed against the earth."* That makes sense as the condition of a fallen sky after 1492 BC. But, in fact, it makes more sense in that the "rubbing" would represent the huge shape seen in the night and day skies, the inner Van Allen belt toroid in glow mode, seen more or less in the center of the sky, on both sides of the equatorial, and stretching from the east horizon to the west.

Now about Katun 9-Ahau and the reason for placing this event in Katun 7-Ahau: Elsewhere I have assumed that approaches by Venus happened repeatedly between 2349 BC (the "flood of Noah") and 2193 BC (the fall of Akkad), for a total of four contacts. Earlier occurrences of Katun 9-Ahau do not match these dates. Katun 9-Ahau in Baktun 1 ends in 2523 BC (corrected to 2547 BC), too early for the "flood of Noah" by 200 years, and Katun 9-Ahau in Baktun 2 ends in 2266 BC (corrected to 2287 BC), after the "flood of Noah" by one hundred years.

I have assumed in these few paragraphs that this event might have happened in Katun 9-Ahau, it is because nothing in the text signifies that a Katun of a different name is under discussion. Katun 9-Ahau in Baktun 4 ends in 1507 BC, when corrections are applied, and thus only comes close to the time of the Exodus of 1492 BC (or other estimates from 1495 to 1491 BC). That would place the Exodus of 1492 BC 15 years after the end of the Katun.

I think, in fact (and as I have pointed out earlier), that this rubbing of Earth and heaven did not occur in Katun 9-Ahau, but happened in the next Katun, 7-Ahau, even though the text is silent about this. There is a pattern developed in the text of assigning appearances of planets to Katun 9-Ahau, at times by inference and at times by the neglect of naming the actual Katun. This becomes obvious when it is realized that the event of 2349 BC (the "third creation") is assigned to a Katun 9-Ahau in complete error, as I will describe further below.

This then is what we have: Since all of pre-history is assigned to a Katun 11-Ahau, the start of the current era (from 3147 BC) is assigned to the assumed first Katun of the era, 9-Ahau. This despite the fact that the current era started with Katun 2-Ahau. But the next event, the ten close passages of Mars (Ten-Sky) are then correctly assigned to Katun 9-Ahau, and the Katun is named. The next event, the electric contact of Venus in 1492 BC, is, however, assigned to the same Katun 9-Ahau only by the fact that no mention is made of a new Katun. The text shifts to this event as if it belonged to Katun 9-Ahau. But, in fact, the corrected ending date for Katun 9-Ahau in Baktun 4 is 1507 BC -- too early for an event in 1492 BC. The next Katun in order, Katun 7-Ahau of Baktun 4, spans the date of 1492 BC, plus any of the variations of this date as calculated in antiquity -- 1491 BC, 1495 BC.

Now it is possible that the scribe making the transcription simply neglected to mention that the event, "Ah Uuc Chek Nal rubs the earth," occurred in Katun 7-Ahau. But it is significant that the shift of events to Katun 9-Ahau happens 4 times, one by an implication, two by neglect, and one as a purposeful falsification. This last, the Katun year for the "third creation" stands out, for it involved moving the event so that the "first day of Kan" of the Katun would fall on the Gregorian equivalent calendar date of July 26th. Only Katun 9-Ahau of Baktun 1 does this in all of the 5200 years of the 13-Baktun cycle of time. This trick will be detailed further below.

I have to make note again of the fact that, because of the Maya understanding of the cyclical nature of time, repeated appearances of visiting planets are not separately listed, except in their titles, as in "Nine-Lives," "Ten Skies," and "He Who Fertilizes the Maize Seven Times." That would seem to explain why there is no notice of Venus between 2349 and 2293 BC. The other events of this same period are listed separately further below.

To return to the seven appearances of "Ah Uuc Chek-nal," I count four appearances of Venus between 2349 BC and 2193 BC, and 700 years later one each in 1492 BC and 1442 BC. This adds up to six overflights. It is possible that the nova event of Venus in 685 BC, another 755 years later, represented the seventh. But this last event is not attributed to Venus in the *Chilam Balam*. Only mention is made of the Sun going off course in 685 BC (further below). I think, however, that all references to Venus in 685 BC, when Quetzalcoatl lived and died, were carefully avoided in the record -- for fear of revealing information to the Spanish priests.

The other likely explanation is that the "cow" form associated with Venus, the change of the Van Allen Belt to glow mode, appeared also directly after 3147 BC, since at that time the Earth would have switched to experiencing the electric field of the Sun from the prior experience of only sensing the electric field of Saturn (being within the plasmasphere of Saturn). This initial event was not associated with an actual electric contact by Venus, except by inference. Since all of pre-history was held to happen in a Katun 11-Ahau, this first cow would have been assigned to the next Katun, 9-Ahau. It is possible that Earth was jolted by Venus directly after 3147 BC. This would constitute the seventh contact with Venus, and might explain why (apparently) the year changed from 225 days to 240 days in 3147 BC. [note 19]

The *Chilam Balam* continues with how the people walked in darkness:

"They moved among the four lights, among the four layers of the stars. The world was not lighted; there was neither day nor night nor moon. Then they perceived that the world was being created. Then creation dawned upon the world."

"They" probably refers to the people, but could also refer to the Gods. That they (the people) "moved" may suggest a migration, as is likely under the conditions of the climatic downturn of 1492 BC. The whole of the paragraph seems almost lifted from the Bible -- speaking of the wanderings of Israel in the desert after 1492 BC.

The "four lights" might be the great luminaries -- the Sun, Moon, Jupiter, and Saturn, although the same paragraph reads that there was no Moon yet. In 1492 BC there was a Moon. Roys suggests "candles" also for the "lights." That suggests stationary lights. Bolio uses "the fourth fire" for the "four lights." I think that the "four lights" are the four "trees" at the cardinal points, the two impinging plasma plumes at the poles and the edges of the equatorial toroid of the Van Allen belt. If a cloud cover obscured the Sun and the stars, as seems implied, then perhaps we are seeing the north and south plasma plumes at least in glow mode, possibly in arc mode near Earth. That might then be true for the east and west plumes also, if these are associated with the toroidal Van Allen belt. This also suggests that the plumes may have lasted for decades.

I also should not neglect that in 1492 BC the Earth went through a wild swing -- it all but tipped over, or at least was placed on its side, as I have suggested in earlier text. Midrashim commentary on Exodus suggests that in 1492 BC the sweep of the pole, "when the stars stopped moving," took a little over a year (Velikovsky). But the major effect is more likely due to a very dense cloud cover, although it is difficult to imagine that a cloud cover (unlike stratospheric dust) would extend to twenty years and obscures the stars.

The use of "the four lights," even if meant to signify the directional trees, might thus be a simile for wandering over a wide geographical area. The language in this case, especially when the following line is considered, which suggests an enormous time span of 8000 years, seems lifted from Book 11 of the *Chilam Balam* which relates the time leading up to the "first creation."

"During the creation thirteen infinite [400] series (added) to seven was the count of the creation of the world. Then a new world dawned for them."

The word translated as "series" can also mean "steps." The "seven" might be the count of the Katun (chronologically). "Infinite" is often the translation of "400," a Baktun. 13 Baktuns would be 5200 years. 13 plus seven would be 8000 year. Thus the "infinite series of steps" might represent a very long time.

On the other hand, thirteen plus seven is 20 years -- one Katun. Other Mesoamerican sources speak to "a generation" of darkness. Bolio translates as:

"Infinite rungs of the ladder of time and seven moons later were counted since Earth woke up and then the dawn came for them."

Seven moons would represent a half year. Most of this phrasing remains unclear except to suggesting the passage of a lot of time, or, as I have suggested, some twenty years. But that could have been stated in terser terms. Perhaps we are here seeing a poetic metaphor for "long time."

It might be suggested, in fact, that the "rungs of the ladder of time" is a metaphor for Uinal months, periods of 20 days. Then we have **(400*20 + 7*20)/365 = 22.3 years** roughly the duration of one Katun.

The 2349 BC Event

The following, although grouped with the start of a new creation, is, I suspect, from a different source. It details events of 2349 BC, the time of Noah, but not all of them. Some are listed further down in the text. The events are also not introduced by listing a Katun name. We would have to assume that Katun 9-Ahau continues.

I think, from the following text, that the copyist is opening a new book, perhaps one titled "the third creation." Unlike before, he copies the pages in the correct order, but leaves off the fall of the Absu, which is recounted much later.

The information is, in fact, not out of "literary" order, since the previous text ended with mention of the start of a new creation, although the reference was to 1492 BC. (We see this sort of connection used much later to describe events of the 8th century BC.) The "third creation," however, points to events in 2349 BC. All the events listed over the next few paragraphs belong to 2349 BC, not 1492 BC.

The text starts with:

"The two-day throne was declared, the three-day throne."

The phrase "two-day throne, three-day throne" is used elsewhere in the *Chilam Balam* to denote short-term leadership, especially in reference to the governing councils of the Itza. Bolio, however, has a more sensible reading:

"the reign of the second period, the reign of the third period was felt."

That makes a lot more sense. The alliteration of the text makes it look like a chapter heading. The question again is, where are we in the Katun counts? They are not mentioned in the following texts. We could assume that the text simply continues with the next Katun in order (Katun 7-Ahau or 5-Ahau), but this results in events which cannot be placed at dates known from other sources. I will therefore suggest that the listing of events continues to be assigned to a Katun 9-Ahau, as had been implied for the event of 1492 BC.

But of course this is incorrect, although it continues the obsession of placing all planetary events in Katuns named 9-Ahau. The "third reign" started at 3147 BC, and ended in 2349 BC. This is not Katun 9-Ahau (see listing at endnote 29). There is a reason for insisting that we are still in Katun 9-Ahaw. As I will detail further below, the Katun name for the event was changed in antiquity to conform to the notion that the events involving the "third creation" had to have happened on a "day of Kan." This was an important aspect in later analysis of older texts. It was an important notion because it was apparently held that the Tzolkin calendar governed celestial events, rather than the other way around. The "third creation" was the most important event of the past, celebrated with ballcourts and site names, and therefore had to end on the correct day.

There are five events listed before we return to naming Katuns. These are the plasma mountain of Jupiter (which may presumably be correctly dated to an earlier Katun 9-Ahau ending in 2547 BC), the return of a coma of Jupiter (which happened in 2349 BC), the first view of the "planted timber," the appearance of the Moon (in 2349 BC or soon after), and the complete extinction of Jupiter (199 years later). I have listed some of the above in correct order, rather than as the events are listed in the *Chilam Balam.* Some of the events fall in even numbered Katuns, mention of which is avoided throughout the book of the *Chilam Balam.*

There may still be a question if this represents the "second creation" or the "third creation," because we are, in fact, first presented with what seems to be an element of the second reign. Saturn, the *Chilam Balam* reads, develops a cometary coma. I think there is an error here.

"Then began the weeping of Oxlahun-ti-ku [Saturn]. They wept in this reign. The reign became red; the mat became red; (because of them) the first tree of the world was rooted fast."

Bolio has, instead of "rooted":

"... the tree became red."

And Bolio also has:

"And then the three gods began to cry."

The "three gods" would have been Jupiter, Mars, and Venus. These are the "three gods" of the Classical era of the Maya. Roys, however, only has Saturn (not one of the "three gods" above) crying, which perhaps makes more sense. The "three" of the "three gods" could be a misreading of the "three" of "the thirteen" by Bolio. "Crying" is a plasma discharge -- a coma and tail. Saturn, however, never had a tail -- it is too positively charged.

I wonder if what we read here is a transcription error, that is, the author meant to write that "Bolon-ti-ku," that is, Jupiter, developed a coma and a sub polar tail (started weeping) rather than "Oxlahun-ti-ku," Saturn. We have no record of either Saturn or Mars ever developing a tail, even when Saturn was "attacked" by Jupiter in 3147 BC. I don't think that Saturn is meant above. Saturn by this time had receded into insignificance.

The (corrected) date of 2567 to 2547 BC for the Katum 9-Ahau (in Baktun 1), mentioned above, coincides with the time when the Egyptian pharaohs first add "Re" to their names -- after 2600 BC. "Re" is the midnight sun, Jupiter. I will suggest that this is what is being described here with the "tree turning red."

Thus in this instance, the supposition that we are in a Katun 9-Ahau is correct. This is a record of the re-appearance of the plasma discharge of Jupiter after it had cleared the asteroid belt in receding from the Sun -- about 500 years after 3147 BC. My earlier diagrammatic estimate of when Jupiter first exited from the asteroid belt (shown in a previous chapter) is the year 2527 BC, which is 20 years after the end of this Katun 9-Ahau (2567 to 2547 BC, corrected). Since the dates of the graph are estimates, it is certainly close enough.

The redness of the apparition cannot be neglected. Although Mesopotamian sources do not mention colors, the Egyptians always depicted Jupiter as a huge red ball. This huge red coma lasted for about 300 years, from about 2550 BC (Katun 9-Ahau in Baktun 1) to sometime before 2349 BC and then returned in 2349 BC. The interruptions will be noted in the text.

The "tree," which Bolio translates as a "red tree," is probably what Mesopotamian cultures had identified as a mountain. It is the plasma discharge of Jupiter from its southern polar region. Notice that the plasma expulsion has changed from green to red. This could mark a change in the ionized gases at the outer edges of the plasmasphere, but it could as likely be a change in the density of these ions. This last is more than likely with a change in the experience of a lower value of the external (solar) electric field.

What the Egyptians called a mountain, the Olmecs identified as a tree. It was earlier identified as the "green tree" of the center. This green mountain described as a "tree" first appeared directly after 3147 BC, but disappeared after 300 years as Jupiter entered the asteroid belt, to reappear 330 years later, as described above.

The Moon

At the following part of the text we still seem to be in the time after the end of the "third creation," the period after 2349 BC. But again, a Katun name is not disclosed. It suggests that we are to understand that events of some named Katun 9-Ahau continue to be listed. The following text is about the Moon, and reports that Jupiter was not weeping. The *Chilam Balam* reads:

> *"The entire world was proclaimed by Uuc-yol-zip; but it was not at the time of this reign that Bolon-ti-ku [Jupiter] wept."*

There is no indication, from the translators, of who "Uuc-yol-zip" is. I would take a wild guess and suggest that, if we are chronologically in the period after 2349 BC, that Uuc-yol-zip is the Moon, which was an independent inner planet already orbiting the Sun at the location to which the Earth moved in 2349 BC. (Lunar calendars are established worldwide only after 2349 BC.)

Earth suddenly picked up a satellite, or, more properly, started to share an orbital location with the Moon, for the Moon travels in the ecliptic, not on the Earth's equatorial. A rapid discharge of the Earth via the Moon, could have destroyed any of the remaining Absu in record time. More on that below.

Uuc-yol-zip is never mentioned again and remains unidentified. Roys, on the basis of other informants, suggests a Deer God, which makes some sense if you have never seen the Moon before and you are suddenly confronted by its changing shape and nightly relocations. The Moon will relocate from the southeast sky to the northeast in the course of a week. But what Katun are we in?

The first appearance of the Moon (the Deer God) should be placed after 2349 BC, but this date falls in a Katun 4-Ahau, rather than the implied Katun 9-Ahau. In fact, I should point out another source, the only other Maya source of ancient history other than the *Popol Vuh*. The Temples of the Cross at Palenque (built in circa AD 690) claims that Jupiter, Mars, and Venus were all born in 2360 BC (corrected to 2336.8 BC a decade after 2349 BC). The Moon was their mother. Later, the Moon "let blood" in 2302.3 BC and "crowns herself" as ruler ("Ahau") in 2282.6 BC. These last two are corrected dates. [note 20]

We don't know exactly what these last two events were. But they can be placed, the first ("letting blood") in Katun 11-Ahau (ending in 2286 BC, corrected to 2307 BC), and the second event ("crowning herself") in Katun 9-Ahau (ending in 2266 BC, corrected to 2287 BC). Perhaps the second Palenque event records the regularization of the Moon's orbit. The wording of *"the entire world was proclaimed"* suggests the same assumption of rulership, which was as deep a concern of the Maya as it seemed to have been for most civilizations in the world. I would thus suggest that the event quoted from the *Chilam Balam* above should probably be assigned to Katun 9-Ahau, and equated to the Palenque record of the Moon "crowning herself" as ruler. This would place it in Katun 9-Ahau (a Long Count of 2.3.0.0.0), even though this is later than what I think it should be. The following will elucidate where this concern comes from.

That Jupiter did not "weep" at the time the Moon appeared (or assumed rulership) is interesting. It suggests that Jupiter had lost its coma and tail. I know that this happened some time after 2400 BC, but I have been unable to determine exactly when. I'll attempt to zero in on that first.

In my diagram of the recession of Jupiter from the Sun, the date when Jupiter encounters the last clump of asteroids at 3.9 to 4.0 AU is shown as 2438 BC to 2349 BC. This may be a high date because I have used a constant radial recession for the calculation.

In Egypt the title "Son of Re" had been in use already by the pharaohs who completed the Giza pyramids before 2500 BC, and was used by all the following pharaohs. During the following fifth dynasty, which spans 2490 BC to 2350 BC, "sun-temples" were built (or rebuilt) along with the pyramid graves of the first six pharaohs of that dynasty, in the period of 2490 BC to 2445 BC. "Sun-temples" are steep pyramids on a flat base. In Egypt these pyramids are the "symbol" of Re, Jupiter, representing the mountain form of the plasma outpouring below its south pole.

Further construction of "sun-temples" was abandoned before the end of the fifth dynasty. These dates suggest that the coma and tail of Jupiter (Re) might have disappeared by 2445 BC (the last "sun-temple"), but we do not know exactly when, or how long it took before this showed up as a change in religious monuments. On the basis of the above information the loss of a coma would be placed sometime before 2445 BC. There is thus a 20-year period where Jupiter seems to have disappeared or, more properly, diminished considerably in size.

The Chinese *Annals of Shu* speak of Yao (Jupiter) gaining the throne as "emperor" in 2357 BC, as if to say that Jupiter again developed a coma at that time. The first few dates of the *Annals of Shu* should probably be placed about a decade later, thus the above date should probably be nearer to 2349 BC.

There is also an interesting passage in the Babylonian *Enuma Elish* which recalls the disappearance of Jupiter's coma tail (as a garment) and its reappearance. Since the *Enuma Elish* clearly recounts the contact with the plasmoid from Venus in 2349 BC, it could be suggested that the disappearance of the coma and tail of Jupiter should be placed before 2349 BC. A period longer than 20 years would perhaps not allow this disappearance event to pass into a narrative. But an exact measure of time was not needed to be recalled, since the *Enuma Elish* was written 500 or 600 years after the events of 2349 BC.

The second instance of the coma of Jupiter disappearing during this time might have coincided with the first appearance of the Moon (at that time perhaps not yet in orbit around Earth). From Palenque, that would be the corrected date of 2336.8 BC (when the planets were "born") -- and thus 12 years after the spectacular blazing of 2349 BC, when Jupiter developed its large coma. But other records contradict this. The *Annals of Shu* claim that Jupiter (Yao) and the Moon (Shun) shared the throne for 30 years. The victory stele of Naram-Sin, "Beloved of the Moon" (2254 - 2218 BC), the great-grandson of Sargon, erected in 2250 or 2200 BC shows the two Gods at the top as stars. Jupiter is shown on his mountain; the Moon is without a support.

Jupiter Returns

"Then came the counting of the mat in its order."

The "counting of the mat" is the start of a new Katun. This has to be Katun 5-Ahau, if the Katuns are taken in order, that is, as if this text is a recital of prophecies associated with various named Katuns. But the naming of Katun 7-Ahau has been skipped, perhaps by accident, perhaps on purpose. The present Katun starts with the seating of Jupiter.

"Red was the mat on which Bolon-ti-ku [Jupiter] sat. His buttock is sharply rounded, as he sits on his mat."

Now we have another plasma outpouring of Jupiter, and again without a clear reference to what Katun has turned. I am tempted to believe that this is the **return** of a coma and tail in 2349 BC. That would place this event in Katun 2-Ahau, at 2.0.0.0.0 in the Long Count.

But it is more tempting to place this event (which seems to have been important for its redness) in a Katun 9-Ahau at the time when Jupiter first exited from the asteroid belt. I have already mentioned this event, above. The red mountain had not been seen for 300 years. This would be a Katun 9-Ahau in the first Baktun (1.10.0.0.0), with a corrected span of dates of 2567 to 2547 BC.

Roys suggests that "his buttock is sharply rounded" could also mean pointed or rounded like a hat. I do not know what to make of this except that it would perhaps fit the emblem -- a circle above a horizontal line -- used for Jupiter (Marduk) in Mesopotamia, and one of the magic symbols of the Egyptians, called the "shen," where the circular part is rendered in red. In Egypt Re (Jupiter) is always shown as a large solid red disk. A "sharply rounded buttock" does not readily match a giant lower plasma stream.

"Then descended greed from the heart of the sky, greed for power, greed for rule."

The phrase, *"Then descended greed from the heart of the sky, greed for power, greed for rule"* exactly expresses the earlier parallel experience after 2700 or 2600 BC in Mesopotamia (the kingship at Uruk) and Egypt (the third dynasty which starts the Old Kingdom). It was coincident (within a hundred years) in both cases with the return appearance of Jupiter on his mountain.

It is also the period after Mars had stopped making close calls to Earth. It is possible that both in the Eastern Mediterranean and in Mesoamerica a change happened -- a change from celestial rulers (and their priests) to human rulership. I would not make this suggestion if it were not for the fact that with the withdrawal of Mars and Mercury from the neighborhood of Earth, there was a worldwide change in conditions. Nothing would keep up the temple economies, when they were no longer needed to placate or plead with the destructive Gods, except the insistence of an autocratic leadership. If this can be accepted -- that at this time we see the first kingships -- then all other explanations, which place causes closer to us in time, can be dispensed with.

The period after 2300 BC saw the predecessors of the Olmecs establishing sites in the tropical region along the Pacific coast of Guatemala, some of which are today dated to about 2000 BC. In 1450 BC the first site on the Caribbean coast in Veracruz, Mexico, was established, San Lorenzo. It seems strange that complaints about leaders would be part of a history of the Gods except that this is also a history of the world. By the time of San Lorenzo, when we see what absolutely stupendous constructions the "greed for power" can accomplish, "leaders" had been well established for a thousand years.

Based on the complaints about leaders, as suggested above, I think we are in the period after about 2700 BC here (and for San Lorenzo, after 1440 BC). Here follows the third listing of trees. The remainder of this section deals with rulers, in association with the color of the trees at the cardinal points. It is a very generic presentation, unlike the exaltation of the leaders of Egypt, who built the Giza pyramids.

> *"Then the red foundation was established; the white foundation of the*
> *ruler was established; the black foundation was established; the yellow*
> *foundation was established."*
>
> *"Then the Red Ruler was set up, he who was raised upon the mat,*
> *raised upon the throne."*
>
> *"The White Ruler was set up, he who was raised upon the mat,*
> *raised upon the throne."*
>
> *"The Black Ruler was set up, he who was raised upon the mat, raised*
> *upon the throne."*
>
> *"The Yellow Ruler was set up, he who was raised upon the mat,*
> *raised upon the throne."*

This is followed by more complaints about these rulers, and their
limitations. It is interesting that the geographical concerns (the colors of the
cardinal directions) seem to have shifted to actual persons or sites at this time.
[note 21]

> *"As a god, it is said; whether or not gods, their bread is lacking, their*
> *water is lacking. There was only a portion (of what was needed) for*
> *them to eat together (...) but there was nowhere from which the quantity*
> *needed for existence could come."*
>
> *"Compulsion and force were the tidings, when he* [Jupiter] *was*
> *seated (in authority); compulsion was the tidings, compulsion by misery;*
> *it came during his reign, when he arrived to sit upon the mat. (...)"*

NOTE: "(...)" above represents lacunas in the original text.

There are similar sentiments about rulers expressed in a later section. I
should point out that later text will claim the rulership of Saturn extended
over the era before 3147 BC (after 6347 BC), and the rulership of Jupiter
extended from after 3147 BC to the time of the arrival of the Spanish. Thus
Jupiter's rulership extends over all of the "third creation."

The above text, and the ones following below, will seem confusing if the
actual sequence of events in the era of 2500 BC to 2200 BC is lost sight of.
To orient the reader, let me list a summary of events of the "Fall of the Absu"
-- what is otherwise known as the "flood of Noah." The details of these were
developed from more extensive sources from the Eastern Mediterranean
region, India, and China, and presented in the chapter "The Career of Jupiter."

- Near the beginning of the third dynasty in Egypt, Jupiter exits from the
  main portion of the Asteroid Belt, and again assumes a gigantic lower

plasma outpouring -- the mountain. Pharaohs of this dynasty, which built the pyramids at Giza start to add "Re" to their names. This happened in a Katun 9-Ahau, ending about 2500 BC.

- This event of Jupiter again showing as an enormous globe on a mountain is taken in the *Chilam Balam* as the "reign of the third period." This event is taken as an anchor in this book of the *Chilam Balam* to list other events related to the later events of 2349 BC. The reason why the Olmecs or other people of antiquity selected Katun 9-Ahau will be detailed further below.

- I should note that a separate page of the *Chilam Balam* actually recounts all the events of 2349 BC in the proper order. This will be detailed in the next chapter.

- At some time before 2349 BC the coma and tail of Jupiter disappeared again. From the fact that no additional "sun-temples" were built in Egypt after 2445 BC, we can suggest that Jupiter since that time had neither upper plumes nor a lower mountain of plasma. Jupiter was dead. My diagrammatic analysis of the travels of Jupiter away from the Sun, shown in the chapter "The Career of Jupiter," places this at 2438 BC, about 100 years before the "flood of Noah" in 2349 BC.

- In 2349 BC a transit of the Sun by Venus caused an Earth shock, tilting up the equatorial, which was hit by a plasmoid from Venus some hours later, identified in the Middle East as a gigantic dragon that waded in the blood of humans seen in the ocean of the sky for days. The initial plasmoid was followed by some nine additional, lesser plasmoid lightning bolts.

- The Absu turned red, and lightning fired across the rings. The equatorial rings disappeared soon after, and the southern stars first showed. Most prominent was the appearance of the Pleiades, high in the sky in the south at midnight.

- On the third night Jupiter had regained its coma, upper plumes, and lower mountain form. Jupiter was back from the dead.

- When the Absu collapsed, the Pleiades appeared for the first time -- an event which continued to be used in the future as a signal for celebrations of the "Day of the Dead" worldwide. At the same time the roof beams of the sky -- the intersection of the equatorial and the ecliptic -- showed up as a yellow road (the ecliptic) and a blood-red road (a remnant ring below the equatorial).

- The Moon showed up near Earth soon after. This was listed in the text above. But with the appearance of the Moon, the *Chilam Balam* notes that Jupiter was "not crying" at that time. The appearance of the Moon, or, more likely, its settling into a regular orbit, is assigned to Katun 7-Ahau, and this might in fact be so.

- One additional event, although it happened 200 years later, is noted in this collection of associated events: the giant coma of Jupiter blazed as if on fire and then disappeared to have Jupiter assume the look of a star. This is described below as "The Burning Tower," and it can (most likely) be placed in a Katun 8-Ahau.

The Burning Tower

As I warned, the events of the 24th and 22nd century BC are presented completely out of order. Thus we start with an event of the 22nd century, the burning of Jupiter. In what is assumed to be Katun 7-Ahau, although not altogether clear from the previous text, we have this strange incident described:

"Suddenly on high fire flamed up. The face of the sun was snatched away, taken from earth."
"This was his garment in his reign. This was the reason for mourning his power, at that time there was too much vigor. At that time there was the riddle for the rulers."

This duplicates the "Tower of Babel" story from the bible and supposedly other similar tales worldwide. We are between the year 2200 BC and 2000 BC. Since it follows the description of the rulership of Jupiter, it suggests the sudden demise of Jupiter, especially when we consider the phrase, *"The face of the sun was snatched away, taken from earth."* The Sun's face, after all, has not been taken away from Earth. This could only be a reference to Jupiter, who was still called "the Midnight Sun" by the Maya even in Classical times, and "Lord Sun."

In other text I have suggested that the Chinese dates for Yao's demise should probably be moved 100 years into the future, thus to 2150 BC. This would also be the death of Abraham. The year is fairly certain. Katun 8-Ahau (2.10.0.0.0), corrected to span 2167 BC to 2147 BC, would match this date. This date is also supported by other sources, as I have noted earlier.

The Planted Timbers

The following text follows on the "burning tower" without notification of a change in Katun. I think, however, considering what we know of the fall of the Absu in 2349 BC, and the events which accompanied this, that the sequence is completely incorrect. The planted timber and the crossroads mentioned below, follow directly on the removal of the Absu (the "flood of

Noah") in 2349 BC, and have nothing to do with the later blazing of Jupiter. The coincident events are:

- The collapse of the "House of Nine Bushes" and the "baptism from the center of the sky" -- listed further below
- The appearance of the Pleiades -- listed directly below.
- The appearance of the ecliptic and the equatorial in the south skies (the cross roads or roof beams).
- The appearance of the Moon (but could be later) -- listed above.
- The north and south polar plumes -- the "timbers" below,
- The return of Jupiter -- already listed above.

This is Katun 2-Ahau, which ends nominally in 2325 BC (2.0.0.0.0), but the dates should be corrected to be from 2367 BC to 2347 BC. This thus includes the date from the Eastern Mediterranean of 2349 BC for the fall of the Absu and the "flood of Noah." By coincidence this Katun falls at the end of a Baktun.

"The planted timber was set up. Perishable things are assembled at that time. The timber of the grave-digger is set up at the crossroads, at the four resting places. Sad is the general havoc, at that time the butterflies swarmed."

Roys reads this paragraph as a local event, suggesting that rulers were assembled and executed at the intersection of two roads in the land of the Maya. I doubt if it has this specificity, for the few other political events which are recalled in other books of the *Chilam Balam* list the names of the actors, in one instance from 700 years earlier. If this execution of chiefs had happened within the last 1000 years, we would have been told the names of the assailants and victims. The language of the Maya (and other people of the region) demands identification of an action in terms of the agents.

The "assembly of perishable things" are the Pleiades. Even in postclassical times the Maya held that the Pleiades were a sprinkling of seed maize. Certainly "precious things" is appropriate, because maize was held the highest status in all the Classical Maya culture. Since 2349 BC the Pleiades were seen above the intersection of the ecliptic and the equatorial, that is, at the location of the equinox, at the start of the constellation Taurus, as I have pointed out in other texts. As I have also pointed out previously, both the ecliptic and the equatorial were outlined as bright bands even still 1500 years ago, with the band of the ecliptic lasting into the 19th century. [note 22]

The equatorial showed at night as a band of glowing matter because of the debris still circling the Earth far above the equator -- left over from previous ages. After the Absu collapsed and most of the material dispersed away from Earth (and continued to fall to Earth until AD 1700), a single band remained, blood-red in color. The red ring is identified as the celestial snake Apep or Apophis in the Eastern Mediterranean region.

The remnant ring would probably show as spikes rising up into the sky at the east and west cardinal points. These regions, being beyond the edges of the Earth, would be lighted by the Sun (but with the west band being in shadow). These might have been the two "trees" of the east and west cardinal points, although I am more comfortable with assigning the trees to the lower Van Allen belt.

Near the time of the equinox the shadow of Earth would fall on the equatorial band but not on the band of the ecliptic (which is much too far away). Thus it looked like the red equatorial band crossed behind the ecliptic, although in actuality it was just the reverse. These crossed bands, with one band falling behind the other (a graphical representation known as the "Saint Andrew's Cross"), were used by the Olmecs and Maya as graphical indicators of the ecliptic throughout remote antiquity and through the Classical Era.

The ecliptic showed as a band of reflecting material which did not fade away until about AD 1840. This is the "Yellow Road" of the Chinese. The two bands intersected at Taurus, below the Pleiades, or probably near the end of Aries, since the red ring was below the equatorial. Mention of the assembly of "precious things" occurs directly before the mention of the timbers at the crossroads. In Southern Mexico and the Yucatan these two bands were displaced only some 20 degrees from being directly overhead where they crossed. In the *Popol Vuh* they are the roof beams of the house of the grandmother of Hunahpu and Xbalanque. They are also the river of pus and the river of blood which have to be crossed to get to the underworld. In remote antiquity the red band appeared only after the Absu had fallen. Because the planets traveled in one of the bands, they were called the crossroads.

Two timbers are mentioned. The "planted timber" is most likely the north polar plasma plume, the other, the "beam of the gravedigger" is the south polar plume, located at the crossroads (and close to the intersection). At a much later time (AD 400 to AD 700) the Milky Way was substituted, which became a primary symbol of creation and access to the underworld for the Classical Maya (as well as archaeologists). The Milky Way had not been seen in the south skies before the fall of the Absu.

The word "gravedigger," Roys notes, can also be translated as "hiders" -- "anyone who buries or hides things." I have no idea what the Maya had in mind in attributing the new view of the bands of the sky (or the south polar beam) to the action of "hiders," but, typical of Mesoamerican grammatical constructions, anything that appears has to be attributed, via an action-oriented verb, to some being. Perhaps the complete Absu and the moving waves of the rings were meant as the "hiders."

From the *Popol Vuh* we have the interesting tale of the Giant called "Mountain" who digs a hole for the Four Hundred Boys and is nearly impaled by the timber which was to be the center post of the house. This timber was set up at the crossroads, under the crossbeams of the sky but also under the crossbeams of the house of the Four Hundred Boys.

The swarming butterflies probably visually represent the dispersal of the Absu or the lightning between the atmosphere and the rings of the Absu. A little later the "flood" will be mentioned.

Despite his demise, Jupiter certainly remained as the chief celestial deity. Of course his status as the ruler of creation would be reinforced by the returning plasma, called a "flower" later in the text, and the plasma bolt delivered in 685 BC. He will appear in Classical times as "God GIII" of the Palenque triad, and be called "Lord Sun."

Katun 3-Ahau: the Sun

The following describes the eruption of Venus in 685 BC. It is also listed out of place, because the event of 685 BC follows the repeated close calls by Mars and Mercury in the 8th and 7th century BC, which are described (out of place) further below. The Katuns are here named, but the individual pages are again being read in the wrong order.

"Then there came great misery, when it came about that the sun in Katun 3-Ahau was moved from its place for three months."

First, as I have noted earlier, the period of three 20-day months (60 days) exceeds the best estimate (from Zoroastrian sources) of the duration of the eruption of Venus by a month. Since the movement of the Sun was most likely charted to sunset locations along the horizon, I think the "sixty days" deal with the horizon setting location of the Sun.

The time interval here is one of three instances in this Book of the *Chilam Balam* where the period is given as an inclusive count. I first realized this for another instance, which caused me to look again at the other two. The three months are thus an interval of two "Uinal" months of 20 days, a total of 40 days. Having independently determined the ending date of the blazing of Venus and Mercury as July 25th, and a starting date as a new Moon before that, it was satisfying to realize that the "three 20-day months" mentioned here represent the 40-day interval between two new moons at June 15 and July 25 (Gregorian calendar dates).

I think we can suggest the veracity of these data from the fact that in all three instances, by allowing for inclusive counting, the intervals can be matched against other known dates and made sense of. This also again verifies the fact that the Long Count existed only since 747 BC, for no such accurate dates or intervals exist before 747 BC. (The inscriptions at Palenque were retrocalculated.)

> *"After three years* [three heaps of years] *it will come back into place in Katun 3-Ahau. Then another Katun will be set (in its place)."*

Roys notes that "three years" literally reads "three heaps of years" which could be a longer period than three "Tun years" (of 360 days), or it could mean a shorter period, but apparently not longer than the 17 or 18 years it would take to reach the end of Katun 3-Ahau. I think a "heap" is likely to be a group of five, but of the 260-day Tzolkin calendar years. (As explained by other contemporary commentators on the mathematics of the Maya, this would be a "bundle" -- a line representing a count of five dots in the numeric notation. Of course a group of 20 is also called a bundle, as is, in later Central Mexico, a group of 52 years.)

The 15 "years" (three heaps of five) is probably a measure on the Tzolkin calendar which rotated the same day-name and day-number combination into place at the same horizon sunset location for a zenithal passage of the Sun. I am assuming a zenithal passage because these were deemed to be very important to each ceremonial site.

In actuality the location along the horizon of the zenithal sunset remained the same after 685 BC as it had been before 685 BC, to within a fraction of a degree, but the calendar day (our calendar) would move back by 10 to 17 days, as follows, depending on the latitude.

location	latitude	zenithal passage of the Sun before 685 BC,	after 685 BC	difference in days
Izapa	14.960	August 21	August 11	10
Monte Alban	17.033	August 16	August 4	12
La Venta	18.125	August 14	July 31	14
Teotihuacan	19.638	August 10	July 25	16

The Tzolkin calendar, not being an annual calendar, would rotate a different day-name into place each following year. Normally, after 20 rotations of the Tzolkin, the same day-name would appear again on the same day of the Gregorian calendar (without accounting for the slippage due to leap days).

As so tersely expressed by the *Chilam Balam*, it would take three times five rotations of the Tzolkin ("bundles of years"), not the normal twenty, for the Sun to again return to the same day-name and day-number combination. We can find this easily, for we do not need to access the Long Count calendar, and we do not need to know the starting date or ending date. But we will have to "discount" the author's quirky inclusive accounting. "Fifteen years until" will mean a difference of "fourteen years." This is the second instance of an interval expressed as an inclusive count. It is then a simple matter to subtract 14 multiples of the 260-day Tzolkin from multiples of the 365.25-day year, until a difference is found which matches the differences in calendar days in the chart above.

In fact, 14 Tzolkin rounds are 12.5 days short of ten 365.25-day years. **14 * 260 - 10 * 365.24 = - 12.40 days**. This is the change in days experienced at Monte Alban. Monte Alban may thus be the source of the lowland Yucatan Maya author's original books. Already 600 years old (since the collapse of the Maya kingdoms) at the time they were read in the 16th century AD, the original source dates back well over 2000 years to 685 BC.

The first date of a zenithal passage of the Sun at Monte Alban, before 685 BC, would have been August 16, 686 BC, 6.3.3.6.11 7-Chuen. Fourteen times 260 days is 0.0.10.2.0 Long Count days. Adding, this gives 6.3.13.8.11 7-Chuen. This falls on August 3rd, 676 BC. One more day needs to be advanced to complete the count, thus August 4. Either way, the difference is 12 or 13 days. (This calculation is unaffected by the change in the calendar instituted at a later date by Monte Alban, in 607 BC. See the chapter "The Day of Kan.")

The same addition of 14 Tzolkin periods to the pre-685 BC dates results in (subtracting 12.5 days as 13 days):

- Izapa: August 9, not 11;
- La Venta: August 1, not July 31;
- Teotihuacan: July 22, not 25.

La Venta is close, however, and might stand as an alternate source for the original glyphic books from which Book 10 of the *Chilam Balam* was eventually composed. La Venta is somewhat north in latitude from Monte Alban.

I should also follow up on my earlier note on the *Chilam Balam* that the return of the Sun was accomplished before the end of the Katun, "it will come back into place in Katun 3-Ahau." As outlined above, the displacement on the Tzolkin calendar would have amounted to less than ten (current) years. The year 685 BC less ten years is 675 BC. This Katun 3-Ahau starts in 689 BC and ends in 669 BC, bracketing both the nova event of Venus in 685 BC and the date of the return of the Sun.

Only a short paragraph is recorded for all of Katun 3-Ahau, although the writer will repeatedly return to the event of Katun 3-Ahau. This was one of the most monumental events in prehistory. It changed the religions and probably the enterprises of Mesoamerica and started people on a path of independent thinking, as elsewhere in the world.

The writer continues with laments, presumably related to Katun 3-Ahau:

"The 'ramon' fruit is their bread, the 'ramon' fruit is their drink; the 'jícama cimarrona' is their bread, the 'jícama cimarrona' is their drink; what they eat and what they drink."
"The 'ix-batun,' the 'chimchim-chay,' are what they eat."

The foods listed are those eaten at a time of famine. Roys notes, however, "Most of the preceding paragraph concerning Katun 3-Ahau appears to be an interpolation. It is not found in the Tizimin and Mani versions," and notes that two other versions of the *Chilam Balam* list the misfortunes ("for each of the twenty years") of Katun 5-Ahau instead.

This is followed by a most curious sentence:

"These things were present here when misery settled, father, in Tun 9."

The Katun 3-Ahau text missing from other copies of the *Chilam Balam* may reflect the care the Maya took in hiding all notice of Kukulkan (Quetzalcoatl) from the Spanish priests. Is the meaning of "father" from a statement about of the exact genesis of Kukulkan, addressed to a Spanish priest?

It might very well be that this interpolation is a confession to a Spanish priest. But it is couched in talk of miseries, rather than the significance of Kukulkan's death and resurrection. Which may be why "the miseries" as well as the reference to "Tun 9" and to "father" is missing in other *Chilam* texts.

If correct as posed by me, then we have here the most valuable aspect of this document, a clear statement about the year of the Kukulkan event -- the earthly appearance of Quetzalcoatl and his death.

"Tun 9" is the ninth year of Katun 3-Ahau. Then "these things" would have happened in 680 BC. My first reaction was that the scribe had the Tun date wrong. If the event happened in 685 BC, then it should have been Tun-4 of Katun-3 (6.3.4.5.15). If the event happened in 680 BC, however, then it would have been Tun-9 (6.3.9.5.15) instead.

Then I remembered that my selection of 685 BC was based on correcting the established error in Eastern Mediterranean chronology. It actually was the year 680 BC on the Julian calendar, the very calendar that the Spanish priests had introduced into the Yucatan. The scribe thus did not make a mistake, but properly identified the year. At least, that is what it looks like to me: he identified the year in the calendar of the invaders when the Sun "did not follow its course for three months." In fact, he managed to retrocalculate the Julian calendar into an era before the Julian calendar was established.

The importance of this short paragraph about the Sun can be gauged from the inclusion of three specific date values: it lasted "three months," the Sun "returned" in 14 Tzolkin periods, and it happened -- ended -- in year (Tun) nine of Katun 3-Ahau -- 680 BC on the actual retrocalculated Julian calendar of the invaders.

Two more data points will be added further below: the date of the release of the plasmoid by Jupiter will be identified and the interval between the last close sighting of Mars and the day the plasmoid arrived will be given.

At this point the list of Katuns is interrupted. To this point the phantom Katuns have progressed in the correct order, that is, Katun 11-Ahau, Katun 9-Ahau, Katun 7-Ahau, Katun 5-Ahau (though I have some problems locating Katun 5-Ahau), and Katun 3-Ahau. Katun 11-Ahau was used at the beginning simply from the notion that all history starts in Katun 11-Ahau. But Katun 3-Ahau can certainly be assigned to a definite time in the past which matches what we know from other sources.

The next Katun should have been Katun 1-Ahau, but now the writer introduces Katun 13-Ahau, with a single line about foreigners.

After introducing Katun 13-Ahau, the *Chilam Balam* then continues with a radically different listing of events. Events are now listed by Katuns in order, in the manner of the "prophecies" of the other Books of the *Chilam Balam*. This has all the look of an additional record from another original source. Near the end, when the writer restarts in Katun 11-Ahau, yet another primary source seems to have been accessed.

"At that time there were the foreigners. The charge (of misery) was sought for all the years of (Katun) 13-Ahau."

It is possible that the mention of Katun 13-Ahau is a very early transcription error (reading 13 for 3), or this may be a reflection of the expected content similar to other Books of the *Chilam Balam*, where Katun 13-Ahau is indeed associated with prophecies of foreigners, the Spanish. In another Book the foreigners arrive in Katun 5-Ahau and are Caribs. Other copies of the *Chilam Balam* have nothing on Katun 3-Ahau, and list "miseries," year by year for Katun 5-Ahau, which is missing from this copy of the *Chilam Balam* -- which is the version from Chumayel.

The 8th Century BC

The approaches by Mars in the 8th century BC (and the 7th century), which devastated Persia, Anatolia, Greece, and Italy, at 35 to 40 degrees latitude, did the same damage in Central America, as indicated by the fact that the number of villages in Mesoamerica decreased markedly in the 8th century BC.

But the *Chilam Balam* at this point is given over to descriptions of flowers, colors, and fragrances -- arcane celestial details never noticed (or mentioned) in the Middle East. Perhaps we are now seeing the transcription from another source, "The Book of Flowers." Mars is only mentioned twice.

From dates extracted from the records of the Middle East the destructive events of the 8th and 7th century should be spread over four Katuns, from 747 BC to about 687 BC -- if we start in 747 BC. This would be the time span of Katun 11-Ahau (767 BC to February of 747 BC), Katun 9-Ahau, Katun 7-Ahau, and Katun 5-Ahau (ending in 687 BC). There is no reference to the last two, but the first two are listed and the events are described.

If, on the other hand, we start with what seems to be the full record, based on archaeological data of destructions in the Mediterranean, then we need to start in 806 BC. The record would have to include the additional Katun 4-Ahau (ending in 806 BC) through Katun 13-Ahau (ending in 768 BC). (Katun 4-Ahau, Katun 2-Ahau, and Katun 13-Ahau.) But there is no reference to these Katuns. Most likely this is because there were no Long Count records compiled before 747 BC. Checking back at later times, nothing was seen of the first four close passes of Mars, except as implicit in the name "Bolon Dzacab," "Nine Lives" -- for Mars did show up a total of nine times.

It is interesting that Mars is known as "Nine Lives" during the 8th and 7th century BC -- when he had also appeared close to Earth nine times before 3147 BC (as I surmised from Eastern Mediterranean sources). At first I thought that it was the nine appearances in the 8th and 7th century BC that became the basis for his name. But it seems to be a coincidence. His name was selected in remote antiquity, before 3147 BC, later known as "this first Bolon Dzacab." The giant greenstone mask-shaped floors at Olmec La Venta, apparently buried as a means of warding off or appeasing Mars, represent the face of a Jaguar in the form of the glyph for "nine." This name might thus have existed before it could have been determined how many times Mars would show up during these two centuries.

It is strange that the first four close passes of Mars between 806 BC and 747 BC were not recorded and, in fact, there were apparently no preventative ceremonial sculptures dedicated to Mars in the Olmec Veracruz region of

Mexico during this period. Tres Zapotes, which had taken over primacy from San Lorenzo in about 850 BC, continued to carve "Venus heads" during the 100-year period before 747 BC, and thus only paid attention to the simultaneous appearance of Venus and Mars in 776 BC.

But the close pass of Mars in 747 BC seems to have destroyed Tres Zapotes, and La Venta was established to celebrate (or ward off) the comings and goings of Mars. La Venta was aligned to a sunset over the mountain Popocatepetl for the day of the Earth shock of 747 BC, when the length of the year changed (but not the axial inclination) and the Olmec Long Count was instituted. The close pass of 747 BC, plus the next four (a total of five), were all remembered at La Venta.

The actual date for the alignment at La Venta is February 28th, but for an angle representing a sunset under the condition of an axial inclination of 30 degrees for the Earth. There are two additional alignments, representing a sunset on April 19th, to the mountains Citlaltepetl and Volcan La Malinche, also selected for an axial inclination of 30 degrees. After 685 BC, when the axis of the Earth changed to an inclination of 23.5 degrees to the normal of the orbit, La Venta was reconstructed to have its long axis at right angles to a sunset on February 28 for the current axial inclination of 23.5 degrees. (Details in a later chapter.)

Thus the close pass of Mars in 747 BC was noted in the reconstruction of the ceremonial center at La Venta, and the visit is recorded in the *Chilam Balam*, appropriately in a Katun 11-Ahau -- the Katun which actually ended the previous era on February 28, 747 BC. A little later in the text the nine concurrent visits by Mercury are recorded as the descent -- with Bolon Dzacab -- of Bolon Mayel, Nine Fragrances. I'll detail Bolon Mayel further below.

> *"Then it was that the lord of (Katun) 11-Ahau spread his feet apart."*
> *"Then it was that the word of Bolon Dzacab [Mars] descended to the tip of his tongue."*

Bolon Dzacab ("Nine Lives") is Mars, to be distinguished from the Mars seen before 3147 BC, who is called "this first Bolon Dzacab," and also differing from Lahun Chaan ("Ten Sky") who appears to be Mars for 300 years after 3067 BC. The "tip of the tongue" is the bottom of the electric arc from Mars (or an extended cone of plasma perhaps in the form of dust). Mars, as God K or God G-II, is often depicted in Maya iconography with a single leg, acknowledged as representing lightning. (On the much later Aztec "Calendar Stone" he is presented in the center with his tongue hanging down.) "Spread his feet" refers to how a growing child is carried on the hip (after Luxton). It is thus a simile for "establish."

The text here is perhaps with reference to all of the period of 806 BC to 747 BC. But notice that, as elsewhere, nothing is said of the change in calendars which happened after 747 BC. (There is, however, a note about the introduction of a calendar at the time of the "third creation," listed on a separate page of the *Chilam Balam*.) Except for the complaints about the rulers who imposed themselves on the Olmecs or Maya, no civil events are ever touched upon in Book 10.

With respect to the phrase "tip of his tongue," there are some Olmec rock carvings from this era of an iguana (or what looks like an iguana) with his tongue reaching up and touching the bottom of cloud glyphs. Cloud glyphs look like pancakes with down-curled edges. It would be appropriate of Mars appearing in the skies, reaching down to Earth with a sustained lightning bolt. Although the tongue here goes in the wrong direction.

But the following Katun 9-Ahau, from 747 BC to 727 BC (further below) includes a surplus of observations, mostly in terms of flowers. Fragrances are also mentioned, which we recognize from Velikovsky's collected anecdotes, although Velikovsky places these in 1492 BC during the interaction with Venus. [note 23]

The Day of Kan

Another event is inserted here, related, as the text states, to Katun 9-Ahau, but we are no longer in the 8th century BC. It is, in fact, in error. The event listed below, the fall of the Absu -- the flood of Noah -- happened in Katun 2-Ahau (2.0.0.0.0), corrected to end in 2347 BC. There is, of course, a Katun 9-Ahau before the "flood of Noah," 148 years too early, just as there is a Katun 9-Ahau after the "flood of Noah," 40 years too late.

I am inclined at this point to suggest an alteration of the original text which was made on purpose in antiquity. More on this below.

> *"Then the charge of the Katun was sought; nine was its charge when it descended from heaven. Kan was the day when its burden was bound to it."*
>
> *"Then the water descended, it came from the heart of the sky for the baptism of the House of Nine Bushes.*

Except for the fact that we are presented with a deluge, the rest does not make much sense at first.

Bolio translates these two lines as:

> *"Nine were their cargoes when he came from the sky. The day of Kan was the day when his cargo was tied up. It was when the water came*

*from the sky for the second birth, from the house of the one of the
'innumerable years.'"*

This relates the fact that we are in a Katun named 9-Ahau, as well as the
fact that the event, the baptism, happened on the day of Kan. The author of
the *Chilam Balam*, on the basis of his sources, has full confidence that the
"day of Kan" should be associated with the "second baptism." I will address
this first.

The "second birth" is a second flood. The flood is suggested by Bolio.
The history we are dealing with ignores hurricanes and tsunamis, and has so
far only listed one other flood, the event of 3147 BC. The flood mentioned
here is the only other mention of a flood. Notice that it "came from the center
of the sky" and that it baptized (wet) the "House of Nine Bushes."

I think we are looking at the event which in other parts of the world is
recognized as the "flood of Noah." The "House of Nine Bushes" is the Absu
or Duat, the last described in Egypt (at 30 degrees latitude) as consisting of
seven rings. In the Yucatan (at 20 degrees latitude) it was seen as consisting
of nine rings -- or rows of bushes. The Maya or their predecessors saw an
additional two rings closer to the Earth's equator.

In Egypt and Mesopotamia the seven rings of the Duat or Absu were
understood to be an ocean in the south, but also as access to the
"Underworld." In the Yucatan the 9 layers were also the underworld, the
domain of "The Nine." But the Olmecs or Maya did not equate the rings to a
sea, as far as I know. This may be because of the steep angle at which the
rings stood in the sky, and the intimate contact of the land with real oceans.

This passage, like so many others, is not only displaced from its proper
sequence, but also seems referenced to the wrong double-decade (Katun). The
question thus remains, if most of the other events are properly slotted in
Katuns of the correct names, why is this "flood" event -- plus the appearance
of the Moon, the first showing of the Pleiades, the appearance of the rafters of
the sky, and the polar plasma plumes -- all of which deal with the flood of
Noah, late by 40 years? The "flood of Noah" can be placed with good
certainty in 2349 BC from the efforts of many chronographers of the
Mediterranean region (and matches good guesswork from China in 200 BC).

[Image: 4-Ahau and 9-Ahau.]

First, it could be suggested that the assignment of the "second baptism" to

Katun 9-Ahau is a transcription error and that Katun 9-Ahau was misread from Katun 4-Ahau.

Errors in transcription, both at the time the *Chilam Balam* was written and at earlier times, are certain. Roys notes a number of them for the *Chilam Balam* text. J.E. Thompson has noted some dozen errors in the *Dresden Codex*, dating from about AD 1200. Vincent H. Malmstrom, in *Cycles of the Sun, Mysteries of the Moon* (1997), has noted a transcription error in Stele C from Tres Zapotes. The task of transcribing the codexes to new plaster-coated bark books by painting the glyphs, illustrations, and diagrams, must have represented a mind-numbing task which could easily result in subtle errors, like the addition of a bar to the glyph for 4-Ahau.

But there is a more elegant solution which comes forward to resolve the "Katun 9-Ahau" issue. The details, which I have promised a number of times in this text already, are as follows:

The day-name "Kan" is the fourth day of any Katun. The first day of Kan in the Katun 9-Ahau after the "flood of Noah" is July 26, 2286 BC -- 2.2.0.0.4 2-Kan, on the "August 11" correlation (this will suggest that it was a very old alteration of the text). If the year is wrong, it is the only one in all of the *Chilam Balam* (making allowances for the scribe's insistence of placing all planetary events in Katun 9-Ahau). With both the Katun and the day listed, it would seem to pinpoint a very certain date. It could signify the completion of the fall of the Absu, but this would have been accomplished in a few days, not 40 years later.

However, July 26th was the celebration of New Year (as "the day of Kan") among the Maya when the Spanish invaded in the 16th century. Bishop Landa (in circa AD 1590) mentions that the new-year day of the Maya was on July 26 and always fell on the Tzolkin days Kan, Muluc, Ix, and Cauac -- in rotation. July 26 was celebrated as the new-year day, not only by the Yucatan Maya and regulated by the priests of the ceremonial center of Edzna, but also at Teotihuacan in Mexico, a thousand miles west from Edzna. Teotihuacan was established in circa 200 BC as an Olmec outpost. Of course it should be understood that this was not our calendar date of July 26th, but is the day when the Sun rose and set at a certain location along the horizon, which today equates to July 26th. For both Edzna and Teotihuacan this included the passage of the Sun directly overhead.

The resolution of why Katun 9-Ahau was understood to be the year of the end of the "third creation," rather than the correct year of Katun 4-Ahau, is buttressed by four concepts.

First, it was known that a calendar had been instituted at the time of the "second baptism" (as was true worldwide). Actually, I suspect that this was the addition of 13 numbered days to the established 20 day-names of the Tzolkin calendar.

Secondly, the start of the year was celebrated among the Maya, as at Teotihuacan in the Valley of Mexico, on July 26th. July 26th actually celebrated the day after the delivery at the Sun of the plasmoid from Jupiter in 685 BC. If this last was a "fourth creation" of the world, it might seem reasonable to the Maya that the previous creation of the world would also start on the same Tzolkin day-name.

Third, the Maya and the Olmecs seemed to have been convinced that the Tzolkin calendar determined celestial events. I'll explore this more in a following chapter. It was this thinking which led to an active search by the Maya (or more likely, the Olmecs) for the "day of Kan" among the records of the past -- a day of Kan which fell on the equivalent calendar date (sunset location) of July 26.

We must allow that the Maya were perfectly capable of calculating backwards to discover on what day in prehistory the setting Sun on July 26th coincided with the fourth day, named Kan, of a newly started Katun.

Of course, a day named Kan falls on July 26th every few years (at about 20-year intervals). However, the Long Count date of 2.2.0.0.4 2-Kan is **the only instance** in the whole Long Count calendar -- 5200 years -- that the **first day** of Kan falls on July 26.

"The day of Kan," July 26th, marked the end of the nova event of the Sun in 685 BC (the termination by the plasmoid of Jupiter) as it was celebrated a few hundred years later. Even though July 26 did not fall on a day of Kan in 685 BC, it became celebrated as the "new year day" among the Maya, having inherited this significant date from the teachings of Olmec Teotihuacan. Much later, before perhaps 300 BC, scribes assigned this "important date" to the event of the "second baptism." The Katun during which July 26 fell on the first day of Kan, was researched and found to have occurred only once in five thousand years since the start of the current era -- in the second Katun of the second Baktun (2.2.0.0.4). [note 24]

Last, as was known among the Maya, all important celestial events happened in Katun-9 periods. The first day of Kan, July 26th, also occurred in a Katun-9.

This has to be the solution to this apparent error in chronology. We are looking at a correction to the historical records, made in antiquity, which seemed eminently reasonable at the time. There is no way that we can manipulate Katuns and Baktuns to account for the difference of 40 years and find the "day of Kan" elsewhere in the past. We could attempt to add together surplus days to the solar year for the periods between 747 BC, 1492 BC, 2193 BC, and 2349 BC, but these will not add up to 40 years. [note 25]

If the Olmecs in antiquity investigated the "day of Kan" for the end of the "third creation," they must have had something to go on besides the notion that the recreation of the world would (or should) have happened when the first day of Kan of a Katun fell on July 26th. I would suggest that, because Jupiter had shown up in a full display three days after September 8th, 2349 BC, this would be "day three" of a Tzolkin calendar round which started with the plasmoid from Venus. The next day is the "day of Kan" -- always the fourth day of a new Katun, and New Year's day for the "third creation."

The error in assignment in the *Chilam Balam* stems from the fact that the day of the "third creation" simply could not be retrocalculated 1600 years later when the Long Count was adopted, and certainly not another 800 years later, when the Maya attempted it (using a 365.24-day year), for the length of the year had changed three times since 2349 BC.

The Maya knew the Tzolkin calendar governed the Gods responsible for creation, and so the new Katun would be a Katun 9-Ahau. This was logical since it was well known from 747 BC that all of pre-history could be assigned to the previous Katun 11-Ahau. Katun 9-Ahau follows directly on Katun 11-Ahau.

It is also possible that a Katun 9-Ahau had actually started at the time of the "third creation" in 2349 BC. In which case the fourth day would be a day of Kan. This is the day after Jupiter returned from the dead. What a separate page of the *Chilam Balam* says, as part of a list of events associated with the fall of the Absu (the flood of Noah), is:

"And then days of the year were introduced."

Let's assume from this that the 260-day Tzolkin was introduced on September 6, 2349 BC, using a rotation of 13 days to follow the waxing and waning of the Moon (even though the Moon may not have shown up exactly that soon). It is difficult to imagine how soon this calendar was devised. But once established, it would have been obvious that the fourth day of the new calendar, which would have been a New Year's Day, was a day of Kan. This would celebrate the end of the "third creation."

Since Baktuns and Katuns had certainly been tallied since 3147 BC, it is very possible that this day of Kan -- September 9, 2349 BC -- was indeed the fourth day of a Katun named 9-Ahau. That also means that, as had happened in 3147 BC, the previous Katun would have been named 11-Ahau -- the Katun which always represents all of prehistory. This coincidence of ending an era with a Katun 11-Ahau would happen again in 747 BC. And a day of Kan shows up on a retrocalculation for April 19, 1493 BC (Exodus, my date of 1492 BC).

Thus if a "day of Kan," which coincided with an equivalent calendar date of July 26th, was found as the fourth day of a Katun 9-Ahau, then the Olmecs would have been justified in suggesting that during this particular double decade the world had been recreated. Even though 40 years late, only Katun

9-Ahau of the second Baktun (2.2.0.0.4) qualified in the complete record of the 5200 years of the cycle of 13 Baktuns.

Now to a previous sentence, which seems out of place. This is a sentence which may need to be separated from the line about "the baptism of the House of Nine Bushes":

"Kan was the day when its burden was bound to it."

The day of Kan here is most likely 6.3.4.5.4 17-Chen 2-Kan which is July 14, Gregorian, 685 BC (July 21, Julian). It is the day, I suspect, that the plasma bolt left Jupiter in 685 BC. The "burden" which "was bound to it" is the plasmoid from Jupiter. The day of binding was the start of the travel from Jupiter. "It" is the day named Kan, not any other entity.

The "day of Kan" had been known to be the day that creation ended in remote times, both in 2349 BC (although assigned to the wrong Katun) and in 1492 BC (of which the time-keepers were more certain). A change to the August 13 Tzolkin calendar had found that the equivalent calendar date of the latest change, July 14, 685 BC, also happened on "the day of Kan."

This note about the "day of Kan" when "the burden was bound to it" -- bound like a pack carried by a trader -- is the fourth chronological reference to the events of the year 685 BC. This date only becomes important later, when we learn that it signifies the decision of Jupiter not to have Mars destroy creation.

The calendar dates mentioned above become clear on an inspection of alignments with horizon location for Olmec coastal and Valley of Mexico ceremonial sites (for which see a following chapter). Alignments were made, at different sites, for April 19th (representing the Earth shock of 1492 BC), February 28th (the shock of 747 BC), and July 9th, 21st, and 25th (all dealing with Jupiter in 685 BC). The start of the blazing of Venus and Mercury in 685 BC, 40 days before July 25th, was not celebrated. The Maya, and, in fact, all of Mesoamerica, only celebrated completions, not the start of events.

The Flowers

The next few lines first attribute the deluge (of 2349 BC) to Mars. The reading seems to present a simultaneous close passage of Mars, as Bolio's translation, above, suggests. (This may reflect the events after 1936 BC, the destruction if Sodom and Gomorrah, which followed on 2349 BC.) Any passage of Mars would have brought torrential rain storms and hurricanes to the region, in addition to destruction. The lines following this do not return to the topic of Mars, but introduce a new player, Mercury.

"With it descended Bolon Mayel [Nine Fragrances]*; sweet was his mouth and the tip of his tongue. Sweet were his brains."*

I suspect that the insertion further above is meant to relate the "water from the sky" (at the time of "Noah's flood") to Mars in the 8th century BC (or Mercury, as here), even though no mention is made of rains or hurricanes associated with Mars. I have a note further below on the sudden topical grouping of events by the author.

"Sweet was his mouth, etc.," -- Meaning either that this celestial agent was not a threat to humans, or the sweet mouth is associated with the "fragrances."

"Bolon" -- nine -- suggests nine appearances of Mercury. Mercury might have been seen close to Earth nine times. But I think that this started in 806 BC. As I have suggested earlier, the orbit of Mercury was elongated since 3147 BC, extending past the orbit of Earth, -- equivalent to what Mars was doing. It was likely in sync with Mars, possibly showing up near Earth when Mars did so. The two planets were known throughout the world as "the twins." The Earth shock by Mercury in 686 BC follows directly on an appearance of Mars, as substantiated by a note on the timing of this further below in the *Chilam Balam*. "With it descended.." affirms that Mars also showed up 9 times.

More on Mercury after another interruption. At this point the text returns to Mars, or the satellites of Mars, rather than Mercury, except that the "honey of the flowers" would have to refer to Mercury.

"Then descended the four mighty supernatural jars [or, two mighty demon bats]*, this was the honey of the flowers."*

Roys's footnote reads:

"For this sentence the following is substituted in the Mani and Tizimin versions of this narrative: 'Then descended two mighty demon bats who sucked the honey of the flowers.'"

That might make sense in representing the two satellites of Mars, which are elsewhere in the world described (during this period) as raging spirits, scorpions, snakes, and chariot wheels. Mars, lacking a magnetic field, would have had a closely held plasmasphere (coma), which might very well have consisted entirely of ionized dust (as is seen today). Once Mars entered Earth's plasmasphere the coma of Mars would have expanded to meet the Earth's electric field, rather than being subjected only to the Sun's much lower electric field outside of Earth's plasmasphere. The two satellites of Mars would have continuously distorted the coma of Mars. Seen on the day side of Earth, this might have presented itself as a flapping dark shape. (The satellites of Mars would be seen east and west of the globe of Mars because Mars passed Earth laterally.)

As I have noted before, according to the modeling by Patten and Windsor, Mars would alternately appear near Earth in going toward the day side of Earth and going toward the night side of Earth. That might account for the appearance of "two" mighty demon bats, rather than 4 or 5 (between 747 BC and 687 BC). Thus two times out of the five recorded appearances of Mars.

This would have happened in the fall of the year, and likely represented a passage of Mars on the day side. The spectacle in the skies, back-lighted by the Sun, would have been astoundingly different from the view of a passage of Mars at night. We may have to assume that the Mani and Tizimin versions of the *Chilam Balam* corrected the information presented in the books of Chumayel.

The "four mighty supernatural jars," on the other hand, might also describe Mercury. After four appearances with Mars (and likely close by), the fifth appearance of Mercury was distinctly different, for it was jolted by Earth (686 BC), and disappeared to a new orbit close to the Sun. Nothing is made of the "burning tower" apparition, however, the sight of which might have only been experienced much further north.

Thus, after having mentioned the appearance of Bolon Dzacab, Mars, in 747 BC, the *Chilam Balam* now has reference to the four additional appearances of Mars -- as "mighty demon bats" or "supernatural jars" rather than as Bolon Dzacab. This coincides with the four giant heads found at La Venta, which were buried in a line north of the pyramid.

Since the "mighty demon bats" suck the honey of the flowers (mentioned above), it suggests the near simultaneous appearance of Mars and Mercury in the skies. The Olmec Jaguar sculptures at La Venta, and later, add the snout and fangs of a snub-nosed bat to the jaguar face. [note 26]

Of course I have here selectively taken the number of appearances from one source (four jars) and the description from another (two bats). But I think the number "four'" is completely justified from the number of heads found at La Venta, and the "bat" description is justified from the sculptures of bat-faced jaguars at La Venta.

In the next few lines of the text, all about flowers, clearly refers to Mercury, which has a minor magnetic field, and would thus support tri-lobed plasma forms at its poles -- looking like flowers. Mars, without a magnetic field, would not.

"Then there grew up for it the red unfolded calyx, the white unfolded calyx, the black unfolded calyx and the yellow unfolded calyx, those

which were half a palm (broad) and those which were a whole palm (in breadth)."

The four colored "calyxes" again look like a distribution to the four compass directions. The half palm and full palm widths describe the lower and upper tri-lobed plasma cones above and below the magnetic poles of Mercury. I should point out that Mercury and Mars were seen in a side view from Earth, since the rotational axis of both planets would nearly parallel that of the Earth. Thus the flowers of Mercury would have extended in a north and south direction.

The flower forms, by the way, are understood in Egypt and the eastern Mediterranean region as wings. From this we have the "winged disk" iconography, which is clearly associated with Mercury.

The north magnetic pole would have a much larger size ("a whole palm") flower form. If these represented the polar plasma forms of a planet, the planet need not have come that close to Earth, since Mercury's coma might easily have been twenty times the diameter of the planet itself, with the polar plumes much larger. Yet, what a threatening image this would have presented! It is a palm held at arm's length. The "whole palm" representing the size of the flower shape at the top, and the "half palm" representing the width of the flower shape at the bottom. A "palm" in width is about 5 degrees of the sky -- ten times the diameter of the Moon.

"Then there sprang up the [1] five-leafed flower, [2] the five drooping (petals), [3] the cacao (with grains like) a row of teeth, [4] the 'ix-chabil-tok,' [5] the little flower, [6] 'Ix Macuil Xuchit,' [7] the flower with the brightly colored tip, [8] the 'laurel' flower, and [9] the limping flower."

On a whim I decided to count the specific flower species, as listed above, to see if this would account for the name Bolon Mayel, "Nine Fragrances."
Bolio has:

And at the same time blossomed [1] the flower that is watered and [2] the one that has holes; and [3] the wavy flower of cocoa and [4] the one never sucked on [this is Ix Macuil Xuchit, "Five Flower," the Mexican god of music and dance], *and [5] the flower of the spirit of color, and [6] the one that always is a flower, and [7] one with a crooked stem."*

With Bolio's rendition we are two flower species short of a count of nine, and obviously there is a pun inserted in the middle of the list. It is interesting that these flower forms could be counted over a period of 120 years from 806 BC, if, as I have assumed, Mercury accompanied Mars in these instances, even though the record of Mars is only shown for the instances after 747 BC. The last appearance of Mercury, in 686 BC, was aborted, of course.

"After these flowers sprang up, there were the vendors of fragrant odors, there was the mother of the flowers."

Fisher adds the following to Bolio's translation,

"These flowers that came out were the 'Comayeles' [Ah Con Mayeles, "the offerers of perfume"], *the mother of flowers."*

Roys notes,

"In the Tizimin and Mani versions we find: 'there was the house of the flowers.'"

... meaning that it (or something) was seen as a celestial apparition.

This is followed by yet additional complaints about rulers. But first let me point out again that both the "flowers" and the "fragrances" could only refer to a planet with a magnetic field and with an atmosphere. This could not be Mars. In fact, I will also suggest that the "house of flowers," mentioned above, is Jupiter, to which the text will get soon. On about June 9th Jupiter developed a coma and became a "house of flowers." "House of flowers" is the Mesoamerican name for a pyramid, actually, "flower mountain." The lightning bolt to the Sun did not leave Jupiter until July 14th.

"Then there sprang up the bouquet of the priest, the bouquet of the ruler, the bouquet of the captain;"
"... this was what the flower-king bore when he descended and nothing else, so they say. It was not bread that he bore."

"So they say," is a reflection on earthly rulers. Bolio has:

"When the latter [the flower God, Mercury] *came down he had no equal. 'Look at him,' they said, 'he does not spill his cargo.'"*

... which has a somewhat different sense. It suggests that the flower shapes were not dropped to Earth, or (more likely) that no electric contact was made with Earth. How Bolio arrived at this reading, which seems correct, is inexplicable. It would seem to suggest that the close overhead passages of Mercury were harmless to Central America -- in clear distinction to the destructiveness of Mars. Mercury may not have come very close, like Mars, but remained at a considerable distance. The last contact with Mercury, at any rate, was felt in North America in Alabama. (As developed in an earlier chapter.) From this, too, we would get the sense that the text has shifted entirely to a description of Mercury, and perhaps the reference to the satellites of Mars, above, is in error.

The sense to me is that the lines about the rulers are an editorial comment on the crop surpluses required by the ruling elite and the luxury goods being extracted from the citizens by the Maya ceremonial centers and through the long-distance trade which flourished since about 1500 BC. Unlike Egypt, and especially Mesopotamia, where feathers, metals, and precious stones were collected for the benefit of the gods of the temples, these goods (plus the food staples required to sustain both the trade functions and the leadership) were for the personal consumption and adornment of the rulers. This is similar to the situation in China. The rulers, in their shamanistic functions, were more important than the Gods. [note 27]

A few more lines on flowers, but now we turn to Jupiter:

"Then it was that the flower sprang up, wide open, to introduce the sin of Bolon-ti-ku [Jupiter].*"*
   "(After) three years was the time when he said he did not come to create Bolon Dzacab [Mars] as the god in hell."

The "sin of Bolon-ti-ku" is a plasma display, but initiated by Jupiter, not Mars. This text seems out of place and recalls the final event of the Venus nova, except that mention is made here of Mars, not of Venus (as in the Mediterranean). In other chapters I have spelled out the details of how this event was differently seen and understood in Mexico from how it was seen and understood in Europe and Asia.

The sentence makes it clear that Jupiter, who was still considered the reigning God, has decided that Mars would not be the agent of death for the current creation, "the God of hell." As the Sun's electric field expanded outward into the region of the planets, it not only caused Venus and Mercury to blaze like suns, but Jupiter suddenly needed to adjust to a completely different electric potential. The flower which "sprang up" to initiate ("introduce") the plasmoid is the coma and funnel-like plasma extensions above and below the poles of Jupiter. This is clearly shown in the earliest iconography of the Olmecs, after 650 BC.

The eruption of Jupiter was followed by a plasmoid bolt ("the sin") directed toward the Sun, and although it was understood to be directed at Venus by the people of the Mediterranean region, it was understood to be directed at Mars by the people of Mesoamerica -- a difference of a half day in seeing the plasmoid land (or not seeing but guessing).

The timing of the plasmoid event was carefully preserved in the original documents and is here quoted by the *Chilam Balam,* probably as a matter of pride in how the cycles of the Tzolkin constituted high science. But the numbers initially do not add up.

"(After) three years.."

Mars was in inferior conjunction with Earth on February 22, 687 BC (-686 Julian). If we add three solar years (of 365.24 days), or Tun years (of 360 days), or even three Tzolkin cycles (of 260 days) to the last date that Mars was seen, we will pass beyond the year of the Venus and Mercury nova event in 685 BC. The word "after," however, was added by the translator, Roys. The sentence should have the meaning of "in the third year," in effect another inclusive span of time.

I certainly don't think we are dealing in solar years here, but in Tzolkin cycles instead. If we add just two Tzolkin cycles of 260 days, we reach July 25, 685 BC on the Gregorian calendar -- the traditional day before New Year's day of the Maya and Olmecs, and the day when the lightning bolt of Jupiter landed at the Sun. This is no mere coincidence. The records of the past as maintained by the Olmecs and subsequent Maya have proven to be dead accurate.

This is also the third instance of inclusive counting in reporting an interval. Since we are dealing with Mesoamerican concepts and language, we have to recognize that the first Tzolkin cycle is completed on the day after Mars was last seen on February 22, which is 6.3.2.15.16 14-Uo 1-Cib on the Long Count (August 13 correlation). The day of 1-Cib has to be counted, for it completes the previous Tzolkin cycle. This is how "three years" is arrived at. The "three years" represent an interval of 520 days, two Tzolkin cycles.

This reference to the 520-day interval is the fifth instance of chronological details of the events of the year 685 BC.

The text about Nine Fragrances starts with a shift to Katun 9-Ahau, the next in order after Katun 11-Ahau, when the first recorded approach by Mars was made (in 747 BC). This would propose that the nine descendings of Mercury are a count of both planets, extending only from 747 BC (the close of the previous Katun 11-Ahau) to 687 BC (the end of Katun 5-Ahau), where for the first and the last visit he is properly identified as Bolon Dzacab, Mars. That would extend the visitations to a total period of 60 years, ending with the last visit in 687 BC. The date of 687 BC (actually -686) is the year which Velikovsky had identified as the year of the second Earth shock received from Mars, although actually this last contact was by Mercury.

Reconsidering now the comment about Mars, it might be suggested that it was the sacrifice of Venus (Quetzalcoatl) which appeased (or controlled) Jupiter. This could certainly have set the tone for human sacrifices for the next 2000 years. Quetzalcoatl, Venus, not only died, but was fully expected to return from the dead, as Jupiter had done a number of times. The reappearance of the coma of Jupiter, which had not been seen since circa 2150 BC, had demonstrated that. Jupiter, too, had died by fire.

Was the decision by Jupiter "not to end the world," or, as the "Chilam Balam" reads, "not to create Bolon Dzacab [Mars] as the god in hell," the promise of a new religion, a new religious practice, or a new contract between God and man? This certainly was the reaction in the Eastern Mediterranean region, as it was in China and India. Perhaps it was also understood this way by the later Maya who listened to the recital of this text that Kukulkan had been the savior of the world. This suggestion would be fully in line with the other couched references to Kukulkan -- Quetzalcoatl -- found in the remainder of the *Chilam Balam* text.

Saturn

The next section, which continues with descriptions of flowers, is, I feel, completely misplaced, perhaps placed here at an early time when the actual sequence of events was already no longer understood. I suspect that the following sections are from a source completely different from the text above.

What here follows is a portrait of Saturn from the earliest time in remotest antiquity. This is followed by a portrait of Jupiter. The portraits of the first two stationary Gods on their mats is deserved. The visitations made by Venus and Mars are ephemeral in comparison. It was Saturn and Jupiter who were the two supreme Gods who sat in rulership in the sky, a thousand years for Saturn, 4500 years for Jupiter, although during Jupiter's reign there were, as elsewhere in the world, numerous other Gods who acted as his agents or provide the role of intermediary. This is followed by a section which turns "rulership" over to the God of the Christians.

The portrait presented of Saturn is more than descriptive, for it records a sequence of events which is missing from the first description of Saturn at the start of this document: the changes from the time the bees blinded his face and the descent of fire and the rope, to the point of his demise at the hands of Jupiter in 3147 BC.

"Then descended Pizlimtec to take the flower [the root of the flower]*; he took the figure of a hummingbird with green plumage on its breast, when he descended."*

As will have been noticed, over the last few paragraphs the collection of events has been sorted topically into like images -- Mars followed water from heaven, and here the flower of Saturn in 4077 BC follows the flowers of

Mercury in the 7th century BC.

Pizlimtec is the God of music and song, or a human revered as a musician. So says Roys. This might also represent one of Peratt's plasma instabilities represented by the Kokopelli petroglyphs, the flute player, which have been carved as petroglyphs and painted on cliffs worldwide. Except, of course, that here he is transformed into a quetzal bird.

The hummingbird with green plumage can be equated with Venus, although as an overall description of the bird on top of the central tree of heaven, and thus the whole Saturnian Polar Configuration. But in the limited context of this description, the "descent" is more likely the visual lowering of Uranus as the Earth started to take up an orbit more directly below Saturn. That started to happen perhaps as early as 5800 BC. Because of the smaller size of Uranus compared to Saturn (even with the considerable offset from the north pole of Neptune), by 4077 BC Uranus had probably disappeared visually behind Saturn.

"Then he sucked the honey from the flower with nine petals."
  "Then the five-petaled flower took him for her husband, Thereupon the heart of the flower came forth to set itself in motion."

Uranus (if he is Pizlimtec) is male here. In the previous text he was identified as Saturn's sister. This suggests, of course, diverse sources for the *Chilam Balam* texts, or differing "readings" of the illustrations. The "heart of the flower" is Mars, which as we know from Mesopotamian and Egyptian texts, will start to lower toward Earth and wander away from the axis of Saturn.

The observation of a flower of nine or five petals, with Uranus lowering into the flower, taken together with the bees which initially wrapped the face of Oxlahun-ti-ku, Saturn, is a reminder of one of the oldest insignias of the pharaohs of Egypt, the bee and the sedge, neither of which has ever been explained as a symbolic source of power or majesty, and has only with difficulty been related by archaeologists to bees of Lower Egypt and the sedge of Upper Egypt (when it should be the other way around).

But a flower of nine and five petals can only be the much later plasma streams from Saturn to Mercury and thence to Mars, both located below Saturn, after Saturn went nova.

Or, following the next entry (see below), this might place the event (allowing Uranus to be seen as a distinct entity) much earlier than my estimate, well before the Earth had taken up a station below Saturn, for there is no other way to record the visual effect of seeing Uranus being lowered into Saturn. But it depends on how "and" and "then" are translated from the Mayan. We should also realize that the author was reading old books which conveyed little sense of the scope of time, so that 1000-year and 2000-year intervals passed unnoticed.

> *"Four-fold* [four branched] *was the plate of the flower, and Ah Kin Xocbiltun was set in the center."*

Ah Kin Xocbiltun is Pizlimtec, claims Roys. But Bolio translates the last line as, *"When the chalice of this flower was opened, the Sun* [Ah Kin Xocbiltun] *was within and in its middle his name could be read."* The glyph for Sun, "Kin," looks like a flower with four petals and a small central circular area, like a four-petaled daisy. The dot in the center is Mercury. The sign or hieroglyphic for "Sun" used elsewhere in the world (Egypt, Mesopotamia, China) is a circle with a central dot, but here we have the addition of four streams of plasma in arc mode impinging on Mercury and seen from below. It is amazing that the illustration from thousands of years ago was misread in this manner, but not totally unexpected.

> *"At this time Oxlahun-ti-ku* [Saturn] *came forth, but he did not know of the descent of the sin of the mat, when he came into his power."*
> *"The flower was his mat, the flower was his chair."*

The sin of the mat, again, is a plasma discharge to Earth. The flower mat resounds throughout other people's mythology too. The Gods of the Canopic jars of the dead pharaoh sit on a lotus flower, as do the creation Gods of the Hindus. The flower mat might be the rings of Saturn, or more likely is Mercury. I suspect that the previous line and most of what follows is placed here in the text to give reasons for why Saturn has to give up rulership at some point. The Maya of the *Chilam Balam* are notorious complainers.

> *"He sat in envy, he walked in envy. Envy was his plate, envy was his cup. There was envy in his heart, in his understanding, in his thought and in his speech."*
> *"Ribald and insolent was his speech during his reign. At that time his food cries out, his drink cries out, from the corner of his mouth when he eats, from the back of his claw* [hand] *when he bites his food."*
> *"He holds in his hand a piece of wood, he holds in his hand a stone."*

The stone is Venus, the piece of wood is Uranus.

> *"Mighty are his teeth; his face is that of Lahun Chan, as he sits."*

Lahun Chan is Mars as Ten Sky. The implied look is that of a red planet.

"Sin is (in) his face, in his speech, in his talk, in his understanding (and in) his walk."

"His eyes are blindfolded. He seizes, he demands as his right, the mat on which he sits during his reign."

"Forgotten is his father, forgotten is his mother, nor does his mother know her offspring."

As almost everywhere else in the world, there is no history before Saturn shows up. Thus he has no parents or has forgotten them. This more or less contradicts what is found on another page of the *Chilam Balam*, where, if not parents, at least there is a long lineage of sacred stones leading up to Oxlahun-ti-ku (Saturn), as the Christian God the Father. This is detailed in Book 11 of the *Chilam Balam*.

"The heart is on fire alone in the fatherless one who despises his father, in the motherless one."

His "heart is on fire" is an exact expression of the change to arc mode of Saturn, or descriptive of surface flames like are seen on the Sun.

"He shall walk abroad giving the appearance of one drunk, without understanding, in company with his father, in company with his mother."

The drunken walk is also recalled from Vedic sources which claim that Saturn traveled in a circle in the north sky. I cannot explain the sudden addition of the mother and father, unless this is another reference to Venus and Uranus.

"There is no virtue in him, there is no goodness in his heart, only a little on the tip of his tongue."

"He does not know in what manner his end is to come; nor does he know what will be the end of his reign, when the period of his power shall terminate."

Bolio translates the last few lines as:

"His heart burning only among the orphans, insulting his father, he must walk in the midst of the homeless, his countenance drunk, his understanding lost, to the place of his father and his mother. He has no kindness; there is no good in his heart; only a little bit on the tip of his tongue. He does not know how he must end up; he does not know what there will be at the end of his reign, or what is going to end in time with his power."

The drunken walk among the "orphans" and "homeless" catches the circular movement of Saturn ablaze in the middle of its satellites.

Before leaving this section, I should point out my suspicion that this extensive description of the faults of Saturn is starting to sound like a prophetic analog of a hoped-for fate for the Spanish invaders.

Jupiter

The following portrait is of Jupiter, but almost at once changes to a couched prediction of the return of Kukulkan.

"This is Bolon-ti-ku [Jupiter]."

This line reads as if it is a caption to an image in a codex.

"(Like that of) Bolon Chan [Lahun Chan is meant here] *is the face of the ruler of men, the two day* [or, second] *occupant of the mat and throne."*

"The two day occupant" is, as before, probably a misreading of "second occupant" or "second reign," which would place the description as starting in 3147 BC.

Roys thinks that "Bolon Chan" ("Nine Sky") is a transcription error, since this name occurs nowhere else in any Maya documents or inscriptions, and that "Luhun Chan" ("Ten-Sky") was meant. "Ten-Sky," as I suggested above, is Mars after 3147 BC. "The face of" presumably just means "looks like," it does not mean "is." The concept, in fact, is that the face of Jupiter looks red, like Mars. This was probably not true initially, since at first, from 3147 BC to circa 2900 BC, Jupiter was green (or, at least so was the lower plasma expulsion). But on its return as a giant entity in the sky in about 2550 BC, it certainly was red. Bolio accepts Nine Sky as meaning "nine faces" and ends up with a reading of:

"These Nine gods ['Bolon-ti-ku,' Jupiter] *will be manifested in nine faces* ['Bolon Chan'] *of Men-Kings, of the mat of the Second time, of the throne of the Second Time, came inside the 'beast Ahau Katun.'"*

The *Chilam Balam* continues with the following, where Roys reads "beast" as "three":

"He came in Katun 3 Ahau."

I initially did not think that Jupiter was meant by "he" here. I thought the author was talking about Kukulkan and referring to the nova event of Venus in 685 BC, which falls in Katun 3-Ahau. But Bolio's "mat of the second time" or Roys's use of "two day throne" is probably meant as the second reign (not to be confused with creations), and thus the reign of Jupiter. What we are then being told here is that Jupiter reappeared in 685 BC in Katun 3-Ahau. That's true.

> *"After that there will be another lord of the land who will establish the law of another Katun, after the law of the lord of Katun 3-Ahau shall have run its course."*
>
> *"At that time there shall be few children; then there shall be mourning among the Itza who speak our language brokenly."*
>
> *"Industry (and) vigor finally take the place, in the first Tun (of the new Katun), of the sin of the Itza who speak our language brokenly."*

The first Tun is the first 360-day period of the next Katun. It could be the next Katun after 685 BC, or it could be any Katun in the future. "Industry" had traditionally been attributed to the enterprising Itza.

> *"It is Bolon-ti-ku [Jupiter] who shall come to his end (with) the law of the lord of Katun 3-Ahau."*

Take note of the three references to Katun 3-Ahau (and more below), and especially the line, *"After that there will be another lord of the land who will establish the law of another Katun, after the law of the lord of Katun 3-Ahau shall have run its course."* This is a veiled reference to the return of Quetzalcoatl, Kukulkan of the Maya, who disappeared in Katun 3-Ahau, but over the next few paragraphs this is turned into the God of the Christians. The "lord of Katun 3-Ahau" is Venus -- Kukulkan -- who shall, in time, that is, at some time in the future, end the reign of Jupiter, substituting another -- but not himself. This will fit history as it was played out with the arrival of the Spanish.

The End of History

A few lines of prediction, in effect incorporating the 16th-century condition of the conversion of the Maya to Christianity, complete the section. The prediction of another flood and the descent of Jesus on a cloud are perfectly in line with the history of the elder Gods.

> *"Then those of the lineage of the noble chiefs shall come into their own, with the other men of discretion and with those of the lineage of the*

chiefs."

"Their faces had been trampled on the ground, and they had been overthrown by the unrestrained upstarts of the day of the Katun, the son of evil and the offspring of the harlot, who were born when their day dawned in Katun 3-Ahau."

This is the fourth reference to Katun 3-Ahau. Some of these lines repeat text from the section "Interrogation of the Chiefs" elsewhere in the "Chilam Balam."

Bolio renders this a little more cohesively, although no clearer, as:

"When the Katun has ended, one will see the lineage of the noble Princes appear, and new wise men, and the descendants of the Princes whose faces were crumbled against the ground, who were insulted by the rage of the time by the crazy ones of their Katun, by the son of evil who called them "children of indolence"; those who were born when the Earth awoke, inside the Three Ahau Katun."

"When the Earth awoke in Katun 3-Ahau" is an interesting concept, and stands as the only reference to a change in the religious philosophy of Mesoamerica in the 7th century BC, although it is clearly demonstrated in the alignments of the ceremonial centers after 600 BC. No new alignments were ever added (except for additional alignments for 2349 BC).

Clearly also, in the above quoted paragraph, "those" refers to the Princes. In Roys's rendition it is not clear who "who were born" refers to -- it could be read as the "son of evil" and the "offspring of the harlot." Interestingly, this sort of language is to be found in the condemnations of Biblical prophets. The scribe thus betrays his Christian upbringing. From the very start of the Spanish overlordship the children of chiefs and officials were separated from their parents and educated separately.

"When their day dawned" becomes, with Bolio, "when the Earth awoke." That in effect suggests a "fourth creation" as yet to come. [note 28]

Roys's text continues with an "end of creation" scenario:

"Thus shall end the power of those who are two-faced toward our Lord God."

"But when the law of the Katun shall have run its course, then God will bring about a great deluge again which will be the end of the world."

"When this is over, then our Lord Jesus Christ shall descend over the Valley of Jehoshaphat beside the town of Jerusalem where he redeemed us with his holy blood."

"He shall descend on a great cloud to bear true testimony that he was once obliged to suffer, stretched out on a cross of wood."

"Then shall descend in his great power and glory the true God who created heaven and earth and everything on earth. He shall descend to level off the world for the good and the bad, the conquerors (and) the captives."

Typically, once again there will be a new creation, for God will level off the world. The promised deluge, however, never came.

Recap of Book 10

It should be clear to the reader that this Book of the *Chilam Balam* is only tendentiously in chronological order, and, from our perspective, the mark is missed. The copyist did not have counts of Baktuns (periods of 20 Katuns) available or neglected them. This seems odd, for the texts of the Temple of the Cross at Palenque correctly place past events in the proper Baktun. Otherwise we would have to assume that, for example, the reason the events of 1492 BC and the events after 2349 BC (the "third creation") were listed in reverse order was simply to adhere to the late Maya historical format of lumping all events of the same-named Katun together.

Some chronological order exists, as in how the prehistory (the "second creation") is grouped at the beginning and in correct order (and expanded on near the end), and the events of the 8th and 7th century BC are placed near the end (with the fall of the Absu in 2349 BC inexplicably added). And another form is used also. Events are sorted into activities and like imagery. Thus, near the end, all the flower episodes are grouped together.

The conclusion is reached compositionally, calling up the imagery of Kukulkan, starting with the event of the Sun going off its course in 685 BC. The ending reads as a subtle attempt to simultaneously satisfy the politics of the new Christian overlords and not counter the traditions of the Maya citizens.

I have appended lists of Katuns for the time period of 3147 BC through 668 BC, with the events inserted. [note 29]

Special thanks to M Harris for corrections.

Endnotes

Note 1 --

The Maya, as well as other Mesoamerican people, certainly recognized the continuous progress of time along a single axis, as we do. So perhaps it would be more accurate to say that time was conceived of as the delivery of the separate Katuns, which carried with them certain qualities which predetermined the conditions of the world when a Katun arrived. This would be similar to recognizing the seasons of the year as a repeating cycle, where each month brings with it certain weather conditions. The "weather" of the Maya Katun cycle extended over twenty-year periods.

Note 2 --

Munro S. Edmonson, in "Some Postclassic Questions About The Classic Maya" (*Fifth Palenque Round Table*, 1978), writes about this:

"The Colonial texts produce the impression that their obscurity may have been partially designed to keep Maya traditions from the Spanish. They were not at all intended to be secret from the Maya peasantry, who are frequently apostrophized directly. And there are even now in Quintana Roo Mayas who can read and understand them."

But he immediately qualifies his opinion by pointing to an earlier tradition:

"It seems to me quite possible therefore that the glyphic texts of the Classic period could have contained a substantial esoteric and metaphoric element without necessarily impeding their intelligibility for the commoners and laymen to whom they must have been in part addressed. A certain deviousness and indirection may well be part of Mayan tradition. Flies are ancestors; the moon is the end; the sun is the beginning; stalks are lineages; monkeys are peasants."

My feeling is that Book 10 includes very little metaphorical material, although Book 11 and two other short pages of the *Chilam Balam* (dealing with earlier history) do, at a severe cost in understanding.

Amazingly, Richard Luxton in translation and commentary in *The Book of Chumayel* (1996), interprets all of Book 10 as a highly metaphorical poetical discourse on the political and social changes in the Yucatan in the late 16th century AD, based on a conflict and resolution between two calendars -- personified by Luxton as "The Thirteen" and "The Nine."

Book 11 does not escape this treatment either. I think this is nonsense created from the inability to make any sense of the texts. Luxton also frequently points up puns which make no sense. However, he also has the ability to clear up many strange words, like "opilla" and "expleo." More on these in the following chapter.

Note 3 --

More recent archaeological finds have placed the first Maya monumental construction at 150 to 50 BC, and in some isolated cases as early as 800 BC (Takalik Abaj, in clay) and 600 BC (El Mirador, in stone).

Monuments raised in Palenque (in circa AD 700) present dates before 3114 BC, note celestial events in 2360 and 2305 BC, and record the birth of a "prehistoric king" of Palenque in 993 BC.

The first Tzolkin date inscriptions were in use at the Zapotec site of San José Mogote in the Oaxaca region by about 600 BC. By 400 BC the Tzolkin and Haab calendars were in use at Monte Alban (Oaxaca). The earliest Olmec long-count is depicted on Stele C from Tres Zapotes as 32 BC.

Note 4 --

The *Popol Vuh* clearly notes that the authors had used four source books, and, in fact, the *Popol Vuh* spends more than half of the text with descriptions of events from the first two books, called "The Dawn of Life" and "Our Place in the Shadows." This is not the case here for the *Chilam Balam*, although Book 11, and an additional page do specifically source these two.

Most of the information for Book 10 of the *Chilam Balam* seems to rely on abstracts from the last two books mentioned by the *Popol Vuh*, the book called "The Light that Came from Beside the Sea" and the book called "The Council Book." It would be expected that the Maya had already consolidated events by same-named Katuns, for this represents the layout of Book 10. It would also be expected that the significant event of 2349 BC, the fall of the Absu, would be sourced from a separate book. But this event is inexplicably split up to different sections of the text. Book 11 of the *Chilam Balam* treats the event of 2349 BC separately.

Note 5 --

In the *Popol Vuh* the tribal gods of the Quiche turn to stone when the Sun first shines. The Quiche continue to feed these stones with blood.

Note 6 --

Considering the bees as satellites holds if Saturn (and later Jupiter) were close enough to Earth to be seen clearly. There are enough references to the satellites of both these planets among "mythological" sources from other parts of the world to confirm that this would have been the case.

I have only seen limited "bee iconography" among Olmec carvings or stelae, but there are some Maya murals depicting bees. Bees recur, however, in other pages of the *Chilam Balam* dealing with the history of much more remote times. There is an instance of wasps being used as weapons in the *Popol Vuh*, but this is likely a recollection of a particularly busy meteor shower.

Note 7 --

The prominent satellites of Saturn (those discovered before the 20th century AD) number 7. Adding Uranus, Neptune, Mercury, Mars, and Venus, and Saturn itself, the number adds up to 13. I originally (before 2010) excluded Neptune (as not visible) and Mercury (not discovered by me until 2009), and added Iapetus (at an orbital radius of 3,561,300 km) and Phoebe (orbiting at 12,952,000 km) to make up the count of 13. But I have removed these two distant satellites from consideration. Venus, although strictly a satellite, is not listed below, although included in the count. This is the count after 4077 BC when Venus was expelled from Saturn.

```
Moon         Radius (km)   Mass (kg)   Distance (km)   Discoverer   Date
-------      -----------   ---------   -------------   ----------------

(7 satellites known before the 19th century, in order...)

Mimas          196         .380e+20       185,520      W. Herschel 1789
Enceladus      250         .840e+20       238,020      W. Herschel 1789
Tethys         530        7.55e+20        294,660      G. Cassini 1684
Dione          560       10.5e+20         377,400      G. Cassini 1684
Rhea           765       24.9e+20         527,040      G. Cassini 1672
Titan        2,575      1350.e+20       1,221,850      C. Huygens 1655
Hyperion 205x130x110     .177e+20       1,481,000      W. Bond 1848
```

Seven is the traditional number recognized in antiquity, as, for example, the "seven helpers of the king (Osiris)" in Egyptian mythology.

It was known in more remote antiquity among the Olmecs that Neptune was one of the stack of planets as related in Book 11 of the *Chilam Balam* -- See the chapter "The Earlier Olmec Record." Then the planets (Uranus, Neptune, Saturn, Venus, Mars) plus the "seven helpers of the king" add up to

12. It has long been my suspicion that Mercury should probably be added to the "Saturnian planets" to substitute for the globe identified as Venus and called "Sovereign Plumed Serpent" in the *Popol Vuh*.

The *Popol Vuh* identifies the northern planets as five in number during the time of the negotiations between the southern ball plasmoids and the northern planets (all within the period ending in 8347 BC, 2500 years after 10,900 BC), but the *Popol Vuh* seems to misidentify Mercury as Venus -- both were white spheres -- calling Mercury "Sovereign Plumed Serpent." This suggests that Venus only came into existence much later -- in 4077 BC.

Note 8 --

See Linda Schele and David Freidel, *A Forest of Kings* (1990). The temple images at Palenque are named as the "Tablet of the Foliated Cross," the "Tablet of the Cross (the World Tree)," and the "Tablet of the Sun (the War Stack)" -- in three separate temples of the same names, of which the "Temple of the Cross" is the central structure.

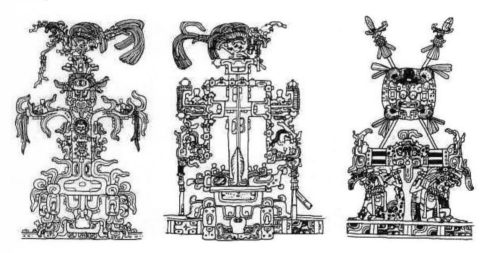

[Images: Palenque, circa AD 700. "Tablets of the Temple of the Foliated Cross," the "Temple of the Cross," and the "Temple of the Sun." After Linda Schele and David Freidel "A Forest of Kings" (1990).]

The tablets above are flanked with figures of the ruler Chan-Bahlum and his (dead) father. Both the accompanying texts and the iconography make it clear that the three panels are dedicated, in order (left to right), to Mars, Venus, and Jupiter. These are the "Palenque Triad" of gods, named GII, GI, and GIII.

The aged God L (GIII) on the left of the third panel above is Jupiter. God

GI-prime, who is seen on the right of the panel, is Saturn, the father of GI (Venus). This last panel would seem to represent the lines of electrons connected to the far south as spears, not unlike the North African depiction of Neith of the Arrows. The two older Gods assigned to this would be appropriate, since this predated everything else, 5000 years ago.

Note 9 --

I have assumed a synchronous rotation Earth and Saturn, which means that in effect Saturn's period was 24 hours, not 10.6 hours which is the period of rotation today. The speeding up of the rotation of Saturn can probably be justified from the loss in orbital rotational momentum due to its later relocation to 9.5 AU.

What would certainly account for the "beating of things with wood and stone" would be a misalignment of the axis of Earth and Saturn, which I have estimated at about 15 degrees. Saturn would be seen as revolving in a circle of about 30 degrees diameter around the center of the Earth's polar axis on a daily basis.

Note 10 --

Wal Thornhill has suggested that the weak magnetic field of Mercury is probably due to its wildly eccentric orbit. This would also apply to Venus before it circularized.

Note 11 --

The easily seen satellites of Jupiter number 4. These are in excess of 3000 km in diameter and were noted by Galileo. The next four in size and prominence, ranging from 50 to 200 km in diameter were discovered by the beginning of the 20th century AD. The satellites are listed below in order of distance from Jupiter. There are many more small and odd satellites.

It should be suggested that the satellites of Jupiter seen in antiquity consisted only of those relatively close to the planet, large enough to be seen, and not at extreme distances. That suggests the numbered satellites listed above. Since Thebe was not discovered until 1979, it might be left off the list. Then "the nine" would consist of 8 numbered satellites plus Jupiter. This follows the same reasoning as for Saturn.

A number of mythological sources (Asia and Africa) claim nine satellites or Gods who accompany Jupiter. Maybe Thebe was included. The last four are all at 10,000,000 km or more, and are unlikely to be part of the set.

```
          Distance  Radius   Mass
Satellite   (km)     (km)     (kg)   Discoverer  Date   comment
---------  --------  ------  -------  ----------  -----  -------
Metis       128,000     20   9.56e16  Synnott     1979   close in, small
Adrastea    129,000     10   1.91e16  Jewitt      1979   close in, small
Amalthea    181,000     98   7.17e18  Barnard     1892   1
Thebe       222,000     50   7.77e17  Synnott     1979   too late
Io          422,000   1815   8.94e22  Galileo     1610   2
Europa      671,000   1569   4.80e22  Galileo     1610   3
Ganymede  1,070,000   2631   1.48e23  Galileo     1610   4
Callisto  1,883,000   2400   1.08e23  Galileo     1610   5
Himalia  11,480,000     93   9.56e18  Perrine     1904   6
Elara    11,737,000     38   7.77e17  Perrine     1905   7
Lysithea 11,720,000     18   7.77e16  Nicholson   1938   8
Leda     11,094,000      8   5.68e15  Kowal       1974   smallest
Pasiphae 23,500,000     25   1.91e17  Melotte     1908   too far
Sinope   23,700,000     18   7.77e16  Nicholson   1914   too far
Carme    22,600,000     20   9.56e16  Nicholson   1938   too far
Ananke   21,200,000     15   3.82e16  Nicholson   1951   too far
```

Note 12 --

See Linda Schele and David Freidel, *A Forest of Kings* (1990), and *Maya Cosmos* (1993).

The quetzal plumage is a plasma connection between Venus and Saturn. If the connection were in arc mode it would be a display in green or violet, or at any rate brilliantly colored -- like the feathers of the quetzal bird (*Pharomachrus mocinno*). At a later time it would be the green plasma tail of Venus.

Note 13 --

The two-headed serpent uses Venus as one head and the Sun as the other. This is an image of the plasmoid bolt of Jupiter as seen in July of 685 BC. The vision serpent is distinct from this and might be a representation of the last red ring in the sky, the snake Apep of the Egyptians. Alternately it might represent a polar plasma plume which showed periodically, and ended in a ball form with a feather headdress.

Note 14 --

Although it is possible that the "nine" of "Bolon Dzacab" refers to the rising of Mars to Saturn, which is specifically noted by the *Chilam Balam*, it is more likely that the "nine" refers to the nine close approaches of Mars in the era of 806 BC to 687 BC.

Note 15 --

It is just as possible that the contact was much closer to Mesoamerica, for it could be suggested that the north magnetic pole was located at or near Hudson Bay at this time. That would still have the location of the plasma contact be viewed in the northwest direction from England, in the northeast from Mongolia, but seen in the wrong direction from China (although Chinese myth is fuzzy on this). But the plasma connection to Saturn would present itself as directly over the North Pole as seen from Northern Pakistan and India -- and thus without the curvature as seen from other locations.

This view from India might be justified from the extensive use of really giant swings as religious monuments at a number of locations. Any plasma connection in glow mode would look to have well-defined left and right edges. As I have mentioned earlier, the plasma stream may have looked as if there was very little change in the width from its lowest to its highest location.

See, in this regard, Willard Van De Bogart's essay presented at [The Giant Swing]. He writes:

"In India the swing has been used for thousands of years with its early beginnings going back to the aboriginal cultures which populated the Indian sub-continent long before the Hindu culture began. The swing has been used in fertility rites, religious rituals and as a symbol for the cosmological understanding of the universe and developed as a way to celebrate the beginnings of the New Year by cultures worldwide."

Note 16 --

Schele and Freidel, *A Forest of Kings* (1990), endnote 33 to page 246. To repeat a previous endnote: Ballcourt A-IIb at Copan in Honduras was built during the sixth or seventh century AD, and soon remodeled. The remodeling preserved three central alley markers.

A tree is shown on the outside area of the north and south markers. Suspended from each tree is a large playing ball. The tree of the north is labeled "Nine Successions"; the tree of the south is labeled "Seven Successions." If, as I suspect, the trees represent the plasma plumes of the north and south, then we have here an inventory of how many times the *axis mundi* reappeared. It would be appropriate to reappear more frequently in the north, since the north magnetic pole would facilitate a larger movement of electrons.

The dates for the return of the directional trees are as follows:

- (1) after 3147 BC (trees mentioned)
- (2) after 2349 BC (trees mentioned)
- (3) after 2193 BC
- (4) after 1492 BC (trees mentioned)
- (5) after 1442 BC
- (6) after 747 BC
- (7) after 686 BC
- (8) after 685 BC

The date of 686 BC is not at all certain. I added the date of 685 BC to the list. There was no change in the Earth's orbit in 686 or 685 BC, but the electric field of the Sun changed significantly in 685 BC. I also have the suspicion that there might have been two additional changes in the orbit of Earth between 2349 BC and 2193 BC, which have remained unrecorded. The name "Nine Successions" is one more "succession" than noted in the records at Palenque, where the first northern plasma plume is called "north-eight-house."

Note 17 --

The choppy transliterations of the dedicatory texts of monuments of the Maya seldom are very clear on purposes, except to prove the exceptional nature of the Long Count calendar. In this case, too, it is unknown why the "raised-up-sky north-eight-house GI" had to be invoked.

In the quoted text, the glyph "GI" is used with other modifiers, and it is uncertain what it would mean. It could be a possessive, "the eight-house of Venus." This would match the first recognition by the Egyptians of Venus flying around the tree of Biblos in the north. It could also read as "raised-up-sky north-house eight-GI," but GI (Venus) only shows up seven times near Earth, as I will detail in this text, not eight.

Maya representations of Gods as face-glyphs are called God GI, GII, GIII, and God A, B, C, etc., by archaeologists because it has not been easy to identify the faces with well-known and named Gods. But based solely on iconography I can readily associate some of these numbered and alphabetically identified face-glyphs with the planets as follows:

```
named God          planet
B, GI              Venus
D, GI-prime        Saturn
K, GII             Mars
L, GIII            Jupiter
```

Note 18 --

[*Image: The four flames which surround the cosmos, an illustration from the Egyptian* Book of the Dead.]

Note 19 --

If Hathor in Egyptian iconography and literature can be identified with electric contacts by Venus, then the occurrence of the "Seven Hathors" (as sculpted, for example, at the Roman Period temple of Denderah in Egypt) might signify a similar recognition of the repeating nature of interferences by Venus.

In Copic "Hathor" is the name for the seven stars of the Pleiades.

Note 20 --

In the texts at the Maya Temples of the Cross in Palenque (AD 690), the Moon, although born before creation according to the texts (in 3121 BC) and bearing planetary children in 2360 BC, becomes "ruler" ("crowns herself") in 2305 BC. After correction (see below), this date would fall in a Katun 9-Ahau. Saturn is her husband; he is also born before the retrocalculated nominal date of the second creation of 3114 BC. The birth of the Moon can be attributed to seeing Jupiter on a nearby outer orbit before it clashed with the Saturnian system.

The specific seasonal dates used at Palenque are likely selected for their numerological value (so think some archaeologists), although I would think that probably the correct era was used -- that is, the correct Baktun and the correct Katun. The inscriptions were meant to be seen by local Ahobs and visiting dignitaries from other Maya ceremonial centers -- all of whom where literate and acquainted with the written history of the world.

That the three planets were "born" in 2360 BC would suggest that they became visible at this time, that is, as star-like objects, but more importantly it would mean that they were freed from the obscuring Absu into which the ecliptic dipped for half of each year before 2349 BC. This could also suggest that the Absu had clearly disappeared at this time. As I have pointed out in another chapter, the date of 2360 BC is incorrect by 22 years. It should be 2337 BC, which places it after the "flood of Noah" of 2349 BC by 12 years. The "flood of Noah" is the start of the removal of the Absu from the skies.

The "corrections" noted in the text are based on the assumption that the Palenque dates were retrocalculated on the basis of a 365.24-day solar year, whereas the Olmec who instituted the Long Count originally used a 360-day solar year. Thus the retrocalculations place all the calculated Baktuns and Katuns too far into the past by 5.24 days per year since 747 BC.

The crowning of the Moon as Ahau in 2305 BC should be corrected by 22 years to 2283 BC, which, by the way, is close to the date that the Moon "Shun" joins the Chinese emperor (God) Yao (Jupiter) on the throne (2287 BC traditionally, corrected to 2277 BC).

Note 21 --

But note that in the chapter, "The Day of Kan," I identify Monte Alto in Guatemala, dating to about 2000 BC, as an earlier important ceremonial center. Monte Alto was destroyed or left behind after (what looks like) 520 years of use, to be replaced by San Lorenzo in about 1440 BC.

Note 22 --

An ephemeris program needs to be set at 2000 BC to show the Pleiades aligned with the intersection of the equatorial and the ecliptic. Except for the horizon and zero degrees longitude lines, this is the condition of the sky in June of 685 BC and anytime earlier. This would not be true after July of 685 BC, when the intersection had moved 15 degrees west along the horizon.

Note 23 --

The sweet smells are quoted by Velikovsky from the *Papyrus Anastasi*, Ginsberg's *Legends*, and the *Vedas*. It is reminiscent of the smell of the exhaust of diesel engines, thus the burning of hydrocarbons.

Note 24 --

July 26 is the day after July 25, and therefore is New Year's Day. July 25 represents the overhead passage of the Sun at Edzna in the Eastern Yucatan, as also at Teotihuacan in the Central Valley of Mexico. Both are located at a latitude of 19 degrees and 41 minutes north.

At the time of the Spanish invasion, after AD 1556, July 26th was rotating through the days Kan, Muluc, Ix, and Cauac (using the August 13 correlation), reaching the day of Kan on July 26, 1557 (Gregorian), as Landa reported. But it would not have mattered what Tzolkin day-name fell on July 26th. It was known as "the day of Kan" -- as the day the world was destroyed and recreated.

Note 25 --

I attempted to apply any number of corrective measures to the calendar calculations, but only the substitution of 365.24 days for the 360 days, as assumed both by us and by the Classical Era Maya for the period prior to 747 BC, yielded results. Thus the scribal "error correction" for the day of Kan was accomplished well after 685 BC.

In researching the "day of Kan" over a span of 5000 years I became aware of how relatively easy it was to access the Long Count for particular combinations of the Tzolkin and Haab.

Note 26 --

We should be able to check locations of Mars and Mercury with an ephemeris program; however, fully accurate results cannot be expected, for even though the Earth's orbit was determined by 747 BC, the orbit of Mercury changed in 686 BC. The location of the planet Mercury for the date of March 23, -686, the second Earth shock, is "off" by some days, as I show in Appendix B, "The Celestial Mechanics." Since this is likely to have been the last alteration of the orbit of Mercury, it can be expected to be close to today's values in that instance only -- which represents the starting position (in fact, the aphelion) of the current orbit.

Earlier positions cannot be found for the simultaneous appearance of Mars and Mercury. This is to be expected for an ephemeris based on the current tight orbit of Mercury. It is amazing, yet expected, that a point of coincidence was found with the orbit of Earth in 686 BC. If the earlier orbit of Mercury was simply an elongated version of today's orbit, that is, the same orbit with extreme eccentricity, then the orbital period would be the same, although the location of the planet at any point in time along its orbit would vary considerably.

Certainly both Mars and Mercury would appear together in the skies on occasion, since Mercury (today) has a fairly short orbital period, and even

Mars would pass Earth approximately every two years. An inspection of the series of the Julian (ephemeris) years 748, 733, 718, 703, and 688 BC, shows Mercury near the sky location of Mars in four out of five years in March or February. It does not happen in 688 BC but happens two years later. (The series was developed by repeatedly subtracting 15 years from astronomical year -747.)

I am adding this note only to demonstrate that the condition of the simultaneous appearance of Mars and Mercury is very possible. In all these cases an ephemeris program will show Mars outside the orbit of Earth and both Mars and Earth in line with the Sun.

Note 27 --

Schele and Freidel (in *A Forest of Kings*) are of the opinion that the accumulation of wealth, resulting from harvest surpluses and wider trading, which had come into effect after 300 BC (although earlier dates could very well be suggested), constituted an unprecedented crisis among the Maya, whose social interactions were based on egalitarianism. They write of "a culture which regarded the accumulation of wealth as an aberration," and note:

"We know that the problem the Maya were trying to resolve was one of social inequality because that is precisely the state of affairs that the institution of ahau defines as legitimate, necessary, and intrinsic to the order of the cosmos."

Acceptance of this social sinkhole for wealth did not keep Maya scribes from complaining incessantly, as we see in the *Chilam Balam* texts, both in this Book and elsewhere.

The surpluses of maize, by the way, are astounding. Typically, in well-watered territory, only one-third of the corn crop was needed to feed the family of the farmer year round -- a family which could easily consist of 10 people. That means 20 people could be fed for a year from the remaining crop.

Note 28 --

If we assume that the "lineage of the noble chiefs" and those whose "faces had been trampled on the ground" represent the orthodox upholders of the relationship between the Maya and the cosmos, then the "unrestrained upstarts of the day and of the Katun," who had inflicted the overthrow of the orthodox nobility, most likely represent a second wave of religious philosophy entering the Yucatan from the west.

The archaeological record of the Classical Era shows the arrival of emissaries from Teotihuacan (in Mexico) some time before AD 700. They bring the flayed human face shield and the dart thrower, which were in general use in the Valley of Mexico at that time. The Maya adopted these to some degree, but it is more likely that they adopted aspects of the religious philosophy and practices of the westerners.

Of course the Maya had already adopted both the temple mound and the script and time keeping of the Olmecs by circa 100 BC (and possibly much earlier). And the later invasion by the Itza, after AD 900, certainly brought with them a religion of hope for the return of Quetzalcoatl which differed from the concept about Venus which the Classical Maya had already established.

In the main text I have postulated the changes in attitudes toward the older Gods in China, India, and the Middle East after 600 BC, which spread in waves of new religions. I have suggested that the same would have happened in Mesoamerica, and would propose that the first and primary epicenter was Olmec Veracruz.

It could therefore be suggested that, as elsewhere in the world, a number of different solutions came forward. We certainly see this in Central Mexico in the period after 600 BC, with new interpretations of the control of the Gods established at intervals through to the time of the Aztecs.

We have no clear idea from the text of the *Chilam Balam* of when new philosophies were introduced which would have caused the overthrow of the older nobility, although the Itza are repeatedly blamed for "introducing idolatry" to the Yucatan, possibly to cast blame away from the indigenous Maya. But what is interesting is that this is referenced to the events Katun 3-Ahau -- in 685 BC. Since Katun 3-Ahau would repeat, any number of other incidents could be tied to this. This history certainly holds Katun 3-Ahau as significant.

Note 29 --

The following lists every one of the ending years of Katun 9-Ahau, 7-Ahau, 5-Ahau, and 3-Ahau. I have listed the years as "BC" rather than in their astronomical nomenclature. The Katuns all start 20 years earlier. Where I skip a range of Katuns, I have placed a series of dots.

The corrections listed on the right of some lines are based on the assumption that the Olmecs had listings of Baktuns and Katuns available which reflected solar years, so that a Baktun would be 400 solar years, and a Katun would be 20 solar years, without regard to the actual length of the year. Thus the corrections below are based on subtracting 6 Baktuns (2400 years) from 747 BC to arrive at 3147 as the year of the end of the "Era of the Gods."

The correction is thus **3147 - 400 * Baktuns - 20 * Katuns**. The corrected years are shown as "sb" -- "should be."

- Before 3114 BC (0.0.0.0.0) sb: 3147 BC
  -- Oxlahun-ti-ku (Saturn) is blindfolded.
  -- Bolon-ti-ku (Jupiter) attacks Saturn.
  -- Nine-Lives (Mars) rises 9 times.
- Katun 11-Ahau ends in 3055 BC (0.3.0.0.0)
- Katun 9-Ahau ends in 3033 BC (0.4.0.0.0) sb: 3087-3067
  -- Ten-Sky (Mars) arrives.
- Katun 7-Ahau ends in 3015 BC (0.5.0.0.0)
- Katun 5-Ahau ends in 2996 BC (0.6.0.0.0)
- Katun 3-Ahau ends in 2975 BC (0.7.0.0.0)
  ....
- Katun 9-Ahau ends in 2779 BC (0.17.0.0.0)
- Katun 7-Ahau ends in 2759 BC (0.18.0.0.0)
- Katun 5-Ahau ends in 2739 BC (0.19.0.0.0)
- Katun 3-Ahau ends in 2720 BC (1.0.0.0.0)
  ....
- Katun 9-Ahau ends in 2523 BC (1.10.0.0.0) sb: 2567-2547
  -- The Third Creation
  -- Jupiter clears the asteroid belt and develops a coma
- Katun 7-Ahau ends in 2503 BC (1.11.0.0.0)
- Katun 5-Ahau ends in 2483 BC (1.12.0.0.0)
- Katun 3-Ahau ends in 2463 BC (1.13.0.0.0) sb: 2507-2487
  -- Jupiter loses its tail for 20 years.
  ....
- Katun 4-Ahau ends in 2345 BC (1.19.0.0.0) sb: 2387-2367
- Katun 2-Ahau ends in 2325 BC (2.0.0.0.0) sb: 2367-2347
  -- Fall of the Absu (misplaced below).
  -- (no Katun listed:) Jupiter develops a coma again.
- Katun 13-Ahau ends in 2305 BC (2.1.0.0.0) sb: 2347-2327
  -- (no exact Katun:) Moon appears.
  -- (Palenque) Moon first appears, 2336.8 BC
- Katun 11-Ahau ends in 2286 BC (2.2.0.0.0) sb: 2327-2307
- Katun 9-Ahau ends in 2266 BC (2.3.0.0.0) sb: 2307-2287
  -- (Palenque:) Moon "lets blood," 2302.3 BC
  -- (Annals of Shu) Moon birth 2301 BC
  -- Fall of the Absu (misplaced event).
- Katun 7-Ahau ends in 2246 BC (2.4.0.0.0) sb: 2287-2267
  -- (Palenque:) Moon "crowns herself," 2282.6 BC
  -- (Annals of Shu) Moon employed 2288 BC

- Katun 5-Ahau ends in 2226 BC (2.5.0.0.0) sb: 2267-2247
- Katun 3-Ahau ends in 2206 BC (2.6.0.0.0)
....
- Katun 8-Ahau ends in 2128 BC (2.10.0.0.0) sb: 2167-2147
  -- Yao dies 2150 BC
  -- Gudea, brightness of Ningursu, ca 2150 BC
  -- Shu, celestial event" of 2155 BC
  -- Death of Abraham at 199, 2150 BC
  -- Jupiter in flames -- "fire on high"
- Katun 6-Ahau ends in 2108 BC (2.11.0.0.0) sb: 2147-2127
- Katun 4-Ahau ends in 2089 BC (2.12.0.0.0) sb: 2127-2107
- Katun 2-Ahau ends in 2069 BC (2.13.0.0.0) sb: 2107-2087
- Katun 13-Ahau ends in 2050 BC (2.14.0.0.0) sb: 2087-2067
- Katun 11-Ahau ends in 2030 BC (2.15.0.0.0) sb: 2067-2047
  -- Rockenbach, Tower of Babel, 2060 BC
- Katun 9-Ahau ends in 2010 BC (2.16.0.0.0) sb: 2047-2027
- Katun 7-Ahau ends in 1990 BC (2.17.0.0.0) sb: 2027-2007
- Katun 5-Ahau ends in 1971 BC (2.18.0.0.0)
- Katun 3-Ahau ends in 1951 BC (2.19.0.0.0)
....
- Katun 9-Ahau ends in 1754 BC (3.9.0.0.0)
- Katun 7-Ahau ends in 1734 BC (3.10.0.0.0)
- Katun 5-Ahau ends in 1714 BC (3.11.0.0.0)
- Katun 3-Ahau ends in 1695 BC (3.12.0.0.0)
....
- Katun 9-Ahau ends in 1497 BC (4.2.0.0.0) sb: 1527-1507
- Katun 7-Ahau ends in 1478 BC (4.3.0.0.0) sb: 1507-1487
  -- Ah Uuc Chek Nal (Venus) rubs the Earth.
- Katun 5-Ahau ends in 1458 BC (4.4.0.0.0)
- Katun 3-Ahau ends in 1438 BC (4.5.0.0.0)
....
- Katun 9-Ahau ends in 1241 BC (4.15.0.0.0)
- Katun 7-Ahau ends in 1221 BC (4.16.0.0.0)
- Katun 5-Ahau ends in 1202 BC (4.17.0.0.0)
- Katun 3-Ahau ends in 1182 BC (4.18.0.0.0)
....
- Katun 9-Ahau ends in 985 BC (5.8.0.0.0)
- Katun 7-Ahau ends in 965 BC (5.9.0.0.0)
- Katun 5-Ahau ends in 945 BC (5.10.0.0.0)
- Katun 3-Ahau ends in 926 BC (5.11.0.0.0)
....
- Katun 11-Ahau ends in 747 BC (6.0.0.0.0) actual

-- Mars contacts Earth; (start of Long Count)
- Katun 9-Ahau ends in 729 BC (6.1.0.0.0) actual
  -- Further sightings of Mars.
- Katun 7-Ahau ends in 708 BC (6.2.0.0.0)
- Katun 5-Ahau ends in 688 BC (6.3.0.0.0)
- Katun 3-Ahau ends in 668 BC (6.4.0.0.0) actual
  -- Venus nova, Kukulkan disappears.

Calculations are in Unix bc notation, where ∧ denotes exponentiation; the functions a(rctangent), s(ine), and c(osine) use radians; angle conversions to radians or degrees by the divisors rad=.017+ and deg=57.2+; other functions are shown as f( ); tan( )=s( )/c( )
units: million == 1,000,000; billion == 1,000,000,000;
AU == 93,000,000 miles.

Visit the website at http://saturniancosmology.org/

Feel free to email me with any comments or corrections:
jno@saturniancosmology.org